183

• About the Cover

Throughout history both artists and mathematicians have been fascinated by geometric shapes and their interrelationships. Right angles, rectangles and triangles are some geometric figures in the abstract painting shown on the cover. Can you see others?

• About the Title Page

Sculpture based on geometry uses balance among lines and planes in solids. Artist Ursula Meyer sculptured two identical geometric forms shown on the title pages. Can you see these two identical shapes in each picture?

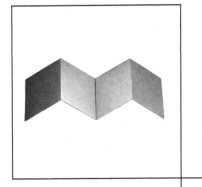

RAY C. JURGENSEN

ALFRED J. DONNELLY

MARY P. DOLCIANI

EDITORIAL ADVISERS
ANDREW M. GLEASON
ALBERT E. MEDER, JR.

Modern School Mathematics
GEOMETRY

HOUGHTON MIFFLIN COMPANY · BOSTON

NEW YORK · ATLANTA · GENEVA, ILLINOIS · DALLAS · PALO ALTO

■ ABOUT THE AUTHORS

Ray C. Jurgensen, Chairman of Mathematics Department and holder of Eppley Chair of Mathematics, Culver Military Academy, Culver, Indiana. Mr. Jurgensen has been a member of the School Mathematics Study Group (SMSG) writing team on geometry and a lecturer at the National Science Foundation institutes for mathematics teachers.

Alfred J. Donnelly, Master Instructor and holder of the William Pitt Oakes Chair of Mathematics, Culver Military Academy. Mr. Donnelly brings to his authorship a rich background of both study and teaching of mathematics.

Mary P. Dolciani, Professor and Chairman, Department of Mathematics, Hunter College of the City University of New York. Dr. Dolciani has been a member of the School Mathematics Study Group and a director and teacher in numerous National Science Foundation and New York State Education Department institutes for mathematics teachers.

Editorial Advisers

Andrew M. Gleason, Professor of Mathematics, Harvard University, is prominently associated with curriculum changes in mathematics. Professor Gleason was Chairman of the Advisory Board for SMSG as well as co-chairman of the Cambridge Conference which wrote the influential report, *Goals for School Mathematics.*

Albert E. Meder, Jr., Dean and Vice Provost and Professor of Mathematics, Rutgers, The State University. Dr. Meder was Executive Director of the Commission on Mathematics of the College Entrance Examination Board, and has been an advisory member of SMSG.

CONTENTS

CREDITS

PAGE

Cover, i   Painting reproduced courtesy the Celanese Corporation

ii–iii   Sculpture "Xerxes" by Ursula Meyer, Courtesy of the A. M. Sachs Gallery, New York

xii   Sherman Howe, Jr.

49   New York Picture Research

50   Black Star

90   Courtesy of Pullman Incorporated

116   New Mexico State Tourist Bureau

146   Frank Lloyd Wright, architect — Hedrich-Blessing Studio

190   Courtesy of Corning Glass Works

230   Courtesy of Corning Glass Works

275   Courtesy of Mrs. George D. Birkhoff

276   Courtesy of U. S. Department of Commerce, Weather Bureau, W. B. Bentley

312   Courtesy of the United States Atomic Energy Commission

358   John Littlewood, The Christian Science Monitor

405   Courtesy of Columbia University Library, D. E. Smith Collection

406   The Museum of Contemporary Crafts, Ferdinand Boesch

439   Courtesy of Columbia University Library, D. E. Smith Collection

442   Collection of C. V. S. Roosevelt, Washington, D. C.

482   Courtesy of the Marley Company

512   Barbara Ferrell-Hero, WHITE RIVER SERIES, acrylic and casein on canvas, Courtesy of the Eleanor Rigelhaupt Gallery, Boston

542   Courtesy of Lennox Industries Inc.

584   Murphy and Mackey, architects — Hedrich-Blessing Studio

617   Keystone View Company, Inc.

618   Wide World Photos, Inc.

The publishers are grateful to the authors for the use of certain portions of their text copyrighted © 1965, 1963 by Houghton Mifflin Company under the title *Modern Geometry, Structure and Method.*

SYMBOLS

$\lvert x \rvert$	absolute value of x	p	perimeter
$\angle$, $\measuredangle$	angle, angles	$\perp$	perpendicular, is perpen-dicular to
A	area		
$\overset{\frown}{AB}$	the arc AB	π	pi
$O - \overset{\frown}{AB}$	the sector AB	n-gon	polygon of n sides
B	area of base	P	postulate
$\odot$	circle	r	radius
c	circumference	$a : b$	the ratio of a to b
$\overline{X}$	"X-bar," the complement of X	$\{\,\}$	set
		N	set of natural numbers
$\cong$	congruent, is congruent to	W	set of whole numbers
$\ncong$	not congruent, is not con-gruent to	J	set of integers
		$\mathcal{R}$	set of real numbers
$\wedge$	conjunction	U	universal set
$\vee$	disjunction	$\emptyset$	empty set
cos	cosine	$\in$	is an element of
$^\circ$, $'$, $''$	degrees, minutes, seconds	$\notin$	is not an element of
d	diameter; distance	$\subset$	is a subset of
e	base edge	$\not\subset$	is not a subset of
$=$	equals, is equal to	$\cap$	intersection
$\ne$	is not equal to	$\cup$	union
$>$	is greater than	$\ldots$	and so on up to; and so on indefinitely
$\ge$	is greater than or equal to		
$<$	is less than	$\sim$	similar, is similar to
$\le$	is less than or equal to	$\sim$	negation of a statement, it is false that
$\doteq$	is approximately equal to		
h	height	sin	sine
$\overleftrightarrow{AB}$	the line through A and B	l	slant height
$\overline{AB}$	the segment with end-points A and B	m	slope
		S	area of sphere
AB	the length of the segment $\overline{AB}$	$\sqrt{a}$	positive square root of a
		tan	tangent
$\overrightarrow{AB}$	the ray $\overrightarrow{AB}$	$\therefore$	therefore
$\overrightarrow{OA}$	the vector OA	$\triangle$, $\triangle\!\!\!\triangle$	triangle, triangles
$m \angle ABC$	measure of angle ABC	V	volume
		$\to$	approaches, approaches as a limit
$m \overset{\frown}{AB}$	measure of arc AB		
(x, y)	ordered pair	$\to$	implication (if-then) or conditional
(x, y, z)	ordered triple		
O	origin	$\leftrightarrow$	equivalence of statements; is equivalent to
$\parallel$	is parallel to		
$\nparallel$	is not parallel to	$M: X \to X'$	the function or mapping M that maps point X into point X'
$\square$	parallelogram		

1 Elements of Geometry

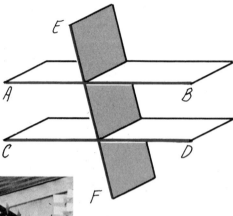

This Vermont designer-craftsman used the basic elements of geometry creatively to build these models. Do you see the model that is represented in part by the drawing above?

Mathematics is today among the most active of all the sciences. In order to meet the demands of industry, the professions, and mathematics itself, mathematicians have been called upon to extend and combine old branches of mathematics as well as to develop new ones. While geometry is one of the oldest branches of mathematics, it is today finding new areas of application in such fields as space exploration and rocket design.

Among the properties of points, lines, surfaces, and solids now being extensively used in the solution of space problems are many first recognized by the early Babylonians and Egyptians (4000–3000 B.C.). It is believed that these early peoples arrived at conclusions about relationships in certain geometric figures on the basis of observations made in repeated measurements. They formulated rules which enabled them to save time in their surveying and pyramid-building activities. Later geometers developed means of proving many of these same conclusions, as well as additional ones, without having to resort to measurement. You will learn about their methods as you progress in this course.

Some of the material in this chapter will already be familiar to you. You have worked with numbers, lines, and angles in previous mathematics courses. Some of the definitions presented may seem to be a little different and, at first, somewhat more complex. However, the definitions selected are those which will be the most useful to you in both this and later mathematics courses.

■ The Language of Sets

1–1 Representing Sets

In this course you will be working with various geometric figures such as lines, planes, angles, and circles. Since every geometric figure will be regarded as a set of points, it would be well to start by refreshing your knowledge of sets.

A set is any collection of objects that are clearly identified. The objects in a set are called its **members** or **elements** and are said to **belong to** or to **be contained in** the set.

1

To specify a set you must identify its members. One way to do this is to list its members within braces { }. For example, you write $A = \{2, 4, 6\}$ which is read

"*A* is the set whose members are 2, 4, and 6"

or

"*A* is the set that contains 2, 4, and 6."

In this case Set *A* is said to be **specified by roster.** The order in which the members are listed is not significant. Thus, you could specify *A* by writing $A = \{4, 2, 6\}$.

Often it is inconvenient or impossible to specify a set by roster. For example, you cannot list all the members of the set of real numbers between 0 and 1. However, you can specify this set by writing a **description** or **rule** within braces.

$B = \{$the real numbers between 0 and 1$\}$,

which is read

"B is the set of the real numbers between 0 and 1."

A set may contain any number of elements. If the elements of a set can be counted with the counting process coming to an end, the set is said to be a **finite set** (**fy**-nite). Otherwise, it is an **infinite set** (**in**-fi-nit). Thus, the set of light bulbs in Florida is a finite set even though an exact count of the members of the set would be difficult to make. However, the set of all odd integers is an infinite set since a count of the elements would never end.

It is possible to have a set that contains no members. For example, the set of odd integers whose squares are even integers contains no members. A set that contains no members is called the **empty set** or the **null set** and is designated by the symbol ∅. We agree to classify the empty set as a finite set with a count of zero elements.

Two sets are said to be **equal sets** if and only if they contain the same members. Thus if *A* and *B* are sets and $A = B$, *A* and *B* are simply different designations for the same set.

The following will help you recall the meaning of other symbols used in working with sets.

NOTATION	HOW READ
$x \in A$	x is a member of A. (or) x belongs to A.
$x \notin A$	x is not a member of A. (or) x does not belong to A.
$\{3, 4, 5, \ldots, 25\}$	The set whose members are 3, 4, 5, and so on through 25.
$\{1, 2, 3, \ldots\}$	The set whose members are 1, 2, 3, and so on indefinitely.
$\{x: x \in A\}$	The set of all x such that x belongs to A.
$\{x: 2x + 8 = 12\}$	The set of all x such that the sum of twice x and 8 is equal to 12.
$x \in \mathfrak{R}$	x belongs to the set of real numbers.

ORAL EXERCISES

Given: $A = \{1, 2, 3, 4\}$ $B = \{5, 6, 7, 8\}$
$C = \{1, 2, 3, \ldots, 20\}$ $D = \{2, 4, 6, \ldots\}$
$E = \{0\}$ $F = \{5, 8, 7, 6\}$

1. Which of these sets are finite? Which infinite?
2. What is the number of elements in B? in E?
3. Does D have a greatest element?
4. Is E the empty set?
5. Describe D in words.
6. Is $5 \in C$? Is $5 \in D$?
7. Are any two of these sets equal?
8. What is meant by the symbol $\emptyset$?
9. Name the three greatest elements in C.
10. Are all elements of B also elements of C?

Read each statement aloud and tell whether or not the statement is true.

11. $5 \in$ {the positive real numbers}

12. $\frac{3}{4} \notin$ {the real numbers}

13. {0} $= \emptyset$

14. {the whole numbers between 3 and 4} $= \emptyset$

15. {x: $5x = 10$} $=$ {2}

16. {x: $x^2 = 25$} $=$ {5}

WRITTEN
EXERCISES

Use the roster method to specify each of the following sets. In each case, state whether the set is finite or infinite.

EXAMPLE. {the whole numbers from 10 to 15, inclusive}

Solution: {10, 11, 12, 13, 14, 15}, finite

|A|

1. {the even integers between 11 and 19}

2. {the integers greater than 7 and less than 12}

3. {the months whose names begin with the letter A}

4. {the days of the week whose names begin with the letter T}

5. {the integers greater than 7}

6. {the positive integers}

7. {the integers greater than 20 but less than 105}

8. {the multiples of 5 between 10 and 200, inclusive}

9. {the coefficients in the expression $2x^5 + 7x^3 + 5x^2$}

10. {the exponents in the expression $2x^5 + 7x^3 + 5x^2$}

11. {the roots of the equation $x^2 = 9$}

12. {the roots of the equation $x^2 - 16 = 0$}

13. {the days of the week that begin with the letter K}

14. {triangles that have four sides}

Use the rule method to specify each of the sets in Exs. 15–24. In each exercise several rules are possible. However, you need give only one rule.

EXAMPLE. {11, 12, 13, . . . , 20}

Solution: {the whole numbers from 11 to 20, inclusive}
or {the whole numbers greater than 10 and less than 21}

B **15.** {1, 3, 5, 7}

16. {10, 12, 14, 16, 18}

17. {January, June, July}

18. {red, white, blue}

19. {1, 2, 3, . . .}

20. {2, 4, 6, . . .}

21. {Alaska, Alabama, Arizona, Arkansas}

22. {Saturday, Sunday}

23. {a, b, c, . . . , z}

24. {a, e, i, o, u}

Capital letters are used to name certain points lying within regions 1 and 2 in the given diagram. Make a roster for each of of the following sets.

EXAMPLE. {the points in region 1}

Solution: {A, B, C, D, E}

25. {the points in region 2}

26. {the points in either region 1 or region 2}

27. {the points in both region 1 and region 2}

28. {the points in region 1 but not in region 2}

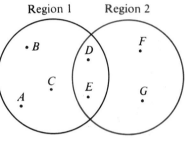

Exs. 25–28

1–2 Relationships between Sets

Consider the two sets *A* and *B* where

$$A = \{1, 2, 3\} \quad \text{and} \quad B = \{1, 2, 3, 4, 5\}.$$

Notice that every member of *A* is also a member of *B*. When two sets *A* and *B* are such that every element of *A* is an element of *B*, *A* is said to be a **subset** of *B*. This relationship is expressed in symbols by $A \subset B$ (read "*A* is a subset of *B*"). To indicate that *A* is not a subset of *B*, you write $A \not\subset B$.

The definition of a subset does not rule out the possibility that the sets contain exactly the same elements. Thus, every set is a subset of itself. From the definition it also follows that the empty set is a subset of every set.

EXAMPLE 1. List all subsets of {1, 2, 3}.

Solution: {1}   {1, 2}   ∅

{2}   {1, 3}   {1, 2, 3}

{3}   {2, 3}

Two sets *A* and *B* are said to **intersect** if there is at least one element that belongs to both sets. Two sets that do not intersect are said to be **disjoint.** Thus, {1, 2, 3} and {3, 4} intersect, while {1, 2} and {3, 4} are disjoint.

The **intersection** of two sets *A* and *B* is the set whose elements belong to *both A and B.* The intersection of sets *A* and *B* is expressed in symbols by $A \cap B$ (read "the intersection of *A* and *B*").

EXAMPLE 2. Given $A = \{2, 3\}$, $B = \{2, 3, 4\}$, $C = \{4, 5\}$.
Identify (a) $A \cap B$, (b) $A \cap C$, (c) $B \cap C$.

Solution: (a) $A \cap B = \{2, 3\}$, (b) $A \cap C = \emptyset$, (c) $B \cap C = \{4\}$.

Care must be exercised in interpreting the verb "intersect" and the noun "intersection." A statement that two sets intersect implies that they have at least one element in common. However, reference to the intersection of two sets does not exclude the possibility that the intersection contains no elements.

The **union** of two sets *A* and *B* is the set of all elements that belong to *at least* one of the two sets. The union of *A* and *B* is written $A \cup B$ (read "the union of *A* and *B*"). Each of the sets *A* and *B* is a subset of their union, $A \cup B$.

EXAMPLE 3. Given $A = \{1, 2, 3\}$, $B = \{2, 3, 4\}$, $C = \emptyset$.
Identify: (a) $A \cup B$, (b) $B \cup C$, (c) $(A \cup B) \cup C$.

Solution: (a) $A \cup B = \{1, 2, 3, 4\}$, (b) $B \cup C = \{2, 3, 4\}$,
(c) $(A \cup B) \cup C = \{1, 2, 3, 4\}$.

Shown below are two lines *l* and *m* each of which represents an infinite set of points. Their intersection, $l \cap m$, is exactly one point, *P*. Their union, $l \cup m$, is an infinite set of points containing all points of *l* and all points of *m*.

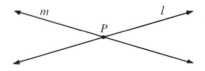

In the diagrams at the top of the next page, the interiors of regions

R and *S* contain infinite sets of points. Shading is used to indicate the union and intersection of regions *R* and *S*.

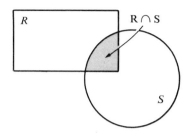

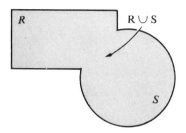

Given: A = {1, 2, 3, 4, 5}   B = {1, 2, 3}   C = {4, 5, 6}
        D = {1, 2, 3, ..., 10}   E = {3, 4, 5, ...}   F = ∅

1. Is *B* a subset of *A*? of *C*?

2. Which of the given sets are finite?

3. Name the elements of *A* ∩ *B*.

4. Is *B* ∩ *C* = *F*?

5. Name the elements of *B* ∪ *C*.

6. Is *F* a subset of *C*?

7. Can the union of two nonempty sets be the empty set?

8. Can the intersection of two nonempty sets be the empty set?

9. Is {4, 5, 6} a subset of *C*?

10. Is 4 ∈ *A*? Is 2 ∉ *E*?

11. If $x \in A$ and $x \in B$, is $x \in (A \cup B)$?

12. If $x \in A$ and $x \in B$, is $x \in (A \cap B)$?

13. Are sets *B* and *C* disjoint?

14. Do two disjoint sets have any common subsets?

15. Name the elements in $\{x: x \in A$ and $x \in B\}$.

16. Name the elements in $\{x: x \in A$ or $x \in B\}$.

Read each statement aloud and tell whether or not the statement is true. Explain the reason for your answer.

17. If $x \in S$ and $x \notin T$, then $S \cup T = \emptyset$.

18. If $R \subset S$ and $S \subset T$, then $R \subset T$.

19. If $R \subset S$ and $R \neq S$, then $R \cap S = S$.

20. If $R \subset S$ and $S \subset R$, then $R = S$.

WRITTEN EXERCISES

Given: $X = \{3, 8, 12\}$. List all the subsets of X that meet the specified condition.

EXAMPLE. Contain exactly two elements.

Solution: $\{3, 8\}$, $\{3, 12\}$, $\{8, 12\}$

A

1. Contain exactly one element.

2. Contain at least one element.

3. Contain exactly three elements.

4. Contain no elements.

5. All elements are even integers.

6. All elements are odd integers.

Given: $A = \{1, 2, 3, 4, 5, 6, 7, 8, 9\}$. Which of the following are subsets of A?

7. $\{1, 2\}$

8. $\{8\}$

9. $\{3, 5, 11\}$

10. $\{7, 8, 9\}$

11. $\{0\}$

12. $\{1, 2, 3, 8\}$

13. $\{1, 2, 3, 4, 5, 6, 7, 8, 9\}$

14. $\emptyset$

Given: $X = \{a, b, c\}$, $Y = \{c, d, e, f\}$, $Z = \{a, c, d, g\}$. List the elements contained in each of the following sets.

15. $X \cap Y$

16. $Y \cup Z$

17. $Z \cup X$

18. $Y \cap Z$

19. $X \cap \emptyset$

20. $Y \cup \emptyset$

21. $(X \cap Y) \cup Z$

22. $(X \cup Y) \cap Z$

In the following, the phrase "contains n elements" means "contains exactly n elements." If A is a set containing five elements and B is a set containing three elements, which of the following statements must be true?

B

23. $A \cap B$ contains five elements.

24. $A \cup B$ contains at least five elements.

25. $A \cup B$ contains four elements.

26. $A \cap B$ is a subset of A.

27. A is a subset of B.

28. $A \cup B$ can contain no more than eight elements.

29. If $A \cap B = \emptyset$, then $A \cup B = \emptyset$.

30. If $x \in A$ and $x \in B$, then $A \cap B$ is not an empty set.

31. If $A \cap B$ contains three elements, then B is a subset of A.

32. If $A \cup B$ contains six elements, then $A \cap B$ contains two elements.

C **33.** Set C contains $x + 2$ elements and set D contains $2x - 1$ elements. If $C \cap D$ contains 3 elements and $C \cup D$ contains 10 elements, find the number of elements in C and in D.

34. Specify by roster $\{x: 2x^2 - x = 3\}$.

35. If $A = \{(x, y): x + y = 5\}$ and $B = \{(x, y): 2x - 3y = 4\}$, find $A \cap B$.

36. (a) Find the number of subsets of a set that contains four elements.

(b) Find the number of subsets of a set that contains five elements.

(c) Observing your answers in (a) and (b), write an expression for the number of subsets of a set that contains n elements.

1–3   Venn Diagrams

The relationship between two or more sets can be pictured by a *Venn diagram.* In such a diagram a set is represented by the region within a closed curve.

Consider sets X and U where $X = \{$girls exactly 16 yrs. old$\}$ and $U = \{$all girls$\}$. The Venn diagram shown depicts the relationship that X is a subset of U. It is not essential that the closed curves used be a rectangle and a circle. The essential requirement is that the region representing the subset X must lie within that representing U.

In the diagram shown, that region of U not lying inside circle X represents the set of all girls not exactly 16 yrs. old. This set, called the **complement** of X, is denoted by $\overline{X}$ (read "X-bar").

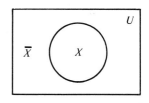

When each set in a particular discussion is thought of as a subset of some particular set U, the set U is called the **universal set** or **universe.** In any discussion the universal set must be specified and it is essential that it contain each set being dealt with as a subset.

The example that follows illustrates the use of shading to represent the relationship between sets which are subsets of the same universal set.

EXAMPLE.

Given: $U = \{$girls$\}$ $Y = \{$girls with long hair$\}$
       $X = \{$girls exactly 16 yrs. old$\}$ $Z = \{$girls exactly 17 yrs. old$\}$

Complement   Intersection   Union

$\overline{X} = \{$girls not exactly $X \cap Y = \{$girls exactly $X \cup Y = \{$girls either
       16 yrs. old$\}$ 16 yrs. old   exactly 16
                              and having   yrs. old, or
                              long hair$\}$ having long
                                                     hair, or
                                                     both.$\}$

Intersection   Union   A Combination

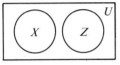

$X \cap Z = \emptyset$ $X \cup Z = \{$girls either $\overline{X \cap Y} = \{$girls except
$X \cap Z = \{$girls both   exactly 16   those both
       exactly 16   or exactly   exactly 16
       and exactly   17 yrs.   yrs. old and
       17 yrs. old$\}$ old$\}$ having
                                                   long hair$\}$

ORAL EXERCISES

Given: $A = \{$male mathematics teachers$\}$
       $B = \{$males over 6 feet tall$\}$
       $U = \{$males$\}$

Tell what numbered regions you would shade to
show each of the following.

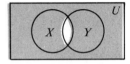

   1. $\{$male mathematics teachers$\}$
   2. $\{$males over 6 feet tall$\}$
   3. $\{$males who are over 6 feet tall and who teach mathematics$\}$
   4. $\{$males who either teach mathematics or are over 6 feet tall$\}$
   5. $\{$males who are not mathematics teachers$\}$

6. {males who are neither over 6 feet tall nor mathematics teachers}

7. {males who are not both mathematics teachers and over 6 feet tall}

8. {males over 6 feet tall who are not mathematics teachers}

State a universal set U of which both given sets are subsets.

EXAMPLE. {all white cats} ; {all black cats}

Solution: $U = $ {all cats}

9. {the even integers} ; {the odd integers}   **11.** {apple trees} ; {pear trees}

10. {algebra books} ; {geometry books}   **12.** {trout} ; {salmon}

WRITTEN EXERCISES

Using a Venn diagram similar to the one shown, represent the indicated set by shading regions.

1. $A \cup B$

2. $A \cap B$

3. A but not B

4. Neither A nor B

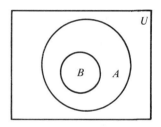

Which of the Venn diagrams shown below pictures:

5. Two disjoint sets?   **7.** A nonempty intersection of two sets?

6. A union of two sets?   **8.** One set as a subset of another?

a.

b.

c.

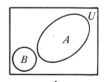

d.

Copy the diagram at the right for each of Exercises 9–16. Then shade the region representing the given set.

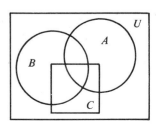

9. $A \cap B$ **13.** $(A \cup B) \cup C$

10. $\overline{A}$ **14.** $\overline{A \cap B}$

11. $B \cup C$ **15.** $\overline{B \cup C}$

12. $(A \cap B) \cap C$ **16.** {$x: x \in A$ or $x \in \overline{B}$}

Sketch a Venn diagram to indicate the relationship
between the given sets.

EXAMPLE. $U = $ {the positive integers}
$X = $ {the even positive integers}
$Y = $ {the positive integers less than 20}

Solution:

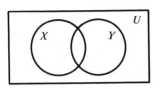

(*X* and *Y* intersect since some
elements belong to both sets.)

B   **17.** $U = $ {animals} $X = $ {baby rabbits} $Y = $ {rabbits}

18. $U = $ {the positive integers} $X = $ {the positive integers less than 6}
$Y = $ {the positive integers greater than 30}

19. $U = $ {geometric figures}   **20.** $U = $ {four-sided plane figures}
$X = $ {triangles} $X = $ {parallelograms}
$Y = $ {right triangles} $Y = $ {four-sided plane figures
that have no parallel
sides}

1–4   Number Lines

Consider the two sets R and S.

$$R = \{ \triangle \; \bullet \; \blacksquare \} \qquad\qquad S = \{ a, \; b, \; c \}$$

Although these sets are not equal, there is an important relationship
between them. The diagrams below show various pairings that assign
to each member of either set *one and only one* member of the other set.
Such a pairing of the elements of two sets is called a **one-to-one correspondence.**

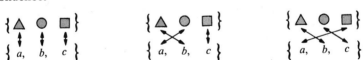

In previous mathematics courses when you worked with number
lines you were making use of certain assumptions about points, lines,
distance, and a particular one-to-one correspondence between the set
of points of a line and the set of real numbers. The following statements
describe those assumptions.

1. For every two points, there is exactly one line that contains both
points.

2. Corresponding to any two points A and B there is a unique positive number called the **distance** between them. (This number is denoted by AB or BA.)
3. The points of a line can be placed in correspondence with the real numbers in such a way that
   (a) to every point of the line there corresponds exactly one real number,
   (b) to every real number there corresponds exactly one point of the line,
   (c) the distance between any two points is the absolute value of the difference of the corresponding numbers.

The pairing between points of a line and real numbers as described in 3 above is said to establish a real number **coordinate system** on the line. A line on which a coordinate system has been established is called a **number line.** Each point of the line is called the **graph** of the number with which it is paired, and the number is called the **coordinate** of the point.

The *coordinate* of A is 3. The *graph* of -2 is C. Point B is the **origin.**
Recall that the **absolute value** of any real number a is the greater of the number a and its opposite $-a$. The symbol $|a|$ denotes the absolute value of a. From the definition of the absolute value of a it follows that: If a is a positive number or zero, $|a| = a$.
$$\text{If } a \text{ is a negative number, } |a| = -a.$$

EXAMPLE. Evaluate each of the following.

        (a) $|3|$ (b) $|-5|$ (c) $-|-3|$ (d) $|8 - 2|$ (e) $|2 - 8|$

Solution: (a) 3   (b) 5   (c) -3 (d) 6   (e) 6

Note: Exs. (d) and (e) illustrate an important absolute-value relationship, $|a - b| = |b - a|$.

Given any two points A and B in space you can find the distance between them once you have set up a coordinate system on the unique line through them. The distance is simply the absolute value of the difference of the coordinates of A and B. In the diagrams that follow, note that the distance between A and B (AB) is not affected by the position of the origin of the coordinate system set up on the line through them.

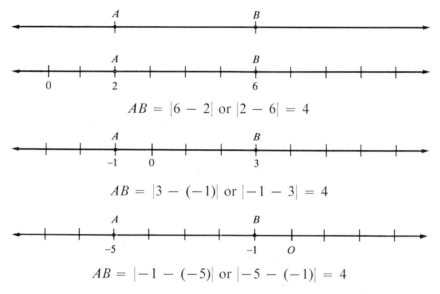

$$AB = |6 - 2| \text{ or } |2 - 6| = 4$$

$$AB = |3 - (-1)| \text{ or } |-1 - 3| = 4$$

$$AB = |-1 - (-5)| \text{ or } |-5 - (-1)| = 4$$

Although number lines are usually pictured in a horizontal position with points having positive coordinates to the right of the origin, a coordinate system can be set up on any line with points having positive coordinates to either side of the origin.

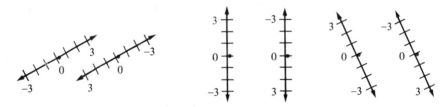

In earlier courses you were introduced to the symbols used in comparing real numbers. These symbols convey information about the relative positions of the graphs of real numbers on a number line on which positive coordinates lie to the right of the origin.

If $a < b$, then the point corresponding to a
lies to the left of the point corresponding to b.

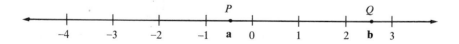

If $a > b$, then the point corresponding to a lies to the right of the point corresponding to b.

A list of the order symbols commonly used in comparing real numbers follows. Check to be sure that you recall the meaning of each.

$a > b$	a is greater than b
$a < b$	a is less than b
$a \geq b$	a is greater than or equal to b
$a \leq b$	a is less than or equal to b
$a < b < c$	a is less than b *and* b is less than c

The set of real numbers $\Re$ is the union of two disjoint sets — the set of rational numbers and the set of irrational numbers. Therefore, there are points corresponding to irrational numbers such as $\sqrt{2}$, π, $\sqrt[3]{7}$, etc. Recall that a repeating or terminating decimal numeral names a *rational number* while a nonrepeating, nonterminating decimal numeral names an *irrational number* The following list will help you to refresh your memory of certain special subsets of real numbers and the letter used to denote each.

{the natural numbers}	$N = \{1, 2, 3, 4, \ldots\}$
{the whole numbers}	$W = \{0, 1, 2, 3, \ldots\}$
{the integers}	$J = \{0, 1, -1, 2, -2, \ldots\}$

ORAL EXERCISES

In the following exercises N, W, and J denote the special subsets described above. The variables a and b represent any two real numbers. Tell whether the assertion made is true or false.

1. $N \subset W$

2. $\frac{3}{4} \in J$

3. $0 \notin W$

4. $\sqrt{3} \in \Re$

5. $\frac{7}{0} \in \Re$

6. $\frac{3}{5} \leq \frac{3}{4}$

7. $J \subset W$

8. $.3 > .333\ldots$

9. If $a > b$, then $-a > -b$.

10. If $a \in W$, then $a \in J$.

11. $|a - b| = |b - a|$

12. $|a| - |b| = |b| - |a|$

In answering Exercises 13–20 refer to the number line below.

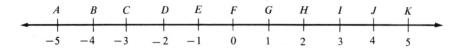

13. What is the coordinate of point D?
14. What point is the graph of 4?
15. What is the distance between B and E?
16. Name two points at a distance 3 from E.
17. Between what two labeled points does the graph of $\sqrt{3}$ lie? π lie?
18. By how much does the coordinate of H exceed that of C?
19. Is the coordinate of D greater than the coordinate of B?
20. Is there more than one point on the number line that is twice as far from F as it is from G?

WRITTEN EXERCISES

Which of the following decimal numerals name rational numbers? (Recall that $8.2\overline{351}$ indicates that the block of digits 351 repeats indefinitely while 8.2351 ... indicates that the decimal is non-ending and nonrepeating.)

1. $\frac{3}{4}$ 3. $-.65$ 5. $1.\overline{6}$ 7. $.00\overline{531}$

2. $.8$ 4. $5.241\ldots$ 6. $\dfrac{2.8}{.5}$ 8. $1.7243\ldots$

Express the given numeral as the ratio of two integers.

EXAMPLE. 2.146

Solution: $2.146 = 2 + .146 = 2 + \frac{146}{1000} = \frac{2146}{1000}$

9. $.65$ 11. 2.3 13. $\dfrac{1\frac{1}{2}}{3}$ 15. $1.\overline{3}$

10. $-.135$ 12. $.\overline{6}$ 14. $\dfrac{-\frac{3}{4}}{\frac{2}{3}}$ 16. $(-1\frac{1}{2})^2$

Which of the following are true for all real numbers a and b such that $a > b$? For those not always true, give an example for which the assertion is false.

17. $a - b > 0$ **21.** $a + b = b + a$ **25.** $|a| = a$

18. $\dfrac{1}{a} > \dfrac{1}{b}$ **22.** $\dfrac{6}{a} \in \mathcal{R}$ **26.** $|a| + |b| = |a + b|$

19. $a^2 > b^2$ **23.** $(a - b)^2 = (b - a)^2$

20. $|a| > |b|$ **24.** $|a - b| = |a| - |b|$

Find the distance on the number line between two points having the indicated coordinates.

27. 2 and 9   **29.** -6 and -2 **31.** $a - 1$ and $a - 4$

28. -3 and 0   **30.** -3 and -8 **32.** a and $-a$ $(a < 0)$

33. Is the quotient of two real numbers always a real number? Explain.

34. Is there a smallest real number? a largest real number?

35. Is the set of rational numbers a finite set?

36. Describe the set of numbers specified by $\{x: x = \dfrac{a}{b}, a \in W, b \in N\}$.

Given: $S = \{-1, 0, 5, 7, 9\}$ and $T = \{-3, 0, 2, 5, 8\}$

37. Draw a number line and graph those points whose coordinates are elements of T.

38. Draw a number line and graph those points whose coordinates are elements of $S \cap T$.

39. How many points have coordinates that are elements of $S \cup T$?

40. For what values of x is the statement "$x \in S$ and $x \in T$" true?

Which of the following are true statements when x is -2?

B

41. $3x \le -6$ **45.** $-3x < 3$ **49.** $4x + 8 = 0$

42. $4 - x > 2$ **46.** $8 - x > x - 8$ **50.** $x^3 > x$

43. $x^2 \ge -2x$ **47.** $x^2 - x = 6$ **51.** $\dfrac{1}{x} > x$

44. $2 - x = x - 2$ **48.** $\frac{1}{2}x < x$ **52.** $x(x + 1) < 0$

In Exercises 53–58 the coordinates of two points are given. Find the coordinate of the point halfway between the two points.

EXAMPLE. -3 and 7

Solution: Distance $= |-3 - (7)| = |-10| = 10$
Half the distance $= 5$
The midpoint coordinate is $-3 + 5 = 2$ or $7 - 5 = 2$, **Answer.**

53. 4 and 12   **55.** -4 and $2\frac{1}{2}$ **57.** a and 0

54. -2 and 6   **56.** $\frac{3}{4}$ and $-1\frac{1}{3}$ **58.** a and b

Find the solution set of the given open sentence.

EXAMPLE. $|2x - 1| = 5$

Solution: $2x - 1 = 5$ or $2x - 1 = -5$
$2x = 6$ $2x = -4$
$x = 3$ $x = -2$

 *Check:* $|6 - 1| \overset{?}{=} 5$ *Check:* $|-4 - 1| \overset{?}{=} 5$
$5 = 5\checkmark$ $5 = 5\checkmark$

$\therefore$ The solution set is $\{3, -2\}$, **Answer.**

59. $|x| = 3$ **61.** $|x - 2| = 5$ **63.** $|6 - 2| = x$

60. $|x + 1| = 7$ **62.** $|2x + 3| = 7$ **64.** $|6 - x| = 8$

■ Points, Lines, and Planes

1–5   Basic Undefined Terms

In discussing the number line, the words "point" and "line" were repeatedly used with no attempt made to define either word. This was no oversight. These two words along with the word "plane" are taken without definition. Any attempt to define them would only involve the use of less familiar geometric terms. The paragraphs that follow *describe* rather than define these terms.

A **point** (pt.) is represented on paper by a dot. Dots vary in size with even the smallest having some area. A point in mathematics has no size; it has position only. Thus, no mention is ever made of the size of a point. Points are identified by capital letters.

$\cdot B$

$\bullet C$

$\bullet A$

A **line** in this course will always mean a straight line that extends indefinitely in two opposite directions.   The arrowheads used in representing a line emphasize the fact that the line extends indefinitely.

A line has no width.   It is thought of as an infinite set of points. A line is usually identified by naming two points on the line and placing a double-headed arrow over the names.   Thus, a line through A and B is designated by $\overleftrightarrow{AB}$.

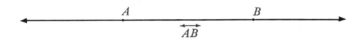

A line may also be named by a single lower-case letter, as below.

A **plane** is a flat surface which extends indefinitely.   A pane of glass or a flat desk top will help you to visualize a plane.   Although a plane has infinite length and width, it has no thickness.   Like the line, a plane is regarded as an infinite set of points.   Recall that the **intersection** of any two geometric figures is the set of points common to both figures.

A plane is usually represented in drawings by a four-sided figure like those shown in the diagrams that follow.   A single capital letter is frequently used to identify a plane.   A plane has no edges, but edges cannot be avoided in drawings representing a plane.

Horizontal sides in a drawing suggest that planes be viewed as horizontal.

Horizontal Planes

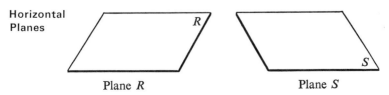

Plane R Plane S

Vertical sides in a drawing suggest that planes be viewed as vertical.

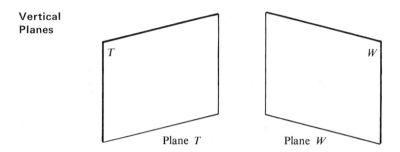

Vertical Planes

Plane *T*   Plane *W*

Dashed lines are used to indicate parts of a figure that would be hidden from view by other parts if the figure were made of material objects.

Intersecting Planes

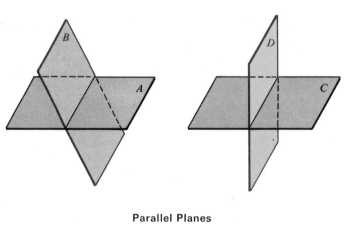

Parallel Planes

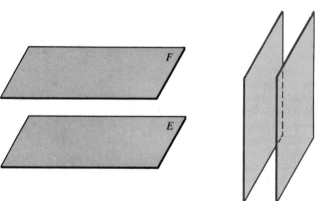

A Rectangular Solid   **A Triangular Pyramid**

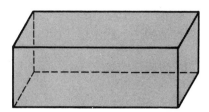
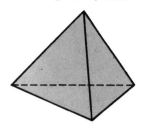

A circle lying in a plane is often represented by an oval. However, not all ovals represent circles. In the figure at the right below, the intersection of the cylinder and the plane actually represents an oval (an ellipse).

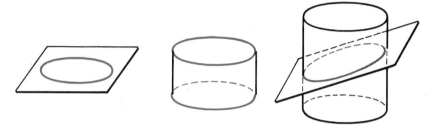

Circle in a Horizontal Plane   **Cylinder**   **Ellipse**

In drawing space figures keep these points in mind.

1. Represent planes by parallelograms.
2. Represent circles by ovals.
3. When important parts of a figure are behind other parts of the figure, show the concealed parts by using dashed lines.
4. When two parts of a figure intersect, be sure to show the intersection in your drawing.

Accompanying the figures that follow are some expressions commonly used to describe relationships between points, lines, and planes.

A lies on or *lies in l.*
A is a point of l.
l passes through A.

l and *m* *intersect* at *P.*
P belongs to the *intersection* of *l* and *m.*

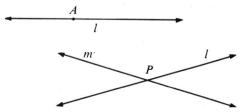

B lies in or *lies on M.*
l lies in or *lies on M.*
M contains l and *B.*

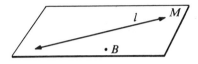

G contains t.
G intersects r at P.
r does not lie in G.

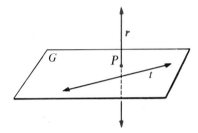

P and *Q* *intersect in* $\overleftrightarrow{XY}$.
$\overleftrightarrow{XY}$ *is the line of intersection.*
$\overleftrightarrow{XY}$ *lies in* both planes.
P and *Q* *contain* $\overleftrightarrow{XY}$.
$\overleftrightarrow{XY}$ *lies in P* and *Q.*

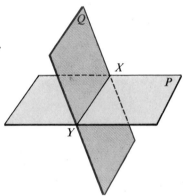

ORAL EXERCISES

1. How many lines can be passed through one point?

2. How many planes can be passed through one point?

3. Can more than one line be passed through two distinct points?

4. How many planes can be passed through two distinct points?

5. Is it possible to have more than one line intersecting a plane at one point?

6. How many planes can intersect a line at one point?

7. Is it possible for two planes to meet in just one point?

8. How many points does a line contain?

9. How many lines does a plane contain?

10. Can two planes contain the same line?

11. Can three planes meet in just one point?

12. If three points do not all lie on the same line, how many different planes can contain all three points?

Refer to the given figure and classify each of the given statements (1–8) as either true or false.

1. *l* lies in *S*.

2. *P* lies in *R*.

3. *S* contains *P*.

4. $\overleftrightarrow{XY}$ is the intersection of *R* and *S*.

5. A line passing through *P* and *A* must lie in *R*.

6. *l* and *m* intersect at *A*.

7. Any line in *R* must intersect $\overleftrightarrow{XY}$.

8. $\overleftrightarrow{XY}$ contains all points common to *R* and *S*.

Draw and label the figure described.

9. A line *l* lying in a horizontal plane *C*.

10. Lines *c* and *d* lying in a vertical plane *R* and intersecting at *P*.

11. Two nonintersecting horizontal planes *X* and *Y* and a line *l* that intersects both planes.

12. A circle *O* lying in a vertical plane.

13. A rectangle *ABCD* lying in a horizontal plane.

14. A plane *S* containing one of two intersecting lines *l* but not containing the other line *m*.

Make drawings similar to those shown, replacing dashed segments by solid ones where appropriate.

B **15.** 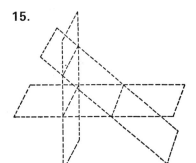 **16.**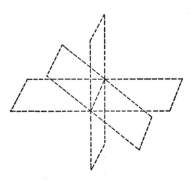

Draw and label the figure described.

17. A plane *X* intersecting two parallel planes *A* and *B*.

18. A rectangular solid all of whose edges appear to have equal length.

19. Three planes *X*, *Y*, and *Z* intersecting in a line.

20. Three planes *A*, *B*, and *C* having exactly one point in common.

In Exercises 21–24 draw a figure that supports your answer.

C **21.** Can a plane always be passed through any two given lines?

22. Can a line be parallel to each of two intersecting planes?

23. Can the intersection of a plane and a cylinder be a rectangle?

24. Given four random points with no three on a line and not all in one plane. If planes are passed through each possible set of three points, how many planes are there?

1–6   Some Basic Definitions

Although "point," "line," and "plane" are used without definition, other essential terms can be defined in terms of them.

Space: The set which consists of all possible points.

Collinear (ko-**lin**-ee-er) **Points:** A set of points all of which lie on the same line.

Coplanar (ko-**plain**-er) **Points:** A set of points all of which lie in the same plane.

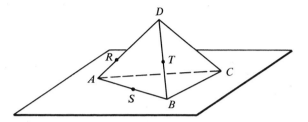

A, R, and D are collinear.

A, S, and B are collinear.

B, T, and D are collinear.

A, B, and C are noncollinear.

B, C, and D are noncollinear.

A, S, B, and C are coplanar.

B, C, D, and T are coplanar.

A, S, B, T, D, and R are coplanar.

A, B, C, and D are noncoplanar.

A, D, C, and T are noncoplanar.

Betweenness of Points: Point B is said to lie between points A and C if and only if all three points are distinct points on a line and $AB + BC = AC$.

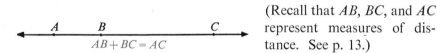

(Recall that AB, BC, and AC represent measures of distance. See p. 13.)

Line Segment: For any two distinct points A and B, line segment AB is the set of points consisting of A, B, and all points between A and B. A line segment is usually referred to simply as a segment. The symbol for segment AB is $\overline{AB}$.

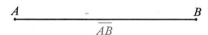

Note how the drawing and symbol for segment $\overline{AB}$ differ from those for line AB.

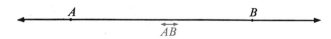

Length of a Segment: The length of a segment is the distance between its endpoints. The length of $\overline{AB}$ is therefore designated by writing AB or BA. The length of a segment is a number. No arrows or bars are ever used in representing the length of a segment.

Congruent Segments: Two segments are said to be congruent if they have the same length. The symbol ≅ stands for "is congruent to." Thus, if $\overline{AB}$ and $\overline{CD}$ have the same length, $\overline{AB} \cong \overline{CD}$. If two segments are congruent, each segment is said to be congruent to the other.

Midpoint of a Segment: A point X is the midpoint of a segment $\overline{AB}$ if X lies between A and B and $AX = XB$.

Bisector of a Segment: A line or segment whose intersection with a given segment $\overline{AB}$ is the midpoint of $\overline{AB}$ is a bisector of that segment.

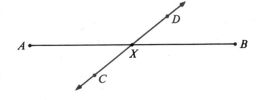

Ray: Ray AB is the union of segment $\overline{AB}$ and the set of all points X such that B lies between X and A. A is called the **endpoint** of ray AB. Informally speaking, "ray AB" means that the ray starts at A, goes through B, and continues indefinitely. The symbol $\overrightarrow{AB}$ is used to designate "ray AB." Note that the first letter in a ray symbol names the endpoint of the ray.

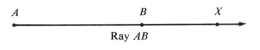

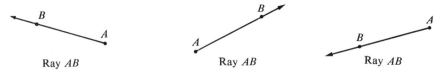

Opposite Rays: $\overrightarrow{AB}$ and $\overrightarrow{AC}$ are called opposite rays if A, B, and C lie on a line and A is between B and C.

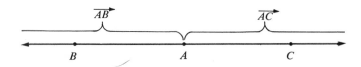

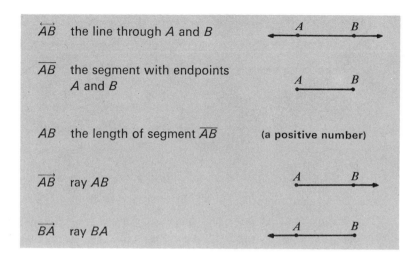

$\overleftrightarrow{AB}$ the line through A and B

$\overline{AB}$ the segment with endpoints A and B

AB the length of segment $\overline{AB}$ (a positive number)

$\overrightarrow{AB}$ ray AB

$\overrightarrow{BA}$ ray BA

ORAL EXERCISES

1. Must three distinct points be collinear? coplanar?
2. Can you refer to the length of $\overleftrightarrow{AB}$? of $\overrightarrow{AB}$? of $\overline{AB}$?
3. Does AB represent a number? a set of points?
4. If X is the midpoint of $\overline{AB}$, which of the following assertions are correct? $\overline{AX} = \overline{XB}$; $\overline{AX} \cong \overline{XB}$; $AX \cong XB$.
5. Is a ray an infinite set of points?
6. If two rays have the same endpoint must they be opposite rays?
7. Is the union of two opposite rays a line?

In answering Exercises 8–12 refer to the adjacent diagram.

8. Do $\overrightarrow{AB}$ and $\overrightarrow{BA}$ name the same ray?
9. Do $\overrightarrow{CA}$ and $\overrightarrow{CB}$ name the same ray?
10. Name two opposite rays. Name three segments.
11. Is $CA + AB = CB$?
12. Give a simpler name for: (a) $\overrightarrow{AB} \cap \overrightarrow{AC}$ (b) $\overrightarrow{AB} \cup \overrightarrow{AC}$.

Exercises 1–8 refer to the adjacent figure in which X is the midpoint of $\overline{AB}$.

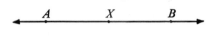

A

1. Are A, B, and X collinear?

2. Does $\overrightarrow{XA}$ pass through B?

3. Does $\overleftrightarrow{XA}$ pass through B?

4. Is $AX = XB$?

5. Is $\overline{AX} \cong \overline{XB}$?

6. Is $AB = 2AX$?

7. If X has coordinate -2 and B has coordinate 3, find the coordinate of A.

8. If A has coordinate -3 and B has coordinate 7, find the coordinate of X.

9. If $\overrightarrow{CD}$ and $\overrightarrow{CE}$ are opposite rays, which one of the points C, D, or E is between the other two?

10. If R, S, and T are collinear points with coordinates 2, 3, and $\sqrt{7}$, respectively, which point lies between the other two?

11. What is the intersection of $\overleftrightarrow{XY}$ and $\overrightarrow{XY}$? What is the union?

12. Do $\overline{CD}$ and $\overline{DC}$ name the same segment? Do $\overrightarrow{CD}$ and $\overrightarrow{DC}$ name the same ray?

Refer to the given diagram and represent by an appropriate symbol the set of points whose coordinates x satisfy the given condition.

EXAMPLE. $x \leq 2$

Solution: $\overrightarrow{CA}$ or $\overrightarrow{CB}$

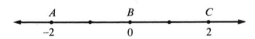

B

13. $x \geq 0$

14. $x = 2$

15. $-2 \leq x \leq 2$

16. $|x| \leq 2$

17. $|x| \geq 0$

18. $-2 \leq x \leq 0$

Given D, E, F, and G located as shown. In Exercises 19–24, classify the assertion made as true or false.

19. $\overrightarrow{FG} \subset \overrightarrow{EG}$

20. $\overrightarrow{FD} \cap \overrightarrow{EF} = \overline{EF}$

21. $\overrightarrow{EF} \subset \overline{EF}$

22. $\overrightarrow{FD} \cap \overrightarrow{FG} = \emptyset$

23. $\overrightarrow{ED} \cup \overrightarrow{EG} = \overleftrightarrow{DG}$

24. $\overrightarrow{ED} \cap \overrightarrow{FG} = \emptyset$

25. Draw a figure in which $AB = BC$ and yet B is not the midpoint of $\overline{AC}$.

26. Draw two different figures showing collinear points A, B, C, and D so located that both $AC + CD = AD$ and $CD + DB = CB$ are true.

Refer to the given figure and describe
the set of points represented by each of
the following:

EXAMPLE 1. $C \cap A$

Solution: {all points on l}

EXAMPLE 2. $B \cup l$

Solution: {all points in B together with
all points on l}

27. $l \cup A$ **30.** $m \cap A$

28. $m \cup B$ **31.** $C \cap B$

29. $l \cap m$ **32.** $C \cap l$

Indicate whether the graph of the given inequality is: (a) a segment (b) a segment,
except for its endpoints (c) a ray (d) a ray, except for its endpoint (e) a point
(f) a line

$\boxed{\text{C}}$ **33.** $x \leq -3$ **35.** $|x| \leq 0$ **37.** $x < 3$ and $x > 1$

34. $2 < x < 5$ **36.** $-3 \leq x \leq 2$ **38.** $x < 3$ or $x > 1$

■ Angles and Their Measure

1–7 Angle

An **angle** ($\angle$) is the union of two noncollinear rays that have the same
endpoint. The two rays are called the **sides** of the angle and their
common endpoint the **vertex** of the angle.

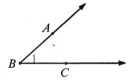
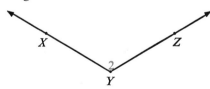

The angle at the left above is the union of $\overrightarrow{BC}$ and $\overrightarrow{BA}$. Its vertex
is B and its sides are $\overrightarrow{BC}$ and $\overrightarrow{BA}$. It can be designated in symbols by
$\angle ABC$, $\angle CBA$, or $\angle 1$. The angle at the right is the union of $\overrightarrow{YZ}$
and $\overrightarrow{YX}$. It can be designated in symbols by $\angle XYZ$, $\angle ZYX$, or $\angle 2$.

Note that when three letters are used, the letter at the vertex is always placed between the other two letters.

When there is no possibility of confusion, the single letter naming the vertex may be used in referring to an angle. Thus, the angles pictured at the bottom of page 29 could be denoted by $\angle B$ and $\angle Y$.

You should *never* refer to an angle by a single letter when two or more angles have the same vertex.

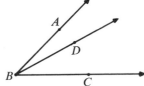

$\angle B$ could mean:

$\angle ABC$

$\angle ABD$

$\angle DBC$

The sides of an angle extend indefinitely since they are rays rather than segments. One angle therefore does not have longer sides than another.

In the discussion of the measure of an angle the term "half-plane" will be used. An informal description of the meaning of "half-plane" follows.

The diagram pictures a line *l* in plane *M*. Line *l* separates *M* into three subsets. One subset is *l*. Each of the other subsets is an infinite set of points called a **half-plane.** Each of the half-planes has edge *l*. Neither half-plane contains *l*. Coplanar half-planes that have the same edge are called *opposite half-planes.*

In the figure shown
m is the **edge** of each half-plane.
m does not lie in either half-plane.
A and *B lie in* the same half-plane.
B and *C lie in* opposite half-planes.
B and *C lie on* opposite sides of *m*.

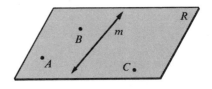

P lies in the **interior** of $\angle ABC$ in this figure. Notice that *P* and *C* lie in a half-plane with edge $\overleftrightarrow{AB}$, and *P* and *A* lie in a half-plane with edge $\overleftrightarrow{BC}$. The **interior** of $\angle ABC$ is the intersection of the half-plane that contains *C* and has edge $\overrightarrow{AB}$ and the half-plane that contains *A* and has edge $\overrightarrow{BC}$. Points *A*, *B*, and *C* lie on $\angle ABC$. Points *S* and *R*, which lie neither in the interior nor on $\angle ABC$, lie in the **exterior** of $\angle ABC$.

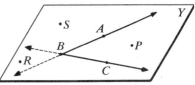

1. State four ways of referring to the angle at the right.

2. What point is the vertex of the angle?

3. Name the sides of the angle.

4. Does *A* lie in the interior of the angle?

5. Does *R* lie in the interior of ∠*RTS*?

6. Does a point separate a plane into half-planes?

7. Does a ray separate a plane into half-planes?

8. If two points lie in the same half-plane, does the segment joining them intersect the edge of the half-plane?

9. If two points lie in opposite half-planes with edge *l*, does the segment joining them intersect *l*?

10. Does the vertex of an angle lie in the interior of the angle?

11. Is the intersection of two rays always a point?

12. What point is the vertex of ∠*CDE*?

13. Name the rays that are the sides of ∠*CDE*.

14. Is the union of two coplanar rays necessarily an angle?

1. State the sides of ∠*XAB*.

2. Are $\overrightarrow{AC}$ and $\overrightarrow{AB}$ opposite rays?

3. Name three angles with vertex *A*.

4. Of what angle are rays $\overrightarrow{AC}$ and $\overrightarrow{AB}$ sides?

5. Is *X* in the interior of ∠*CAB*?

6. Is *Y* in the interior of ∠*XAB*?

Exs. 1–8

7. What ray is a common side of ∠*BAX* and ∠*BAC*?

8. Does $\overrightarrow{AX}$, excluding point *A*, lie in the interior of ∠*CAB*?

9. Are the two half-planes determined by $\overleftrightarrow{ST}$ disjoint sets of points?

10. Do A and B lie in the same half-plane with edge $\overleftrightarrow{ST}$?

11. Is A in the interior of $\angle RST$?

12. Does $\overrightarrow{ST}$ divide X into two half-planes?

13. Describe the intersection of a half-plane and its edge.

14. If P is the midpoint of $\overline{AB}$ and l is a line intersecting $\overline{AB}$ at P, do A and B lie on opposite half-planes with edge l?

1–8 Measure of Angles

When an angle is represented on paper, it is possible to find its approximate measure in degrees by using an instrument called a **protractor**. A protractor consists of a segment together with a semicircle marked off in units from 0 to 180. Most protractors have the 0 to 180 scale indicated in both directions on the arc. While one scale would be sufficient, the two make it possible to measure a greater variety of angles with less effort.

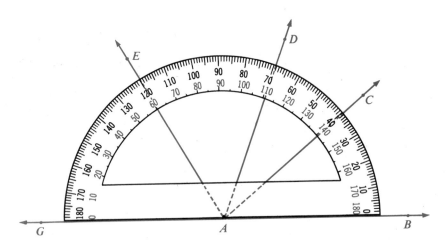

In the above figure the protractor indicates a measure of 41 for $\angle CAB$. The number 41 names the number of degrees in the angle. The *number* itself is called the **measure** of $\angle CAB$. By defining the measure of an angle as a number, we make it unnecessary to add the word "degrees" or to use the symbol for degrees (°) when giving the measure of an angle. To indicate that $\angle CAB$ has a measure of 41, you write $m\angle CAB = 41$. The measure of other angles shown is:

$$m\angle DAB = 70 \qquad\qquad m\angle EAG = 60$$

$$m\angle EAB = 120 \qquad\qquad m\angle DAG = 110$$

$$m\angle GAC = 139$$

While you could find the measures of $\angle DAC$ and $\angle EAD$ by shifting the position of the protractor, you could use subtraction.

$$m\angle DAC = 70 - 40 = 30 \qquad m\angle EAD = 120 - 70 = 50$$

The degree symbol is used when the measure of an angle is indicated in a diagram. However, when you use the words "the measure of an angle is," you report only a number and do not say "degrees." Here you see four ways of describing $\angle ABC$.

$\angle ABC$ has measure 50.
The measure of $\angle ABC$ is 50.
$m\angle ABC = 50$.
$\angle ABC$ is a 50° angle.

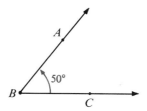

In using a protractor, you must exercise care to see that it is properly placed and correctly read. The following suggestions will help you acquire skill in using a protractor to find the approximate measure of an angle.

1. If possible, estimate whether the angle measure is greater or less than 90.
2. Place the straight edge of the protractor along one side of the angle with the center of the straight edge at the vertex of the angle.

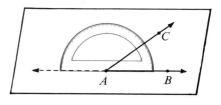

3. Read the scale that has 0 (not 180) at one side of your angle.
4. If the sides of the angle in a drawing are not long enough to reach the scale, extend them.

This figure illustrates proper placements of a protractor to determine the approximate measures of the angles of a triangle.

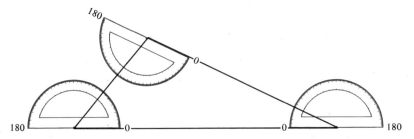

Earlier we assumed that for every point on the number line there is exactly one real number, and that for every real number there is exactly one point on the number line. Somewhat similar assumptions are made about a correspondence between the real numbers between 0 and 180 and the rays in a half-plane drawn from a given point in the edge of the half-plane.

1. Corresponding to every ray that lies in the union of a half-plane and its edge, and has as end-point a given point in the edge of the half-plane, there is exactly one number between 0 and 180 inclusive.

2. Corresponding to every number between 0 and 180 inclusive, there is exactly one ray that lies in the union of a half-plane and its edge, and has as endpoint a given point in the edge of the half-plane.

Our assumptions permit us to conclude that there is exactly one number between 0 and 180 corresponding to $\overrightarrow{PA}$. That number is the measure of $\angle APB$.

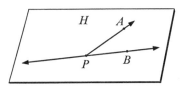

It is sometimes convenient to obtain the measure of an angle without using a particular half-plane whose edge contains a side of the angle.

As shown below, you need merely compute the absolute value of the difference between the numbers corresponding to the sides of the angle.

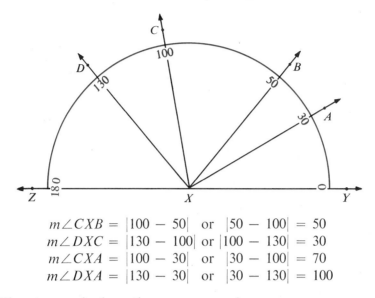

$$m\angle CXB = |100 - 50| \quad \text{or} \quad |50 - 100| = 50$$
$$m\angle DXC = |130 - 100| \quad \text{or} \quad |100 - 130| = 30$$
$$m\angle CXA = |100 - 30| \quad \text{or} \quad |30 - 100| = 70$$
$$m\angle DXA = |130 - 30| \quad \text{or} \quad |30 - 130| = 100$$

When two angles have the same measure they are called **congruent angles.** The angles pictured, $\angle ABC$ and $\angle XYZ$, are **congruent** ($\angle ABC \cong \angle XYZ$), because each has measure r. Do you see that the following statements are equivalent?

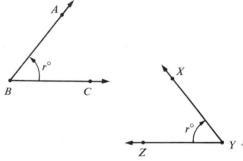

$$\angle ABC \cong \angle XYZ \qquad m\angle ABC = m\angle XYZ$$

In practical problems, angle measures that are not integers are still sometimes expressed in degrees, minutes (') and seconds ("). Recall that $1' = \frac{1}{60}^\circ$ and $1'' = \frac{1}{3600}^\circ$. The following example indicates how you can find a decimal numeral that is the measure of the pictured $\angle ABC$.

$$35°48'36'' = 35° + 48' + 36''$$
$$= 35° + \tfrac{48}{60}^\circ + \tfrac{36}{3600}^\circ$$
$$= 35° + .8° + .01°$$
$$= 35.81°$$
$$\therefore m\angle ABC = 35.81$$

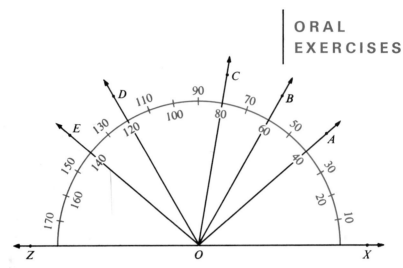

1. State the measure of $\angle AOX$, $\angle BOX$, $\angle BOA$, $\angle COB$, $\angle DOX$.
2. Name three angles whose measure is 20.
3. Does $\angle EOZ$ have the same measure as $\angle AOX$?
4. Name the angle whose sides are $\overrightarrow{OB}$ and $\overrightarrow{OD}$.
5. What ray is a common side of $\angle COB$ and $\angle BOA$?
6. Does $\overrightarrow{OB}$ divide $\angle COA$ into two angles of equal measure?
7. Is the measure of $\angle ZOE$ 140?
8. Name three angles that have $\overrightarrow{OA}$ as a side.
9. Is $m\angle COX = m\angle AOX + m\angle COA$?
10. Name three angles that have measure 60.
11. By how much does the measure of $\angle COA$ exceed that of $\angle COB$?
12. Is it correct to say "the measure of $\angle BOX$ is 60 degrees"?
13. Name all the angles that have $\overrightarrow{OC}$ as a side.
14. Which of the following are correct statements?

$$\angle EOD \cong \angle COB, \quad \angle EOD = \angle COB, \quad m\angle EOD = m\angle COB$$

15. Are $\angle COB$ and $\angle BOA$ congruent angles?
16. How many minutes are there in $2°$?
17. How many seconds are there in $\frac{1}{2}'$?
18. What part of a degree is $20'$?
19. If two angles have the same vertex and the same measure, are they the same angle? congruent angles?
20. If three distinct noncollinear rays in a half-plane have a common endpoint, how many angles do they form?

A 1. Using a straight edge draw a large triangle and a large quadrilateral on your paper. Then, using a protractor, find the approximate measure of each angle in each figure. Compute the sum of the angle measures in each figure.

2. Express $\frac{2}{3}°$ in minutes.

3. What fractional part of a degree is 48'?

4. Express $\frac{3'}{4}$ in seconds.

5. What fractional part of a minute is 24''?

6. Is 24°59'60'' equivalent to 25°?

In Exercises 7–10 assume that the sizes of ∠ABC and of ∠DBC were indicated on the adjacent figure. What would you write on the figure to indicate the size of ∠ABD?

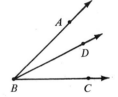

7. ∠ABC; 62°20'   ∠DBC; 43°40'

8. ∠ABC; 61°42'   ∠DBC; 42°38'40''

9. ∠ABC; 65°32'12''   ∠DBC; 43°42'20''

10. ∠ABC; 64°18'   ∠DBC; 45°25'34''

11. Name the six angles in the adjacent figure.

12. What angle has $\overrightarrow{XB}$ and $\overrightarrow{XC}$ as sides?

13. Without measuring, name the largest angle.

14. Is $m\angle CXA = m\angle BXA + m\angle CXB$?

15. Is $m\angle DXB - m\angle DXC = m\angle CXA - m\angle BXA$?

16. If $m\angle BXA = 30$ and $m\angle CXB = 40$, find $m\angle CXA$.

17. If $m\angle DXB = 70$ and $m\angle DXC = 30$, find $m\angle CXB$.

18. $m\angle DXC + m\angle CXB = m\angle$? .

19. $m\angle DXA - m\angle BXA = m\angle$? .

20. If $\angle DXB \cong \angle CXA$, is $\angle DXC \cong \angle AXB$?

21. If $m\angle DXA = a$ and $m\angle CXD = b$, find $m\angle CXA$.

22. If $m\angle DXB = a$ and $m\angle CXB = b$, find $m\angle DXC$.

Exs. 11–22

1-9 Some Special Angles and Angle Relationships

You should already be familiar with most of the terms defined below.

Acute Angle: an angle of measure less than 90.

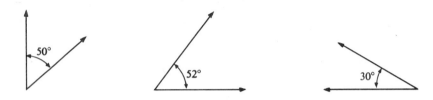

Right angle (rt. $\angle$): an angle of measure 90.

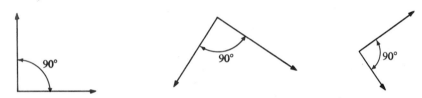

Obtuse Angle: an angle of measure greater than 90 but less than 180.

Adjacent Angles (adj. $\measuredangle$): two angles in the same plane that have a common vertex and a common side but have no interior points in common. The rays not common to both angles are called the **exterior sides** of the two adjacent angles.

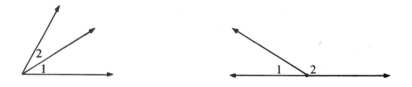

Vertical angles (vert. $\measuredangle$): angles whose sides form two pairs of opposite rays. (Recall that opposite rays form a straight line.)

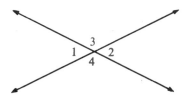

∠1 and ∠2 are vertical angles.

∠3 and ∠4 are vertical angles.

Complementary Angles: two angles the sum of whose measures is 90. Each angle is called a **complement** of the other.

Supplementary Angles: two angles the sum of whose measures is 180. Each angle is called a **supplement** of the other.

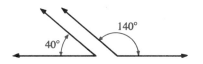

When the exterior sides of two adjacent angles are opposite rays, the sum of the angle measures is 180.

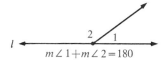 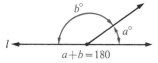

Congruent Angles: Angles which have the same measure.

Bisector of an angle: Ray $\overrightarrow{BD}$ is the bisector of ∠ABC if D lies in the interior of ∠ABC and ∠ABD ≅ ∠DBC.

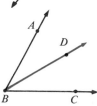

Dihedral Angle (dy-**hee**-dral): The union of a line and two noncoplanar half-planes having the line as edge. Each half-plane is called a **face** of the dihedral angle.

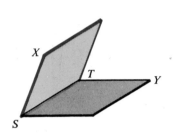

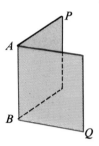

Dihedral Angle **X-ST-Y**
or **Y-ST-X**

Dihedral Angle **P-AB-Q**
or **Q-AB-P**

The expression *"dihedral angle"* is used to describe the union of certain sets of points in a space figure. In this expression, the word "angle" is not to be interpreted as meaning the union of two rays.

ORAL EXERCISES

Given the adjacent figure with $\overleftrightarrow{BD}$ and $\overleftrightarrow{AC}$ intersecting at O.

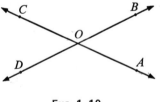

1. Which angles are acute angles?
2. Which angles are obtuse angles?
3. Name two pairs of vertical angles.
4. Name four pairs of supplementary angles.
5. What two angles are supplements of $\angle BOA$?
6. What two angles have $\overrightarrow{OC}$ as a common side?
7. Name two pairs of opposite rays.
8. What angles appear to have equal measures?
9. Is $\angle COD$ a supplement of $\angle BOA$?
10. Name two angles that are adjacent to $\angle DOA$.

Exs. 1–10

Given the figure below in which $\overleftrightarrow{AB}$ and $\overleftrightarrow{CD}$ intersect at X and $m\angle 5 = 90$. Refer to angles by numbers in answering.

11. Are $\angle 1$ and $\angle 2$ adjacent angles?

12. Are $\angle 4$ and $\angle 2$ adjacent angles?

13. Name one pair of supplementary angles.

14. Name a right angle.

15. What angles appear to be acute angles?

16. Are $\angle 1$ and $\angle 2$ complementary angles?

17. Are $\angle 1$ and $\angle 4$ vertical angles?

18. Name a pair of vertical angles.

19. If $m\angle 1 = 50$, what is the measure of $\angle 2$?

20. If $m\angle 3 = a$, what is the measure of $\angle 1$?

21. What is the sum of the measures of $\angle 1$ and $\angle 3$?

22. Can you say that $\angle 1$, $\angle 5$, and $\angle 2$ are supplementary angles?

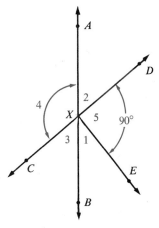

Exs. 11–22

WRITTEN
EXERCISES

In the given figure $\overleftrightarrow{AB}$ and $\overleftrightarrow{CD}$ intersect at X. Refer only to numbered angles.

1. What pairs of angles are vertical?

2. What angles appear to be acute?

3. What angles appear to be obtuse?

4. Are $\angle 3$ and $\angle 4$ adjacent angles?

5. Are $\overrightarrow{XC}$ and $\overrightarrow{XA}$ opposite rays?

6. What two angles are supplements of $\angle 5$?

7. Name two pairs of opposite rays.

8. Are $\angle 2$ and $\angle 3$ adjacent angles?

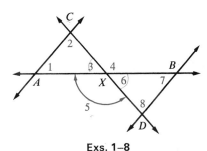

Exs. 1–8

9. Can two acute angles be supplementary?

10. Can two vertical angles, both acute, be adjacent?

11. If two angles are congruent and complementary, find the measure of each.

12. If two angles are congruent and supplementary, find the measure of each.

13. Can two angles be both complementary and adjacent?

14. How many dihedral angles are formed when two planes intersect?

EXAMPLE 1. $\angle A$ and $\angle B$ are complementary.
   $\angle A$ is an angle of 23°18′56″.
   $\angle B$ is an angle of ?°?′?″.

Solution: 90°   89°60′   89°59′60″
         $-$23°18′56″ $-$23°18′56″ $-$23°18′56″
                                   $\angle B$ is an angle of 66°41′ 4″, **Answer**

EXAMPLE 2. From 36°20′15″ subtract 10°40′48″.

Solution: 36°20′15″   35°80′15″   35°79′75″
         $-$10°40′48″ $-$10°40′48″ $-$10°40′48″
                                              25°39′27″, **Answer**

15. $\angle A$ and $\angle B$ are complementary. $\angle A$ is an angle of 23°18′56″; $\angle B$ is an angle of ?°?′?″.

16. $\angle C$ and $\angle D$ are supplementary. $\angle C$ is an angle of 110°28′. $\angle D$ is an angle of ?°?′?″.

17. By how many degrees and minutes does 28°26′ exceed 15°40′?

18. By how many degrees and minutes does 50°40′ exceed 12°52′?

19. An angle has measure $2k$. Express the measure of its complement.

20. An angle has measure $5k$. Express the measure of its supplement.

In Exs. 21–26, it is given that the measure of $\angle A$ is three times that of $\angle B$.

[B] **21.** If $\angle B$ is an angle of 45°20′30″, then $\angle A$ is an angle of ?°?′?″.

22. If $\angle A$ is an angle of 16°18′24″, then $\angle B$ is an angle of ?°?′?″.

23. If $\angle A$ and $\angle B$ are complementary, find the measure of each.

24. If $\angle A$ and $\angle B$ are supplementary, find the measure of each.

25. Find the measure of each angle if the sum of their measures is 60.

26. Find the measure of each angle if the difference of their measures is 80.

EXAMPLE 3. The measure of one of two supplementary angles is 24 less than twice the measure of the other. Find the measure of each angle.

Solution: Let $x =$ the measure of the first angle;
       then $2x - 24 =$ the measure of the second angle.

   $3x - 24 = 180$
          $3x = 204$ *Check:* 112 is 24 less than twice 68.
            $x = 68$ The sum of 112 and 68 is 180.
   $2x - 24 = 112$ 68, 112. **Answer.**

27. The measure of one of two complementary angles is 18 less than twice the measure of the other. Find the measure of each angle.

28. The measure of one of two supplementary angles is 20 more than four times the measure of the other. Find the measure of each angle.

29. Two complementary angles have measures of $3x - 10$ and $2x + 10$ respectively. Find the measure of each angle.

30. Two supplementary angles have measures of $2x - 15$ and $x + 30$. Find the measure of each angle.

31. By what number does the measure of the supplement of an acute angle exceed the measure of the complement of the angle?

32. Represent as a single fraction the measure of the complement of an angle whose measure is $\frac{2}{3}x - 10$.

$\boxed{\text{C}}$ **33.** The sum of the measures of a complement and a supplement of an angle is 184. Find the measure of the angle.

34. If $3x - 15$ is the measure of an acute angle, what restrictions are placed on x?

35. Two adjacent supplementary angles have measures of a and b respectively. Find the measure of the angle whose sides are rays that bisect the given angles.

36. The sum of the measures of two complementary angles exceeds the difference of their measures by 86. Find the measure of each angle.

CHAPTER SUMMARY

1. A set is usually specified by a roster or a rule. A set of numbers can also be specified by a graph. Sets are classified as infinite or finite with the empty set (∅) considered as finite. Union (∪) and intersection (∩) are two operations that can be performed on sets.

2. Every element of a subset of a given set must be an element of the given set. Any set is a subset of itself. The empty set is a subset of every set.

3. The relationship between two nonempty subsets of a given set can be depicted by a Venn diagram.

4. Real numbers may be pictured as points on a line with exactly one point corresponding to each real number and exactly one real number corresponding to each point. The distance between two points on a number line is the absolute value of the difference of their coordinates.

5. No attempt is made to define the terms "point," "line," and "plane." $\overline{AB}$, $\overrightarrow{AB}$, and $\overleftrightarrow{AB}$ denote sets of points. AB denotes a positive number, the length of $\overline{AB}$.

6. The measure of an angle is a real number lying between 0 and 180. When two angles have equal measures the angles are said to be congruent. If $m\angle ABC = m\angle DEF$, then $\angle ABC \cong \angle DEF$.

Vocabulary and Spelling

set (*p. 1*)
member of set (*p. 1*)
element of set (*p. 1*)
specifying a set (*p. 2*)
  by roster (*p. 2*)
  by rule (*p. 2*)
finite set (*p. 2*)
infinite set (*p. 2*)
empty set (*p. 2*)
null set (*p. 2*)
equal sets (*p. 2*)
subset (*p. 5*)
intersection of sets (*p. 6*)
disjoint sets (*p. 6*)
union of sets (*p. 6*)
Venn diagram (*p. 9*)
complement of a set (*p. 9*)
universal set (*p. 9*)
one-to-one correspondence (*p. 12*)
distance between points (*p. 13*)
coordinate system on a line (*p. 13*)
number line (*p. 13*)
  coordinate of a point (*p. 13*)
  graph of a number (*p. 13*)
  origin (*p. 13*)
absolute value (*p. 13*)
order symbols (*p. 15*)
point (*p. 18*)
line (*p. 19*)
plane (*p. 19*)
intersection of geometric figures
  (*p. 19*)

space (*p. 24*)
collinear points (*p. 24*)
coplanar points (*p. 25*)
betweenness of points (*p. 25*)
line segment (segment) (*p. 25*)
  length of (*p. 25*)
  congruent (*p. 26*)
  midpoint of (*p. 26*)
  bisector of (*p. 26*)
ray (*p. 26*)
  endpoint of (*p. 26*)
  opposite rays (*p. 26*)
angle (*p. 29*)
  sides of (*p. 29*)
  vertex of (*p. 29*)
half-plane (*p. 30*)
  edge of (*p. 30*)
interior of angle (*p. 30*)
exterior of angle (*p. 30*)
measure of angle (*p. 32*)
congruent angles (*p. 35*)
acute angle (*p. 38*)
right angle (*p. 38*)
obtuse angle (*p. 38*)
adjacent angles (*p. 38*)
vertical angles (*p. 38*)
complementary angles (*p. 39*)
supplementary angles (*p. 39*)
bisector of angle (*p. 39*)
dihedral angle (*p. 40*)

CHAPTER TEST

1–1 **1.** If $A = \{3, 4, 5, \ldots\}$, then A is a(n) __?__ set.

2. Specify by roster: {the even integers between 5 and 20}.

1–2 **3.** If $A = \{1, 2, 3\}$ and $B = \{2, 3, 4\}$, then $A \cap B = \{\_?\_\}$.

4. List the four subsets of $\{a, b\}$.

1–3 In the Venn diagram below name by number the regions you would shade to represent each of the following:

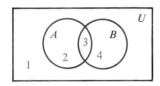

5. $A \cup B$ **6.** $A \cap B$ **7.** $\overline{A \cap B}$

1–4 **8.** Find the distance between two points whose coordinates are -3 and 5.

9. Is the coordinate of every point on a real number line a rational number?

1–5 **10.** Can two planes intersect in just one point?

11. If A, B, and C lie on a line, do $\overleftrightarrow{AB}$ and $\overleftrightarrow{BC}$ both denote that line?

1–6 **12.** If 3 points are coplanar, must they also be collinear?

13. If R, S, and T are collinear points such that $RT + TS = RS$, which point lies between the other two?

14. Does $\overline{AB}$ denote a line, a segment, or a distance?

1–7 **15.** Is the edge of a half-plane contained in the half-plane?

16. Name the ray that is a common side of $\angle RST$ and $\angle PST$.

1–8 **17.** Can the measure of an angle be a negative number?

18. If $m\angle ABC = m\angle RST$ is $\angle ABC \cong \angle RST$?

1–9 **19.** Is a right angle an acute angle, an obtuse angle, or neither?

20. If two angles are both congruent and complementary, what is the measure of each?

CHAPTER REVIEW

1–1 Representing Sets   *Pages 1–5*

   1. A set that contains no elements is called the __?__ .
   2. The symbol $\in$ is read "__?__".
   3. Is the set of rational numbers between 2 and 3 an infinite set?
   4. Do $\{0\}$ and $\emptyset$ represent the same set?

1–2 Relationships between Sets   *Pages 5–9*

   5. Two sets that do not intersect are said to be __?__ .
   6. If $x \in A$ and $x \in B$, must A and B intersect?
   7. $A \cap B$ denotes the __?__ of A and B while $A \cup B$ represents the __?__ of A and B.
   8. The intersection of $\{a, b, c, d\}$ and $\{b, c\}$ is $\{\underline{\ ?\ }\}$.

1–3 Venn Diagrams   *Pages 9–12*

   9. Draw a diagram which depicts the relationship between the sets:

$$U = \{\text{all integers}\}$$
$$A = \{\text{all positive integers}\}$$
$$B = \{\text{all positive odd integers}\}$$

1–4 Number Lines   *Pages 12–18*

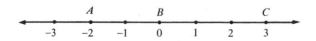

   10. The __?__ of point A is -2.
   11. Point B is called the __?__ .
   12. The coordinate of a point halfway between A and C is __?__ .
   13. Evaluate $|-8| - |3|$.

1–5 Basic Undefined Terms   *Pages 18–24*

   14. When two lines cross they are said to __?__ .
   15. Is a line an infinite set of points?
   16. If a line lies in a plane, the plane __?__ the line.
   17. If points X and Y lie in a plane, must $\overleftrightarrow{XY}$ lie in that plane?

1–6 Some Basic Definitions *Pages 24–29*

18. If three points lie on a line, they are __?__.
19. $\overline{AB}$ represents a __?__ with endpoints __?__ and __?__.
20. The endpoint of $\overrightarrow{BA}$ is point __?__.
21. The length of $\overline{RS}$ is denoted by __?__.

1–7 Angle *Pages 29–32*

22. An angle is the __?__ of two __?__ rays that have the same endpoint.
23. A line separates a plane into two __?__.
24. A point on the edge of a half-plane __?__ ($\in$ or $\notin$) the half-plane.
25. The sides of $\angle DEF$ are $\overrightarrow{\underline{\quad ? \quad}}$ and $\overrightarrow{\underline{\quad ? \quad}}$.

1–8 Measure of Angles *Pages 32–37*

26. If $m\angle RST = m\angle ABC$, then $\angle RST$? $\angle ABC$.
27. If r is the measure of an angle then __?__ $< r <$ __?__.
28. If the numbers on a protractor that correspond with the sides of an angle are 110 and 70, then the measure of the angle is __?__.
29. If an angle of 25°20′ is bisected, each resulting angle is an angle of ?°?′.

1–9 Some Special Angles and Angle Relationships *Pages 38–43*

Given $\overleftrightarrow{AB}$ and $\overleftrightarrow{DC}$ are lines.

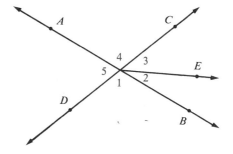

30. $\angle 1$ and $\angle$? are vertical angles.
31. $\angle 2$ and $\angle 3$ are a pair of __?__ angles.
32. $m\angle 1 + m\angle 5 =$ __?__.
33. If $m\angle 4 > 90$, then $\angle 4$ is a(n) __?__ angle.

• EXTRA FOR EXPERTS

Testing Laws of Set Algebra

There is an algebra of sets just as there is an algebra of numbers. A variety of laws or formulas can be developed by combining the operations of union, intersection, and complement in this set algebra. One method of testing the validity of a formula in set algebra is that of "numbering parts." An illustration of the use of this technique in testing a formula involving three sets follows:

Given: The universal set U with subsets A, B, and C.

Verify: $A \cap (B \cup C) = (A \cap B) \cup (A \cap C)$

Procedure:

1. Make a Venn diagram and number each distinct region.

2. Represent each set by enclosing within brackets the numbered regions within its boundaries.

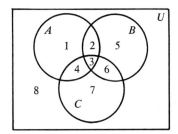

$$A = [1, 2, 3, 4]$$
$$B = [2, 3, 5, 6]$$
$$C = [3, 4, 6, 7]$$

3. Determine the regions in each member of the formula and show that they are the same.

$$A \cap (B \cup C) = [1, 2, 3, 4] \cap ([2, 3, 5, 6] \cup [3, 4, 6, 7])$$
$$= [1, 2, 3, 4] \cap [2, 3, 4, 5, 6, 7] = [2, 3, 4]$$
$$(A \cap B) \cup (A \cap C) = ([1, 2, 3, 4] \cap [2, 3, 5, 6])$$
$$\cup ([1, 2, 3, 4] \cap [3, 4, 6, 7])$$
$$= [2, 3] \cup [3, 4] = [2, 3, 4]$$

Therefore $A \cap (B \cup C) = (A \cap B) \cup (A \cap C)$, since both consist of regions 2, 3, 4.

EXERCISES

Using Venn diagrams and the method of "numbering parts," test the validity of the following formulas.

1. $A \cap (A \cup B) = A$

2. $A \cup (A \cap B) = A$

3. $(A \cap \overline{B}) \cup (A \cap B) = A$

4. $(A \cap B) \cap (A \cap \overline{B}) = \emptyset$

5. $\overline{A} \cap \overline{B} = \overline{A \cup B}$

6. $A \cup (B \cup C) = (A \cup B) \cup C$

7. $A \cap (B \cap C) = (A \cap B) \cap C$

8. $A \cup (B \cap C) = (A \cup B) \cap (A \cup C)$

▶ Father of Greek Mathematics

Who could be more appropriate to begin this series of stories about the history of geometry than the man who bears the title "Father of Greek Mathematics"? Thales, an important geometer, lived in the period around 600 B.C. As a young man, he was a successful merchant whose affairs took him to many lands. While in Egypt, he became fascinated by the arithmetic and geometry known to the priests. There he worked out a method for finding the heights of pyramids by using their shadows.

Retiring from commerce at an early age, Thales devoted himself to the study of mathematics and philosophy. He set out to prove properties of geometric figures by deduction rather than by measurement. Among his proved conclusions were two theorems you will study:

Two vertical angles are congruent.
If two sides of a triangle are congruent, the angles opposite them are congruent.

Thales was also interested in astronomy. For his many contributions, which included the correct number of days in a year, he became known as the first of the Seven Wise Men of Greece, about whom many legends exist today.

The following account illustrates the strong practical side of Thales. On one occasion as a merchant, he was transporting several large sacks of salt by donkeys to a neighboring town. While crossing a shallow river, one of the donkeys slipped and fell. Naturally some of the salt dissolved in the water, resulting in a lighter load. When the same donkey came to the second water crossing, it purposely fell in an effort to further lighten its load. At the next seaboard town, Thales purchased a large number of sponges and loaded them on the donkey's back. At the next water crossing, the donkey again went into its stumbling act, needless to say, for the last time!

2

Induction and Deduction

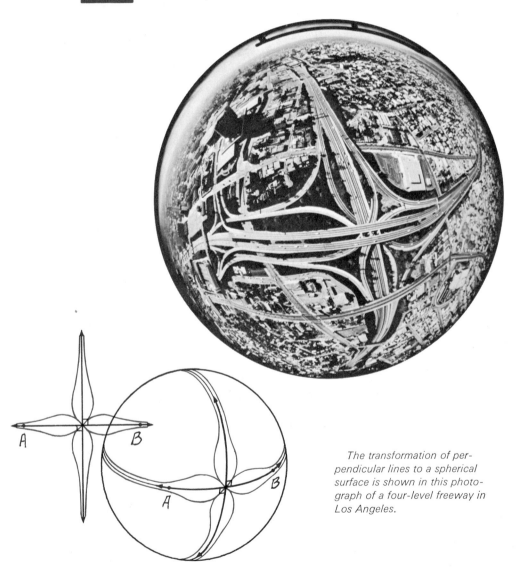

The transformation of perpendicular lines to a spherical surface is shown in this photograph of a four-level freeway in Los Angeles.

Centuries ago, in the land of Egypt, the art of measurement developed out of practical necessity. The annual overflowing of the Nile River benefited the people of the valley by enriching their soil, but it also washed out their property lines. History tells us that every year specialists had to determine boundaries so that each farmer could again cultivate his part of the rich land.

The measurement specialists also designed buildings for grain storage, temples for worship, and pyramids for royal burials. They developed accurate means of determining north-south and east-west lines. North-south lines, based upon observations of the sun and stars, were laid out first. Then came east-west lines. The priests insisted that the lines be laid out carefully in temple construction so that temple doors would face due east.

The mathematician of the Egyptian era found east by using ropes. Consequently he was called a rope-stretcher. He found his east-west line from a north-south line by making a right angle in this way:

He tied knots in a rope to get twelve equal spaces. He chose knots S and T to divide the rope into lengths of 3, 4, and 5 units.

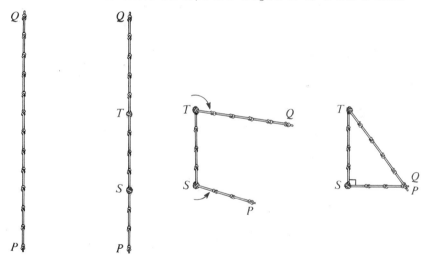

He put S and T on a north-south line, drove stakes at S and T, kept the rope tight, and swung ends P and Q.

When P and Q met he had a right angle at S.

The rope-stretcher happened to be correct. He did not know why he had a right angle, but many trials had taught him a principle that worked.

The Egyptians arrived at their geometric rules through inductive (in-**duk**-tiv) thinking. This means that they tried things out many times, observed results, and then guessed at general laws. You

51

probably suspect that the Egyptians made some mistakes. They did. For example, they decided that a formula for the area of a circle was $A = (\frac{8}{9}d)^2$. This formula, while in error by about one-half of one percent, would give results accurate enough for many purposes even today.

■ Induction, A Method of Discovery

2–1 Meaning of Induction and Intuition

You have done inductive thinking throughout your life. As a small child you thought inductively when you decided that touching a hot stove would burn you. Now you think inductively when you decide, after many trials, which of two soda fountains makes the tastier sundaes. Inductive thinking occurs when you observe individual events and then guess at a general law. **Induction** (in-**duk**-shun) is the process of finding a general principle based upon the evidence of specific cases. The statement of the general principle is also called an induction.

Notice that induction involves guessing. While the process does not always lead to correct results, inductive thinking is a valuable method of discovering likely conclusions. A scientist often uses induction, and so does a politician. You should use the method, as such people do, with reasonable caution.

Nobody can give you a fool-proof set of rules for using induction. You must develop your own judgment. Right now you can easily detect foolish extremes. Think of the man who concludes that he will always be able to lift a calf as the calf grows up just because he has been able to lift the calf each day so far. That man is an optimistic guesser quite different from a man so cautious that he sees no reason to expect the sun to rise in the east tomorrow just because it has always risen there before.

Consider a poor use of induction in mathematics: the case of a man whose experience leads him to believe that every integer is less than one billion. The man could even spend his life presenting evidence to support his opinion. He might say, "Take one. One is less than one billion. Take two. Two is less than one billion." And so on. The man is blinded by details. Very likely you see a quick way to settle the billion matter. You need merely think of the number one billion and one.

When you "sense" something, when you "just feel sure" that something is true, you are doing *intuitive* (in-**too**-i-tiv) thinking. **Intuition** is that kind of mental activity which gives you information or beliefs which are based on hunches or insight. Here is an example of a simple intuitive discovery in geometry:

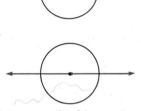

Draw a circle. In the plane of the circle draw a line through the center of the circle.

It is intuitively evident that the line divides the circle into two regions of equal area. Furthermore, you can "see," without a single additional drawing, that any line through the center of any circle must divide that circle into two regions of equal area.

You should recognize induction and intuition as valuable tools. They are used for making discoveries in daily life, in science, and in mathematics. But you must remember that a principle supported by inductive or intuitive thinking is based upon a guess. An intelligent guess is only the beginning of a mathematician's work. Since a major part of his work is to prove statements to be correct or incorrect, this book will emphasize proofs.

ORAL EXERCISES

Tell whether the process used is inductive, intuitive, or neither.

1. The boys present at a meeting of their club give their ages as 11, 12, 11, 11, 13, 12, 12, 12, 11 and 12. A visitor decides, "All boys in this club are at least eleven years old."

2. A girl looks into several robins' nests and says, "All robins' eggs are blue."

3. A courtroom spectator merely looks into a defendant's eyes before saying, "He's guilty, I tell you."

4. A juror serves on a case in which the charge is speeding. Upon finding out that the defendant has already been convicted several times for speeding, a juror mutters to himself: "That speeder is guilty."

5. Some scientists have controlled a gorilla's environment so that it has never seen any kind of tool used. One day, after gazing hungrily for some time at a banana that is just out of reach, the gorilla suddenly seizes a stick and rakes the banana up to his cage.

6. A gorilla, though it has always been kept in a cage without any sticks, has often seen animals in adjoining cages use sticks to move objects. One day when he is given a stick he promptly uses the stick to rake a banana up to his cage.

7. On Mary's fourth birthday her mother baked a birthday cake. Later that year the mother baked a birthday cake for Ann, and later still one for John. Mary then said, "Mother makes a cake whenever one of us has a birthday."

8. Jim had just transferred to East High. He knew of the rule that a transfer student was not eligible for a varsity team until he had been in East High for a semester. He said, "I'm not going out for basketball. I wouldn't be eligible anyhow."

9. Sue learned that she was older than Peggy, and that Peggy was older than Mary. She then said, "I am older than Mary."

10. Elmer was sent to the office on four consecutive days for being late to class. As he arrived late the fifth day he murmured, "I will be sent to the office."

11. On his way to the office Elmer said to himself, "I was late because the bell rang early."

WRITTEN EXERCISES

State conclusions that seem reasonable.

EXAMPLE. Five radish seeds soaked in a certain chemical develop later into yellow radishes. Six spinach seeds soaked in that chemical develop into grasslike plants. Four kernels of corn soaked in that chemical develop into unusually tall stalks.

Solution: That chemical so affects seeds that normal plants do not develop.

[A]
1. You eat a new kind of fruit and then suffer from hives for the first time in your life. A week later you try the fruit again, only to have hives again. You have a similar experience a month later.

2. You watch an ant taste a liquid and die. Then several more ants sample the liquid and die.

3. A man uses a weed-killer on his lawn and notices that most of the clover plants die.

4. One colony of virus X flourishes when placed in a certain gelatin. Five other trials with virus X in that kind of gelatin give similar results.

5. You find a nest of strange eggs, similar to each other. The first three eggs hatch into lizards.

6. The ambassador to the United States from country Z states his country's position on an issue, but the very next day country Z acts in a way that contradicts the ambassador. The ambassador then states that all political prisoners in Z will be freed. Within a week twelve political prisoners in Z are hanged.

7. A teacher gave all her classes true-false tests on seven consecutive Tuesdays.

8. A boy questioned all fifty of the seniors in his high school and learned that English was the only course all fifty were taking in common.

In Exercises 9–16 predict the *n*th term of a sequence of terms of which the first five terms are shown.

EXAMPLE. 6, 7, 8, 9, 10

Solution: Each term shown is 5 greater than the number of the term. Prediction: the *n*th term is $n + 5$. **Answer.**

9. 1, 2, 3, 4, 5, . . .

10. 4, 5, 6, 7, 8, . . .

11. 2, 4, 6, 8, . . .

12. 2, 4, 8, 16, 32, . . .

13. 5, 10, 15, 20, 25, . . .

14. $-3, -2, -1, 0, 1, . . .$

15. $1, \frac{1}{2}, \frac{1}{3}, \frac{1}{4}, \frac{1}{5}, . . .$

16. $\frac{1}{2}, \frac{2}{3}, \frac{3}{4}, \frac{4}{5}, \frac{5}{6}, . . .$

In Exercises 17–20 make a statement based upon inductive thinking.

EXAMPLE. The sum of the first two positive integers is 3, or $\dfrac{2 \cdot 3}{2}$.

The sum of the first three positive integers is 6, or $\dfrac{3 \cdot 4}{2}$.

The sum of the first four positive integers is 10, or $\dfrac{4 \cdot 5}{2}$.

Solution: Is the sum of the first five positive integers $\dfrac{5 \cdot 6}{2}$?

Yes, $1 + 2 + 3 + 4 + 5 = 15$, and $15 = \dfrac{5 \cdot 6}{2}$

The sum of the first *n* positive integers is $\dfrac{n(n + 1)}{2}$. **Answer.**

B

17. The sum of the first 2 positive even integers is 6, or $2 \cdot 3$.
The sum of the first 3 positive even integers is 12, or $3 \cdot 4$.
The sum of the first 4 positive even integers is 20, or $4 \cdot 5$.

18. The sum of the first 2 positive odd integers is 4, or 2^2.
The sum of the first 3 positive odd integers is 9, or 3^2.

19. Join all pairs in a set of 3 points and 3, or $\dfrac{3 \cdot 2}{2}$, segments are formed whose endpoints belong to the given set.

Join all pairs in a set of 4 points and 6, or $\dfrac{4 \cdot 3}{2}$, segments are formed whose endpoints belong to the given set.

20. 12, 15, 21, 30, and 126 are all multiples of 3. The sums of the digits of these numbers, 3, 6, 3, 3, and 9, are also multiples of 3.

$\boxed{\text{C}}$　**21.** Tom tested the expression $n^2 + n + 17$ and reported: No matter what positive integer you use for n, the number $n^2 + n + 17$ is a prime number. Show that Tom's induction is not correct.

22. Predict the nth term of a sequence of terms in which the first term is 7, the second term 0.49, and the third term 0.0343.

2–2　Perpendicular Lines and Circles

You already know many things about perpendicular lines and circles, but you will want to check your knowledge against the definitions shown below.

When two lines meet to form congruent adjacent angles, the lines are said to be **perpendicular** ($\perp$), and each line is a perpendicular to the other line. Segments or rays which are parts of the lines are also called perpendicular. A line, ray, or segment which is perpendicular to a segment at its midpoint is a **perpendicular bisector** of that segment.

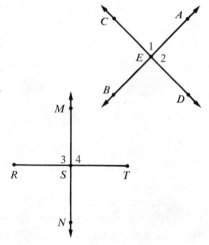

If $m\angle 1 = m\angle 2$ in the adjacent figure then $\overleftrightarrow{AB}$ is perpendicular to $\overleftrightarrow{CD}$. This is denoted by writing $\overleftrightarrow{AB} \perp \overleftrightarrow{CD}$. Also in this figure $\overrightarrow{AB} \perp \overline{CD}$, $\overrightarrow{EA} \perp \overrightarrow{ED}$, and so on, for other appropriate combinations of lines, rays, or segments.

If $m\angle 3 = m\angle 4$ and $RS = ST$, then $\overleftrightarrow{MN}$, $\overline{MN}$, $\overrightarrow{SM}$, and $\overrightarrow{SN}$ can each be described as a "perpendicular bisector" of $\overline{RT}$. In a given plane the expression "the perpendicular bisector of a segment," unless specified otherwise, refers to a line.

A *line is perpendicular to a plane* when the line is perpendicular to every line in the plane that passes through its foot (the point of intersection). Here $\overline{PQ}$, as well as $\overleftrightarrow{PQ}$, is perpendicular to plane X provided that $\overline{PQ} \perp \overleftrightarrow{QA}$, $\overline{PQ} \perp \overleftrightarrow{QB}$, $\overline{PQ} \perp \overleftrightarrow{QC}, \ldots$

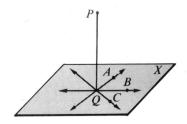

A **circle** ($\odot$) is the set of all points in a plane that are at a given distance from a given point in the plane. That given point is the **center**. $\odot P$ denotes a circle whose center is P.

A circle separates the set of points of a plane into three subsets: the circle itself, the interior of the circle, and the exterior of the circle.

A **radius** is a segment joining the center of a circle to a point on the circle. $\overline{PA}$ is a radius. $\overline{PA}$, $\overline{PB}$, and $\overline{PC}$ are radii.

A **chord** (kord) is a segment whose endpoints lie on a circle. Both $\overline{RS}$ and $\overline{AC}$ are chords.

A **diameter** is a chord that contains the center. $\overline{AC}$ is a diameter.

A line that contains a chord is called a **secant**. $\overleftrightarrow{RS}$ is a secant, and so is $\overleftrightarrow{AC}$.

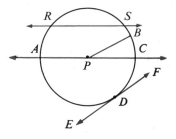

A **tangent** to a circle is a line in the plane of the circle which intersects the circle in exactly one point. That point is called a **point of tangency** or **point of contact**. In the figure shown above, point D is a point of contact and $\overleftrightarrow{EF}$ is a tangent. Circle P is said to be tangent to $\overleftrightarrow{EF}$ at point D. Two or more circles that lie in the same plane and have the same center are called **concentric circles**.

Radius and diameter are names for segments. At times the same words denote lengths of segments. For example, $\overline{ON}$ is a radius of the circle shown. The radius of the circle is 5.

Tangent and secant are names for lines, but are also names for segments. Thus "tangent PQ" in relation to this figure can mean: $\overleftrightarrow{PQ}$, a line through P tangent to $\odot O$ at Q; $\overline{PQ}$, a segment from P to Q, a point of tangency. Similarly "secant AC" can mean: $\overleftrightarrow{AC}$, the line containing chord $\overline{BC}$; $\overline{AC}$ the segment from A to C. When there might be doubt about the intended meaning, use an additional word as in Oral Exercise 1 below.

ORAL EXERCISES

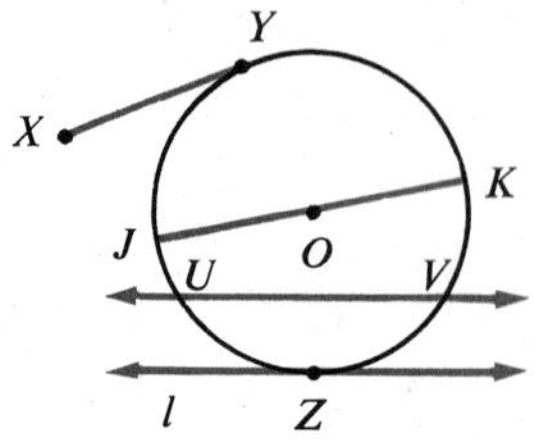

1. In the given diagram, name the center; a radius; a diameter; two chords; a secant; a tangent (line); a tangent (segment); two points of tangency.
2. State the diameter of a circle whose radius is 3; $11\frac{1}{2}$; 13.2; n.
3. State the radius of a circle in which the longest chord has length 10; 9; 15.46; k.
4. Can a tangent to a circle contain a given point not in the plane of the circle?
5. Given a point in the interior but not at the center of a circle. That point lies on how many radii of the circle? diameters? chords? secants? tangents?
6. Given two points in the interior but not at the center of a circle. Both points lie on how many radii of the circle? diameters? chords? secants? tangents?
7. The radius of $\odot O$ is 5, and point X lies in the plane of $\odot O$. What can you say about the position of X if $OX = 5$? if $OX = 2$? if $OX > 5$?
8. The radius of $\odot P$ is 6, and points Y and Z lie in the plane of $\odot P$. What can you say about YZ if Y and Z are both on the circle? in the interior of the circle? in the exterior of the circle?

WRITTEN EXERCISES

Exercises 1–12 in this section deal with plane figures.

A

1. Draw a line. In one of the half-planes sketch several circles that have congruent radii and are tangent to the line. What figure contains the centers of all the circles?

2. Select a point on a line and draw several circles tangent to the line at that point. What figure contains the centers of all the circles?

3. Draw a circle and a set of parallel chords of that circle. What figure contains the midpoints of all chords in the set?

4. Draw two nonparallel chords of a circle. Draw the perpendicular bisector of each chord. Where do the perpendicular bisectors meet?

Make a sufficient number of sketches for reasonable inductions or intuitive discoveries. Then complete the statements.

EXAMPLE. A line drawn perpendicular to a tangent at the point of tangency passes __?__ .

Draw: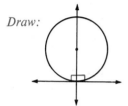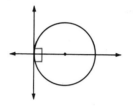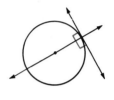

Solution: through the center of the circle.

B

5. A line perpendicular to a radius at the outer end of the radius is __?__ .

6. Two lines tangent to a circle at the ends of a diameter are __?__ .

7. The two tangents (segments) to a circle from an outside point are __?__ .

8. A radius that is perpendicular to a chord __?__ the chord.

9. If two chords of a circle are equally distant from the center, then __?__ .

10. If two chords are unequally distant from the center of a circle, then those chords have __?__ , and the one at the greater distance from the center __?__ .

11. If $\overrightarrow{PX}$ and $\overrightarrow{PY}$ are tangent to $\odot O$ at X and Y, then $\overrightarrow{PO}$ __?__ $\angle XPY$.

12. If $\overrightarrow{PX}$ is a tangent from P to $\odot O$, then $\overline{XO}$ __?__ $\overline{PX}$.

2–3 Spheres

Many properties of a circle suggest related properties of a sphere. Notice, for example, that we define a sphere just as we defined a circle, except for omitting the restriction *in a plane*.

A **sphere** is the set of all points at a given distance from a given point.

You will see that you can often define terms which are used for spheres as well as for circles simply by replacing the word *circle* by the word *sphere*.

You usually represent a sphere by drawing a circle. Sometimes you draw an oval as well so that the reader is sure to "see" a sphere, not just a circle. Here is shown a sphere *P*.

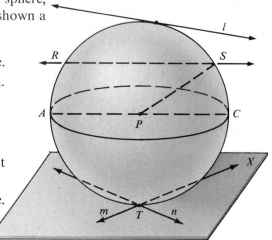

P is the center of the sphere.

$\overline{PA}$, $\overline{PS}$, and $\overline{PC}$ are radii.

$\overline{RS}$ and $\overline{AC}$ are chords.

$\overline{AC}$ is a diameter.

$\overleftrightarrow{RS}$ is a secant.

Lines *l*, *m*, and *n* are tangent lines.

Plane *X* is a tangent plane. Sphere *P* is tangent to plane *X* at *T*.

A sphere separates all the points of space into three subsets: the exterior of the sphere, the sphere itself, and the interior of the sphere.

A **common tangent** of two spheres is a line that is tangent to both spheres. A **common tangent plane** of two spheres is a plane that is tangent to both spheres.

ORAL EXERCISES

1. What word would you use to describe two spheres which have the same center?

2. What is the greatest number of points in which a sphere can intersect a line?

3. The radius of sphere *O* has length *n*. Describe the position of a point *X* (a) if $OX = n$; (b) if $OX < n$; (c) if $OX > n$.

4. Two concentric spheres with center *O* have radii *p* and *q* respectively. What can you say about point *Y* if $p < OY < q$?

5. How many diameters of a sphere does a plane through the center of the sphere contain?

6. How many radii (segments), no three in one plane, can be drawn in a sphere?

7. How many planes containing a given point can be drawn tangent to a given sphere if the point (a) is an interior point? (b) is a point of the sphere? (c) is an exterior point?

8. Suppose that a plane intersects a sphere in more than one point. How many points of intersection are there? What single word describes the set of points in the intersection? *circle*

9. How many spheres can be tangent to a given plane at a given point of the plane? What word describes the set of points which are centers of such spheres?

10. How many spheres can be tangent to a given sphere at a given point? Must their centers lie in the exterior of the given sphere?

**WRITTEN
EXERCISES**

Write a definition for

 1. A radius of a sphere.   3. A line tangent to a sphere.

2. A diameter of a sphere.   4. A plane tangent to a sphere.

Tell how many common tangent planes two spheres with unequal radii have when:

5. One sphere lies in the interior of the other.

6. Each sphere lies in the exterior of the other.

7. The spheres intersect in exactly one point and have no interior points in common.

8. The spheres intersect in exactly one point and have interior points in common.

9. What does intuition tell you about two planes tangent to a sphere, one at each end of a given diameter? Draw a figure.

10. Draw a figure showing two perpendicular radii, $\overline{OA}$ and $\overline{OB}$, of a sphere. Lines *l* and *m* are coplanar with $\overline{OA}$ and $\overline{OB}$ and are tangent to the sphere at *A* and *B* respectively. What does intuition suggest about lines *l* and *m*?

 11. Draw a figure showing $\overline{AB}$, $\overline{AC}$, and $\overline{AD}$ tangent to a given sphere at points *B*, *C*, and *D* respectively. Use sticks and a globe or ball if you cannot picture the situation. Tell what appears to be true about *AB*, *AC*, and *AD*.

12. Spheres Q and P each lie in the exterior of the other. The radius of sphere Q is less than that of P. $\overline{A_1B_1}$ is tangent to spheres P and Q at A_1 and B_1 respectively; likewise $\overline{A_2B_2}$ and $\overline{A_3B_3}$. $\overleftrightarrow{A_1B_1}$, $\overleftrightarrow{A_2B_2}$, $\overleftrightarrow{A_3B_3}$ all pass through a point X. Draw a figure. Tell what you believe to be true about A_1B_1, A_2B_2, and A_3B_3.

Using induction and intuition, complete the following statements.

EXAMPLE. A line perpendicular to a radius of a sphere at its outer endpoint __?__.

Solution: is tangent to the sphere.

13. A radius of a sphere drawn to the point of contact of a line tangent to the sphere __?__.

14. A plane perpendicular to a radius of a sphere at its outer endpoint __?__.

15. A line containing the center of a sphere and perpendicular to a plane that is tangent to the sphere passes __?__.

16. A line is tangent to a sphere. A plane perpendicular to that line at the point of tangency passes __?__.

C **17.** The centers of three spheres are the vertices of an equilateral triangle. The length of the radius of each sphere is one-fourth the length of the side of the triangle. How many distinct planes, each one tangent to every sphere, can be drawn?

18. Use the three spheres of Exercise 17. How many new spheres, each tangent to each of the given three, can be drawn?

▪ Deduction, A Method of Proof

2–4   Deductive Reasoning

Suppose you know that the following two statements are true.

1. Every cheerleader in Laville High is a junior.
2. Maria is a cheerleader in Laville High.

On the basis of these two statements you can reason to the following conclusion:

Conclusion: Maria is a junior.

Although you never before heard of Maria of Laville High, common sense, with no guessing involved, tells you that if statements 1 and 2 are correct, then the conclusion shown is also correct.

The type of reasoning used in reaching the conclusion in this example is called **deductive reasoning.** When you accept some statements and reason from them to a conclusion you are reasoning *deductively* (dee-**duk**-tiv-ly). The process is called *deduction* (dee-**duk**-shun). Sometimes the conclusion is itself called a *deduction.* You can say that you *deduce* a new fact from accepted facts.

The following examples show that you sometimes reason deductively without stating some fact that you expect everybody to accept as true.

EXAMPLE 1.

Let us analyze the following *assertion* to see how deductive reasoning is involved:

Since Martinez plays major league baseball, he gets a good salary.

In this assertion, the following *accepted statement* is made:

Martinez plays major league baseball.

You expect people to make and accept the following statement:

All major league baseball players get good salaries.

You can reach the *conclusion:* Martinez gets a good salary.

EXAMPLE 2.

Assertion: If $\frac{1}{3}x = 5$, then $x = 15$.

Accepted statement made: $\frac{1}{3}x = 5$.

Statement you expect people to make and accept: For any numbers a, b, and c, if $a = b$ then $ca = cb$.

Conclusion: $3(\frac{1}{3}x) = 3 \cdot 5$, or $x = 15$.

When a mathematician is searching for new mathematical ideas, he uses *induction.* When he wants to put accepted ideas together and draw conclusions from them, he uses *deduction.*

ORAL EXERCISES

Is the thinking illustrated inductive or deductive?

1. A child examines eight acorns and concludes that all acorns are hard.

2. If $3x = 12$, $x = 4$.

3. Since today is Tuesday, tomorrow will be Wednesday.

4. It will rain on Christmas again this year since it has done so for the last five years.

5. If the perimeter of a square is 4 in., then each side is 1 in. long.

State a conclusion based on the given information.

6. Lead is heavier than iron. Iron is heavier than aluminum.

7. The Whites always have hot dogs on Tuesday. Today is Tuesday.

8. b is greater than a, and a equals c.

9. Only bright students get all A's. Bob gets all A's.

10. The product of p and q is negative, but p is positive.

11. All librarians love books. Mary's aunt is a librarian.

12. $x + y = 10$ and $x = 6$.

WRITTEN EXERCISES

In Exercises 1–6 state, if possible, whether Sue is older or younger than Bill.

1. Sue is ten years old and Bill is nine years old.

2. Sue is twelve years old and Bill is twelve years old.

3. Bill is more than fourteen and Sue is less than fourteen.

4. Sue is older than Mary and Bill is older than Mary.

5. Sue is older than Mary and Bill is younger than Mary.

6. Sue is older than Mary and Bill is older than Tom.

A teacher told a student that she had two of the three numbers 1, 2, 3 in mind. The student then made the statements listed below. Which of them represent conclusions arrived at by correct deductive reasoning?

7. At least one of your numbers is odd.

8. The average of your two numbers is greater than $1\frac{1}{4}$.

9. One of your numbers is 3.

10. The difference between your numbers is 1.

11. The first number you have in mind is greater than the second.

12. The sum of the squares of your numbers is less than 14.

State a conclusion, when possible, based on the given statement.

13. x is a number such that $5x = 10$.

14. g is a number such that $7g = 7h$.

15. t is a whole number between 22.3 and 23.7.

16. k is a number whose square is 81.

17. The product of a and b is 12.

18. $a \cdot 0 = 0$.

19. The square of the integer n is an odd number.

20. The square of the integer n is an even number.

In each of the following exercises the first two statements are accepted as facts. These are followed by a conclusion. State whether the conclusion represents correct or faulty deductive reasoning.

21. A student must study in order to pass his exams. John studies. Therefore, John will pass his exams.

22. A rectangle has four right angles. A square is a rectangle. Therefore, a square has four right angles.

23. Nobody works at the mill during a strike. Nobody is working today at the mill. Therefore, there is a strike at the mill.

24. Jane's dad goes fishing every Saturday. Today is Saturday. Therefore, Jane's dad will go fishing.

State a conclusion, when possible, based on the given data.

EXAMPLE 1. n is the larger root of the equation $x^2 - x - 12 = 0$.

Solution: Since $x^2 - x - 12 = 0$ is a quadratic equation, we try to solve the equation by the factoring method.

$$(x - 4)(x + 3) = 0$$
$$x - 4 = 0 \qquad x + 3 = 0$$
$$x = 4 \qquad x = -3$$

The two possible roots, 4 and -3, both check. Of the two roots, 4 is the greater. We deduce that $n = 4$.

EXAMPLE 2. All bears like honey, and my pet likes honey.

Solution: No definite conclusion is possible. Perhaps some other animals also like honey.

B   **25.** n is an integer between 7.2 and 9.3.

26. n is a negative number whose square is 9.

27. All rabbits like lettuce, and my pet does not like lettuce.

28. Only girls wear braids, and my child wears braids.

29. n is the larger root of $x^2 - 5x + 6 = 0$.

30. n is the smaller root of $x^2 - 6x + 8 = 0$.

31. $b \cdot c = 0$, and b is not zero.   **34.** $x = 12 - y$, and $y > 0$.

32. $bd = 7$, and $b = 2$.   **35.** $a + b > c + d$.

33. $x + y = 12$, and $x > 6$.   **36.** $a + k < b + k$.

37. No jazz lovers like poetry, and Irene likes poetry.

38. No jazz lovers like poetry, and Kate loves jazz.

39. No jazz lovers like poetry, and Tom does not like poetry.

40. No jazz lovers like poetry, and Sam hates jazz.

41. All right angles are congruent, and $\angle 1$ and $\angle 2$ are congruent angles.

42. Adjacent angles have a common side, and $\angle 1$ and $\angle 2$ do not have a common side.

State a conclusion based on the given information.

43. The measure of the area of a given square is six times the measure of its side.

44. The measure of the area of a given square is less than the measure of its perimeter.

45. n is a root of each of the following equations.

$$x^2 - x - 6 = 0, \ x^2 - 7x + 12 = 0, \ x^3 - 4x^2 + 2x + 3 = 0$$

46. n is a root of each of the following equations.

$$\frac{2}{x} = \frac{x}{8}, \ x^3 = 16x, \ x^3 = x^2 + 48$$

47. x and y are two numbers such that $x + y > 12$, and $x - y < 12$.

48. x is a number such that $x^2 - x < 12$.

2–5   Deduction and Logic

In Section 2–4 you did what people often do; you used reasoning patterns that you intuitively felt to be correct. Intuition is not the only way to distinguish between correct and incorrect reasoning patterns. You can consciously employ principles of **logic** that have been known since the days of early Greece.

When investigating reasoning patterns logicians (lo-**ji**-shuns) use symbols such as p and q to represent statements. That is, p and q are variables whose domain is a set of statements. For p you might substitute the specific statement: $\angle ABC$ *is a right angle.* You could equally well substitute: *Every cheerleader in Laville High is a junior.* In the development of principles of logic the meaning of statements p and q is not important, but the relations between them are. However, in applications of logic to particular subjects both the meanings of statements and the relations between them are important.

For a start in logic, we define and illustrate compound statements.

Conjunction

Where p and q represent any statements, the compound statement "*p and q*," written $p \wedge q$, is called the **conjunction** of p and q.

EXAMPLE. p: Jim is a football player.

q: Jim is a basketball player.

$p \wedge q$: Jim is a football player and Jim is a basketball player.

The adjacent table, called a **truth table,** specifies the conditions under which a conjunction is a true statement. Note that the first two columns, headed p and q, list all possible combinations of truth and falsehood for p and q.

$p \wedge q$ is true if and only if p is true and q is true.

p	q	$p \wedge q$
T	T	T
T	F	F
F	T	F
F	F	F

The conjunction of statements ($\wedge$) is related to the intersection of sets ($\cap$). A Venn diagram illustrates this in our example about Jim:

Let $F = \{$all football players$\}$

$B = \{$all basketball players$\}$

Then $F \cap B = \{$all persons who play both football and basketball$\}$.

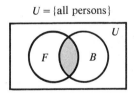

$U = \{$all persons$\}$

If $p \wedge q$ is a true statement in the example about Jim, Jim must belong to the set represented by circle F and also to the set represented by circle B. He must therefore belong to the set represented by the shaded region. Jim $\in (F \cap B)$.

Disjunction

Where p and q represent any statements, the compound statement "*p or q*," written $p \lor q$, is called the **disjunction** of p and q.

EXAMPLE. p: Sue has a part in the operetta.

q: Sue is a cheerleader.

$p \lor q$: Sue has a part in the operetta or Sue is a cheerleader.

p	q	$p \lor q$
T	T	T
T	F	T
F	T	T
F	F	F

As the table shows, the compound statement $p \lor q$ is defined to be true whenever p is true, or q is true, or both p and q are true.

$p \lor q$ is true unless both p and q are false.

The idea of disjunction of statements ($\lor$) is related to the idea of union of sets ($\cup$).

Let $O = $ {all people in operetta}

$C = $ {all cheerleaders}

Then $O \cup C = $ {all people who are in operetta, are cheerleaders, or both}

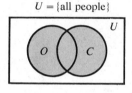

$U = $ {all people}

In the Venn diagram Sue is in the set represented by the shaded region. If statements p and q are both true, then Sue belongs to $O \cap C$ as well as to $O \cup C$. However, if only one of the two statements is true, Sue still belongs to $O \cup C$, and $p \lor q$ is a true statement.

Negation, or Negative, of a Statement

Where p represents any statement, the statement *It is false that p,* usually shortened to *not-p*, written $\sim p$, is called the **negation** of p or the **negative** of p.

EXAMPLE 1. p: John is in the Spanish class.

$\sim p$: It is false that John is in the Spanish class.

$\sim p$: John is not in the Spanish class.

The truth table for $\sim p$ is particularly simple. Since p has only two possibilities (**T** or **F**), the table requires just two rows.

p	$\sim p$
T	**F**
F	**T**

$\sim p$ is true when p is false. $\sim p$ is false when p is true.

The idea of negation of a statement ($\sim$) is closely related to the idea of the complement of a set ($\overline{}$). In Example 1:

Let $X = \{$all students in the Spanish class$\}$

$\overline{X} = \{$all students not in the Spanish class$\}$

$U = \{$all students$\}$

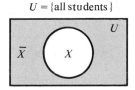

If p is true, John $\in X$. Then John $\notin \overline{X}$, and $\sim p$ is false.

If p is false, John $\notin X$. Then John $\in \overline{X}$, and $\sim p$ is true.

You must exercise care when forming the negation of a statement about *all* the members of a set. In Example 2 all of the forms of the statement $\sim p$ are correct negations of p.

EXAMPLE 2. p: All artists are music-lovers.

$\sim p$: It is false that all artists are music-lovers.

$\sim p$: The set of artists is not a subset of the set of music-lovers.

$\sim p$: Some artists are not music-lovers.

$\sim p$: There is at least one artist who is not a music-lover.

$U = \{$all people$\}$

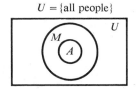

Let $A = \{$all artists$\}$

$M = \{$all music-lovers$\}$

$U = \{$all people$\}$

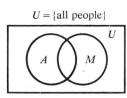

If p is accepted as true, then the Venn diagram at the right above shows the relationship.

If $\sim p$ is accepted as true, then this is the Venn diagram.

ORAL EXERCISES

$U = \{$all men$\}$

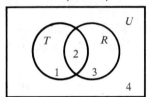

In Exercises 1–8 $T = \{$all Texans$\}$

$R = \{$all ranchers$\}$

$U = \{$all men$\}$

Identify by numbers the regions representing sets that might contain a man when it is known that the man is:

1. a Texan.

2. a rancher.

3. a resident of Dallas.

4. not a resident of Dallas.

5. an old man.

6. not an old man.

7. a Texas rancher.

8. not a Texas rancher.

Classify each simple statement and each compound statement as true or false.

9. $5 + 3 = 8$ and $6 + 2 = 7$.   **10.** $3 \cdot 2 = 7$ or $4 \cdot 3 = 12$.

11. An acceptable negation of *Every trapezoid is a parallelogram* is *Some trapezoid is not a parallelogram.*

12. If $p \wedge q$ is a false statement, then q must be false.

WRITTEN EXERCISES

In each exercise state whether the statements (a) $p \wedge q$ and (b) $p \vee q$ are true or false.

1. p: Every triangle has three sides.
   q: Every square has four right angles.

2. p: Every triangle has three sides.
   q: The intersection of two planes is a circle.

3. p: The intersection of two planes is a circle.
   q: A rectangle has four diagonals.

4. p: The sum of two odd integers is an even integer.
   q: March is the third month of the year.

5. *p*: Every square has four sides.

   q: $|-3| = 3$.

6. *p*: A week has seven days.

   q: The month of February has thirty days.

For the given statement p write out the negation ∼p, using a Venn diagram for assistance.

$U = \{$all students$\}$

EXAMPLE. *p*: Some geometry students
                    do not take Latin.

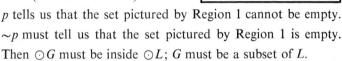

Solution: Let *G* = {all geometry students}

   L = {all Latin students}

   p tells us that the set pictured by Region 1 cannot be empty.

   ∼*p* must tell us that the set pictured by Region 1 is empty.

   Then ⊙*G* must be inside ⊙*L*; *G* must be a subset of *L*.

   ∼*p*: All geometry students take Latin.   **Answer.**

   7. All geometry students take history.

   8. Some geometry students take Spanish.

   9. At least one football player is a track star.

10. Not all girls take home economics.

11. No member of the chorus has a harsh voice.

12. Some debaters speak too quietly.

Make a truth table for the compound statement.

EXAMPLE. ∼*p* ∨ ∼*q*

Solution:

1. Your last column must be headed ∼*p* ∨ ∼*q*. To determine the truth of ∼*p* ∨ ∼*q*, you need to know the truth of ∼*p* and of ∼*q*. Hence, you head columns as shown.

2. Use the definition of the truth of ∼*p* to fill out the third column, and of ∼*q* to fill out the fourth column.

p	*q*	∼*p*	∼*q*	∼*p* ∨ ∼*q*
T	T	F	F	F
T	F	F	T	T
F	T	T	F	T
F	F	T	T	T

3. Write T's or F's in the last column by adapting the definition of the truth of *p* ∨ *q*, page 68, to the case ∼*p* ∨ ∼*q* and referring to the truth values listed in columns 3 and 4.

13. $\sim(\sim p)$ **14.** $p \vee \sim p$ **15.** $p \wedge \sim q$ **16.** $\sim p \vee q$

$\boxed{C}$ **17.** $\sim p \wedge \sim q$ **19.** $\sim(\sim p \wedge q)$

18. $\sim(\sim p \vee \sim q)$ **20.** $[\sim(p \wedge \sim p)] \vee [p \wedge (q \wedge \sim p)]$

■ Principles of Logic

2–6   Conditionals: "If-Then" Statements

Where p and q represent statements, the compound statement "*If p, then q*" is called a **conditional** or **implication** and is expressed in symbols by $p \rightarrow q$. Statement p is the **hypothesis** and statement q the **conclusion** of the conditional $p \rightarrow q$.

The conditions under which a conditional is true are shown in the adjacent truth table. Note that $p \rightarrow q$ is true whenever q is true. However, when $p \rightarrow q$ is true, q is not necessarily true.

The example that follows will help you to understand the reasonableness of the agreement about conditions under which $p \rightarrow q$ is called true.

p	q	$p \rightarrow q$
T	T	T
T	F	F
F	T	T
F	F	T

EXAMPLE. George promises: If I find a five-dollar bill, I'll take you to the movies.

Consider the four possibilities.

1. George finds a five-dollar bill and takes you to the movies. He keeps his promise; his statement was *true*.

2. George finds a five-dollar bill but does not take you to the movies. He broke his promise; his statement was *false*.

3. George does not find a five-dollar bill, but still takes you to the movies. He has not broken his promise; his statement is *true*.

4. George does not find a five-dollar bill and does not take you to the movies. He has not broken his promise; his statement is *true*.

$p \rightarrow q$ is true except when p is true and q is false.

$p \rightarrow q$ is true when q is true or p is false.

The conditional *If p, then q* can be expressed in other ways. Some of these ways are

q, if p. p is a sufficient condition for q.

p, only if q. q is a necessary condition for p.

p implies q. q follows from p.

The expressions "sufficient condition" and "necessary condition" are not to be confused. Consider the conditional "If two angles are right angles, then the two angles are congruent." This statement asserts that a *sufficient condition* for two angles to be congruent angles is that they be right angles. It asserts that a *necessary condition* for two angles to be right angles is that they be congruent angles.

Thus far we have used truth tables to define the conditions under which certain types of compound statements are true. Truth tables are also used to prove the truth of other compound statements.

EXAMPLE. Show that for all combinations of truth values of p and q the statement $p \rightarrow (p \lor q)$ is true.

Solution:

p	q	$p \lor q$	$p \rightarrow (p \lor q)$
T	T	T	T
T	F	T	T
F	T	T	T
F	F	F	T

1. Head columns with p, q, $p \lor q$, and $p \rightarrow (p \lor q)$.
2. List all possible combinations of **T** and **F** in the p and q columns.
3. Using the defined conditions for the truth of $p \lor q$ (p. 68), fill in column 3.
4. Using the truth values in columns 1 and 3 and the defined conditions for the truth of a conditional (p. 72), fill in column 4.
5. The conditional $p \rightarrow (p \lor q)$ is always true since column 4 contains only **T**'s.

In algebra you worked with simple conditionals that contained a variable such as x whose domain was the set of all real numbers. Suppose you were asked to prove that the conditional stated below was true.

If $x + 4 = 6$, then $x = 2$.

When x is replaced by 2, the statements $x + 4 = 6$ and $x = 2$ are both true, and the conditional $x + 4 = 6 \rightarrow x = 2$ is true. However, this establishes the truth of the conditional *only* for the integer 2. Since the domain of x is *all* real numbers, you must still establish the truth of the assertion for the remaining real numbers — those greater than 2, and those less than 2. The truth table shown establishes the truth of the given conditional for all real values of x.

	$x + 4 = 6$	$x = 2$	$x + 4 = 6 \rightarrow x = 2$
when $x = 2$	T	T	T
when $x < 2$	F	F	T
when $x > 2$	F	F	T

The above example illustrates an important point. If p and q involve variables, to assert that $p \rightarrow q$ is true is to assert that $p \rightarrow q$ is true for all replacements in the domain of the variables, *not* just those for which p and q are true statements.

In this text, unless otherwise indicated, you are to assume that in any algebraic equation the domain of each variable is the set of real numbers.

ORAL EXERCISES

State the hypothesis and conclusion in each of these conditionals. In Exercises 1–4, *r, s, t* and *u* represent statements.

1. $r \rightarrow s$.

2. If t, then u.

3. $t \rightarrow (r \lor s)$.

4. $\sim u \rightarrow r$.

5. If it snows, then the game will be postponed.

6. If I save my allowance, then I can go to the movie.

7. If the temperature continues to drop, the lake will freeze over.

8. If Shaun studies his vocabulary list, he will pass the test.

9. John will play in Saturday's game, if his ankle heals.

10. The square of an integer is an even number provided the integer is an even number.

Express each of the following statements in "if-then" form:

11. Two circles which have congruent radii have equal areas.

12. When $3x - 1 = 2x$, it follows that $x = 1$.

13. A square of side 2 inches has a perimeter of 8 inches.

14. When I read without glasses, my eyes get tired.

15. Two opposite rays form a straight line.

16. $|x| > 0$ whenever $x \neq 0$.

17. Two planes intersect provided they are not parallel.

18. For every $x > 1$, $x > \dfrac{1}{x}$.

State whether the conditional $r \to s$ is defined to be true or false under the conditions described.

19. When r is true and s is true.

20. When r is true and s is false.

21. When r is false and s is true.

22. When r is false and s is false.

Complete:

23. Given that s is true. Then, no matter whether r is true or false, the conditional $r \to s$ is defined to be a __?__ statement.

24. Given that r is false. Then, no matter whether s is true or false, the conditional $r \to s$ is defined to be a __?__ statement.

25. Where $t \to u$, __?__ is true only if __?__ is also true.

26. Where $t \to u$, is t a necessary condition or a sufficient condition for u?

WRITTEN
EXERCISES

List the hypothesis and conclusion in each statement.

1. If Susie walks, she will be late.

2. If Sam does not fail algebra, he will be eligible to play.

3. Two integers whose sum is 7 cannot both be even.

4. Two angles have equal measures if they are vertical angles.

5. The product of two consecutive integers is an odd integer.

6. The game will be cancelled in the event of rain.

Express each statement in "if-then" form.

7. Every multiple of 4 is a multiple of 2.

8. When $a - b$ is a positive number, b is less than a.

9. Warren will sing, provided Steve will play the piano.

10. Each angle of an equilateral triangle has measure 60.

Assign p and q to the statements in such a way that $p \rightarrow q$ is true. If such an assignment cannot be made, write "not possible."

11. $\angle A$ and $\angle B$ are right angles. $\angle A$ and $\angle B$ are congruent angles.

12. Lines l and m are parallel. Lines l and m do not intersect.

13. $n^2 = 25$. $n = 5$.

14. $\angle C$ and $\angle D$ are acute angles. $\angle C$ and $\angle D$ are congruent angles.

15. $x \in \{\text{all people}\}$. $x \in \{\text{all old people}\}$.

16. $y \in \{\text{all girls}\}$. $y \in \{\text{all high school students}\}$.

Construct a truth table to prove that each of the conditionals is a true statement for all combinations of truth values of p and q.

B

17. $(p \wedge q) \rightarrow p$ **19.** $p \rightarrow (p \vee q)$

18. $(p \wedge q) \rightarrow q$ **20.** $(p \wedge q) \rightarrow (p \vee q)$

Construct a truth table to prove that the conditional shown is not always a true statement. That is, show that the last column of your table contains at least one **F**.

21. $p \rightarrow (p \wedge q)$ **22.** $(p \vee q) \rightarrow p$

In Exercises 23 and 24 indicate which statements assert the same thing as the given statement.

C

23. Earl must study his lessons or he will have to stay home from the picnic.

    a. If Earl doesn't study his lessons, he will have to stay home from the picnic.

    b. If Earl studies his lessons, then he must go to the picnic.

    c. If Earl stays home from the picnic, then he must study his lessons.

    d. If Earl is not to stay home from the picnic, then he must study his lessons.

24. Fred will pass only if he studies hard.

    a. If Fred studies hard, he will pass.

    b. Either Fred studies hard or he will fail.

    c. If Fred does not study hard, he will not pass.

    d. If Fred is to fail, then he must not study hard.

2–7 The Law of Detachment

Think of a discussion that has progressed to the point where you say:
"If Tony beats me in this next game then he is a better player than
I am." You do not admit that Tony is a better player. You only
admit that a certain conditional is true. Where p and q represent the
statements shown:

> p: Tony beats me in this next game.
>
> q: He is a better player than I am.

you are accepting the truth of the conditional *If p, then q.*

Now Tony beats you in the next game. You are forced to admit:
Tony is a better player than I am. This example suggests that:

When you know $p \rightarrow q$ and know p you can deduce q. The fact that
you can, whenever both $p \rightarrow q$ and p are true, detach p and have q, suggests the name: Law of Detachment.

> *Law of Detachment*
> Whenever $p \rightarrow q$ is true and p is true,
> then q is true.

To establish the law you need only observe, in the truth table on page
72, that $p \rightarrow q$ and p are both true only in the first row. In that
row q is true.

A simple use of the law in geometry is shown below.

Given:

> If $\angle A$ and $\angle B$ are vertical angles, then $\angle A \cong \angle B$.
> $\angle A$ and $\angle B$ are vertical angles.

Conclusion:

> $\angle A \cong \angle B$.

As you proceed in this course and write proofs about geometric figures you will often use the Law of Detachment more than once in a proof. To see how this works, suppose you are given the three statements

$$p \qquad\qquad p \rightarrow q \qquad\qquad q \rightarrow r$$

First detach p in $p \rightarrow q$ and deduce q.

Then detach q in $q \rightarrow r$ and deduce r.

ORAL EXERCISES

1. State the Law of Detachment, using s and t for statements.
2. State the Law of Detachment, using u and v for statements.
3. The conditional $p \rightarrow q$ is known to be true. Which of the following is correct?

   Given p you can deduce q.
   Given q you can deduce p.
4. If given both u and $u \rightarrow v$ you can deduce __?__.
   If also given $v \rightarrow w$, you can deduce __?__.
5. If you accept the facts: *If John lives in Houston, he lives in Texas* and *John lives in Houston,* what can you deduce by using the Law of Detachment?
6. If you accept the facts: *If A lives in K, he lives in M* and *A lives in K,* what can you deduce by applying the Law of Detachment?

WRITTEN EXERCISES

Letters p, q, r, s, t, represent statements. Indicate the statement you can deduce from the information given. If none, write *None.*

A

1. Given: $p \rightarrow t;\ p.$
2. Given: $p \rightarrow t;\ t.$
3. Given: $r;\ r \rightarrow s.$
4. Given: $s;\ s \rightarrow r.$
5. Given: $s \rightarrow \sim t;\ s.$
6. Given: $\sim r \rightarrow p;\ \sim r.$

7. Given: $p \rightarrow q$; $\sim p$.

8. Given: $\sim t \rightarrow \sim r$; $\sim t$.

9. Given: If Sally tries hard, she types well; Sally tries hard.

10. Given: If $\angle C$ and $\angle D$ are right angles, then $\angle C \cong \angle D$; $\angle C$ and $\angle D$ are right angles.

B Indicate a statement you can deduce by one application of the Law of Detachment and a second statement you can deduce by a second application of the law.

11. Given: $p \rightarrow q$; $q \rightarrow r$; p. **13.** Given: $r \rightarrow s$; $s \rightarrow \sim q$; r.

12. Given: s; $s \rightarrow t$; $t \rightarrow q$. **14.** Given: $\sim q \rightarrow p$; $p \rightarrow t$; $\sim q$.

15. Copy and complete the truth table shown.

p	q	$p \rightarrow q$	$(p \rightarrow q) \wedge p$	$[(p \rightarrow q) \wedge p] \rightarrow q$
T	T	?	?	?
T	F	?	?	?
F	T	?	?	?
F	F	?	?	?

16. Construct a truth table to show that the conditional $[(r \rightarrow s) \wedge s] \rightarrow r$ is *not* always true.

C **17.** Construct a truth table to show that the conditional

$$([(p \rightarrow q) \wedge (q \rightarrow r)] \wedge p) \rightarrow r$$

is true for all eight combinations of **T** and **F** for p, q, and r.

18. It is known that the five statements: $p \rightarrow q$, $q \rightarrow r$, $r \rightarrow s$, $s \rightarrow t$, and p are all true. Show how t can be deduced through repeated uses of the Law of Detachment.

2–8 Converses, Inverses, Contrapositives

If you interchange the statements p and q in the conditional *If p, then q,* you get a new conditional *If q, then p* called the **converse** of the original conditional. The *converse* of $p \rightarrow q$ is $q \rightarrow p$. The conditionals $p \rightarrow q$ and $q \rightarrow p$ are converses of each other.

A conditional and its converse are different statements. The examples that follow show that the converse of a true conditional *may be true* or it *may be false.*

EXAMPLE 1. $p \rightarrow q$: If a point lies on a line, then the line contains the point. (*True*)

   $q \rightarrow p$: If a line contains a point, then the point lies on the line. (*True*)

EXAMPLE 2. $p \rightarrow q$: If $n > 5$, then $n \neq 4$. (*True*)

   $q \rightarrow p$: If $n \neq 4$, then $n > 5$. (*False*)

You can show by a truth table that *the converse of a true conditional is not necessarily true.* (See Exercise 18, page 83.)

When the conditional $p \rightarrow q$ and its converse $q \rightarrow p$ are both true, p and q are said to be **equivalent statements.** The statement $p \leftrightarrow q$, called a **biconditional** or **equivalence,** can be read in many ways, some common ways being:

p is equivalent to q.	p is necessary and sufficient for q.
If p then q, and if q then p.	q is necessary and sufficient for p.
If p, then q, and conversely.	p, if and only if q.
If q, then p, and conversely.	q, if and only if p.

Equivalent statements have the same truth value. Either both are true statements or both are false statements.

The simple but important biconditional $p \leftrightarrow \sim(\sim p)$ is left for you to prove as an exercise. (See Exercise 17, p. 82.)

Where *If p, then q* is any conditional, the new conditional *If not-p, then not-q* is called the **inverse** of the original conditional. Thus, the *inverse* of $p \rightarrow q$ is $\sim p \rightarrow \sim q$. Like the converse, the inverse of a true conditional may be true or it may be false.

EXAMPLE 3. $p \rightarrow q$: If the angles of a quadrilateral are congruent, the quadrilateral is a rectangle. (*True*)

   $\sim p \rightarrow \sim q$: If the angles of a quadrilateral are not congruent, the quadrilateral is not a rectangle. (*True*)

EXAMPLE 4. $p \rightarrow q$: If a number is an integer, then it is a rational number. (*True*)

   $\sim p \rightarrow \sim q$: If a number is not an integer, then it is not a rational number. (*False*)

You can show by a truth table that the *inverse of a true conditional is not necessarily true.* (See Exercise 19, page 83.)

Where *If p, then q* is any conditional, the new conditional *If not-q, then not-p* is called the **contrapositive** of the original conditional. Thus, the *contrapositive* of $p \rightarrow q$ is $\sim q \rightarrow \sim p$. You will be asked to prove (See Exercise 20, page 83) that a *conditional and its contra-positive are both true or else are both false.* Thus a conditional and its contrapositive are equivalent statements. This important biconditional is called **Law of the Contrapositive.**

Law of the Contrapositive: $(p \rightarrow q) \leftrightarrow (\sim q \rightarrow \sim p)$

On the basis of this law you can assert that $p \rightarrow q$ is true if you have established that $\sim q \rightarrow \sim p$ is true. Sometimes the most convenient way to prove a statement is to prove the contrapositive of the statement. For example, to prove:

"If the square of an integer is odd, the integer itself is odd"

it is less difficult to prove the contrapositive:

"If an integer is not odd (is even), then the square of the integer is not odd (is even)."

SUMMARY OF RELATED CONDITIONALS

Given Conditional:	If p, then q	$p \rightarrow q$
Converse:	If q, then p	$q \rightarrow p$
Inverse:	If not p, then not q	$\sim p \rightarrow \sim q$
Contrapositive:	If not q, then not p	$\sim q \rightarrow \sim p$

A conditional and its contrapositive are equivalent statements. The converse and the inverse are equivalent statements.

ORAL EXERCISES

Form the (a) converse (b) inverse (c) contrapositive in Exercises 1–4.

1. $r \rightarrow s$

2. $t \rightarrow \sim u$

3. $\sim v \rightarrow w$

4. $\sim y \rightarrow \sim z$

5. Given $r \rightarrow s$.

    a. Is r a sufficient condition for s?

    b. Is s a sufficient condition for r?

    c. Is r a necessary condition for s?

    d. Is s a necessary condition for r?

6. Which of the following is equivalent to *If t, then u?*

  a. *t* only if *u*   **b.** *u* only if *t*   **c.** *t* if and only if *u*

7. When $p \rightarrow q$ and $q \rightarrow p$ are both true conditionals, *p* and *q* are called __?__ statements.

8. Given $v \leftrightarrow w$. Is *v* a sufficient condition for *w*? Is *v* a necessary condition for *w*?

9. If $p \leftrightarrow q$ is true and *q* is true, is *p* true or false?

10. If $p \leftrightarrow q$ is true and *p* is false, is *q* true or false?

WRITTEN EXERCISES

In Exercises 1–8, p denotes the statement "C > 5" and q the statement "C > 3". Translate the given conditional into an "if-then" statement about C and tell whether your statement is true.

A

1. $p \rightarrow q$	**4.** $\sim p \rightarrow \sim q$	**7.** $\sim q \rightarrow p$
2. $p \rightarrow \sim q$	**5.** $q \rightarrow p$	**8.** $\sim q \rightarrow \sim p$
3. $\sim p \rightarrow q$	**6.** $q \rightarrow \sim p$	

Write the converse, inverse and contrapositive of each of the following statements.

9. If two angles are adjacent, then the two angles have the same vertex.

10. If today is Tuesday, then tomorrow is Wednesday.

11. If $x > 5$, then $x^2 > 25$.

12. If a polygon is a square, then it is a rectangle.

Write a conditional that is true and such that

13. the converse is true.

14. the converse is false.

15. the inverse is false.

16. the inverse is true.

In Exercises 17–20, a statement is given followed by a truth table in which the last column expresses the statement in symbols. Copy and complete the table. Explain how the table supports the truth of the given statement.

B   **17.** Statement: The negation of the negation of *p* is equivalent to *p*.

p	$\sim p$	$\sim(\sim p)$	$p \leftrightarrow \sim(\sim p)$
T	?	?	?
F	?	?	?

18. Statement: The converse of a conditional is *not* equivalent to the conditional.

p	q	$p \to q$	$q \to p$	$(p \to q) \leftrightarrow (q \to p)$
T	T	?	?	?
T	F	?	?	?
F	T	?	?	?
F	F	?	?	?

19. Statement: The inverse of a conditional is *not* equivalent to the conditional.

p	q	$\sim p$	$\sim q$	$p \to q$	$\sim p \to \sim q$	$(p \to q) \leftrightarrow (\sim p \to \sim q)$
T	T	?	?	?	?	?
T	F	?	?	?	?	?
F	T	?	?	?	?	?
F	F	?	?	?	?	?

20. Statement: The contrapositive of a conditional is equivalent to the conditional.

p	q	$\sim p$	$\sim q$	$p \to q$	$\sim q \to \sim p$	$(p \to q) \leftrightarrow (\sim q \to \sim p)$
T	T	?	?	?	?	?
T	F	?	?	?	?	?
F	T	?	?	?	?	?
F	F	?	?	?	?	?

By means of a truth table establish the truth of each of the following.

21. $(r \to \sim s) \leftrightarrow (s \to \sim r)$

22. $(r \to s) \leftrightarrow \sim(r \wedge \sim s)$

23. $(r \to s) \leftrightarrow \sim r \vee s$

24. $\sim(r \vee s) \leftrightarrow \sim r \wedge \sim s$

CHAPTER SUMMARY

Inventory of Structure and Method

1. Conclusions based on inductive thinking or intuitive thinking represent intelligent guesses, not proved conclusions.

2. Deductive reasoning involves accepting some statements and reasoning from them to a conclusion. If the reasoning pattern used is logically valid, the conclusion is valid.

3. The compound statement "*p* and *q*" ($p \wedge q$) is called the **conjunction** of *p* and *q*, and is true only when both *p* and *q* are true.

4. The compound statement "*p* or *q*" ($p \vee q$) is called the **disjunction** of *p* and *q*, and is true whenever *p* or *q* or both are true.

5. The **negation** of statement *p* is "not-p" ($\sim p$). If *p* is true, $\sim p$ is false. If *p* is false, $\sim p$ is true.

6. A compound statement of the form "*if p, then q*" ($p \rightarrow q$) is called a **conditional.** A conditional is true except when *p* is true and *q* is false. If *p* and *q* are interchanged the resulting conditional "*if q, then p*" ($q \rightarrow p$) is called the **converse** of *"if p, then q."* The converse of a conditional may or may not be true.

7. By the law of detachment, if the conditional $p \rightarrow q$ is true and *p* is true, then *q* is true.

8. When the conditional $p \rightarrow q$ and its converse $q \rightarrow p$ are both true, *p* and *q* are equivalent statements. The equivalence $p \leftrightarrow q$ is true if and only if *p* and *q* are either both true or both false.

9. The conditional $p \rightarrow q$ and its contrapositive $\sim q \rightarrow \sim p$ are equivalent statements.

Vocabulary and Spelling

induction (*p. 52*)
intuition (*p. 53*)
perpendicular lines (*p. 56*)
perpendicular bisector (*p. 56*)
line perpendicular to plane (*p. 57*)
circle (*p. 57*)
   radius of (*p. 57*)
   chord of (*p. 57*)
   diameter of (*p. 57*)

secant of (*p. 57*)
tangent to circle (*p. 57*)
   point of tangency (*p. 57*)
   point of contact (*p. 57*)
concentric circles (*p. 57*)
sphere(s) (*p. 59*)
   common tangent (*p. 60*)
   common tangent plane (*p. 60*)
deductive reasoning (*p. 63*)

CHAPTER TEST

2–1   State a conclusion suggested by inductive thinking.

   1. On three occasions Jean substituted brown sugar for white sugar when making cookies. Each time the cookies were sticky.

   2. The squares of the odd numbers 1, 3, 5, 7, and 9 are 1, 9, 25, 49, and 81.

2–2   **3.** The longest chord that can be drawn in a circle is a __?__ .

   4. If two circles are concentric they must have the same center and be __?__ .

2–3   **5.** A sphere separates all the points of space into __?__ subsets.

   6. At a point on a sphere __?__ tangent lines can be drawn.

2–4   State a conclusion that follows from the given statements. Assume a, b, and c represent real numbers.

   7. $a > b$ and $a < c$.   **8.** $ab > 0$ and $a < 0$.

2–5   Classify the given statement as true or as false.

   9. If $p \land q$ is true, then q may or may not be true.

   10. If $p \lor q$ is true, then q may or may not be true.

2–6   **11.** $p \to q$ is true except when __?__ is true and __?__ is false.

   12. The conditional $p \to q$ can be expressed: __?__ only if __?__ .

2–7   State a conclusion that follows from the given statements.

   13. If an integer is odd, its square is odd. k is an odd integer.

   14. $p \to q; q \to r; p$

2–8 Given the statement: If $a < 2$, then $a < 5$. Write the converse, the inverse, and the contrapositive of the statement. Indicate which statements are true and which are false.

15. The converse is __?__.　　　　**17.** The contrapositive is __?__.

16. The inverse is __?__.

CHAPTER REVIEW

2–1 **Meaning of Induction and Intuition**　　　*Pages 52–56*

1. When you believe something on the basis of a sudden hunch you are doing __?__ thinking.

2. You (can, cannot) __?__ prove a conclusion by inductive reasoning.

2–2 **Perpendicular Lines and Circles**　　　*Pages 56–59*

3. A line that bisects a segment is (always, sometimes, never) __?__ perpendicular to the segment.

4. A secant intersects a circle in __?__ points, and the segment joining those points is called a __?__.

5. A tangent to circle O at point P is __?__ to $\overline{OP}$ at point P.

2–3 **Spheres**　　　*Pages 59–62*

6. Two spheres with the same center are called __?__.

7. Passing through a point in the exterior of a sphere __?__ lines tangent to the sphere can be drawn.

8. The intersection of a sphere and a plane that passes through the center of the sphere is a __?__.

2–4 **Deductive Reasoning**　　　*Pages 62–66*

Make a deduction about y based on the given information.

9. $x + y = 15$ and $x = 6$.

10. $y^2 > 25$ and $y < 0$.

2–5 **Deduction and Logic**　　　*Pages 66–72*

11. Where p and q are statements, $p \wedge q$ denotes the __?__ of p and q.

12. The statement $p \vee q$ is false only when both p and q are __?__.

13. When p is true and q is false, $p \wedge (\sim q)$ is __?__.

2–6 **Conditionals: "If-Then" Statements**　　　*Pages 72–77*

14. In the conditional $r \rightarrow s$, statement __?__ is the hypothesis and statement __?__ is the conclusion.

15. If $s \rightarrow t$, then t is a (necessary/sufficient) __?__ condition for s.

16. If $p \rightarrow q$ is true and p is false, then q (may be/must be) __?__ true.

2-7 The Law of Detachment   *Pages 77-79*

17. If $p \rightarrow q$ is true and p is true, then __?__ is true.

18. If $p \rightarrow q, q \rightarrow s$, and p are all true, then s (must/may) __?__ be true.

19. If $p \rightarrow q$ is true and q is true, you (can/cannot) __?__ deduce that p is true.

2-8 Converses, Inverses, Contrapositives   *Pages 79-83*

20. $\sim p \rightarrow \sim q$ is the __?__ of $p \rightarrow q$.

21. A conditional and its __?__ are equivalent statements.

22. "p, *if and only if* q" is represented in symbols by __?__.

• EXTRA FOR EXPERTS

Some Errors in Reasoning

When a person uses a reasoning process that is not valid (is not correct) we say that there is a *fallacy* in his thinking. Of course you need not grant a conclusion that is based on a fallacious argument. On the other hand, you cannot be sure that a conclusion is a false statement just because it was supported by invalid reasoning. For instance, it is entirely possible that you should vote for a particular candidate even though the reasons he offers in seeking your vote are unsound.

Non Sequitur.

A conclusion that does not follow from other statements offered in support of that conclusion is called a *non sequitur*.

EXAMPLE.

Given: A particular number n satisfies the equation $n^2 + 3 = 28$.

Reasoning (faulty): Since $n^2 + 3 = 28$, $n^2 = 25$, $n = 5$, and the particular number is 5.

The error: From $n^2 = 25$ it does not follow that $n = 5$. The strongest conclusion you can reach is: $n \in \{5, -5\}$.

Fallacy of Circular Reasoning

When a person "proves" a statement S by assuming at some point in his argument S itself, he is said to *argue in a circle*. An extreme form of circular reasoning is shown in the following conversation. Four year-old Tom: *I'm bigger than you are.* Kathy: *Why?* Tom: *Because I'm bigger than you are.*

Fallacy of Asserting the Consequent

When a person proceeds from the knowledge that $p \rightarrow q$ is true and q is true to the conclusion that p is true, his error in reasoning is called *asserting the consequent or reasoning on the converse.*

EXAMPLE. All good athletes are strong competitors.
The members of this club are strong competitors.
Therefore the members of this club are good athletes.

The error: The first statement does not say anything about *all* strong competitors. So the mere fact that a club is made up of strong competitors does not mean that the members are athletes. The club may, for instance, be made up of checker players. A Venn diagram makes the situation clear.

$A = \{$good athletes$\}$
$M = \{$members of club$\}$

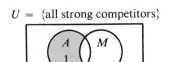

$U = \{$all strong competitors$\}$

We cannot conclude that the set indicated by Region 1 is the empty set.

Fallacy of Denying the Premise

When a person proceeds from the knowledge that $p \rightarrow q$ is true and p is false to the conclusion that q is false, his error in reasoning is called *denying the premise.*

EXAMPLE. All dogs like to chase cats.
No rabbits are dogs.
Therefore no rabbits like to chase cats.

The error: The first statement does not assert that dogs are the *only* animals that like to chase cats. No conclusion can be reached about non-dogs.

$U = \{$all animals$\}$

$C = \{$cat chasers$\}$
$D = \{$dogs$\}$
$R = \{$rabbits$\}$

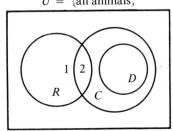

The first statement tells us that circle D lies inside circle C. The second statement tells us that circles R and D lie outside each other. We cannot tell from the first two statements whether Region 2 indicates an empty set. Of course, we know that the conclusion in the example is correct in spite of the faulty reasoning process.

Faulty Reasoning from Analogy

When a person uses similarities between two objects to conclude incorrectly that something true of one object must be true of the other, his process is one of *faulty reasoning from analogy*.

EXAMPLE. A sphere is the three-dimensional figure analogous to a circle, a two-dimensional figure. Since at a point on a circle there is exactly one line tangent to the circle, there is exactly one line tangent to a sphere at a point on the sphere.

The error: The fact that spheres and circles are alike in some ways does not mean that they are alike in all ways. Known properties of circles may suggest possible properties of spheres, but the properties must be tested for spheres.

EXERCISES

Point out what is wrong with the reasoning.

1. I know that Jim is older than Peggy because Peggy is younger than Jim. And Peggy must be younger than Jim because Jim is older than Peggy.

2. Skiing and skating are similar because in each sport you fasten runners to your feet. Since skiers wax their skis, skaters must wax their skates.

3. Given: $r \rightarrow s$; s. Therefore r.

4. Given: $r \rightarrow s$; $\sim r$. Therefore $\sim s$.

Draw a Venn Diagram to show that the reasoning is faulty.

5. All tigers eat meat.
   No lamb is a tiger.
   Therefore no lamb eats meat.

6. All cheerleaders have pleasant personalities.
   The Jones girls are not cheerleaders.
   Therefore the Jones girls do not have pleasant personalities.

7. All fishermen like outdoor life.
   The members of this club like outdoor life.
   Therefore the members of this club are fishermen.

8. All senators are citizens of the United States.
   The men in this room are citizens of the United States.
   Therefore the men in this room are senators.

3 Deduction and Geometry

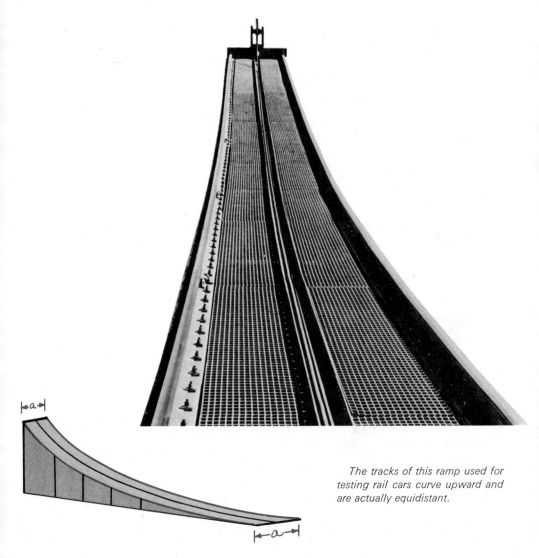

The tracks of this ramp used for testing rail cars curve upward and are actually equidistant.

If it had been necessary for man to depend solely on experimentation and inductive reasoning to organize, extend, and apply his mathematical knowledge, progress would indeed have been at a snail's pace. Fortunately, Greek scholars in the period beginning around 600 B.C. recognized that if a few geometric facts were assumed, other geometric facts could be arrived at by deductive thinking, without the need for repeated experimentation, observation, and intelligent guessing.

These early Greek scholars approached the study of geometry with little concern for its applications. They were interested in it as a subject in which the principles of logic could be applied. They concerned themselves with defining terms, listing basic assumptions, and organizing systematically the conclusions which could be based on these definitions and assumptions.

One of the best known of the ancient geometers was a Greek scholar named **Euclid.** Around 300 B.C. he produced a thirteen-volume work called *The Elements.* Six of the volumes dealt with geometry of the plane. These were the basis for all plane geometry texts until well into the present century.

In this chapter you will begin to do deductive thinking about geometric figures. First, however, since your study of algebra included much deductive reasoning, it will be good for you to review algebra briefly.

■ Mathematical Systems

3–1   Postulates and Theorems in Algebra

Do you recall that, in studying algebra, you assumed some basic properties of equality, of inequality, and of the real numbers? Basic assumptions are called **axioms** or **postulates.** Since you will use algebraic properties when you reason deductively about geometric figures, lists for you to use in refreshing your memory are provided in this section. In the lists the variables a, b, and c are variables whose domain is the set of real numbers.

/ 7

Assumed Properties of Real Numbers

For Addition

Closure Postulate	The sum $a + b$ is a unique real number.
Commutative Postulate	$a + b = b + a$.
Associative Postulate	$(a + b) + c = a + (b + c)$.
Additive Postulate of Zero	$\Re$ contains a unique element 0 having the property that $a + 0 = a$ and $0 + a = a$.
Postulate of Additive Inverses	For every real number a there is a unique real number $-a$ such that $a + (-a) = 0$ and $(-a) + a = 0$.

For Multiplication

Closure Postulate	The product ab is a unique real number.
Commutative Postulate	$ab = ba$.
Associative Postulate	$(ab)c = a(bc)$.
Multiplicative Postulate of One	$\Re$ contains a unique element 1 having the property that

$$a \cdot 1 = a \text{ and } 1 \cdot a = a.$$

Postulate of Multiplicative Inverses	For every real number a except zero, there is a unique real number $\dfrac{1}{a}$ such

$$\text{that } a \cdot \frac{1}{a} = 1 \text{ and } \frac{1}{a} \cdot a = 1.$$

Distributive Postulate of Multiplication with Respect to Addition

Distributive Postulate	$a(b + c) = ab + ac$ and $(b + c)a = ba + ca$.

Assumed Properties of Equality   *15*

Reflexive Property	$a = a$.
Symmetric Property	If $a = b$, then $b = a$.
Transitive Property	If $a = b$ and $b = c$, then $a = c$.

Assumed Properties of Inequality   */6*

Postulate of Comparison	One and only one of the following statements is true: $a < b$, $a = b$, $b < a$.
Transitive Postulate	If $a < b$ and $b < c$, then $a < c$.
Additive Postulate	If $a < b$, then $a + c < b + c$.
Multiplicative Postulate	If $a < b$ and $0 < c$, then $ac < bc$; If $a < b$ and $c < 0$, then $bc < ac$.

Note that the postulates of inequality are expressed in terms of the symbol $<$. You can define the symbol $>$ by saying that the statement $b > a$ has the same meaning as the statement $a < b$. Then the postulates can be expressed in terms of the symbol $>$. The transitive postulate of inequality, for example, can be expressed in the form: If $a > b$ and $b > c$, then $a > c$.

Neither subtraction nor division is mentioned in the postulates. To proceed, we need definitions. If the difference $a - b$ is defined to be that unique number x such that $b + x = a$, and the quotient $a \div b$ ($b \neq 0$) is defined to be that unique number x such that $b \cdot x = a$, it can be proved that:

$$a - b = a + (-b)$$

$$a \div b = a \cdot \left(\frac{1}{b}\right)$$

Each of the above assertions is a *theorem*. A **theorem** is a statement that can be proved.

You may use, in geometry, any theorem that you had in algebra. Some of the algebraic theorems that you will use most often in geometric proofs are listed below.

Some Proved Properties (Theorems)

Of Equality

Addition Property   If $a = b$, then $a + c = b + c$ and $c + a = c + b$.

Subtraction Property   If $a = b$, then $a - c = b - c$ and $c - a = c - b$.

Multiplication Property   If $a = b$, then $ac = bc$.

Division Property   If $a = b$ and $c \neq 0$, then $\dfrac{a}{c} = \dfrac{b}{c}$.

Of Inequality

Subtraction Property   If $a < b$, then $a - c < b - c$.

Division Property   If $a < b$ and $c > 0$, then $\dfrac{a}{c} < \dfrac{b}{c}$;

If $a < b$ and $c < 0$, then $\dfrac{a}{c} > \dfrac{b}{c}$.

Substitution Principle   If $a = b$, "a" may be replaced by "b" and "b" by "a" in any equation or inequality.

Zero-Product Property   If $ab = 0$, then $a = 0$ or $b = 0$.

ORAL EXERCISES

What property of real numbers is illustrated by each of the following?

1. $3 + 2 = 2 + 3$

2. $2(a + b) = 2a + 2b$

3. $5 \cdot 1 = 5$

4. $7 + (-7) = 0$

5. $5 \cdot 3 = 3 \cdot 5$

6. $8 + 0 = 8$

Each of the following exercises uses the addition, the subtraction, the multiplication, or the division property of equality. State which of these is used in each exercise. You need not name other properties that are used.

7. If $5x = 20$, then $x = 4$.

8. If $x + 8 = 10$, then $x = 2$.

9. If $2x - 3 = 11$, then $2x = 14$.

10. If $7 = 13 - 2x$, then $2x + 7 = 13$.

11. If $\frac{1}{3}x = 5$, then $x = 15$.

12. If $.3x + 4 = 7$, then $3x + 40 = 70$.

Name the property of inequality which supports the indicated deduction.

13. If $x + 5 < 8$, then $x < 3$.

14. If $2x < 10$, then $x < 5$.

15. If $-3x > 12$, then $-4 > x$.

16. If $-\frac{1}{2}x > 6$, then $-12 > x$.

Which of the following statements are true for all real numbers a and b?

17. If $a + 1 = b$, then $b > a$.

18. If $a + 2 < b + 3$, then $a < b$.

19. If $-2 > a$, then $4 > a^2$.

20. If $-2a > 6$, then $a > -3$.

WRITTEN EXERCISES

1. Write the additive inverse of each of the following real numbers.

   a. 5   **b.** -3 **c.** $\frac{1}{2}$ **d.** a **e.** $-a$ **f.** $\dfrac{a}{b}$

2. Write the multiplicative inverse of each of the following real numbers.

   a. 3   **b.** -4 **c.** $\frac{1}{2}$ **d.** a **e.** $\dfrac{1}{a}$ **f.** $\dfrac{a}{b}$

Name the property of real numbers illustrated by each of the following.

3. $x + y = y + x$ **6.** $x + 0 = x$

4. $b + (-b) = 0$ **7.** $a(bc) = (ab)c$

5. $r(s + t) = rs + rt$ **8.** $(r + s) + t = r + (s + t)$

Name the property of equality which supports the indicated conclusion.

9. If $3x = 15$, $x = 5$.   **11.** If $2x = k$ and $k = 8$, $2x = 8$.

10. If $5x + 2 = 12$, $5x = 10$.   **12.** If $20 = 4x - 2$, $4x - 2 = 20$.

Name the property of inequality which supports the indicated conclusion.

13. If $x - 4 < 6$, $x < 10$.   **15.** If $x > y$ and $y > 5$, $x > 5$.

14. If $\frac{1}{3}x < -2$, $x < -6$.   **16.** If $-5x > 20$, $-4 > x$.

Which of the following are true for all real numbers a and b ($b \neq 0$)?

B   **17.** $6ab = 2a \cdot 3b$ **20.** $b > \dfrac{1}{b}$

18. $a - b = b - a$ **21.** $|a - b| = |b - a|$

19. $ab + cb = (a + c)b$ **22.** $\dfrac{a^2}{b^2} > \dfrac{a}{b}$

For each step listed in transforming the given equation name a property of real numbers or equality that applies. When more than one property applies, you need name only one.

EXAMPLE. $4x - 6 = 2(x + 3)$

Solution:

Step 1. $4x - 6 = 2x + 6$	*Step 1.* Distributive Law.
Step 2. $\quad\ \ 4x = 2x + 12$	*Step 2.* Addition property of equality.
Step 3. $\quad\ \ 2x = 12$	*Step 3.* Subtraction property of equality.
Step 4. $\quad\ \ \ x = 6$	*Step 4.* Division property of equality.

23. $12 - x = 20 - 5x$ **25.** $x(x + 4) = x(x + 2) + 1$

    Step 1. $12 + 4x = 20$ *Step 1.* $x^2 + 4x = x^2 + 2x + 1$

    Step 2. $\quad\ \ 4x = 8$ *Step 2.* $\quad\quad\ 2x = 1$

    Step 3. $\quad\ \ \ x = 2$ *Step 3.* $\quad\quad\ \ x = \frac{1}{2}$

24. $2(x + 3) = 8$ **26.** $x^2 + 6x + 2x + 12 = 0$

    Step 1. $2x + 6 = 8$ *Step 1.* $x(x + 6) + 2(x + 6) = 0$

    Step 2. $\quad\ \ 2x = 2$ *Step 2.* $\quad\quad (x + 6)(x + 2) = 0$

    Step 3. $\quad\ \ \ x = 1$ *Step 3.* $x + 6 = 0$ or $x + 2 = 0$

                                Step 4. $x = -6$ or $x = -2$

27. In the set of integers does the property of closure hold for the operation of subtraction? for the operation of division?

28. In the set of real numbers is the operation of subtraction commutative? the operation of division commutative?

Given $A = \{$all positive odd integers$\}$. If $x \in A$, which of the following numbers belong to A?

C

29. $3x$ **31.** $x + 6$ **33.** $\dfrac{1}{x + 2}$ **35.** $x^3 + 2$

30. $7 - 9x$ **32.** x^2 **34.** $x^2 + x$ **36.** x^4

For what values of x is each of the following fractions meaningless (not defined)?

37. $\dfrac{12}{x^2 - 9}$ **38.** $\dfrac{2x - 3}{2x^2 - x - 3}$ **39.** $\dfrac{8}{2x^3 - 8x}$ **40.** $\dfrac{2x - 1}{8 - |2x|}$

3–2 Geometry as a Mathematical System

Using principles of logic discussed in Chapter 2, this book will develop geometry as a mathematical system. To help understand what this means, consider this proof about real numbers a, b, c, and n.

Proof of the statement: If $a < b$ and $b = c$, then $c + n > a + n$.

STATEMENT	REASON
$a < b$	Given.
$a + n < b + n$	Additive postulate of inequality.
$b + n > a + n$	Definition of the symbol $>$.
$b = c$	Given.
$c + n > a + n$	Substitution principle.

Each reason in the proof is either "Given" or is a postulate (step 2), a definition (step 3), or a property previously established (step 5). The proof illustrates the fact that algebra is a mathematical system in which properties about numbers are proved by reasoning deductively from some assumed facts and defined terms.

In any mathematical system:

1. Some basic terms are left undefined.
2. All other terms are carefully defined.
3. Some basic properties are accepted without proof (Postulates).
4. All other properties are established by proofs (Theorems).

In beginning to develop geometry as a mathematical system, we introduced the undefined terms "point," "line," and "plane" in

Chapter 1. Some basic terms must be accepted without definition for, if you attempted to define those terms, you would have to use, in your definitions, less familiar terms that would in turn have to be defined.

In Chapter 1, we also included some definitions of geometric terms, for example, "ray," "segment," and "angle."

Can you recognize a good definition? First, it should contain no word whose meaning is not already known, except the word being defined. For example, the only geometric terms used in defining another geometric term should be ones previously defined or accepted as undefined. Secondly, a good definition should classify the term being defined with a minimum number of restrictions. It should not be a listing of all the special properties of the term.

Two definitions of a square follow. The first definition is inadequate whereas the second is merely inefficient.

1. **A square is a four-sided figure in which all sides are congruent.**

This definition is not restrictive enough. It does not restrict the figure to a plane. It does not contain sufficient information to distinguish a square from a parallelogram in which all sides are congruent but not all angles are congruent.

2. **A square is a quadrilateral in which all sides and angles are congruent and the diagonals are both congruent and perpendicular.**

This definition contains too many restrictions. It lists properties over and above the essential ones.

In mathematics some definitions are best expressed in symbols. For example, the square of any real number a can be defined by the equation $a^2 = a \cdot a$.

ORAL
EXERCISES

Which of the following definitions would you classify as acceptable?

1. Pear: a fruit which can be eaten.

2. Equilateral triangle: a triangle in which all three sides are of equal length.

3. Basketball: a game in which a spherical-shaped ball is used.

4. Largest: that which is larger than the next largest.

5. Triangle: a geometric figure which has three sides, three angles, and a perimeter.

6. Ice: solid form of that substance which, in liquid form, is water.

Complete:

7. The kind of reasoning used within a mathematical system is __?__ reasoning.

8. In a mathematical system a statement accepted without proof is called a(n) __?__.

9. In a mathematical system a proved statement is called a(n) __?__.

10. In a mathematical system some terms are defined, but some terms must be left __?__.

WRITTEN EXERCISES

In Exercises 1–8 classify the given definition as "acceptable" or "unacceptable." Give a reason to support your classification of any definition as "unacceptable."

EXAMPLE.   A *scholar* is one who exhibits the traits of a scholar.

Solution: Unacceptable — uses the word being defined.

A

1. A *sphere* is a round object of spherical shape.

2. *Forever* is until the end of time.

3. *Concentric circles* are two different circles which lie in the same plane and have the same center but have radii of different lengths.

4. *Up* is the opposite direction from down.

5. A *week* is a period of time consisting of seven consecutive days.

6. A *teacher* is a person who is employed in a school.

7. The *bisector of an angle* is a ray which divides an angle into two congruent angles that have the same measure.

8. An *exponent* is a little number frequently used in algebraic expressions.

A person asserting that the following statements are true is making a hidden assumption in each case. Indicate the assumption being made.

EXAMPLE. If $a > b$, then $ac > bc$.

Solution: Assumption is made that $c > 0$.

B

9. The square of a positive rational number is less than the number itself.

10. Two lines which do not meet are parallel.

11. If two angles are supplementary, one is acute and the other obtuse.

12. If $a < b$, then $\dfrac{a}{t} < \dfrac{b}{t}$.

13. Two distinct lines, each perpendicular to the same line, are parallel.

14. The measure of the area of a square is greater than the measure of its perimeter.

Suppose you accept as a postulate the statement, *Vertical angles have equal measures.* Which of these conclusions can be deduced from the postulate?

15. Two angles which have equal measures are vertical angles.

16. Two angles which are not vertical angles cannot have equal measures.

17. Two angles which do not have equal measures cannot be vertical angles.

18. Two angles which are vertical angles cannot be complementary angles.

Suppose you accept as a postulate the statement, *Any acute angle can be bisected.* Which of these conclusions can be deduced?

19. Any acute angle can be divided into two angles of equal measure.

20. Any acute angle can be divided into three angles of equal measure.

21. Any angle that can be bisected is an acute angle.

22. The complement of any acute angle can be bisected.

23. The supplement of any acute angle can be bisected.

24. An angle which is not acute cannot be bisected.

Given: A = {all positive integers} B = {all negative integers}
C = {all rational numbers} D = {all real numbers}

On the basis of your knowledge of number facts, tell for which of the given sets the statement listed would not be a reasonable postulate.

EXAMPLE. The product of any two members of the set is a member of the set.

Solution: This statement would not be a reasonable postulate for *B* since the product of two negative integers is not a member of *B*.

25. The sum of any two members is a member of the set.

26. The difference of any two members is a member of the set.

27. The quotient of any two nonzero members is a member of the set.

28. For any two members a and b, $a^2 > b^2$ if $a > b$.

29. For any two members a and b, $a - b = b - a$.

30. For any member a there is a member b of the set such that $ab = 1$.

■ Initial Postulates and Theorems

3–3 Points, Lines, and Planes

Before we can *prove* conclusions in geometry, we must have some postulates as well as definitions to support our assertions. Five postulates about points, lines, and planes are listed below. Additional postulates will be introduced from time to time as we proceed to develop geometry as a mathematical system. A postulate will always be designated by "**P**" with a subscript indicating its number.

POSTULATES 1–5

P_1 A line contains at least two points; a plane contains at least three points not all on one line; and space contains at least four points not all in one plane.

P_2 Through any two different points there is exactly one line.

P_3 Through any three points which are not on one line there is exactly one plane.

P_4 If two points lie in a plane, then the line containing them lies in that plane.

P_5 If two different planes intersect, then their intersection is a line.

On the basis of these postulates it is possible to prove some theorems about points, lines, and planes. Once a theorem has been proved, it can be used along with definitions and postulates in proving later theorems.

The first theorems in a deductive system often state obvious conclusions which follow from combining definitions and postulates. Unfortunately, detailed proofs of such theorems are tricky and not too meaningful to students just beginning the study of proofs. Therefore, this book will merely present a supporting argument for each of the first few theorems. You will not be required to reproduce these arguments. You should, however, know the statement of each theorem.

THEOREM 3–1 If two lines intersect, they intersect in exactly one point.

C **Supporting argument:**

Let *l* and *m* be the two given lines and *R* their known point of intersection. Suppose *l* and *m* had a second point of intersection *S*. Then *l* and *m* would have to be the same line, since by P_2 there could be but one line through both *R* and *S*. This would contradict the given condition that *l* and *m* are different lines. Therefore, they cannot intersect in a second point.

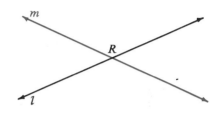

THEOREM 3–2 If a point lies outside a line, exactly one plane contains the line and the point.

C **Supporting argument:**

By P_1 there must be at least two points on *l*. Since *X* is given as not on *l*, there are at least three points not all on a line. P_3 makes it possible to conclude that there is exactly one plane containing these three points. Finally, P_4 insures that *l* lies in that plane since two points on *l* lie in the plane.

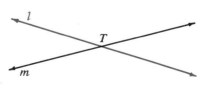

THEOREM 3–3 If two lines intersect, exactly one plane contains both lines.

C **Supporting argument:**

Let *T* be the point at which *l* and *m* intersect. Since P_1 tells us that a line contains at least two points, there must be another point on *m* and another point on *l*. P_3 informs us that there is exactly one plane which will contain these three points. Both *l* and *m* will have to lie in this plane because P_4 says that if two points lie in a plane the line through them lies in that plane.

Notice the phrase *exactly one* in Theorem 3–3. *One and only one* is an equivalent phrase. The following two sentences are both acceptable statements of Theorem 3–3.

If two lines intersect, exactly one plane contains both lines.
If two lines intersect, one and only one plane contains both lines.

ORAL EXERCISES

1. Restate P_2 and P_3 using the phrase *one and only one*.
2. Restate Theorem 3–1 and Theorem 3–2 using the phrase *one and only one*.
3. State a postulate about real numbers.
4. State a postulate about the intersection of two planes.
5. What is meant by collinear points? coplanar points?
6. Do two different points always lie in some line?
7. Does "exactly one line" mean the same as "one and only one line"?
8. Can two points be noncollinear?
9. Does Postulate 3 state that there is exactly one plane through any three points?
10. State the postulate that specifies the minimum number of points in space.
11. Are postulates theorems?
12. Postulate 1 states that a line contains at least two different points. Does this justify a conclusion that two lines contain at least four points?
13. Should two contradictory statements be accepted as postulates?
14. Could Theorem 3–3 be cited as a reason to justify a step taken in proving Theorem 3–1?

WRITTEN EXERCISES

Write in full the postulate that justifies each of the following statements.

A

1. Points A and B lie in one and only one line.
2. If points A, B, C are noncollinear, they lie in one and only one plane.

3. If points A and B are different points in plane X, $\overleftrightarrow{AB}$ lies in X.

4. If points A and B are different points in plane X, there is a third point in X not on $\overleftrightarrow{AB}$.

In Exercises 5–10 draw a figure representing:

5. Three points on one line.

6. Three points not on one line.

7. Four points all in one plane.

8. Four points not all in one plane.

9. Two intersecting planes.

10. Two nonintersecting planes.

Classify the following statements as true or false.

11. An undefined term cannot be used in a postulate.

12. Two different planes can intersect in exactly one point.

13. A postulate is a proved statement.

14. A set of points is collinear if there is a line which contains all the points of the set.

15. Any two lines lie in exactly one plane.

16. If two points on a ray lie in a plane, the ray lies in that plane.

17. Two intersecting lines have just one point in common.

18. A segment has exactly one endpoint.

B

19. State Postulate 2 in "if-then" form.

20. State Postulate 3 in "if-then" form.

21. Given: Point A lies in plane M, and Point B lies in plane M.
  a. What can you conclude about $\overleftrightarrow{AB}$?
  b. State the postulate that supports your deduction.

22. Given: Planes P and Q both contain point C.
  a. What can you conclude about the intersection of P and Q?
  b. State the postulate that supports your deduction.

23. Given: l and m are intersecting lines. Point P lies on l and m. Point Q lies on l and m.
  a. What can you conclude about P and Q?
  b. State the theorem that supports your conclusion.

24. Given: The vertices of triangle ABC lie in plane X.
  a. What can you conclude about the sides of triangle ABC?
  b. State the postulate that supports your conclusion.

25. If three points lie in both of two different planes, can they be the vertices of a triangle? Must they be collinear?

26. $ABCD$ is a quadrilateral whose diagonals intersect in point X. Must the points A, B, C, D, and X all lie in one plane?

C   27. Draw a figure showing four points P, Q, R, and S in such a position that $\overleftrightarrow{PQ}$, $\overleftrightarrow{PR}$, $\overleftrightarrow{PS}$, $\overleftrightarrow{QR}$, $\overleftrightarrow{QS}$, and $\overleftrightarrow{RS}$ (a) are six different lines (b) are contained in four lines (c) are all the same line.

28. Draw figures showing two essentially different ways in which three noncoplanar lines can be coplanar in pairs.

29. If the word "line" were everywhere replaced by the word "circle" in all five postulates, which ones would seem to be reasonable statements about circles?

30. Write a supporting argument in paragraph form for the statement: If a line intersects a plane not containing the line, the intersection is a single point. (Refer to the supporting argument for Theorem 3–1.)

3–4   Lines and Segments

In Chapter 1 you were introduced to the real number line. Certain ideas were developed about the correspondence between points on a line and the real numbers and about the distance between two points. However, since no conclusions were established by deductive proof, these findings must be restated as postulates now before they can be used as a basis on which to build additional conclusions about lines and segments.

P₆   Between any two points there is a unique distance.

$AB = BA = x$, where x is a unique positive real number.

P₇   The set of points on a line can be put in one-to-one correspondence with the real numbers in such a way that:
1. Any particular point is paired with zero;
2. The distance between any two points is equal to the absolute value of the difference between the numbers corresponding to those points.   (Ruler Postulate)

$AB = |y - x|$
$\quad = |x - y|$

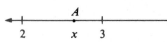
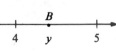

It is important to recall the conditions stated for betweenness of points.

B is said to lie between A and C if and only if:

1. All three are distinct points on the same line.
2. $AB + BC = AC$

P_7 permits you to set up a coordinate system on any line. You can pair zero with any given point on a line. When two distinct points are given on a line, one of the points can be paired with zero and the other with a positive real number.

Two preliminary theorems follow. Again supporting arguments rather than formal proofs are presented. Though you will not be required to reproduce these arguments, you should know the statements of the theorems.

The two theorems state properties that are intuitively evident. However, in developing a mathematical system, you cannot make use of intuitively evident properties that have not been listed as postulates or established as theorems.

THEOREM 3–4   On a ray there is exactly one point at a given distance from the endpoint of the ray.

c **Supporting argument:**

Let $\overrightarrow{AB}$ be the given ray. The zero point of a coordinate system can be placed at A with all other points on $\overrightarrow{AB}$ having positive numbers as coordinates. Let d be the given distance. Postulate 7 gives us two points on $\overleftrightarrow{AB}$ and at distance d from A. One of these points has coordinate d, a positive number. That point, point X in the figure, is the desired point on $\overrightarrow{AB}$. The other point, which has coordinate $-d$, cannot lie on $\overrightarrow{AB}$.

THEOREM 3-5   A segment has exactly one midpoint.

C **Supporting argument:**

Let $\overline{AB}$ be the given segment. We need to show that there is exactly one point M on $\overline{AB}$ which satisfies the conditions that $AM + MB = AB$ and $AM = MB$. From the two equations it follows that AM must equal $\frac{1}{2}AB$. Since $\frac{1}{2}AB$ is a unique number, Theorem 3-4 tells us that there is exactly one point on $\overrightarrow{AB}$ at distance $\frac{1}{2}AB$ from A. That point lies on $\overline{AB}$, for otherwise it would lie beyond B on $\overrightarrow{AB}$, and we would have $AB + BM = AM$, and AM would be greater than MB.

ORAL EXERCISES

1. Give a definition for a segment.
2. Is the distance between two points always a real number?
3. If a and b are real numbers does $|a - b| = |b - a|$?
4. Explain the difference between AB and $\overline{AB}$.
5. What set of numbers does our postulate say can be put in one-to-one correspondence with the set of points on a line?
6. Is it meaningful to refer to the length of $\overleftrightarrow{AB}$?
7. Can two different points on a line have the same coordinate once a coordinate system has been set up on the line?
8. Can one point be said to lie between two other points if the three points are not collinear?

WRITTEN EXERCISES

Refer to the adjacent coordinate system in answering Exercises 1–8.

A 1. What point has a coordinate 0?
2. What is the distance from A to B?
3. What is the length of $\overline{BD}$?

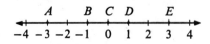

4. What is the coordinate of the endpoint of $\overrightarrow{BC}$?

5. What is the coordinate of the midpoint of $\overline{AE}$?

6. What two points are at a distance 2 from D?

7. Is it true that $AB + BC + CD = AD$?

8. If the zero point were made to correspond to A, would the distances between the indicated points be changed?

9. D, E, and F are collinear points. Can you find an arrangement of the points such that point E lies between points D and F, and at the same time point F lies between points D and E?

10. If x, y, and z are coordinates of three collinear points with $x > y$ and $y > z$, which point lies between the other two?

11. Suppose S is a point, not an endpoint, on $\overline{RT}$. Complete the following:

    a. $RS + ST = \underline{\ ?\ }$ **b.** $RT - ST = \underline{\ ?\ }$ **c.** $RT - RS = \underline{\ ?\ }$

12. B is a point on $\overline{AC}$ such that $AC = 2(AB)$. Compare AB and BC.

13. P, Q, and R are collinear points. P and Q are fixed points 10 units apart. Q is 15 units from R. Illustrate two possible placements of R.

14. Three towns, X, Y, Z, lie on a straight road but not necessarily in that order. It is 16 mi. from X to Y and 25 mi. from Y to Z. Which town cannot lie between the other two?

15. Points J, K, and L lie in some order on a line. If $JK < KL$, which point cannot possibly lie between the other two?

16. Point A lies to the left of point B on a line. C and D are two other points on this line. If $AB = 5$, $BC = 2$, and $CD = 4$, show by scale drawings that it is possible for the points to lie in the order

    a. A, B, C, D **b.** A, D, B, C **c.** D, A, C, B **d.** A, C, B, D

17. A, B, C are three collinear points with coordinates x, y, z respectively. One relationship which might exist between the coordinates would be $x > z > y$. Write five other double inequalities that could exist between the coordinates.

18. Write a supporting argument for the following theorem: If A and C are distinct points and B is any point on $\overleftrightarrow{AC}$ such that $AB = BC$, then B is between A and C.

3–5 Two-Column Deductive Proofs

To prove a statement in geometry or in any other mathematical system means to demonstrate that the statement follows logically from other accepted statements. Thus, only definitions, postulates, or previously proved theorems can be cited to support assertions made in proving statements in geometry.

The two-column form of proof is used extensively in geometry. It enables a person to show each assertion made and the reason which supports it. Assertions are listed in order in the left-hand column. The supporting reason for each assertion is listed in the right-hand column. When the supporting reason for a statement is a theorem or postulate, you are to name the particular theorem or postulate in the reason column. You are not to refer to it by number.

Study the organization of the sample proofs which follow. Note that both the statements and reasons are numbered. Until you have had more experience with proofs, the **Given** (the **Hypothesis**) and the **To Prove** (the **Conclusion**) will be listed for you in proof exercises.

EXAMPLE 1.

Given: P lies on $\overleftrightarrow{AB}$ between A and B.

To Prove: $PB = AB - AP$.

Proof

STATEMENT	REASON
1. P lies on $\overleftrightarrow{AB}$ between A and B.	1. Given.
2. $AP + PB = AB$	2. Definition of betweenness.
3. $PB = AB - AP$	3. Subtraction property of equality. (AP subtracted from both members)

The first two steps of the proof shown in Example 1 are geometric, and the third step is essentially algebraic. Actually, although you proceed easily enough from step 2 to step 3, a more complete algebraic development would involve many steps:

$PB + AP$	$= AB$	Definition of betweenness.
$(PB + AP) - AP$	$= AB - AP$	Subtraction property of equality.
$(PB + AP) + (-AP) = AB - AP$		By use of theorem: $a - b = a + (-b)$.
$PB + (AP + (-AP)) = AB - AP$		Associative postulate for addition.
$PB + \quad 0$	$= AB - AP$	Postulate of additive inverses.
PB	$= AB - AP$	Additive postulate of zero.

Such algebraic detail is rarely shown in proofs of theorems in geometry. In this book just enough algebraic detail will be shown so that readers can proceed with confidence. Although the reason column could simply show, for algebraic steps, the phrase *By algebra*, it is generally helpful to identify some algebraic principle that is being applied. Note how this is done in step 3 of Example 1 and in steps 5 and 6 of Example 2.

EXAMPLE 2.

Given: A, B, C, X on $\overleftrightarrow{AX}$ in the order shown, with $AC = BX$.

To Prove: $AB = CX$.

Proof

STATEMENT	REASON
1. A, B, C, X on $\overleftrightarrow{AX}$ in the order shown	**1.** Given.
2. $AC = AB + BC$	**2.** Definition of betweenness.
3. $BX = BC + CX$	**3.** Definition of betweenness.
4. But $AC = BX$	**4.** Given.
5. $AB + BC = BC + CX$	**5.** Substitution principle. (Substituting for AC and BX in Step 4)
6. $AB = CX$	**6.** Subtraction property of equality.

Note that in the sample proofs care is taken to specify whether a property is one of equality or of inequality.

ORAL
EXERCISES

Name the properties of real numbers, equality, or inequality which justify the deductions made in the following statements.

1. If $AB + BC = AC$, then $BC = AC - AB$.

2. If $AB > AC$, then $AB - AC > 0$.

3. $AB = CD$ if $AB + BC = CD + BC$.

4. $x - 3 = 0$ if $4(x - 3) = 0$.

5. If $AB - BC = CD - BC$, then $AB = CD$.

6. If $2AB = CD$, then $AB = \frac{1}{2}CD$.

7. If $AB = CD$ and $CD = EF$, then $AB = EF$.

8. $3a > 3b$ if $a > b$.

WRITTEN EXERCISES

Write a two-column proof for each of the following. You may assume between-ness of points on the basis of their positions in the given figure.

A   **1.** Given: A, B, C, D on $\overline{AD}$ in the order shown.
    Prove: $AB + BD = AC + CD$.

2. Given: $AB = CD$.   Prove: $AC = BD$.

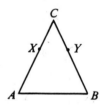
A _____ B C _____ D

3. Given: $AC = BD$.   Prove: $AB = CD$.

4. Given: $AB > CD$.   Prove: $AC > BD$.

5. Given: $AC > BD$.   Prove: $AB > CD$.

6. Given: A, B, C, D on $\overline{AD}$ in the order shown.
    Prove: $AB + BC + CD = AD$.

Points X and Y lie on sides $\overline{AC}$ and $\overline{BC}$ of $\triangle ABC$ as shown.

B   **7.** Given: $AX = BY$; $XC = YC$.
    Prove: $AC = BC$.

8. Given: $AC = BC$; $AX = BY$.
    Prove: $XC = YC$.

9. Given: $AC = BC$; X and Y are midpoints.   Prove: $AX = BY$.

10. Given: $AC > BC$; $AX = BY$.   Prove: $XC > YC$.

CHAPTER SUMMARY

Inventory of Structure and Methods

1. In algebra the steps taken in solving an equation or inequality or in transforming an expression represent deductions based upon certain assumed statements about real numbers, equality, and inequality. In mathematics assumed statements such as these are called **postulates.**

2. Both algebra and geometry are examples of **mathematical systems.** In developing a mathematical system you start with undefined terms, defined terms, and postulates. From these you reason to conclusions called **theorems**. A theorem is a statement to be proved. Once proved, a theorem can be used to support deductions made in proving theorems which follow it.

3. Some particularly useful properties of points, lines, and planes are:

You can specify a unique line when you have:

a. two distinct points,

b. two intersecting planes.

You can specify a unique plane when you have:

a. three noncollinear points,

b. two intersecting lines,

c. a line and a point not on the line.

The distance between two distinct points is a positive real number. If B lies between A and C on a line, then $AB + BC = AC$.

Vocabulary and Spelling

Euclid (*p. 91*)

axiom (*p. 91*)

postulate (*p. 91*)

properties of real numbers (*p. 92*)

properties of equality (*p. 92*)

properties of inequality (*p. 92*)

theorems of algebra (*p. 93*)

mathematical system (*p. 96*)

undefined term (*p. 96*)

definition (*p. 97*)

exactly one (*p. 102*)

one and only one (*p. 102*)

given (*p. 108*)

to prove (*p. 108*)

CHAPTER TEST

3–1   Name the property of equality or inequality that supports the indicated conclusion.

1. If $3x = 12$, then $x = 4$.

2. If $2x - 3 > 17$, then $2x > 20$.

3. If $p = q$ and $q = r$, then $p = r$.

4. If $\frac{1}{7}x = 5$, then $x = 35$.

3–2   Classify *each* statement as true or false.

5. All terms in a mathematical system must be defined.

6. An acceptable definition of a geometric figure lists all the properties of the figure.

7. A statement accepted without proof is called a postulate.

8. Postulates may be used in proofs.

3–3 State the theorem or postulate which enables you to make a deduction about the following:

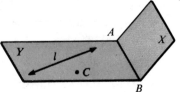

9. The intersection of planes X and Y.

10. The number of planes containing both line l and point C.

11. The number of planes through points A, B, and C.

12. The number of lines containing points A and B.

3–4 Exercises 13–16 refer to the given figure.

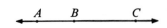

13. What can you say about $AB + BC$?

14. Does $\overleftrightarrow{AC}$ have a fixed length?

15. If A and B have coordinates -6 and -2 respectively, what is the length of $\overline{AB}$?

16. If $AB < \frac{1}{2}AC$, what can you conclude about BC?

3–5 Write the reason which supports each step taken in this two-column proof.

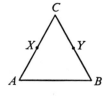

Given: X lies on $\overline{AC}$; Y lies on $\overline{BC}$;
$\qquad\quad AX = BY$; $XC = YC$.

To Prove: $AC = BC$.

Proof

STATEMENT	REASON
17. X lies on $\overline{AC}$; Y lies on $\overline{BC}$.	**17.** __?__
18. $AX = BY$; $XC = YC$.	**18.** __?__
19. $AX + XC = BY + YC$.	**19.** __?__
20. $AX + XC = AC$ and $BY + YC = BC$.	**20.** __?__
21. Therefore, $AC = BC$.	**21.** __?__

CHAPTER REVIEW

3–1 Postulates and Theorems in Algebra   *Pages 91–96*

1. Is the statement $a(b + c) = ab + ac$ a postulate or is it a theorem?

2. The associative postulate for addition states: $(a + b) + c =$ __?__ .

3. If $a < b$ and $c < 0$, then ac __?__ bc. (Write $=$, $<$, or $>$)

4. In proceeding from $\frac{1}{9}x = 2$ to $x = 18$ you use the __?__ property of equality.

3–2 Geometry as a Mathematical System *Pages 96–99*

5. Assumptions made in a mathematical system are called __?__.

6. Three basic terms, each naming a geometric figure, not defined in geometry are __?__, __?__, and __?__.

7. State an undefined term used in the definition of *line segment*.

8. Criticize the following definition of *two*: Two is a number between one and three.

3–3 Points, Lines, and Planes *Pages 100–104*

9. A plane contains at least __?__.

10. If two __?__ intersect, exactly one __?__ contains both __?__.

11. If __?__ points are noncollinear, exactly one __?__ contains those points.

12. If two planes intersect, their intersection is a __?__.

3–4 Lines and Segments *Pages 104–107*

13. If points A, K, and N lie on a line and $AN + NK = AK$, then __?__ lies between __?__ and __?__.

14. Given a positive number d. There is exactly one point on __?__ at distance d from point A. (Write either "$\overleftrightarrow{AB}$" or "$\overrightarrow{AB}$.")

15. The distance between two distinct points must be a __?__ number.

16. If S is the midpoint of $\overline{MN}$, then __?__ $=$ __?__.

3–5 Two-column Deductive Proofs *Pages 107–110*

17. In a two-column proof, assertions appear in the __?__ -hand column and supporting reasons in the __?__ -hand column.

18. Postulates, definitions, and __?__ can be used as reasons to support steps in a deductive proof.

19. If point S is known to lie between points R and T, then a satisfactory reason to support the assertion: $RS + ST = RT$ is __?__.

20. If it is known that $RS + ST = RT$, then a satisfactory reason to use to support the assertion: $RS = RT - ST$ is __?__.

A BRIEF REVIEW OF SPECIAL QUADRATIC EQUATIONS

A polynomial equation of degree two is called a **quadratic equation.** Each of the following is a quadratic equation with x as the variable.

$$x^2 - 9 = 0 \qquad 4x^2 - 5 = 10 \qquad\qquad x^2 = a$$
$$2x^2 - 10x = 0 \qquad x^2 + 16 = 8x \qquad ax^2 + bx + c = 0$$

Every quadratic equation in one variable has two roots. When the two roots happen to be the same number, the solution set contains a single element. In other cases the solution set contains two elements.

This review will consider methods for solving two simple types of quadratics. You may recall that many quadratic equations can be solved only by completing the square or by applying the quadratic formula. Quadratic equations of this type will not be discussed here.

Type 1. Equations which can be transformed into equations of the form $x^2 = a$, where $a > 0$.

Such equations can often be solved mentally.

EXAMPLE 1. $x^2 - 9 = 0$

Solution:
$$x^2 = 9$$
$$x = 3 \text{ or } -3$$

Both numbers check.

The solution set is $\{3, -3\}$, **Answer.**

EXAMPLE 2. $4x^2 - 5 = 10$

Solution:
$$4x^2 = 15$$
$$x^2 = \tfrac{15}{4}$$
$$x = \frac{\sqrt{15}}{2} \text{ or } -\frac{\sqrt{15}}{2}$$

Both numbers check.

The solution set is $\left\{ \dfrac{\sqrt{15}}{2}, -\dfrac{\sqrt{15}}{2} \right\}$,

Answer.

Type 2. Equations which can be transformed into equations of the form $ax^2 + bx + c = 0$, where $ax^2 + bx + c$ is readily factorable.

Such equations can be solved by application of the principle that a product is zero whenever either of its factors is zero.

EXAMPLE 3. $2x^2 - 10x = 0$

Solution:
$$x^2 - 5x = 0$$
$$x(x - 5) = 0$$
$$x = 0 \mid x - 5 = 0$$
$$x = 5$$

Both numbers check.
The solution set is $\{0, 5\}$, **Answer.**

EXAMPLE 4. $x^2 + 16 = 8x$

Solution:
$$x^2 - 8x + 16 = 0$$
$$(x - 4)(x - 4) = 0$$
$$x - 4 = 0 \mid x - 4 = 0$$
$$x = 4 \qquad x = 4$$

The number 4 checks.
The solution set is $\{4\}$, **Answer.**

EXAMPLE 5. x denotes the length of a segment, and $4x^2 + 2x = 30$.

Solution:
$$4x^2 + 2x - 30 = 0$$
$$2x^2 + x - 15 = 0$$
$$(x + 3)(2x - 5) = 0$$
$$x + 3 = 0 \mid 2x - 5 = 0$$
$$x = -3 \qquad x = \tfrac{5}{2}$$

Reject -3. (Though both -3 and $\frac{5}{2}$ check in the original equation, the length of a segment cannot be a negative number.)

The length of the segment is $\frac{5}{2}$, **Answer.**

EXERCISES

Find the solution set of each equation.

1. $x^2 - 25 = 0$
2. $x^2 = 49$
3. $x^2 = 171$
4. $x^2 - b = 0 \ (b > 0)$
5. $x^2 + 2x - 8 = 0$
6. $x^2 - 5x = 14$

7. $x^2 + 12x = 0$
8. $x^2 = 17x$
9. $2x^2 - 2x - 40 = 0$
10. $2x^2 - x - 1 = 0$
11. $3x^2 - 84 = 9x$
12. $3x^2 - 19x - 14 = 0$

In each of the following exercises, x denotes the length of a segment. Find x, rejecting numbers which have no meaning as lengths.

13. $x^2 = 36$
14. $x^2 - 7 = 57$
15. $25x^2 = 16$
16. $x^2 = n \ (n > 0)$
17. $x^2 - 5x = 50$
18. $x^2 - 8x + 15 = 0$

19. $x^2 = 13x$
20. $x^2 - 5x = 0$
21. $x^2 + 8x + 15 = 0$
22. $2x^2 - 14x + 20 = 0$
23. $3x^2 - 3x = 60$
24. $2x^2 + x - 15 = 0$

Angle Relationships; Perpendicular Lines

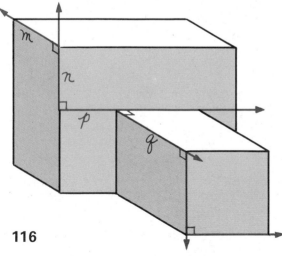

These Taos Pueblo adobe houses in New Mexico reveal an interesting pattern of perpendicular lines.

116

Up to this point only seven statements have been accepted as geometric postulates. These postulates represent assumptions about either our three undefined terms or the measure of distance between points on a line. While you were able to prove some additional conclusions on the basis of these postulates and a few theorems resulting from the postulates, you were restricted to working with lines or points on a line.

Before you can proceed to prove conclusions involving other geometric figures, you must have some accepted basic properties of an angle upon which to build. Though an angle was defined in Chapter 1, no statements about an angle were listed as postulates. Certain conclusions about the measure of an angle were arrived at inductively. However, before these can be used as a basis from which to reason to additional conclusions about angles, they must be restated in the form of postulates.

■ Angle Relationships

4–1 Initial Postulates and Theorems

Postulates 8 and 9 do for angle measure what Postulates 6 and 7 did, in the preceding chapter, for segment length.

P8 To every angle there corresponds a unique real number greater than 0 and less than 180. (Angle measurement postulate)

Postulate 8 is referred to as the angle measurement postulate since the real number specified is called the measure of the angle. Recall that congruent angles have the same measure.

P9 In the union of a half-plane and its edge, the set of rays with a common endpoint in the edge of the half-plane can be put in one-to-one correspondence with the real numbers from 0 to 180 inclusive in such a way that:

1. One of the two opposite rays lying in the edge is paired with 0 and the other is paired with 180.

2. The measure of any angle whose sides are rays of the given set is equal to the absolute value of the difference between the numbers corresponding to its sides. (Protractor postulate)

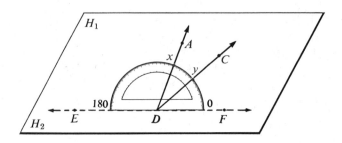

Postulate 9 enables you to conclude that in the situation represented above:

1. There are two unique real numbers x and y corresponding respectively to rays $\overrightarrow{DA}$ and $\overrightarrow{DC}$.

2. x and y are real numbers between 0 and 180.

3. $m\angle ADC = |x - y| = |y - x|$.

An understanding of what is meant by "a ray lying between two given rays" is essential in working with angles which have a common vertex. The three-part definition which follows is not one you will be required to quote. However, you should be familiar with the three conditions that are met when a ray lies between two given rays.

Betweenness of Rays: For $\angle AOC$, $\overrightarrow{OB}$ is said to lie between $\overrightarrow{OA}$ and $\overrightarrow{OC}$ when:

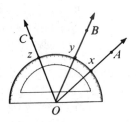

1. All three rays have a common endpoint.

2. $\overrightarrow{OB}$ lies, except for its endpoint, in the interior of $\angle AOC$.

3. The real numbers x, y, and z which correspond to $\overrightarrow{OA}$, $\overrightarrow{OB}$, and $\overrightarrow{OC}$ respectively are such that either $z > y > x$ or $x > y > z$.

THEOREM 4–1   If $\overrightarrow{OE}$ lies between $\overrightarrow{OD}$ and $\overrightarrow{OF}$ in a half-plane, then $m\angle DOE + m\angle EOF = m\angle DOF$.   (Angle addition theorem)

C

Supporting argument:

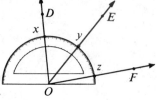

Since $\overrightarrow{OE}$ lies between $\overrightarrow{OD}$ and $\overrightarrow{OF}$ there are three real numbers x, y, and z corresponding to $\overrightarrow{OD}$, $\overrightarrow{OE}$, and $\overrightarrow{OF}$, respectively, such that $x - y$, $y - z$, and $x - z$ are positive numbers.

By the Protractor Postulate:

$$m\angle DOE = |x - y| = x - y \quad \text{(Since } |a| = a \text{ when } a > 0\text{)}$$
$$m\angle EOF = |y - z| = y - z$$
$$m\angle DOF = |x - z| = x - z$$

By the addition property of equality:

$$m\angle DOE + m\angle EOF = (x - y) + (y - z) = x - z$$

But: $\qquad\qquad\qquad m\angle DOF = x - z$

By the substitution principle:

$$m\angle DOE + m\angle EOF = m\angle DOF$$

(*Note:* Simply write **Angle addition theorem** when you use Theorem 4–1 as a reason in proofs.)

THEOREM 4–2   If the exterior sides of two adjacent angles are opposite rays, the angles are supplementary.

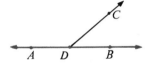

|C| **Supporting argument:**

Let $\angle ADC$ and $\angle CDB$ be any two angles having $\overrightarrow{DC}$ as a common side and in such position that $\overrightarrow{DA}$ and $\overrightarrow{DB}$ are opposite rays. By the protractor postulate $\overrightarrow{DB}$ can be paired with 0 and $\overrightarrow{DA}$ with 180. Let r be the number paired with $\overrightarrow{DC}$. Then:

$$m\angle CDB = |r - 0| = r$$

$$m\angle ADC = |180 - r| = 180 - r$$

Therefore, $\qquad m\angle CDB + m\angle ADC = r + (180 - r)$

$$m\angle CDB + m\angle ADC = 180$$

$\angle CDB$ and $\angle ADC$ are supplementary angles since the sum of their measures is 180.

THEOREM 4–3   In a half-plane, through the endpoint of a ray lying in the edge of the half-plane, there is exactly one other ray such that the angle formed by the two rays has a given measure between 0 and 180.

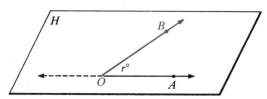

C   **Supporting argument:**

Let $\overrightarrow{OA}$ be the given ray and r be the given measure. It is possible to set up a one-to-one correspondence between rays and numbers in such a way that $\overrightarrow{OA}$ corresponds to zero. Then, there can be but one ray $\overrightarrow{OB}$ that corresponds to the number r since $|r - 0| = r$ when $r > 0$.

THEOREM 4–4   An angle has exactly one bisector.

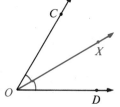

C   **Supporting argument:**

We need a ray $\overrightarrow{OX}$ such that $\angle COX \cong \angle DOX$. Therefore, $m\angle COX$ must equal $\frac{1}{2} m\angle COD$. Let s be the unique real number that corresponds, by the angle measurement postulate, with $\angle COD$. Then $m\angle COX = \frac{1}{2}s$. From Theorem 4–3 it follows that there is exactly one ray in the half-plane (having edge $\overleftrightarrow{OC}$ and containing point D) such that $m\angle COX = \frac{1}{2}s$. This ray is the bisector.

The proofs that follow show how the angle postulates and theorems can be used in proving conclusions. They also illustrate policies regarding information conveyed by diagrams. Whenever a diagram appears in this book:

1. Betweenness relations shown in the diagram can be used in proofs. A diagram serves as a more convenient way to convey betweenness information than a specific listing of all betweenness relationships.

2. A point shown by diagram to be in the interior of an angle can be used, in proofs, as an interior point.

3. No specific conclusions about segment length or angle measure can be drawn from a diagram.

Thus, given only the diagram shown, you can conclude that point M lies on $\overrightarrow{AL}$ between points A and L and that point K lies in the interior of $\angle JAL$. You *cannot* conclude that $\overrightarrow{AJ} \perp \overrightarrow{AL}$ or that $AM = ML$.

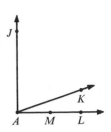

EXAMPLE 1.

Given: $\overrightarrow{BA}$, $\overrightarrow{BX}$, $\overrightarrow{BY}$, and $\overrightarrow{BC}$ as shown.

To Prove: $m\angle ABX + m\angle XBY + m\angle YBC$
$= m\angle ABC.$

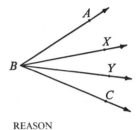

Proof

STATEMENT	REASON
1. $m\angle ABX + m\angle XBY = m\angle ABY.$	1. Angle addition theorem.
2. $m\angle ABY + m\angle YBC = m\angle ABC.$	2. Angle addition theorem.
3. $m\angle ABX + m\angle XBY + m\angle YBC$ $= m\angle ABC.$	3. The substitution principle. ($m\angle ABX + m\angle XBY$ is substituted for $m\angle ABY$ in Statement 2.)

EXAMPLE 2.

Given: $m\angle RPS = m\angle TPW$

To Prove: $m\angle RPT = m\angle SPW$

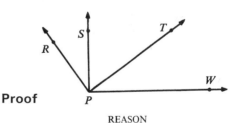

Proof

STATEMENT	REASON
1. $m\angle RPS = m\angle TPW.$	1. Given.
2. $m\angle RPS + m\angle SPT$ $= m\angle TPW + m\angle SPT.$	2. Addition property of equality.
3. $m\angle RPS + m\angle SPT = m\angle RPT.$	3. Angle addition theorem.
4. $m\angle TPW + m\angle SPT = m\angle SPW.$	4. Angle addition theorem.
5. $m\angle RPT = m\angle SPW.$	5. The substitution principle. (In Statement 2, $m\angle RPT$ is substituted for the left-hand member and $m\angle SPW$ for the right-hand member.)

ORAL
EXERCISES

1. Complete the sentence: An angle is the union of __?__.
2. What point is common to rays $\overrightarrow{AB}$ and $\overrightarrow{AC}$?
3. Can an angle have a measure of $\sqrt{120}$? of $\sqrt{9}$?
4. Does "$\angle ABC \cong \angle XYZ$" mean that $\angle ABC$ and $\angle XYZ$ are the same angle?
5. What is the measure of a right angle?
6. What kind of an angle has a measure greater than 90 but less than 180?
7. Name two angles in the diagram that have $\overrightarrow{PT}$ as a common side.
8. Name a pair of adjacent angles.
9. If $m\angle RPT < 90$, what kind of an angle is $\angle RPT$?
10. If $\angle RPS \cong \angle SPT$, what can you conclude about $\overrightarrow{PS}$?
11. What theorem supports the conclusion that $m\angle RPS + m\angle SPT = m\angle RPT$?
12. If $m\angle RPT = a + b$ and $m\angle SPT = a$, what can you conclude about the measure of $\angle RPS$?

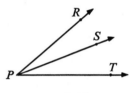

Exs. 7–12

13. How many rays in half-plane H_1 and with endpoint O form a 30° angle with $\overrightarrow{OJ}$? with $\overrightarrow{OS}$?
14. How many rays in half-plane H_2 and with endpoint O form a 120° angle with $\overrightarrow{OJ}$? with $\overrightarrow{OS}$?
15. What must be true if O is the midpoint of $\overline{JS}$?
16. Does $\overrightarrow{OJ}$ lie in the edge of the half-plane H_1?
17. If $a \neq b$ and $|a - b| = a - b$, which of the following are true?

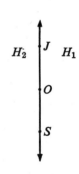

Exs. 13–16

$$a > b \qquad a - b > 0$$
$$a < b \qquad a - b = 0$$

18. If $a < b$, which of the following are true?

$$|a - b| = a - b \qquad b - a > 0$$
$$|a - b| = b - a \qquad a \neq b$$

19. State one pair of adjacent angles whose exterior sides lie in opposite rays. State the theorem that asserts that those two angles are supplementary.

20. Repeat Exercise 19, using a different pair of angles.

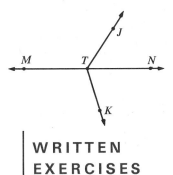

WRITTEN EXERCISES

In the given figure, a, b, c are the real numbers which correspond respectively to the coplanar rays $\overrightarrow{OR}$, $\overrightarrow{OS}$, and $\overrightarrow{OT}$, and $a > b > c$. Use this information in answering questions 1–14.

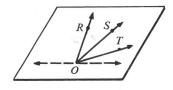

Exs. 1–14

A

1. What angle has measure $b - c$?

2. What angle has measure $a - c$?

3. Are $|c - b|$ and $c - b$ the same real number?

4. If $m\angle TOR = 60$, what can you conclude about $a - c$?

5. Are $\angle TOR$ and $\angle TOS$ adjacent angles?

6. If $\angle TOR$ is an acute angle, what is true about $a - c$?

7. Could the sum of a, b, and c be more than 180?

8. If $a - b = b - c$, what two angles have the same measure?

9. Name two angles of which $\overrightarrow{OR}$ is a common side.

10. Are rays $\overrightarrow{OR}$ and $\overrightarrow{OT}$ opposite rays?

11. If $\frac{1}{2}(a - c) = b - c$, what is true about $\overrightarrow{OS}$?

12. Does $|c - a| = |a - c|$?

13. If $a - b > b - c$, how do $m\angle SOR$ and $m\angle TOS$ compare?

14. Is there more than one plane containing rays $\overrightarrow{OR}$, $\overrightarrow{OS}$, and $\overrightarrow{OT}$?

Write the reason that supports each step in the following sequence.

Exs. 15–20

Given: In the figure at the right, $\angle GSR$ is an acute angle; $\overrightarrow{ST}$ bisects $\angle GSR$.

15. $m\angle GSR < 90$.

16. $m\angle GSR = m\angle GST + m\angle TSR$.

17. $m\angle GST + m\angle TSR < 90$.

18. $m\angle TSR = m\angle GST$.

19. $2m\angle TSR < 90$.

20. $m\angle TSR < 45$.

Write a two-column proof for each of the following exercises. Draw a separate figure for each
exercise and list the Given and the To Prove.

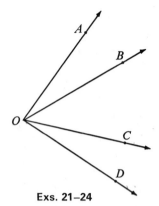

B 21. Given: $m\angle AOB = m\angle COD$.
Prove: $m\angle AOC = m\angle BOD$.

22. Given: $m\angle AOC = m\angle BOD$.
Prove: $m\angle AOB = m\angle COD$.

23. Given: $m\angle AOB > m\angle COD$.
Prove: $m\angle AOC > m\angle BOD$.

24. Given: $m\angle AOC > m\angle BOD$.
Prove: $m\angle AOB > m\angle COD$.

Exs. 21–24

If $\overrightarrow{OA}$ and $\overrightarrow{OB}$ are opposite rays, determine the measures of $\angle 1$ and $\angle 2$ when:

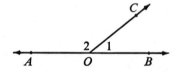

25. $m\angle 1 = x$; $m\angle 2 = 2x + 15$.

26. $m\angle 1 = x - 10$; $m\angle 2 = 3x + 10$.

27. The measure of $\angle 2$ exceeds that of $\angle 1$
by 40.

28. The ratio of the measure of $\angle 1$ to the measure of $\angle 2$ is 2 to 3.

Given: In the plane figure, A, O, and D are collinear points. Find the measure
of $\angle 1$ in each exercise.

C 29. $\angle 1$, $\angle 2$, and $\angle 3$ have measures in the
ratio 4:5:6.

30. $m\angle 1 = 3x + 2$; $m\angle 2 = 3x + 4$; $m\angle 3 = 6x - 18$.

31. $m\angle 1 = 5x$; $m\angle 2 = x + 40$;
$m\angle 3 = x^2 - 20$.

32. $m\angle 1 = 2x + 22$; $m\angle 2 = x + 46$; $m\angle 3 = x^2 + 4$.

33. $m\angle 1 = x^3 - 70$; $m\angle 2 = 185 - 4x^2 - 5x$; $m\angle 3 = 65$.

34. $m\angle 3 = 30$; $m\angle 2 - m\angle 1 = \frac{1}{3}(m\angle 1 + m\angle 3)$.

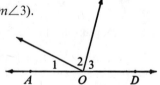

4–2 Right Angles and Perpendicular Lines

The postulates and theorems of the preceding section can be used
to prove theorems about special angles and pairs of angles. Some
definitions are repeated here for your convenience.

Right Angle: an angle with a measure of 90.

Perpendicular (⊥) Lines: two lines which meet to form congruent adjacent angles.

Complementary Angles: two angles the sum of whose measures is 90.

THEOREM 4–5 All right angles are congruent.

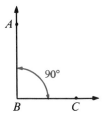 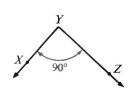

C **Supporting argument:**

Let ∠*ABC* and ∠*XYZ* be any two right angles. Each by definition has measure 90. Since they have the same measure, the angles are congruent.

THEOREM 4–6 If two lines are perpendicular, they meet to form right angles.

C **Supporting argument:**

Let *l* and *m* be any two perpendicular lines. By definition, ⊥ lines form congruent adjacent angles. Therefore, $m\angle 1 = m\angle 2$. Since adjacent angles whose exterior sides are opposite rays are supplementary, $m\angle 1 + m\angle 2 = 180$. By the substitution principle, $2(m\angle 1) = 180$. Then, by the division property, $m\angle 1 = 90$. Likewise, $m\angle 2 = 90$, $m\angle 3 = 90$, and $m\angle 4 = 90$. Each of the angles has measure 90. Therefore, each is a right angle.

THEOREM 4–7 If two lines meet to form a right angle, the lines are perpendicular.

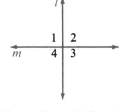

C **Supporting argument:**

Let *l* and *m* be any two lines meeting so that $m\angle 1 = 90$. Since the exterior sides of ∠1 and ∠2 are opposite rays, $m\angle 1 + m\angle 2 = 180$. By the substitution principle, $90 + m\angle 2 = 180$. By the subtraction property, $m\angle 2 = 90$. Thus, ∠1 ≅ ∠2, and lines *l* and *m* are perpendicular, since they meet so as to form congruent adjacent angles.

THEOREM 4–8   If two adjacent acute angles have their exterior sides in perpendicular lines, the angles are complementary.

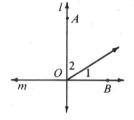

C   **Supporting argument:**

Let $\angle 1$ and $\angle 2$ be two adjacent angles with exterior sides in perpendicular lines *l* and *m*. Since perpendicular lines meet to form rt. angles, $m\angle AOB = 90$. By the angle addition theorem, $m\angle 1 + m\angle 2 = m\angle AOB$. By the substitution principle, $m\angle 1 + m\angle 2 = 90$. Thus, the angles are complementary.

THEOREM 4–9   In a plane, through a given point of a line, there is exactly one line perpendicular to the line.

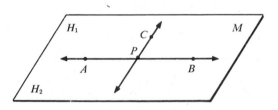

C   **Supporting argument:**

Let *P* be the point of $\overleftrightarrow{AB}$ at which we wish to find the number of lines perpendicular to $\overleftrightarrow{AB}$ and lying in plane *M*. Let H_1 and H_2 be the half-planes into which $\overleftrightarrow{AB}$ separates plane *M*. By Theorem 4–3 there is exactly one ray $\overrightarrow{PC}$, with *C* in H_1, such that $m\angle CPB = 90$. But if $m\angle CPB = 90$, then $\overrightarrow{PC} \perp \overleftrightarrow{AB}$ by Theorem 4–7. Suppose there were a second such perpendicular $\overrightarrow{PD}$ with *D* a point in H_1 not on $\overrightarrow{PC}$. Then $m\angle DPB = 90$ and thus $m\angle DPB = m\angle CPB$. But this would contradict Theorem 4–3. Therefore, there is exactly one line perpendicular to $\overleftrightarrow{AB}$ at *P* and lying in *M*.

It is important to note that Theorem 4–9 specifies the number of perpendicular lines at a point in a line, all lines *lying in a plane*. It is possible to have any number of lines perpendicular to a given line at a given point if this restriction is removed. You see intuitively that they would all lie in a plane perpendicular to the line at the point.

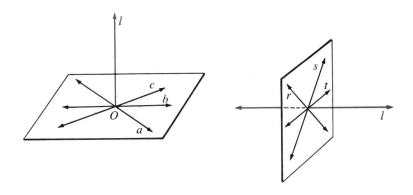

ORAL EXERCISES

The given figure consists of three coplanar lines passing through O with $\overleftrightarrow{AB} \perp \overleftrightarrow{CD}$. Classify the following statements as true or false.

1. $m\angle AOC = 90.$

2. $m\angle EOB > m\angle EOD.$

3. $m\angle FOD = m\angle AOD - m\angle AOF.$

4. $\angle AOD$ is a right angle.

5. $\angle COF$ is an acute angle.

6. $\overleftrightarrow{EF} \perp \overleftrightarrow{CD}.$

7. $\angle AOF$ and $\angle AOD$ are adjacent angles.

8. The exterior sides of $\angle AOF$ and $\angle FOD$ lie in perpendicular lines.

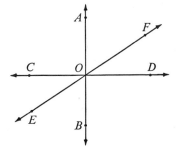

Exs. 1–12

9. $\angle AOC$ and $\angle AOD$ are complementary angles.

10. $\angle COF$ and $\angle FOD$ are supplementary angles.

11. Rays $\overrightarrow{OC}$ and $\overrightarrow{OF}$ are opposite rays.

12. $\angle AOC$ and $\angle AOD$ are congruent adjacent supplementary angles.

State the theorem which supports the conclusion made in each of the following exercises dealing with the plane figure shown.

13. If $\overrightarrow{OR} \perp \overleftrightarrow{XY}$, then $m\angle ROX = 90$.

14. If $\overrightarrow{OR} \perp \overleftrightarrow{XY}$,
then $m\angle SOY + m\angle ROS = 90$.

15. If $m\angle ROX = 90$, then $\overrightarrow{OR} \perp \overleftrightarrow{XY}$

16. If $\overleftrightarrow{XY}$ contains O but not S, then $\angle SOY$ and $\angle XOS$ are supplementary.

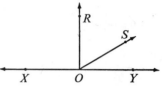

Exs. 13–16

Given: Line l lies in the plane X and is $\perp$ to plane Y at point P. Tell how many lines can be drawn $\perp$ to line l at P that lie in:

17. Plane Y.

18. Plane X.

19. Both planes X and Y.

20. Neither plane X nor plane Y.

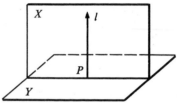

Exs. 17–20

WRITTEN EXERCISES

Given the plane figure in which $\overleftrightarrow{CD} \perp \overleftrightarrow{AB}$.

 A

1. $m\angle 1 + m\angle 2 = \underline{\quad?\quad}$.

2. If $m\angle 1 = 60$, then $m\angle 2 = \underline{\quad?\quad}$.

3. If $m\angle 3 = 50$, then $m\angle 4 = \underline{\quad?\quad}$.

4. Are $\overrightarrow{OT}$ and $\overrightarrow{OS}$ opposite rays?

5. Is $\angle AOT$ a supplement of $\angle TOB$?

6. If $m\angle TOB = 140$, then $m\angle 1 = \underline{\quad?\quad}$.

7. $m\angle 1 + m\angle 2 + m\angle 3 + m\angle 4 = \underline{\quad?\quad}$.

8. If $m\angle 2 + m\angle 3 = 110$,
then $m\angle 1 + m\angle 4 = \underline{\quad?\quad}$.

9. Name, using numbers, two pairs of complementary angles.

10. If $m\angle 4 = 23$, then $m\angle 3 = \underline{\quad?\quad}$.

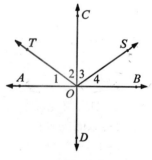

Exs. 1–18

11. Name, using numbers, two angles that are adjacent to $\angle 2$.

12. If $m\angle 1 = 32$, then $m\angle TOB =$ __?__.

13. What rays must be perpendicular if $m\angle 2 + m\angle 3 = 90$?

14. Must $\overrightarrow{OT}$ be perpendicular to $\overrightarrow{OS}$ if $m\angle 1 + m\angle 4 = 90$?

15. If $m\angle 1 = x$, then $m\angle 2 =$ __?__.

16. If $m\angle 4 = 3x$, then $m\angle AOS =$ __?__.

17. If $m\angle 2 = x + 10$, express $m\angle 1$ in simplest form.

18. If $m\angle 3 = 2x - 10$, express $m\angle 4$ in simplest form.

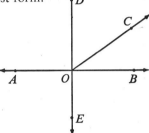

In the given plane figure $\overleftrightarrow{DE} \perp \overleftrightarrow{AB}$ at O. Write
the complete statement of the theorem which sup-
ports each of the following conclusions.

B

19. $m\angle DOB = m\angle DOC + m\angle COB$.

20. $\angle AOD$ is a right angle.

21. $\angle COB$ and $\angle DOC$ are complementary.

22. $\angle AOC$ and $\angle COB$ are supplementary.

Exs. 19–22

Give a reason to support each statement in the following proof.

Given: The plane figure with $\overrightarrow{OA} \perp \overrightarrow{OC}$.

To Prove: $m\angle 1 = 90 - m\angle 2$.

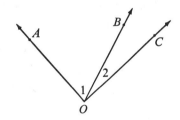

Proof

STATEMENT	REASON
23. $\overrightarrow{OA} \perp \overrightarrow{OC}$.	**23.** ?
24. $\angle AOC$ is a right angle.	**24.** ?
25. $m\angle AOC = 90$.	**25.** ?
26. $m\angle 1 + m\angle 2 = m\angle AOC$.	**26.** ?
27. $m\angle 1 + m\angle 2 = 90$.	**27.** ?
28. $m\angle 1 = 90 - m\angle 2$.	**28.** ?

Give a reason to support each statement in the following proof.

Given: $\overleftrightarrow{AB}$ and $\overleftrightarrow{CD}$ intersecting at O.

To Prove: $\angle 1 \cong \angle 3$.

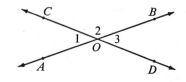

Proof

STATEMENT	REASON
29. $\overleftrightarrow{AB}$ and $\overleftrightarrow{CD}$ intersect at O.	**29.** ?
30. $\angle 1$ and $\angle 2$ are supplementary. $\angle 2$ and $\angle 3$ are supplementary.	**30.** ?
31. $m\angle 1 + m\angle 2 = 180$. $m\angle 2 + m\angle 3 = 180$.	**31.** ?
32. $m\angle 1 + m\angle 2 = m\angle 2 + m\angle 3$.	**32.** ?
33. $m\angle 1 = m\angle 3$.	**33.** ?
34. $\angle 1 \cong \angle 3$.	**34.** ?

■ Formal Proofs

4–3   Supplementary Angles; Complementary Angles; Vertical Angles

So far in this book, informal supporting arguments have been presented to justify theorems. This has been done because we have wished to emphasize the nature of the argument rather than a particular form of presentation. However, there is an approved form for presenting the proof of a theorem, not only because the use of a particular form is customary, but more important, because it helps in understanding the substance of the argument.

The proof of Theorem 4–10 that follows is presented in the form that will ordinarily be used hereafter. In the next section we shall point out the essential elements of this form.

THEOREM 4–10   If two angles are supplementary to the same angle or to congruent angles, they are congruent to each other.

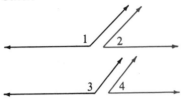

Given: $\angle 2 \cong \angle 4.$
$\angle 1$ is supplementary to $\angle 2.$
$\angle 3$ is supplementary to $\angle 4.$

To Prove: $\angle 1 \cong \angle 3.$

Analysis: Use the equation form to express the fact that certain angles are supplementary. Then use properties of equality.

Proof

STATEMENT	REASON
1. $\angle 1$ is supplementary to $\angle 2.$	1. Given.
2. $m\angle 1 + m\angle 2 = 180.$	2. If two angles are supplementary, the sum of their measures is 180.
3. $\angle 3$ is supplementary to $\angle 4.$	3. Given.
4. $m\angle 3 + m\angle 4 = 180.$	4. If two angles are supplementary, the sum of their measures is 180.
5. $m\angle 1 + m\angle 2 = m\angle 3 + m\angle 4.$	5. Transitive property of equality.
6. $m\angle 2 = m\angle 4.$	6. Given, and definition of congruent angles.
7. $m\angle 1 = m\angle 3.$	7. Subtraction property of equality.
8. $\angle 1 \cong \angle 3.$	8. Definition of congruent angles.

The case where the two angles are supplementary to the same angle can be considered as a special case of the proof presented and need not be established separately. However, it is suggested that you write out a proof similar to the one above for this special case. It will help you to become familiar with the form used in demonstrating theorems.

THEOREM 4–11   If two angles are complementary to the same angle or to congruent angles, they are congruent to each other.

Given: $\angle 2 \cong \angle 4.$
$\angle 1$ is complementary to $\angle 2.$
$\angle 3$ is complementary to $\angle 4.$

To Prove: $\angle 1 \cong \angle 3.$

Analysis: Use the equation form to express the fact that certain angles are complementary. Then use properties of equality.

(The remainder of the demonstration is left for you to provide. Refer back to Theorem 4–10 if you have difficulty in developing a two-column proof.)

THEOREM 4–12   If two lines intersect, the vertical angles formed are congruent.

Given: $\overleftrightarrow{AB}$ and $\overleftrightarrow{CD}$ intersect at $E.$

To Prove: $\angle 1 \cong \angle 2; \ \angle 3 \cong \angle 4.$

Analysis: Use the fact that there are several pairs of supplementary angles. Then apply Theorem 4–10.

Proof

STATEMENT	REASON
1. $\overleftrightarrow{AB}$ and $\overleftrightarrow{CD}$ intersect at $E.$	1. Given.
2. $\angle 1$ and $\angle 3$ are supplementary. $\angle 2$ and $\angle 3$ are supplementary.	2. If the exterior sides of two adj. ∡ are opposite rays, the angles are supplementary.
3. $\angle 1 \cong \angle 2.$	3. Two ∡ supplementary to the same $\angle$ are congruent.
4. $\angle 1$ and $\angle 4$ are supplementary. $\angle 2$ and $\angle 3$ are supplementary.	4. Same as reason for Statement 2.
5. $\angle 3 \cong \angle 4.$	5. Two ∡ supplementary to congruent ∡ are congruent.

ORAL

EXERCISES

1. When two lines intersect, how many pairs of vertical angles are formed?

2. If two angles are complementary, must they be adjacent?

3. If two angles are adjacent, must they be complementary?

4. Can a pair of acute vertical angles ever be adjacent angles?

5. Can a pair of vertical angles ever be complementary?

6. If two angles are both congruent and supplementary, what is the measure of each?

7. Is a supplement of an acute angle always an obtuse angle?

8. If two angles are not congruent, can their complements be congruent?

For the plane figure given, classify the following statements as true or false.

9. $m\angle 2 = m\angle 3$.

10. If $m\angle 1 > m\angle 3$, then $m\angle 2 > m\angle 3$.

11. $\angle 7$ and $\angle 8$ are adjacent angles.

12. If $\angle 1 \cong \angle 6$, then $\angle 3 \cong \angle 5$.

13. $\angle 3$ and $\angle 2$ are both supplementary to $\angle 1$.

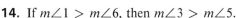

Exs. 9–20

14. If $m\angle 1 > m\angle 6$, then $m\angle 3 > m\angle 5$.

15. If $\angle 1 \cong \angle 3$, then $\angle 3$ is a rt. angle.

16. If $\angle 5 \cong \angle 8$, then $\angle 5$ is a rt. angle.

17. If $m\angle 3 = m\angle 5$, then $m\angle 2 = m\angle 8$.

18. If $\angle 6 \cong \angle 2$, then $\angle 1 \cong \angle 5$.

19. If $m\angle 1 > m\angle 3$, then $\angle 2$ is an acute angle.

20. If $\angle 6$ is a rt. angle, then $m\angle 7 = m\angle 8$.

Given the plane figure in which $\overrightarrow{OA} \perp \overrightarrow{OB}$ and $\overrightarrow{OC} \perp \overrightarrow{OD}$. State a theorem or definition to support the following conclusions.

21. $\angle AOB$ and $\angle COD$ are right angles.

22. $m\angle 2 + m\angle 3 = m\angle AOB$; $m\angle 2 + m\angle 1 = m\angle COD$.

23. $\angle 2$ and $\angle 3$ are complementary, and $\angle 2$ and $\angle 1$ are complementary.

24. $\angle 1 \cong \angle 3$.

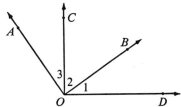

Exs. 19–24

WRITTEN EXERCISES

In the plane figure, $\overrightarrow{PX}$ is perpendicular to $\overleftrightarrow{AB}$ at P. Name the following.

A
1. Two right angles.
2. An obtuse angle.
3. Two complementary angles.
4. A pair of opposite rays.
5. Two angles which are adjacent to $\angle XPY$.
6. Two noncongruent supplementary angles.
7. Two nonadjacent angles.
8. Two congruent supplementary angles.

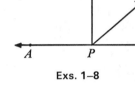

Exs. 1–8

Given plane quadrilateral ABCD. Assuming the angles have the indicated measures, name the following.

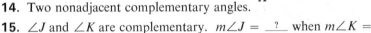

9. Two right angles.
10. An obtuse angle.
11. Two adjacent complementary angles.
12. An angle supplementary to $\angle DAB$.
13. Two segments perpendicular to $\overline{BC}$.
14. Two nonadjacent complementary angles.
15. $\angle J$ and $\angle K$ are complementary. $m\angle J = \underline{\ ?\ }$ when $m\angle K =$
    a. 50   **b.** 60   **c.** n **d.** $90 - x$
16. $\angle R$ and $\angle S$ are supplementary. $m\angle R = \underline{\ ?\ }$ when $m\angle S =$
    a. 110   **b.** 40   **c.** n **d.** $90 - x$
17. If two angles with the same measure are complementary, find the measure of each.
18. If two angles are both vertical and supplementary, find the measure of each.
19. One angle has a measure of $3a$. A second angle has a measure of $90 - a$. What is the value of a if these angles are supplementary?
20. An acute angle has a measure of $60 + 2a$ $(a > 0)$. What can you conclude about the range of values for a?

Give a reason to support each statement in the following proof.

Given: The plane figure with
$\overleftrightarrow{FD}$ intersecting $\overleftrightarrow{CG}$ and
$\overleftrightarrow{EH}$ at A and B re-
spectively   so   that
$m\angle 4 = m\angle 3$.

To Prove: $\angle 2$ and $\angle 1$ are supplementary.

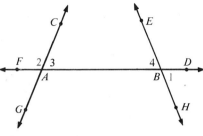

Proof

STATEMENT	REASON
21. $\angle 2$ and $\angle 3$ are supplementary.	**21.** ?
22. $m\angle 2 + m\angle 3 = 180$.	**22.** ?
23. $m\angle 4 = m\angle 3$.	**23.** ?
24. $m\angle 2 + m\angle 4 = 180$.	**24.** ?
25. $\angle 4 \cong \angle 1$.	**25.** ?
26. $m\angle 4 = m\angle 1$.	**26.** ?
27. $m\angle 2 + m\angle 1 = 180$.	**27.** ?
28. $\angle 2$ and $\angle 1$ are supplementary.	**28.** ?

29. If $m\angle A < m\angle B$, what is the relationship between the measures of their complements?

30. If $m\angle A < m\angle B$, what is the relationship between the measures of their supplements?

31. The measure of an angle is 16 less than the measure of its complement. Find the measure of the angle.

32. The measure of an angle is 22 more than the measure of its supplement. Find the measure of the angle.

33. An angle has a measure of $2x + 20$, and its vertical angle a measure of $5x - 34$. Find the measure of each angle.

34. An angle has a measure of $3x - 10$, and its complement a measure of $2x + 20$. Find the measure of each angle.

35. Given: $\overleftrightarrow{AB}$, $\overrightarrow{OX}$, and $\overrightarrow{OY}$ intersecting
at O;
$m\angle XOB = m\angle YOB$.

Prove: $m\angle AOX + m\angle YOB = 180$.

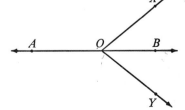

36. Given: $\overrightarrow{AX} \perp \overleftrightarrow{AB}$;
    $\overrightarrow{BY} \perp \overleftrightarrow{AB}$;
    $\angle 1 \cong \angle 2$.
    Prove: $\angle 3 \cong \angle 4$.

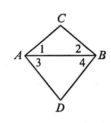

37. Given: $\overrightarrow{AD}$ and $\overrightarrow{AE}$ opposite rays;
    $\overrightarrow{BA}$ and $\overrightarrow{BC}$ opposite rays;
    $m\angle 1 = m\angle 2$.
    Prove: $m\angle 5 + m\angle 4 = 180$.

38. Given: $\overleftrightarrow{AC} \perp \overleftrightarrow{AD}$;
    $\overleftrightarrow{BC} \perp \overleftrightarrow{BD}$;
    $m\angle 1 = m\angle 2$.
    Prove: $m\angle 3 = m\angle 4$.

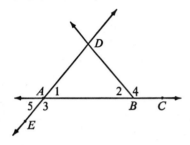

C

39. An acute angle has a measure of $2a + 3b$. What is the difference between the measures of a supplement and a complement of the angle?

40. The measures of two complementary angles differ by x. Express the measure of the larger angle in terms of x.

41. The sum of the measures of a complement and a supplement of an angle is 160. Find the measure of the angle.

42. Two angles are such that the ratio of the measures of their complements is 3 to 2, while the ratio of the measures of their supplements is 9 to 8. Find the measure of each angle.

4–4 The Demonstration of a Theorem

You have now had some experience both in reading and in writing formal proofs. A proof of a statement that is classified as a theorem is often referred to as "a demonstration of the theorem." Let us now study the form used in presenting a demonstration of a theorem.

The demonstration of a theorem consists of six essential parts arranged in order.

   1. **Statement:** a full written statement of the theorem.

2. **Figure:** a lettered figure drawn to illustrate all the given conditions. (Though a diagram is not essential to the logical reasoning, it helps you to visualize the deductions being made.)
3. **Given:** all given conditions expressed in terms of the letters or numbers used in the figure.
4. **To Prove:** all conclusions expressed in terms of the letters or numbers used in the figure.
5. **Analysis:** a brief description of the plan to be used in the proof. Some teachers prefer to call this part *Sketch of Proof* or *Plan of Proof*. You may use either of these if your teacher approves.
6. **Proof:** a series of numbered statements paralleled by like-numbered reasons which lead to the desired conclusion or conclusions.

When you are asked to *demonstrate a theorem*, be sure that your demonstration contains the six essential parts. There are no sure-fire rules which will enable you to discover how to prove the theorem. However, the following general suggestions will prove helpful.

1. Be sure your figure accurately depicts the given conditions. Do not add any special conditions that are not given. (For example, do not draw a right triangle or an isosceles triangle when only a triangle is specified.)
2. If the theorem is not stated in "if-then" form, rephrase it in that form. This will help you to recognize the *given* and the *to prove*.
3. When trying to discover a plan of proof, you can often help yourself by reasoning back from the conclusion. Think "The conclusion will be true if . . . is true. This in turn will be true if . . . is true."
4. Remember that only given data, definitions, postulates, previously-proved theorems, and recognized algebraic properties can be used as reasons.
5. Look back at previously-proved theorems for possible methods of attack.

The proofs of exercises that involve congruence of segments or of angles involve fewer steps when certain basic theorems about congruence can be cited. The meanings of the terms *reflexive, symmetric*, and *transitive*, as they pertain to equality serve as reliable guides to the meanings of the terms as they apply to congruence. Two easily-proved theorems about congruence properties are stated at the top of the next page. The demonstrations are left for you. (See Exercises 9–14, p. 139.)

THEOREM 4–13   Congruence of segments is reflexive, symmetric and transitive.

THEOREM 4–14   Congruence of angles is reflexive, symmetric and transitive.

WRITTEN EXERCISES

For each of the theorems that follow: (a) copy the statement; (b) draw a figure to illustrate the theorem; (c) list the given conditions in terms of your figure; (d) list the conclusions to be proved. **Do not attempt to write a proof.** The proofs of many of these statements involve theorems you have not yet studied.

EXAMPLE.   If two sides of a triangle are congruent, the angles opposite those sides are congruent.

Solution:

Given: $\overline{AC} \cong \overline{BC}$.

To Prove: $\angle A \cong \angle B$
   (or $\angle CAB \cong \angle CBA$.)

A
1. If two angles of a triangle are congruent, the sides opposite those angles are congruent.
2. If the three angles of a triangle are congruent, the three sides of the triangle are congruent.
3. If a segment joins the midpoints of two sides of a triangle, its length is one-half the length of the third side.
4. The sum of the measures of the angles of a triangle is 180.

B
5. If a point lies on a line that is the perpendicular bisector of a segment, then the point is equidistant from the endpoints of the segment.
6. The segments joining the midpoints of the opposite sides of a quadrilateral bisect each other.
7. The bisectors of two adjacent supplementary angles form a right angle.
8. If the four sides of a quadrilateral are congruent, a diagonal will bisect the two angles whose vertices it connects.

9. Write a demonstration of the first part of Theorem 4–13: Congruence of segments is reflexive.

Given: $\overline{AB}$.

$$A \bullet\!\!\!-\!\!\!-\!\!\!-\!\!\!-\!\!\!-\!\!\!-\!\!\!-\!\!\!-\!\!\!-\!\!\!-\!\!\!-\!\!\!-\!\!\!-\!\!\!-\!\!\!-\!\!\!- \bullet B$$

To Prove: ... ?

Analysis: Use the definition of congruent segments.

Proof

STATEMENT	REASON
1. $AB = AB$	**1.** Reflexive property of equality.
2. ... ?	**2.** Definition of congruent segments.

10. Write a demonstration of the first part of Theorem 4–14.

11 and **12.** Write demonstrations of the second and third parts of Theorem 4–13. (Two separate demonstrations.)

13 and **14.** Write demonstrations of the second and third parts of Theorem 4–14. (Two separate demonstrations.)

CHAPTER SUMMARY

Inventory of Structure and Methods

1. *Some useful statements about angles.*

   An angle is the union of two noncollinear rays that have the same endpoint. Congruent angles are angles that have the same measure.

   To every angle there corresponds a unique real number greater than 0 and less than 180. That number is called the measure of the angle.

   In the adjacent figure the **angle addition theorem** justifies the conclusion:

   $$m\angle AOB = m\angle AOX + m\angle XOB.$$

   If the exterior sides of two adjacent angles are opposite rays, the angles are supplementary.

   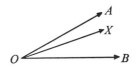

   An angle has exactly one bisector.

2. *Some useful theorems about right angles and perpendicular lines.*

   A right angle has a measure of 90.

   All right angles are congruent.

   Perpendicular lines meet to form congruent adjacent angles.

   If two lines are perpendicular, they meet to form right angles.

   If two lines meet to form a right angle, the lines are perpendicular.

   If two adjacent acute angles have their exterior sides in perpendicular lines, the angles are complementary.

   In a plane, through a point in a line, there is exactly one line perpendicular to the given line.

3. *Some useful theorems about supplementary, complementary, and vertical angles.*

   If the exterior sides of two adjacent angles are opposite rays, the angles are supplementary.

   If two angles are supplementary to the same angle or to congruent angles, they are congruent to each other.

   If two angles are complementary to the same angle or to congruent angles, they are congruent to each other.

   If two lines intersect, the vertical angles formed are congruent.

4. *A demonstration of a theorem consists of the:*

   Statement   Figure   Given   To Prove   Analysis   Proof

**Methods You Now Have for
Proving Two Angles Congruent**

Show that they have equal measures.

Show that they are supplements of the same angle or congruent angles.

Show that they are complements of the same angle or congruent angles.

Show that they are vertical angles.

Vocabulary and Spelling

angle-measurement postulate (*p. 117*)   angle addition theorem (*p. 118*)

protractor postulate (*p. 117*)   demonstration of a theorem (*p. 136*)

betweenness of rays (*p. 118*)   analysis (*p. 137*)

CHAPTER TEST

4–1 Given the plane figure.

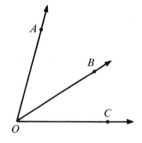

1. $\angle AOC$ is the union of __?__ and __?__.

2. If $\overrightarrow{OB}$ bisects $\angle AOC$, then
$m\angle ? = m\angle ?$.

3. $\overrightarrow{OB}$ lies between __?__ and __?__.

4. The __?__ theorem supports the assertion that
$m\angle BOC + m\angle AOB = m\angle AOC$.

5. If $\overrightarrow{OC}$ lies in the edge of a half-plane and $\overrightarrow{OC}$ is paired with the number 0, then there is a unique __?__ number $> $__?__ and $< $__?__ that is paired with $\overrightarrow{OB}$.

4–2 In the given figure R, S, and T are collinear.

6. __?__ and __?__ are opposite rays.

7. $m\angle PST + m\angle RSP = $__?__.

8. If $m\angle PST = 90$, then $\overrightarrow{SP}$ is __?__ to $\overleftrightarrow{RS}$.

9. If $m\angle RSP = 110$, then $m\angle PST = $__?__.

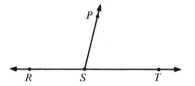

10. If $m\angle PST = a$, then $m\angle RSP = $__?__.

11. If $RS = ST$, then S is the __?__ of $\overline{RT}$.

4–3 In the plane figure shown, $\overrightarrow{OA} \perp \overrightarrow{OB}$ and $\overrightarrow{OD} \perp \overrightarrow{OE}$.

12. $\angle AOB$ is a __?__ angle.

13. $\angle 1$ and $\angle ?$ are complementary angles.

14. $m\angle 2 + m\angle 3 = $__?__.

15. $\angle 1$ and $\angle 3$ are congruent angles because they are both complements of $\angle ?$.

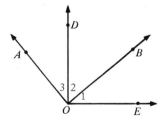

16. Since $m\angle AOE > 90$, $\angle AOE$ is an __?__ angle.

17. If $\angle 1$, $\angle 2$, and $\angle 3$ are congruent angles, the measure of each is __?__.

4–4 Draw a figure and list the "given" and "to prove" for the following statements. (Do not write a proof of the statement.)

18. If a line bisects one of two vertical angles, it bisects the other.

19. If two angles of one triangle are congruent respectively to two angles of another triangle, the third angles are congruent.

20. If all four sides of a quadrilateral are of equal length, then the two diagonals of the quadrilateral are perpendicular.

CHAPTER REVIEW

4–1 Initial Postulates and Theorems   *Pages 117–124*

1. The union of $\overrightarrow{OB}$ and $\overrightarrow{OC}$ is $\angle$?.

2. If $\overrightarrow{OC}$ bisects $\angle BOD$, then $m\angle$? $= m\angle$?.

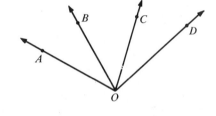

3. $\overrightarrow{OB}$ lies _?_ $\overrightarrow{OA}$ and $\overrightarrow{OC}$.

4. If $\angle BOC$ is an acute angle, its measure is $>$ _?_ and $<$ _?_.

5. By the angle addition theorem, $m\angle BOC + m\angle BOA = m\angle$?.

4–2 Right Angles and Perpendicular Lines   *Pages 124–130*

6. $\angle RST$ is a _?_ angle if $\overrightarrow{RS} \perp \overrightarrow{ST}$.

7. Two adjacent acute angles are _?_ if their exterior sides lie in perpendicular lines.

8. Two lines are _?_ if they meet to form congruent adjacent angles.

9. If two adjacent angles each have measure 90, their exterior sides are _?_ rays.

10. In a given _?_ one and only one line can be drawn perpendicular to a given line at a given _?_.

4–3 **Supplementary, Complementary, and** *Pages 130–136*
Vertical Angles

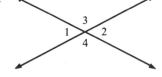

11. Name two angles that are supplements of ∠3.

12. $m\angle 4 + m\angle 2 =$ __?__ .

13. If $m\angle 1 = 70$, then $m\angle 2 =$ __?__ and $m\angle 4 =$ __?__ .

14. If two angles are both vertical and complementary, each has a measure of __?__ .

15. If $m\angle 1 + m\angle 2 = 4a + 20$, then $m\angle 1 =$ __?__ .

4–4 **The Demonstration of a Theorem** *Pages 136–139*

16. In demonstrating a theorem the given and the to prove must be expressed in terms of a lettered __?__ .

17. An outline of the plan of proof of a theorem is called the __?__ .

18. Once a theorem has been proved it __?__ (can, cannot) be cited as a reason to support a step taken in a proof of a subsequent theorem.

CUMULATIVE TEST: CHAPTERS 1–4

Classify the given statement as true or as false.

1. The intersection of two sets is the set of elements common to both sets.

2. For every real number x, $|x| = x$.

3. A segment is a finite set of points.

4. If B lies on $\overline{AC}$ and $AB = BC$, then B is the midpoint of $\overline{AC}$.

5. Every half-plane contains its edge.

6. If the conditional "$p \rightarrow q$" is true, then p and q must both be true.

7. If two angles are complementary, then both angles are acute angles.

8. $a^2 = 25$ if and only if $a = 5$.

9. There is a point on the real number line whose coordinate is $\sqrt{-9}$.

10. If two points on a ray lie in a plane, the ray lies in that plane.

In each sentence replace __?__ by the appropriate word, phrase, or numeral.

11. The supplement of an acute angle is an __?__ angle.

12. A statement formed by joining two statements by the word *and* is called a __?__ .

13. In a mathematical system a statement accepted as true without proof is called a __?__ .

14. A secant intersects a circle in __?__ points, and the segment between those points is called a __?__ .

15. Two coplanar circles that have the same center are __?__ circles.

Given: $A = \{1, 2, 3\}$, $B = \{3, 4, 5\}$. Specify by roster

16. $A \cap B$ **17.** $A \cup B$ **18.** $B \cup \emptyset$

Name the property of real numbers or equality that supports each step in the following solution.

Given: $2(x - 1) = 12$

19. $2x - 2 = 12$ **20.** $2x = 14$ **21.** $x = 7$

Identify the *hypothesis* and *conclusion* in each of the following statements.

22. If two planes intersect, then their intersection is a line.

23. If two angles are congruent, then their supplements are congruent.

Find the measure of a complement of $\angle A$ if, $m\angle A$ equals

24. 54   **25.** $x + 10$ **26.** $90 - x$

Given: The adjacent plane figure with $\overrightarrow{OA} \perp \overleftrightarrow{DC}$.

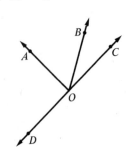

27. $m\angle AOC =$ __?__ .

28. $DO + OC =$ __?__ .

29. Name a pair of opposite rays.

30. $m\angle BOC + m\angle ? = 180$.

31. Name two angles that are complementary.

32. State a conclusion that can be drawn if the following two statements are accepted as true:

The sum of the measures of the angles of a quadrilateral is 360.
A trapezoid is a quadrilateral.

33. Draw a figure and express the *Given* and *To Prove* in terms of your figure for the statement.

In a circle, if a radius is perpendicular to a chord, it bisects the chord.

Give a reason that supports each assertion about the given plane figure.

Given: $\overrightarrow{OC} \perp \overrightarrow{OD}$; $\overrightarrow{OA} \perp \overrightarrow{OB}$.

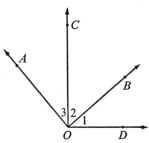

34. $\angle COD$ is a right angle.

35. $\angle 1$ and $\angle 2$ are complementary.

36. $m\angle 3 + m\angle 2 = m\angle AOB$.

37. $m\angle 1 = m\angle 3$.

B

38. Assume that p and q are true statements and that r is a false statement. Indicate the truth value of each of the following.

   a. $p \rightarrow q$ **c.** $r \rightarrow q$ **e.** $p \wedge \sim r$

   b. $p \rightarrow r$ **d.** $p \vee r$ **f.** $p \leftrightarrow q$

39. For each open sentence tell whether the set of all points on the number line with coordinate x that satisfy the condition is a point, a ray, a segment, or a line.

   a. $x \leq 3$ **c.** $|x| \geq 0$ **e.** $2x - 6 = 0$

   b. $-2 \leq x \leq 4$ **d.** $x - 2 \geq 1$ **f.** $x < 3$ or $x > -2$

40. Three times the measure of an angle is 30 less than twice the measure of a supplementary angle. Find the measure of both angles.

41. Given: $m\angle 1 = m\angle 3$.

     Prove: $m\angle 4 + m\angle 2 = 180$.

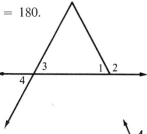

42. Given: Plane figure;

       $\overrightarrow{OA} \perp \overleftrightarrow{CD}$

       $\overrightarrow{OB} \perp \overleftrightarrow{XY}$.

     Prove: $m\angle 1 = m\angle 3$.

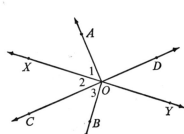

5 Parallel Lines and Planes

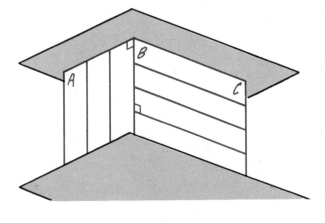

Architect Frank Lloyd Wright used several sets of parallel lines and parallel planes in designing Taliesin East in Spring Green, Wisconsin.

The paths of jet planes flying a straight course in formation suggest parallel lines. This is because the airplanes move in the same direction, in paths which do not meet. The pilots do their best to stay the same distance apart. The vapor trails provide a temporary indication of the success of the pilots.

Of course you realize that airplanes cannot fly in perfectly straight lines and that vapor trails are only crude reminders of mathematical lines. The parallel lines and planes that you will study in this chapter are mathematical figures. Definitions, postulates, and theorems will be stated carefully. You should compare the mathematical statements with the intuitive knowledge you already have about parallel lines and planes.

While you have not yet been able to prove it, you are probably aware of the fact that the sum of the measures of the angles of a triangle is 180. The theorem is a logical consequence of the postulates set down in this chapter.

■ When Lines and Planes Are Parallel

5–1 Basic Properties

Look at the two solid black edges of the rectangular solid. These segments will not meet no matter how far they are extended. The same thing is true of the red edges, but the red segments are not related to each other in the same way as the black segments are. The heavy black segments are parts of *parallel* lines, while the red segments are parts of *skew* lines.

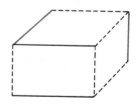

Parallel lines (∥ lines) are lines that lie in the same plane and have no point in common. If a and b are parallel lines, we say that a is parallel to b ($a \parallel b$).

Skew lines are two lines that do not lie in any one plane.

A line and a plane are parallel if they have no point in common.

You can use the symbol ∥ in several ways. Here, for example, line *j* and plane *P* are ∥. Also, *j* ∥ *P* (*j* is parallel to *P*).

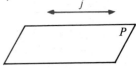

Parallel planes (∥ planes) are planes that have no point in common. Look at the ceiling and floor of your room for an example of parallel planes. Then look at the lines in which the front wall meets the ceiling and floor. The lines seem to be parallel, and a theorem is suggested.

THEOREM 5–1   If two parallel planes are cut by a third plane, the lines of intersection are parallel.

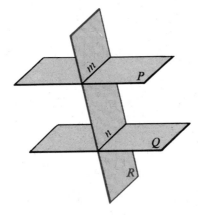

Given: Plane *P* ∥ plane *Q*; *P* and *Q* cut by plane *R* in lines *m* and *n*.

To Prove: *m* ∥ *n*.

Analysis: Lines are ∥ by definition when they satisfy two requirements. *m* and *n* can be shown to satisfy those requirements.

Proof

STATEMENT	REASON
1. *m* is a line, and *n* is a line.	**1.** If two different planes intersect, their intersection is a line.
2. Lines *m* and *n* lie in one plane.	**2.** Given in plane *R*.
3. *m*, which lies in *P*, and *n*, which lies in *Q*, have no point in common.	**3.** Parallel planes have no point in common, by definition.
4. *m* ∥ *n*.	**4.** By the definition of parallel lines.

There are many theorems about the special relationships that exist between certain sets of lines and planes. Time does not permit the development of formal proofs of all such theorems. However, it is important that you develop the ability to visualize the relationships between lines and planes in space. You will find that the use of thin sticks to represent lines, and pieces of cardboard to represent planes, will help you to draw correct conclusions intuitively.

To describe space relationships you need to know a few new terms. Recall from Chapter 2 that a line is perpendicular to a plane when it is perpendicular to every line in the plane that passes through its foot. If two planes are such that one of them contains a line perpendicular to the other, the planes are said to be **perpendicular.** Thus, in the adjacent figure, if $\overleftrightarrow{AB} \perp$ plane R, then plane $P \perp$ plane R.

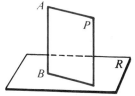

At a point on the earth's surface a line is described as vertical if it contains that point and also the center of the earth. At the same point, a line or plane perpendicular to the vertical line is described as horizontal.

Remember, there are three possible positions for two distinct lines in space: parallel, intersecting, and skew. There are two possible positions for two distinct planes: intersecting and parallel.

ORAL EXERCISES

Using your intuitive understanding of space, classify each statement as always, sometimes, or never true.

1. Skew lines are parallel.

2. A line on the chalkboard and a line on the floor are skew.

3. Two lines that do not intersect are skew.

4. Two planes each perpendicular to a third plane are parallel to each other.

5. A line that intersects one of two parallel planes in one point intersects the other plane also.

6. A plane that cuts one of two parallel lines in one point cuts the other also.

7. A plane that intersects one of two skew lines in one point intersects the other line also.

Assume that cross sections of a flagpole are circles and that the centers of all the circles lie on a line. If that line is a vertical line the flagpole is called vertical. Classify each statement as **always, sometimes,** or **never** true.

8. The line determined by a vertical flagpole passes through the center of the earth.

9. The line determined by a nonvertical pole passes through the center of the earth.

WRITTEN EXERCISES

On the basis of intuitive or inductive thinking, write **always, sometimes,** or **never** on your paper — not in the book.

EXAMPLE. Through a point outside a plane there are infinitely many lines parallel to the plane.

Solution: Hold a marble to represent a point outside your desk top, a plane. Hold a pencil in various positions so that it is parallel to the desk top yet touching the marble.
Always. **Answer.**

A

1. Through a point outside a plane there are infinitely many planes parallel to that plane.

2. A line parallel to the edge of a dihedral angle lies in one of the faces of the dihedral angle.

3. Two lines perpendicular to the same plane are parallel to each other.

4. If a plane and a line not in that plane are perpendicular to the same line, they are parallel to each other.

5. If a plane and a line not in that plane are perpendicular to the same plane, they are parallel to each other.

6. Two lines perpendicular to a third line are perpendicular to each other.

7. Two lines parallel to a third line are parallel to each other.

8. Two lines parallel to the same plane are parallel to each other.

9. Two planes parallel to the same line are parallel to each other.

10. Two planes parallel to the same plane are parallel to each other.

11. Two lines skew to the same line are skew to each other.

12. In a plane, two lines perpendicular to the same line are perpendicular to each other.

B 13. A plane and a line not in that plane which are parallel to the same line are parallel to each other.

14. A plane and a line not in that plane which are parallel to the same plane are parallel to each other.

15. A line which intersects one of two parallel lines intersects the other also.

16. In a plane, a line which intersects one of two parallel lines intersects the other also.

17. A plane not containing any vertex of a triangle but intersecting two sides of that triangle intersects the third side also.

18. A plane that contains two sides of a triangle contains the third side also.

19. If two angles have parallel sides, the angles are either congruent or supplementary.

20. If line k is parallel to plane P and plane Q contains k, and Q intersects P in a line m, then m is parallel to k.

C 21. A vertical pole in New York is parallel to a vertical pole in London.

22. A horizontal line in New York is parallel to a horizontal line in London.

23. Given two skew lines, it is possible to find a plane containing one of the lines and parallel to the other line.

24. Given two skew lines, there exist infinitely many planes parallel to both of the lines.

25. If a, b, c, d, e, f, g, are lines such that $a \parallel b$, $b \perp c$, c is skew to d, $d \parallel e$, $e \parallel f$, and $f \parallel g$, then $a \parallel g$.

26. Given two skew lines, there exists a line perpendicular to both of the skew lines.

5–2 Transversals and Special Angles

A **transversal** (trans-ver-sal, trans.) is a line that intersects two or more other lines in different points. This book will use the word *transversal* only when all the lines lie in one plane. In the plane figure shown at the top of the next page, t is a transversal of m and n.

For lines *m* and *n* cut by transversal *t*, angles 3, 4, 5, and 6 are called *interior angles*, while angles 1, 2, 7, and 8 are *exterior angles*.

Two angles such as 1 and 5, one exterior and one interior, but on the same side of the transversal, are called *corresponding angles* (corr. ∡). The other pairs of corresponding angles are 2 and 6; 3 and 7; 4 and 8.

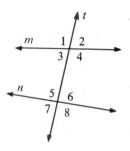

Alternate interior angles (alt. int. ∡), such as 3 and 6, are both interior, are on opposite sides of the transversal, and have different vertices. The other pair of alternate interior angles is 4 and 5.

Alternate exterior angles (alt. ext. ∡) are on opposite sides of the transversal, are both exterior, and have different vertices. The two pairs of alternate exterior angles are 1 and 8; 2 and 7.

The blue lines on your notebook paper roughly illustrate parallel lines. Select two of the lines and draw a transversal. Choose two corresponding angles and measure each of them. Compare the measures.

Repeat the experiment, using other transversals with different slopes. Do you find, in each case, that the measures of the two angles are approximately the same? You should, if you have used your protractor carefully. The relationship suggested by your measurements is taken as a postulate in our geometry.

P10   If two parallel lines are cut by a transversal, corresponding angles are congruent.

You could have chosen in each trial of the experiment performed above any one of four pairs of corresponding angles. Notice in the figure that

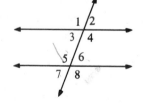

If ∠2 ≅ ∠6, each with a measure of 50,
then ∠1 ≅ ∠5, for each must have a
            measure of 130,
    ∠3 ≅ ∠7, for each must have a
            measure of 50,
and ∠4 ≅ ∠8, for each must have a
            measure of 130.

This illustrates the fact that if one pair of corresponding angles are congruent, then the remaining corresponding angles are congruent in pairs. When we say that corresponding angles are congruent, we mean this for all four pairs.

THEOREM 5–2 If a transversal is perpendicular to one of two parallel lines, it is perpendicular to the other one also.

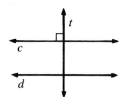

Given: Transversal t cuts ‖ lines c and d; $t \perp c$.

To Prove: $t \perp d$.

Analysis: You can deduce that $m\angle 1 = m\angle 2$. Since $\angle 1$ is a rt. $\angle$, $\angle 2$ must be a rt. $\angle$ also. Then you can show that $t \perp d$.

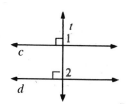

Proof

STATEMENT	REASON
1. $t \perp c$.	1. Given.
2. $\angle 1$ is a rt. $\angle$.	2. If two lines are $\perp$, they __?__.
3. $m\angle 1 = 90$.	3. Definition of rt. $\angle$.
4. $c \parallel d$.	4. Given.
5. $\angle 2 \cong \angle 1$.	5. If two parallel lines __?__.
6. $m\angle 2 = m\angle 1$.	6. Definition of $\cong$ ⊿.
7. $m\angle 2 = 90$.	7. Transitive property of equality.
8. $\angle 2$ is a rt. $\angle$.	8. Definition of rt. $\angle$.
9. $t \perp d$.	9. If two lines meet to __?__.

THEOREM 5–3 If two parallel lines are cut by a transversal, alternate interior angles are congruent.

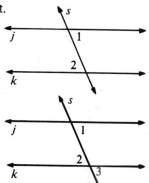

Given: ‖ lines j and k cut by transversal s.

To Prove: $\angle 1 \cong \angle 2$.

Analysis: You can readily show that both $\angle 1$ and $\angle 2$ are congruent to $\angle 3$.

Proof

The proof is left for you.

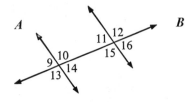

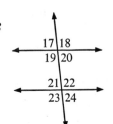

1. In Figure *A* and in Figure *B* name:

   a. Four pairs of corresponding angles.

   b. Two pairs of alternate interior angles.

   c. Two pairs of alternate exterior angles.

   d. Two pairs of interior angles on the same side of the transversal.

   e. Two pairs of exterior angles on the same side of the transversal.

2. In the figure, $m \parallel n$. Name the measure of each of the labeled angles in the figure when the measure of $\angle 1$ is

   a. 110   **b.** y **c.** 90

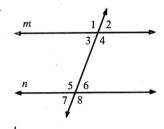

EXAMPLE.

Given: the plane figure;
            $a \parallel b$; $c \parallel b$.

To Prove: $\angle 1 \cong \angle 3$.

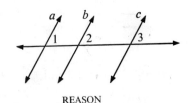

Proof

STATEMENT	REASON
1. $a \parallel b$; $c \parallel b$.	1. Given.
2. $\angle 1 \cong \angle 2$.	2. If $\parallel$ lines are cut by a trans., corr. $\angle$ are congruent.
3. $\angle 2 \cong \angle 3$.	3. Same as Reason 2.
4. $\angle 1 \cong \angle 3$.	4. Transitive property of congruence.

A

1. Given: $m \parallel n$; $\angle 2 \cong \angle 3$.
　　Prove: $\angle 1 \cong \angle 3$.

2. Given: $m \parallel n$; $\angle 1 \cong \angle 3$.
　　Prove: $\angle 2 \cong \angle 3$.

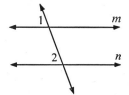

Exs. 1, 2

3. Given: $j \parallel k$; $\angle 4 \cong \angle 7$.
　　Prove: $\angle 5 \cong \angle 6$.

4. Given: $j \parallel k$; $\angle 5 \cong \angle 6$.
　　Prove: $\angle 4 \cong \angle 7$.

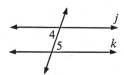

Exs. 3, 4

5. Given: $\overleftrightarrow{XY} \parallel \overleftrightarrow{ZW}$; $\overleftrightarrow{RS} \parallel \overleftrightarrow{TQ}$.
　　Prove: $\angle 1 \cong \angle h$.

6. Given: $\overleftrightarrow{XY} \parallel \overleftrightarrow{ZW}$; $\overleftrightarrow{RS} \parallel \overleftrightarrow{TQ}$.
　　Prove: $\angle b \cong \angle 7$.

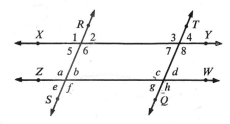

Exs. 5, 6

7. Given: $\overline{HG} \parallel \overline{EF}$; $\overline{HE} \parallel \overline{GF}$.
　　Prove: $\angle GHE \cong \angle EFG$.

8. Given: $\overline{HG} \parallel \overline{EF}$; $\overline{HE} \parallel \overline{GF}$.
　　Prove: $\angle HEF \cong \angle FGH$.

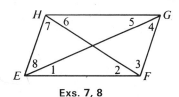

Exs. 7, 8

In Exs. 9–12, it is given that parallel lines a and b are cut by transversal t.

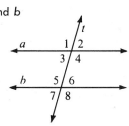

9. Prove: $m\angle 1 + m\angle 7 = 180$.
10. Prove: $m\angle 2 + m\angle 8 = 180$.
11. Prove: $m\angle 3 + m\angle 8 = 180$.
12. Prove: $m\angle 6 + m\angle 1 = 180$.

Exs. 9–12

13. $j \parallel k$; $m\angle 1 = 5x - 11$; $m\angle 2 = 3x + 10$. Find x.

14. $j \parallel k$; $m\angle 3 = 4x + 14$; $m\angle 2 = 7x - 15$. Find x.

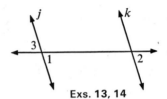

Exs. 13, 14

15. $\angle 1$ and $\angle 2$ have measures of 81 and 82 respectively. Tell, without proof, which lines cannot be parallel in spite of their appearance.

16. $\angle 1$ and $\angle 3$ have measures of 81 and 100 respectively. Which lines cannot, in spite of their appearance, be parallel?

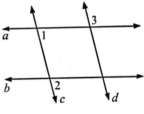

Exs. 15, 16

B **17.** Write a demonstration, showing Figure, Given, To Prove, Analysis, and Proof for: If two parallel lines are cut by a transversal, alternate exterior angles are congruent.

18. Write a demonstration for: If two parallel lines are cut by a transversal, interior angles on the same side of the transversal are supplementary.

19. Given: $j \parallel k$; $\overrightarrow{OA}$ and $\overrightarrow{OB}$ are opposite rays; $m\angle 9 = h$; $m\angle 1 = 180 - h$.

Prove: $m\angle 5 = m\angle 10$.

20. Given: $j \parallel k$; $\overrightarrow{OA}$ and $\overrightarrow{OB}$ are opposite rays; $m\angle 3 = q$; $m\angle 10 = 180 - q$.

Prove: $m\angle 6 = m\angle 9$.

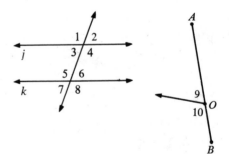

Exs. 19, 20

21. $r \parallel s$; $m\angle 1 = 5x^2 - 3x$; $m\angle 2 = 4(x^2 + x - 3)$.

Find x.

22. $r \parallel s$; $m\angle 3 = x^2$; $m\angle 4 = 11x$.

Find x.

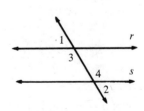

Exs. 21, 22

23. $a \parallel b; m\angle 1 = 2x + y; m\angle 2 = x;$
$m\angle 4 = y + 20.$

Find x and y.

24. $a \parallel b; m\angle 2 = x; m\angle 3 = y;$
$m\angle 4 = 3x - y.$

Find x and y.

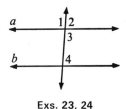

Exs. 23, 24

25. Given: $\overleftrightarrow{RS} \parallel \overleftrightarrow{QT}; \angle 2 \cong \angle 4.$

Prove: $\angle 1$ is supplementary to $\angle 2.$

26. Given: $\overline{QR} \parallel \overline{TS}; \angle 2 \cong \angle 4.$

Prove: $\angle 3$ is supplementary to $\angle 2.$

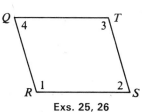

Exs. 25, 26

27. Given: $\overrightarrow{BF}$ bisects $\angle ABC;$
$\overleftrightarrow{DE} \parallel \overleftrightarrow{BC}.$

Prove: $\angle 1 \cong \angle 2.$

28. Given: $\overleftrightarrow{DE} \parallel \overleftrightarrow{BC}; \angle 1 \cong \angle 3.$

Prove: $\overrightarrow{BF}$ bisects $\angle ABC.$

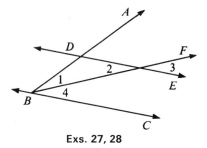

Exs. 27, 28

5–3 Indirect Proof

You have often used indirect proofs, probably without realizing that they are so named. The supporting argument of Theorem 1 is an indirect proof. Here is a simpler example of indirect proof.

When you know that

        Bill and Tom are the same age,

and   Bill and Jack are not the same age,

you deduce that Tom and Jack are not the same age. The indirect proof, so simple in this case that you would not be conscious of using it, goes like this:

Suppose that Tom and Jack are the same age. Then Bill and Jack must be the same age, for each of them is the same age as Tom. But this contradicts the fact that Bill and Jack are not the same age. The supposition must be incorrect, and the conclusion that Tom and Jack are not the same age follows.

Here the same example is put in mathematical form, letters denoting the boys' ages.

Given: $b = t; b \neq j$.

To Prove: $j \neq t$.

Proof: *Suppose* that j does equal t. Then $j = b$, for each of them equals t. But $j \neq b$, given. Consequently the supposed relationship is incorrect, and it follows that $j \neq t$.

Now consider an example of indirect proof in geometry.

EXAMPLE.

Given: Lines j and k cut by transversal;
$\angle 1 \not\cong \angle 2$.

Prove: j and k are not parallel.

Proof: *Suppose* that j and k are parallel.
Then corresponding angles 1 and 2
must be congruent. But this con-
tradicts the given fact that $\angle 1$ is not congruent to $\angle 2$. The supposition must be false, and it follows that j and k are not parallel.

Notice that each indirect proof shown begins with the word *suppose*. To begin an indirect proof, you tentatively accept the negative of the *conclusion* (*to prove*). Then you reason logically until you reach a conclusion, based upon the statement assumed together with things given in the original statement, that contradicts a known fact. When the reasoning is correct, the weakness must lie in the statement assumed. The assumed statement is incorrect, and the desired statement must be correct.

By a *known fact* is meant either a property that is given in the statement being proved, or else a statement considered to be true within our system of geometry. Postulates and theorems are such statements. So are statements of algebraic properties.

This book presents some indirect proofs in paragraph form. There are two reasons for this: Since mathematicians often use the paragraph form, for direct as well as for indirect proofs, you should become familiar with the form. Second, a paragraph presentation of indirect reasoning often seems more natural than a two-column proof.

> ### To Write an Indirect Proof:
>
> 1. Suppose that the negative of the conclusion of the theorem is true.
> 2. Reason from your assumed statement together with statements given in the theorem until you obtain a statement that contradicts a known fact.
> 3. Point out that the assumed statement must be incorrect and that the conclusion of the theorem must be true.

In some cases you can develop a simple proof of a statement by establishing the truth of the contrapositive of the statement. Recall that a conditional and its contrapositive are equivalent. The contrapositive of *If p, then q* is *If not ~q, then not ~p*. By proving the second conditional, you also prove the first one.

EXAMPLE. Prove: If $\angle 1 \not\cong \angle 2$, in the figure shown, then lines j and k are not parallel.

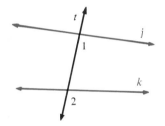

Proof by establishing the contrapositive.

Contrapositive: If lines j and k are parallel, then $\angle 1 \cong \angle 2$. The contrapositive follows directly from P_{10}, and the proof is complete.

ORAL EXERCISES

In Exercises 1–10 tell what the very first sentence of an indirect proof is when you are to prove that:

1. Ann is the same age as Sue.

2. Bill has the same amount of money as Tom.

3. c is equal to d.
5. $\sqrt{5} \neq 2$.
7. Line $r \perp$ line s.

4. e is not equal to f.
6. Line $m \parallel$ line n.
8. $5 \in T$.

9. X is a subset of Y.

10. $J \cup K$ contains more elements than $J \cap K$.

11. To begin an indirect proof you suppose that the __?__ of the *To Prove* is true. Then you proceed by correct reasoning until you reach a conclusion that __?__ a known fact. Your supposition must therefore be __?__. This proves the desired __?__.

12. The success of an indirect proof depends upon showing that your supposition leads to a __?__ which contradicts a __?__.

WRITTEN EXERCISES

In each exercise either write a full indirect proof or else prove by establishing the truth of the contrapositive.

A **1.** Prove: If $\angle 3 \not\cong \angle 4$, in the figure shown, then lines p and q are not parallel.

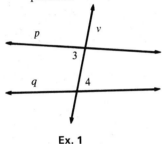

Ex. 1

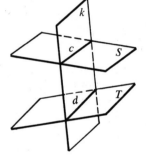

Ex. 2

2. Prove: If lines c and d are not parallel, in the figure shown, then planes S and T are not parallel.

3. Prove: If $\angle A \not\cong \angle B$ then $\angle A$ and $\angle B$ are not vertical angles.

4. Prove: If n is a number such that $n^2 = 3n$, then $n \neq 5$.

B **5.** Prove: If the measure of $\angle R$ is 36 and the measure of $\angle S$ is 64, then $\angle R$ and $\angle S$ are not supplementary.

6. Prove: If the measure of $\angle T$ is 130 and the measure of $\angle Q$ is 53, then $\angle T$ and $\angle Q$ are not supplementary.

C **7.** Prove: If c and d are positive numbers, then $\sqrt{c^2 + d^2} \neq c + d$.

8. Assume that the following properties have been postulated or proved.
Every integer is either even or odd but not both.
The set of integers is closed under addition and subtraction.
The sum of any two even integers is even.
Prove: If x is an odd integer and y is an even integer, then $x - y$ is an odd integer.

5–4 A Parallel to a Line Through an Outside Point

By writing an indirect proof and using Postulate 10 you can prove the following theorem.

THEOREM 5–4   Through a point outside a line not more than one parallel can be drawn to the line.

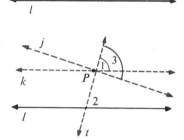

Given: Point *P* outside line *l*.

To Prove: Not more than one line containing *P* is parallel to *l*.

Analysis: If there were two lines containing *P* and parallel to *l*, and if there were a transversal, contradictory statements could be made about the relationship between ∠1 and ∠3.

Proof

Suppose two lines, *j* and *k*, contain point *P* and are parallel to *l*. Through *P* and some point of *l* draw a line *t*. ∠1 ≅ ∠2 because, when two ‖ lines are cut by a transversal, corresponding angles are congruent. ∠3 ≅ ∠2 for the same reason. Hence ∠1 ≅ ∠3. But ∠1 ≇ ∠3, for in a half-plane, through the endpoint of a ray lying in the edge of the half-plane, there is exactly one other ray such that the angle formed by the two rays has a given measure. Therefore, the supposition must be false and it follows that not more than one line containing *P* is parallel to *l*.

The proof of Theorem 5–4 depends on a line, *t* in the figure, that was not mentioned in the statement of the theorem itself. Line *t* is an *auxiliary line*. An **auxiliary line** is a line introduced to make a proof of a theorem possible. When you wish to use such a line you should redraw the figure and indicate the auxiliary part by a dashed line. Your proof must include a step justifying the fact that the line exists.

To use an auxiliary line:

1. Redraw your figure and show the auxiliary line as a dashed line.

2. Put a step in your proof showing that the line exists. You may say, "Draw . . ." realizing that this means, "There exists, and there is now shown in the figure, . . ."

Some writers refer to the statement: "Through a point outside a line not more than one parallel can be drawn to the line" as the **Parallel Postulate.** Other writers use this name for a stronger statement: Through a point outside a line one and only one parallel can be drawn to the line. The latter statement asserts that (1) a parallel actually exists and (2) not more than one parallel exists.

Just as Postulate 10 enabled us to prove that not more than one parallel exists, so a companion postulate, actually the converse of Postulate 10, enables us to prove that there actually is, through a point outside a line, a parallel to that line.

P₁₁   If two lines are cut by a transversal so that corresponding angles are congruent, the lines are parallel.

THEOREM 5–5   Through a point outside a line a parallel can be drawn to the line.

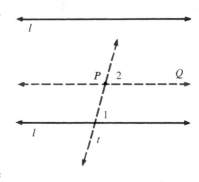

Given: Point *P* outside line *l*.

To Prove: There is a line containing *P* and parallel to *l*.

Analysis: Draw a line that can be used as a transversal. Then draw a line so that ∠2 and ∠1 are congruent angles.

Proof

1. Through point *P* and some point on *l* draw line *t*.	1. Between two points ___?___.
2. In the plane of *P* and *l* draw a ray, $\overrightarrow{PQ}$, such that ∠2 and ∠1 are corresponding angles and $m\angle 2 = m\angle 1$.	2. In a half-plane, through the end point of a ray lying in the edge of the half-plane, there is exactly one other ray such that the angle formed by the rays has a given measure.
3. There is a line, $\overleftrightarrow{PQ}$, containing *P* and parallel to *l*.	3. If two lines are cut by a transversal so that corresponding angles are ≅, the lines are ∥.

Theorems 5–4 and 5–5 are combined in the following statement:

Through a point outside a line exactly one parallel can be drawn to the line.

Replace the word *parallel* in this statement by the word *perpendicular* and you have another theorem.

THEOREM 5–6   Through a point outside a line, exactly one line can be drawn perpendicular to the line.

Proof

The proof is left as an exercise. (Exercise 24.)

In this geometry, Euclidean geometry, there is exactly one parallel to a given line through an outside point. Some geometries are called non-Euclidean, for they have postulates that lead to no parallel or to more than one parallel to a line through an outside point.

ORAL EXERCISES

In Exercises 1–4 is the statement correct? Has the statement been taken as a postulate in this book?

1. Through a point outside a plane, there is exactly one plane parallel to the given plane.

2. Through a point outside a line there is exactly one line parallel to the given line.

3. Through a point outside a line there is exactly one line skew to the given line.

4. Through a point in a line there is exactly one line skew to the given line.

In Exercises 5–8 is the statement true? State the converse. Is the converse true?

5. If a girl has more than two purses, then she has more than three purses.

6. If an integer is even, then it is a multiple of 2.

7. If two lines are parallel, then they do not intersect.

8. If a quadrilateral is a square, then the quadrilateral has four right angles.

9. How many lines can be drawn parallel to line *j* through point *T*? State the postulate or theorem that supports your answer. Is your supporting statement a postulate or a theorem?

10. How many lines can be drawn perpendicular to line *j* through point *T*? State the postulate or theorem that supports your answer. Is your supporting statement a postulate or a theorem?

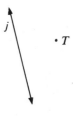

Exs. 9, 10

WRITTEN EXERCISES

A 1. In a certain statement it is given that *l* ∥ *m*, and it is to be proved that ∠1 ≅ ∠2. What are the *Given* and the *To Prove* of the converse?

2. In a theorem it is given that *P* ∥ *Q*, and it is to be proved that *j* ∥ *k*. What are the *Given* and the *To Prove* of the converse?

3. You are given lines *l* and *m* intersecting in a point *X* and a line *k* parallel to *l*. Draw a figure. Tell in one sentence why *k* cannot be parallel to *m*.

4. You are given lines *l* and *m* intersecting in point *X*, and a line *k* perpendicular to *l*. Line *k* does not contain *X*. Draw a figure. Tell in one sentence why *k* cannot be perpendicular to *m*.

5. Given: ∠1 ≅ ∠2; ∠3 ≅ ∠1.
   Prove: $\overline{BC} \parallel \overline{EF}$.

6. Given: $\overline{BC} \parallel \overline{EF}$; ∠1 ≅ ∠3.
   Prove: $\overline{AB} \parallel \overline{DE}$.

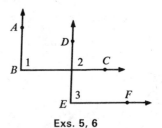

Exs. 5, 6

7. Given: A plane figure with ∠5 ≅ ∠6;
   ∠6 ≅ ∠4.
   Prove: $\overline{QT} \parallel \overline{RS}$.

8. Given: ∠5 ≅ ∠6; $\overline{QR} \parallel \overline{TS}$.
   Prove: $\overline{QT} \parallel \overline{RS}$.

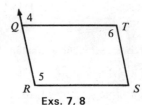

Exs. 7, 8

Write the converse of the statement shown. Is the original statement true? Is the converse true?

9. If each of two angles has measure 58, the two angles have equal measures.

10. If two angles are both obtuse, the two angles are congruent.

11. If $3 - 2z < 13$, then $z > 0$.

12. If $u = 0$, then $uw = 0$.

13. If $b < a$, then $a - b$ is positive.

14. If $x^2 = 25$, then $x = 5$.

B 15. Two squares have equal areas if their sides are congruent.

16. If two angles are supplementary, they are not congruent.

17. People who live in glass houses should not throw stones.

18. Absence makes the heart grow fonder.

19. If two lines are parallel, then there exists a plane to which they are both parallel.

20. If two planes are parallel, then there exists a line to which they are both parallel.

21. Write the converse of Theorem 5–1, beginning with the following: If two planes .... Draw a figure to show that the converse is false.

22. Draw a figure to illustrate the fact that it is not true that a line parallel to one of two perpendicular lines must be perpendicular to the other one.

C 23. Given: Planes W and Z are $\parallel$; planes X and Y cut W and Z in lines $h, j,$ and k.
Prove: $j \parallel k$.

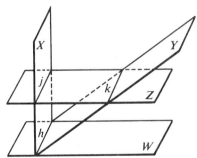

24. Prove Theorem 5–6. You must prove two things: (a) There is one perpendicular. (b) There is not more than one perpendicular. To prove (a), start by drawing that line through the outside point which is parallel to the given line. Use an indirect proof for (b).

5–5 Converses of Earlier Theorems about Parallels

THEOREM 5–7 In a plane, if two lines are perpendicular to a third line, they are parallel to each other.

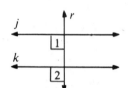

Given: Lines j, k, r in a plane; $j \perp r$; $k \perp r$.

To Prove: $j \parallel k$.

Analysis: Lines can be proved $\parallel$ when corr. ∠s are ≅. Corr. ∠s in this case are rt. ∠s.

Proof

STATEMENT	REASON
1. $j \perp r$; $k \perp r$.	1. ?
2. $\angle 1$ is a rt. $\angle$; $\angle 2$ is a rt. $\angle$.	2. ?
3. $m\angle 1 = 90$; $m\angle 2 = 90$.	3. ?
4. $\angle 1 \cong \angle 2$.	4. ?
5. $j \parallel k$.	5. ?

THEOREM 5–8 If two lines are cut by a transversal so that alternate interior angles are congruent, the lines are parallel.

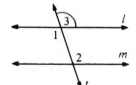

Given: Lines l and m cut by transversal t; $\angle 1 \cong \angle 2$.

To Prove: $l \parallel m$.

Analysis: The lines are $\parallel$ if corr. ∠s are ≅. $\angle 3$ and $\angle 2$ are both ≅ to $\angle 1$.

Proof

The proof is left for you.

1. Which of the following, if given for the plane figure, permits you to deduce that $\overline{AC} \parallel \overline{DB}$: $\angle A \cong \angle D$, or $\angle A \cong \angle B$?

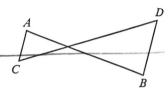

2. Given $l \parallel m$, state the theorem that permits you to deduce that $\angle 1 \cong \angle 2$.

3. Given $\angle 3 \cong \angle 4$, state the theorem that permits you to deduce that $l \parallel m$.

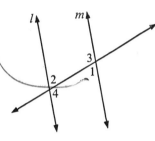

Exs. 2, 3

4. Name segments, if any, which can be deduced to be parallel when, in the plane figure at the left, below:

   a. $\angle 1 \cong \angle A$.
   b. $\angle 3 \cong \angle A$.
   c. $\angle 3 \cong \angle C$.
   d. $m\angle 3 = m\angle 1$.
   e. $m\angle 1 = m\angle C$.
   f. $m\angle A = m\angle B$.
   g. $\angle B$ is supp. to $\angle C$.
   h. $m\angle C + m\angle 2 = 180$.
   i. $m\angle 2 = 163°18'20''$; $m\angle A = 17°42'40''$.
   j. $m\angle 2 = 180 - (n - x)$; $m\angle C = n - x$.

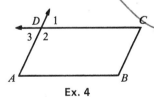

Ex. 4

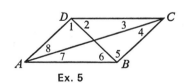

Ex. 5

5. Name segments, if any, which can be deduced to be parallel when, in the plane figure at the right, above:

   a. $\angle 2 \cong \angle 6$.
   b. $\angle 1 \cong \angle 6$.
   c. $\angle 1 \cong \angle 5$.
   d. $\angle 8 \cong \angle 4$.
   e. $m\angle 7 = m\angle 8$.
   f. $m\angle 7 = m\angle 4$.
   g. $m\angle 7 = m\angle 1$.
   h. $m\angle 7 = m\angle 3$.
   i. $\angle 2 \cong \angle ABC$.
   j. $m\angle 1 = m\angle 2 + m\angle 3$.
   k. $\angle 1 \cong \angle 2$.
   l. $m\angle 3 = m\angle 8$.

WRITTEN EXERCISES

1. Given: The plane figure;

$m\angle2 = 122; m\angle4 = 122.$

Prove: $r \parallel s$.

2. Given: The plane figure;

$m\angle2 = 130; m\angle3 = 50.$

Prove: $r \parallel s$.

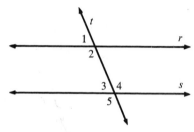

Exs. 1, 2

3. Given: The plane figure;

$\angle6 \cong \angle8; c \parallel d.$

Prove: $b \parallel c$.

4. Given: The plane figure;

$m\angle6 = y; m\angle7 = y; c \parallel d.$

Prove: $b \parallel d$.

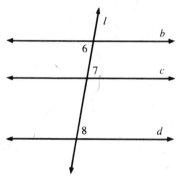

Exs. 3, 4

5. Given: The plane figure; $j \parallel k; \angle1 \cong \angle3.$
Prove: $l \parallel m$.

6. Given: The plane figure; $l \parallel m; \angle1 \cong \angle3.$
Prove: $j \parallel k$.

7. Given: The plane figure; $j \parallel k; \angle2 \cong \angle4.$
Prove: $l \parallel m$.

8. Given: The plane figure; $l \parallel m; \angle2 \cong \angle4.$
Prove: $j \parallel k$.

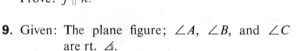

Exs. 5–8

9. Given: The plane figure; $\angle A, \angle B,$ and $\angle C$
are rt. $\angle\!\!\angle$.
Prove: $\overline{AD} \parallel \overline{BC}; \overline{AB} \parallel \overline{DC}.$

10. Given: The plane figure; $\overline{AB} \parallel \overline{DC}; \overline{AD} \perp \overline{DC};$
$\overline{CB} \perp \overline{AB}.$
Prove: $\overline{AD} \parallel \overline{BC}.$

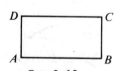

Exs. 9, 10

11. Given: The plane figure; $m\angle 1 + m\angle 5 = 180$;
$m\angle 1 + m\angle 4 = 180$.
  Prove: $\overline{YZ} \parallel \overline{VU}$.

12. Given: The plane figure; $\overline{YZ} \parallel \overline{VU}$; $\angle 1$ and $\angle 5$
are supplementary.
  Prove: $\overline{XY} \parallel \overline{TU}$.

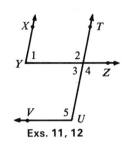

Exs. 11, 12

B

13. Given: The plane figure; $\overrightarrow{JP}$ bisects $\angle KJM$;
$\overrightarrow{MP}$ bisects $\angle JMN$;
$m\angle 2 + m\angle 3 = 90$.
  Prove: $\overline{JK} \parallel \overline{MN}$.

14. Given: The plane figure; $m\angle 1 = m\angle 2 = b$;
$m\angle 3 = m\angle 4 = (90 - b)$.
  Prove: $\overline{JK} \parallel \overline{MN}$.

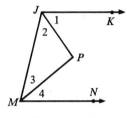

Exs. 13, 14

15. Given: $\angle RST$ and $\angle QTS$ are rt. $\angle$s.
  Prove: $\overline{RS} \parallel \overline{TQ}$.

16. Given: $\angle RST$ and $\angle QTS$ are rt. $\angle$s;
$\angle 1 \cong \angle 4$.
  Prove: $\overline{XS} \parallel \overline{TY}$.

17. Given: $\overline{XS} \parallel \overline{TY}$; $m\angle 1 = m\angle 4$.
  Prove: $\overline{RS} \parallel \overline{TQ}$.

18. Given: $m\angle RST = m\angle QTS$;
$m\angle 1 = m\angle 4$.
  Prove: $\overline{XS} \parallel \overline{TY}$.

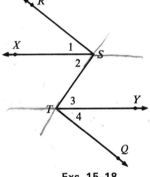

Exs. 15–18

19. Prove: If two lines are cut by a transversal so that alternate exterior angles are congruent, the lines are parallel.

20. Prove: If two lines are cut by a transversal so that interior angles on the same side of the transversal are supplementary, the lines are parallel.

21. Prove: If two lines are parallel to a third line, and all three are cut by a transversal, the first two lines are parallel to each other.

22. Use an indirect proof to prove that: In a plane, if two lines are parallel to a third line, the first two lines are parallel to each other.

23. Given: Planes X, Y, and Z cut by plane W in $\overleftrightarrow{AB}$, $\overleftrightarrow{CD}$, and $\overleftrightarrow{EF}$; $X \parallel Y$; $Z \parallel Y$.
    Prove: $\overleftrightarrow{AB} \parallel \overleftrightarrow{EF}$.

24. Prove: Two lines perpendicular to the same plane do not intersect.

[C] 25. Prove: If two parallel lines are cut by a transversal, then bisectors of corresponding angles are parallel.

26. Prove: If two lines are cut by a transversal and bisectors of alternate interior angles are parallel, then the lines are parallel.

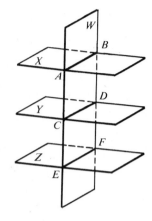

■ Applying Parallels to Polygons

5–6   Applying Parallels to Triangles

You should already be acquainted with most of the terms defined in this section.

A **triangle** ($\triangle$) is the union of the three segments determined by three noncollinear points. A triangle separates the points of a plane into three subsets: the triangle itself, the interior of the triangle, and the exterior of the triangle. The interior of a triangle can be defined as the set of points that lie in the interior of each angle of the triangle.

Each of the points A, B, C is a **vertex** (vert.) of the triangle. The plural form is **vertices.** $\overline{AB}$, $\overline{BC}$, and $\overline{AC}$ are the **sides** and $\angle A$, $\angle B$, and $\angle C$ are the **angles** of triangle ABC.

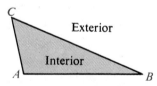

Triangles are sometimes classified according to the number of congruent sides they have. Beneath the name of each kind of triangle below is printed the defining characteristic.

Scalene Triangle	*Isosceles Triangle*	*Equilateral Triangle*
No two sides $\cong$	*At least two sides $\cong$*	*Three sides $\cong$*

Notice that an equilateral triangle is a particular kind of isosceles triangle.

Triangles can also be classified according to their angles.

 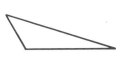

Acute △ *Obtuse △* *Right △* *Equiangular △*
Three acute ∡ *An obtuse ∠* *A right ∠* *Three ≅ ∡*

Angle *TSX* is called an **exterior angle** (ext. ∠) of triangle *RST* when $\overrightarrow{SX}$ and $\overrightarrow{SR}$ are opposite rays. With respect to ∠*TSX*, ∠*R* and ∠*T* are **remote interior angles.** You could find a second exterior angle at vertex *S* by using $\overrightarrow{SR}$ and the ray opposite to $\overrightarrow{ST}$ as sides. There are exterior angles at vertices *R* and *T* also.

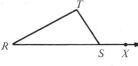

THEOREM 5–9 The sum of the measures of the angles of a triangle is 180.

Given: △*ABC*.

To Prove: $m\angle 1 + m\angle 2 + m\angle 3 = 180$.

Analysis: A line through *B* ∥ to $\overleftrightarrow{AC}$ will provide an angle congruent to ∠1 and an angle congruent to ∠3. Furthermore, there will be three ∡ at *B* whose measures add up to 180.

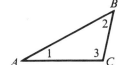

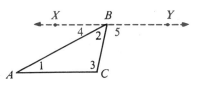

Proof

STATEMENT	REASON
1. Through *B* draw $\overleftrightarrow{XY} \parallel \overleftrightarrow{AC}$.	1. Through a point outside _?_
2. $m\angle XBC = m\angle 4 + m\angle 2$.	2. Angle addition theorem.
3. $m\angle XBC + m\angle 5 = 180$.	3. If the exterior sides of 2 adjacent ∡ _?_.
4. $m\angle 4 + m\angle 2 + m\angle 5 = 180$.	4. Substitution principle.
5. $\angle 1 \cong \angle 4; \angle 3 \cong \angle 5$.	5. If ∥ lines are cut _?_.
6. $m\angle 1 = m\angle 4; m\angle 3 = m\angle 5$.	6. Definition of ≅ ∡.
7. $m\angle 1 + m\angle 2 + m\angle 3 = 180$.	7. Substitution principle.

So far, all proved statements have been called theorems in this book. Sometimes, when a statement can be proved in a few easy steps by application of a theorem, the simply-proved statement is called a *corollary*. **A corollary** is a statement that is readily proved by applying a theorem. An analogy is helpful here: A corollary is to a theorem in mathematics as a by-product is to a main product in industry. A by-product can be very useful, and so can a corollary. You may use a corollary to prove things just as you use a theorem. Try to prove the following corollaries of Theorem 5–9.

COROLLARY 1 If two angles of one triangle are congruent to two angles of another triangle, the third angles are congruent also.

COROLLARY 2 Each angle of an equiangular triangle has measure 60.

COROLLARY 3 A triangle can have at most one nonacute angle.

COROLLARY 4 The acute angles of a right triangle are complementary.

THEOREM 5–10 The measure of an exterior angle of a triangle is equal to the sum of the measures of the two remote interior angles.

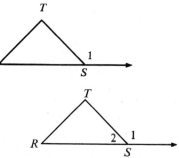

Given: $\triangle RST$ with ext. $\angle 1$.

To Prove: $m\angle 1 = m\angle R + m\angle T$.

Analysis: By Theorem 5–9, $m\angle R + m\angle T + m\angle 2 = 180$. Also, $m\angle 1 + m\angle 2 = 180$.

Proof

The proof is left for you.

ORAL EXERCISES

1. How many congruent sides can a scalene triangle have?

2. Can you have an obtuse triangle that is also an isosceles triangle? an equilateral triangle that is also a right triangle?

3. Give a simple name for the union of pt. X, pt. Y, pt. Z, $\overline{XY}$, $\overline{YZ}$, and $\overline{XZ}$.

4. Give a simple name for the union of $\overleftrightarrow{XY}$, $\overleftrightarrow{YZ}$, and $\overleftrightarrow{XZ}$.

5. For each point A, B, C, tell whether the point lies on $\triangle XYZ$, in the interior of the triangle, or in the exterior.

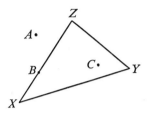

Exs. 3–5

6. Suppose that every point in the interior of some $\triangle RST$ is also in the interior of some $\triangle UVW$, but pt. R is not in the interior of $\triangle UVW$. Where must R lie?

7. Use three letters to name each of the interior angles of $\triangle JKM$; to name each of the exterior angles shown.

8. Name the two interior angles which are remote from ext. $\angle FJK$; from ext. $\angle JME$; from ext. $\angle MKD$.

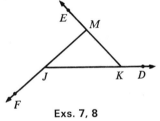

Exs. 7, 8

Supply the missing words or phrases.

9. No right triangle can have an __?__ angle.

10. In $\triangle ABC$ and $\triangle RST$, $m\angle A = m\angle R$ and $m\angle B = m\angle S$. Then __?__.

11. An exterior angle of a triangle and the adjacent interior angle are __?__.

12. In $\triangle ABC$, $m\angle A = 80$ and $m\angle B = 80$. Then $m\angle C = $ __?__.

13. The measure of one acute angle of a right triangle is 30. The measure of the other acute angle is __?__.

14. A certain right triangle has two congruent acute angles. The measure of each acute angle is __?__.

15. The two exterior angles at a vertex of a triangle are __?__ angles and therefore __?__ angles.

16. A statement readily proved by application of a theorem is called a __?__.

17. If one of the angles of an isosceles triangle has a measure of 60, the triangle is a(n) __?__ triangle.

18. The angle determined by the two congruent sides of an isosceles triangle may be __?__ angle, __?__ angle, or __?__ angle.

WRITTEN EXERCISES

EXAMPLE: $m\angle 4 = 150$; $m\angle 3 = 100$. Find $m\angle 2$.

Solution: $m\angle 4 = m\angle 3 + m\angle 2$.
$$150 = 100 + m\angle 2.$$
$$m\angle 2 = 50.$$

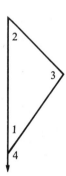

A

1. $m\angle 2 = 50$; $m\angle 3 = 100$. Find $m\angle 4$.

2. $m\angle 1 = 30$; $m\angle 2 = 45$. Find $m\angle 3$.

3. $m\angle 2 = 40$; $m\angle 4 = 150$. Find $m\angle 3$.

4. $m\angle 2 = c$; $m\angle 3 = d$. Find $m\angle 4$.

5. $m\angle 1 = h$; $m\angle 2 = j$. Find $m\angle 3$.

6. $m\angle 2 = (2n)$; $m\angle 3 = (5n)$. Find $m\angle 1$.

Exs. 1–6

In Exercises 7–12, $l \parallel m$.

7. $m\angle 1 = 140$; $m\angle 3 = 50$. Find the measure of each numbered angle.

8. $m\angle 2 = 65$; $m\angle 3 = 70$. Find the measure of each numbered angle.

9. $m\angle 1 = n$; $m\angle 3 = p$. Find the measure of each numbered angle in terms of n and p.

10. $m\angle 5 = j$; $m\angle 6 = k$. Find the measure of each numbered angle in terms of j and k.

11. $m\angle 5 = 7x + 11$; $m\angle 2 = 8x + 4$. Find x.

12. $m\angle 7 = 3x + 5$; $m\angle 4 = 5x + 15$. Find x.

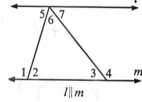

Exs. 7–12

13. Given: $\overline{JK} \perp \overline{MN}$.
Prove: $m\angle 1$ and $m\angle 2$ are complementary.

14. Given: $\overline{JK} \perp \overline{MN}$; $m\angle 1 = m\angle 3$.
Prove: $m\angle 2 = m\angle 4$.

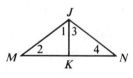

Exs. 13, 14

15. Given: $\angle 5 \cong \angle 6$.
Prove: $\angle 3 \cong \angle 4$.

16. Given: $\triangle$s *RST* and *PQT* are
rt. $\triangle$s with rt. $\angle$s
at pts. *S* and *Q*.
Prove: $\angle 3 \cong \angle 4$.

17. Given: $\angle XYZ \cong \angle BDZ$.
Prove: $\angle YXZ \cong \angle DBZ$.

18. Given: $\overline{AC} \perp \overline{CD}$; $\overline{DB} \perp \overline{AB}$.
Prove: $\angle A \cong \angle D$.

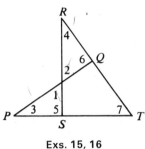

Exs. 15, 16

Exs. 17, 18

EXAMPLE: The measures of the three angles of a triangle are in the ratio
2:4:9. Find the measure of each angle.

Solution: Let the measures be $2x$, $4x$, and $9x$. $2x + 4x + 9x = 180$;
$15x = 180$; $x = 12$. The measures are 24, 48, and 108.

B

19. The measures of three angles of a triangle are in the ratio 2:3:5. Find
the measure of each angle.

20. The measures of three angles of a triangle are in the ratio 4:4:12. Find
the measure of each angle.

21. $m\angle 1 = 2n - 7$; $m\angle 2 = 5n + 3$;
$m\angle 3 = 6n + 2$. Find n.

22. $m\angle 4 = 4n + 15$; $m\angle 2 = 2n$;
$m\angle 3 = 3n$. Find n.

23. $m\angle 1 = \dfrac{x}{5}$; $m\angle 4 = \dfrac{9x - 16}{2}$.
Find x.

24. $m\angle 1 = \dfrac{x}{3}$; $m\angle 4 = \dfrac{x + 20}{4}$. Find x.

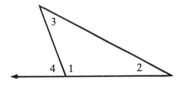

Exs. 21–24

25. The measure of one acute angle of a right triangle is 15 less than twice
the measure of the other acute angle. Find the measure of each acute
angle.

26. The measure of one acute angle of a right triangle is 12 more than
half the measure of the other acute angle. Find the measure of each
acute angle.

27. In the plane figure shown, $\overline{AB} \perp \overline{BC}$. Find the measure of each of the marked angles.

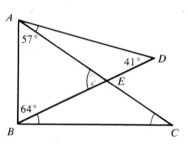

28. In the plane figure shown, $\overline{JK} \parallel \overline{TQ}$, and $\overline{RT} \perp \overline{JQ}$. Find the measure of each marked angle.

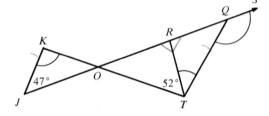

C **29.** $m\angle 2 = c + \dfrac{d}{3}$; $m\angle 3 = 2b + \dfrac{c}{4}$. Express the measure of $\angle 4$ as a single fraction.

30. $m\angle 1 = \dfrac{d - 21}{5}$; $m\angle 2 = \dfrac{f + 3g}{2}$. Express the measure of $\angle 3$ as a single fraction.

Exs. 29, 30

31. Given: The plane figure shown
Prove: $r + s = t + q$
(Hint: Draw an auxiliary line.)

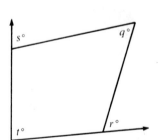

32. Prove Theorem 5–10 without using Theorem 5–9. You may use Theorem 5–5.

You know that

> The sum of the measures of the angles of a polygon with **3** sides is 180 or **1** $\times$ 180,

and that

> The sum of the measures of the angles of a convex polygon with **4** sides is 360 or **2** $\times$ 180.

Inspection of the figure below suggests that

> The sum of the measures of the angles of a convex polygon with **5** sides is 540 or **3** $\times$ 180.

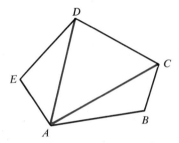

Inductive thinking suggests the following, which you can prove for any particular integer n, $n \geq 3$.

> The sum of the measures of the angles of any convex n-gon is $(n - 2) \times 180$.

Intuition suggests something about the sum of the measures of exterior angles. Think of walking around a convex polygon ABC.... When you reach B you turn through one exterior angle of the polygon. When you reach C you turn through another exterior angle of the polygon. And so on until you return to A. At that time you have turned around once, so the sum of the measures of the angles must be 360.

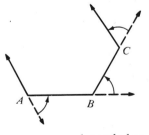

To obtain the result more formally you can use your knowledge about the sum of the measures of interior angles. At each vertex of a convex n-gon the sum of the measures of an exterior angle and the interior angle is 180. The sum of the measures of all n pairs of supplementary angles is $180n$. But, since the sum of the measures of the interior angles is $(n - 2) \times 180$, the sum of the measures of the exterior angles, one at each vertex, is

$180n - (n - 2)180$,

or $180n - (180n - 360)$,

or 360.

> The sum of the measures of the exterior angles of a convex n-gon, one angle at each vertex, is 360.

EXAMPLE 1. The measures of four of the angles of a convex pentagon are 80, 90, 100, and 130. Find the measure of the fifth angle.

Solution: The sum of the measures of all 5 $\angle$s is $(5 - 2) \times 180$ or 540. The sum of the given measures is $80 + 90 + 100 + 130$ or 400. The measure of the fifth angle is $540 - 400 = 140$. **Answer.**

EXAMPLE 2. One exterior angle of a regular convex n-gon has measure 45. Find n, the number of sides.

Solution: Each of n congruent angles has measure 45. The sum of the n measures is 360. $n \cdot 45 = 360$. $n = 8$. **Answer.**

ORAL EXERCISES

1. Which of the figures are polygons? Which are convex polygons?

a.  b.   c.

2. State the number of sides, vertices, and interior angles of each of the following polygons: quadrilateral, decagon, octagon, hexagon, pentagon, n-gon.

3. Can a triangle be equilateral without being equiangular?

4. Can a quadrilateral be equiangular without being equilateral? Equilateral without being equiangular?

5. A point P lies in the interior of a given polygon, and a point Q lies in the exterior. Must $\overline{PQ}$ intersect the polygon?

6. Points R and S both lie in the interior of a convex polygon. In how many points is the polygon intersected by $\overline{RS}$? By $\overrightarrow{RS}$? By $\overleftrightarrow{RS}$?

7. Given polygon $ABCDEF$. Which of the following segments are diagonals of the polygon?

$\overline{CA}$ $\overline{CB}$ $\overline{CD}$ $\overline{CE}$ $\overline{CF}$

8. Given polygon $ABCDEFG$. How many diagonals containing vertex C can be drawn?

9. State the formula for finding the sum of the measures of the angles of a convex n-gon.

10. The sum of the measures of the exterior angles of a convex polygon with 23 sides is __?__ .

WRITTEN
EXERCISES

Draw all possible diagonals from one vertex of a convex polygon of the type named and tell how many triangles are formed.

A

1. Pentagon   **2.** Hexagon   **3.** Octagon   **4.** n-gon

5. Point A is one vertex of a convex n-gon. All diagonals containing point A are drawn. How many triangles are formed?

6. A particular convex polygon is such that when all possible diagonals containing vertex A are drawn, 11 triangles are formed. How many sides does the polygon have?

7. Find the sum of the measures of the angles of a convex polygon of the type named.
   a. quadrilateral   **b.** decagon   **c.** pentagon   **d.** 7-gon

8. Find the sum of the measures of the exterior angles of a convex polygon of the type named.
   a. quadrilateral   **b.** decagon   **c.** pentagon   **d.** 7-gon

9. The measures of three of the angles of a convex quadrilateral are 80, 90, and 103. Find the measure of the fourth angle?

10. Each of five angles of a convex hexagon has measure 130. What is the measure of the sixth angle?

11. What is the measure of one exterior angle of a regular convex polygon with the given number of sides?
   a. 6 sides   **b.** 8 sides   **c.** 16 sides   **d.** n sides

12. How many sides does a regular convex polygon have if the measure of one exterior angle is as given?

  a. 90   **b.** 72   **c.** 24   **d.** 1

B   13. Find the measure of an interior angle of a regular convex polygon with

  a. 8 sides   **b.** 10 sides   **c.** 12 sides   **d.** n sides

14. Find the number of sides in a regular convex polygon in which the measure of one interior angle is

  a. 60   **b.** 108   **c.** 144   **d.** 170

15. The average of the measures of the interior angles of a convex polygon is known to be 108. What is the average of the measures of the exterior angles? How many sides does the polygon have?

16. Each exterior angle of a regular polygon has measure 30. What is the sum of the measures of the interior angles of the polygon?

17. Prove Theorem 5–11.

18. Prove: The sum of the measures of the exterior angles of a convex quadrilateral is 360.

C   19. Prove: The sum of the measures of the angles of a convex pentagon is 540.

20. Discover a formula for the total number of diagonals that can be drawn in a convex n-gon.

PRACTICAL APPLICATIONS

Eratosthenes (**Air**-uh-tos-then-eez), a Greek mathematician of the third century B.C., used the principles studied in this chapter to discover the circumference of the earth. 5000 stadia south of Alexandria lay Syene, the site where men have recently built the Assuan Dam of the Nile. (An Egyptian stadium was a linear measure approximately equivalent to 520 feet.) At a certain time the sun was exactly overhead at Syene and 7°12′ south of the

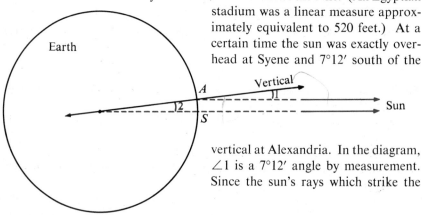

vertical at Alexandria. In the diagram, ∠1 is a 7°12′ angle by measurement. Since the sun's rays which strike the earth are practically parallel, and since the vertical line at A is a transversal, $\angle 2 \cong \angle 1$ and $\angle 2$ is $7°12'$.

The length of arc AS is $\dfrac{7\frac{12}{60}}{360}$ of the earth's circumference.

5000 stadia is $\dfrac{7\frac{12}{60}}{360}$, or $\frac{1}{50}$ of the earth's circumference.

Therefore, by Eratosthenes' argument, the circumference of the earth is 250,000 stadia.

This distance is approximately equal to 24,600 miles and is in error by less than 2%.

CHAPTER SUMMARY

Inventory of Structure and Methods.

1. Relationships of lines and planes.
    Two parallel lines are coplanar; two skew lines are not coplanar.
    A line either lies in, is parallel to, or intersects a plane.
    Two planes either intersect or are parallel.
    When two parallel planes are cut by a third plane, the lines of intersection are parallel.

2. When two parallel lines are cut by a transversal:
    a. Corresponding angles are congruent.
    b. Alternate interior angles are congruent.
    c. The transversal, if perpendicular to one of the lines, is perpendicular to the other also.

3. Two lines cut by a transversal are parallel:
    a. If the corresponding angles are congruent.
    b. If the alternate interior angles are congruent.
    c. If both lines are perpendicular to the transversal.

4. **Indirect proofs** are used in daily life and in mathematics. The method consists of establishing a desired conclusion by showing that the negative of that conclusion leads to a contradiction of a known fact.

5. Through a point outside a line there is exactly one line parallel to the line. (The **Parallel Postulate** of Euclidean geometry.)
    Through a point outside a line there is exactly one line perpendicular to the line.
    The sum of the measures of the angles of a triangle is 180.
    If two angles of one triangle are congruent to two angles of another triangle, the third angles are congruent.

The measure of an exterior angle of a triangle is equal to the sum of the measures of the remote interior angles.

The sum of the measures of the angles of a convex *n*-gon is $(n - 2) \times 180$.

The sum of the measures of the exterior angles, one at each vertex, of a convex polygon is 360.

Vocabulary and Spelling

parallel (‖) lines (*p. 147*)
skew lines (*p. 147*)
parallel line and plane (*p. 147*)
parallel planes (*p. 148*)
perpendicular planes (*p. 149*)
vertical (*p. 149*)
horizontal (*p. 149*)
transversal (trans.) (*p. 151*)
corresponding angles (corr. ⫝̸) (*p. 152*)
alternate interior angles (alt. int. ⫝̸)
  (*p. 152*)
alternate exterior angles (alt. ext. ⫝̸)
  (*p. 152*)
indirect proof (*p. 157*)
auxiliary line (*p. 161*)
Parallel Postulate (*p. 162*)
Euclidean geometry (*p. 163*)
non-Euclidean geometry (*p. 163*)
triangle (△) (*p. 170*)
  interior (*p. 170*)
  exterior (*p. 170*)
  vertex, vertices (*p. 170*)
  sides (*p. 170*)
  angles (*p. 170*)

scalene (*p. 170*)
isosceles (isos.) (*p. 170*)
equilateral (*p. 170*)
acute (*p. 171*)
obtuse (*p. 171*)
right (rt.) (*p. 171*)
equiangular (*p. 171*)
exterior angle (ext.) (*p. 171*)
remote interior ⫝̸ (*p. 171*)
corollary (*p. 172*)
polygon (*p. 177*)
  convex polygon (*p. 177*)
  consecutive vertices (*p. 178*)
  consecutive sides (*p. 178*)
  diagonal (*p. 178*)
  n-gon (*p. 178*)
  equilateral (*p. 178*)
  equiangular (*p. 178*)
  regular (*p. 178*)

CHAPTER TEST

5–1   **1.** In what way are two parallel lines like two skew lines?

2. In what way do two parallel lines differ from two skew lines?

3. Draw sketches showing parallel lines, parallel planes, and skew lines.

4. You can prove that a plane which cuts two parallel planes cuts them in parallel lines by showing that the lines meet two requirements. Name those requirements.

5–2 In Exercises 5–8, $j \parallel k$.

5. Name three angles in the diagram that have measures equal to the measure of $\angle 6$.

6. Name four angles which are supplementary to $\angle 6$.

7. $m\angle 1 = 2n + 3$. Find $m\angle 7$.

8. $m\angle 3 = 5x + 3$. $m\angle 7 = 6x - 9$. Find x.

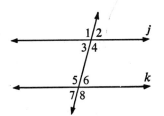

Exs. 5–8

5–3 9. Write an indirect proof: If $k^2 = 5k$, then $k \neq 4$.

5–4 10. What name describes a geometry that postulates more than one line parallel to a line through a point outside the line?

11. Complete the statement in two different ways: Through a point outside a line exactly ___?___.

12. In the figure it is known that $\angle 1 \cong \angle 2$. State the postulate or theorem that supports the conclusion that $r \parallel s$.

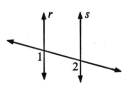

Ex. 12

5–5 13. Name six pairs of angles which, if known to be equal, would enable you to conclude that $m \parallel n$ in the plane figure shown.

14. Name a pair of angles which, if known to be supplementary, would enable you to conclude that $m \parallel n$.

15. Suppose that lines a, b, and c are coplanar, that $a \perp b$, and that $b \perp c$. State the theorem which supports the deduction that $a \parallel c$.

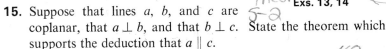

P 153
Theorem **Exs. 13, 14**
5-2

5–6 16. $m\angle 1 = 80$. $m\angle 2 = 50$. $m\angle 3 = $ ___?___.

17. $m\angle 4 = 100$. $m\angle 2 = 40$. $m\angle 3 = $ ___?___.

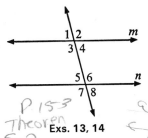

Exs. 16, 17

5–7 18. The number of diagonals containing a particular vertex of a polygon of ten sides is ___?___.

19. The sum of the measures of the interior angles of an n-gon is ___?___.

20. The measure of one exterior angle of a regular polygon of twenty sides is ___?___.

Proof Exercises

21. Prove: If two lines are cut by a transversal so that exterior angles on the same side of the transversal are supplementary, the lines are parallel.

22. Prove that the sum of the measures of the exterior angles of a triangle, one at each vertex, is 360.

CHAPTER REVIEW

5–1   Basic Properties   *Pages 147–151*

1. It is known that lines *l* and *m* do not intersect. Then *l* and *m* must be either __?__ or __?__.

2. If two parallel planes are cut by a third plane, __?__.

3. Two planes, each parallel to a third plane, must __?__.

4. Two lines parallel to the same plane may be parallel lines, __?__ lines, or __?__ lines.

5–2   Transversals and Special Angles   *Pages 151–157*

In Exercises 5–8, *a* ∥ *b*.

5. Name three angles which have measures equal to that of ∠5.

6. Name four angles which are supplementary to ∠2.

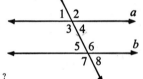

Exs. 5–8

7. $m\angle 3 = 3x + 40$. $m\angle 6 = 5x$. $x =$ __?__.

8. $m\angle 3 = 10x$. $m\angle 4 = 5x + 30$. $x =$ __?__.

5–3   Indirect Proof   *Pages 157–160*

9. Write the negative of "The triangle is isosceles." Write the negative of "The lines are not parallel."

10. In an indirect proof, do you begin by assuming the negative of *hypothesis* or of the *conclusion*?

11. An indirect proof is used to show: "If ∠3 ≅ ∠2, then *j* ∥ *k*." Write the first sentence of the proof.

12. Indirect proofs are based upon the principle that two __?__ statements cannot both be __?__.

5–4   A Parallel to a Line Through an Outside Point   *Pages 161–165*

13. Is the geometry of this book Euclidean or non-Euclidean?

14. Lines *j* and *k* intersect. Is it true that through each point of *j* there is a line parallel to *k*?

15. Write the *Given* and the *To Prove* for the converse of the statement: If $\angle 1 \cong \angle 2$; then $j \parallel k$.

16. Write the converse of: If two parallel planes are cut by a third plane, the lines of intersection are parallel. Is the converse true?

5–5   Converses of Earlier Statements about Parallels

Pages 166–170

17. State lines, if any are shown in this plane figure, which must be parallel when:

    a. $\angle 1 \cong \angle 7$ **c.** $\angle 1 \cong \angle 6$
    b. $\angle 4 \cong \angle 9$ **d.** $\angle 1 \cong \angle 2$
    e. $m\angle 4 + m\angle 5 = 180$
    f. $m\angle 2 = m\angle 3 + m\angle 5$
    g. $m\angle 8 + m\angle 9 = 180$
    h. $l \parallel m$, and $\angle 6 \cong \angle 7$

18. State three theorems you can use to prove lines parallel.

5–6   Applying Parallels to Triangles

Pages 170–176

19. The sum of the measures of the angles of any triangle is ___?___.

20. The acute angles of a right triangle are ___?___.

21. The exterior angle at vertex C of $\triangle ABC$ has measure 105. $m\angle A = 60$. $m\angle B = $ ___?___.

22. State the measure of each of the other two angles when:

    a. $m\angle 3 = g$; $m\angle 4 = h$.
    b. $m\angle 2 = j$; $m\angle 3 = k$.
    c. $m\angle 4 = m$; $m\angle 1 = n$.
    d. $m\angle 1 = p$; $m\angle 3 = q$.

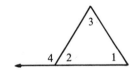

5–7   Applying Parallels to Polygons

Pages 177–182

23. State the number of sides in an octagon, a pentagon, a hexagon, a decagon.

24. The sum of the measures of the interior angles of a convex quadrilateral is ___?___.

25. The measure of each interior angle of a regular polygon having nine sides is ___?___.

26. Write an indirect proof of the fact that a triangle can have at most one obtuse angle.

27. Prove: If two angles in a plane have parallel sides, the angles are congruent or supplementary.

• EXTRA FOR EXPERTS

Many people "study Euclid" without realizing how very much material, both geometric and otherwise, he included in this treatise. Book IX, for example, deals with arithmetica, now called *number theory*. Proposition 20 of Book IX is translated to read: *Prime numbers are more than any assigned multitude of prime numbers.* In other words, the number of primes is infinite.

An indirect proof works nicely. Suppose that the number of primes is finite rather than infinite. Then there is a greatest prime number, say p, and the sequence of primes is 2, 3, 5, 7, 11, . . . , p. Now consider the number $q = (2 \cdot 3 \cdot 5 \cdot 7 \cdot 11 \ldots p) + 1$, and investigate the smallest integer > 1 that divides q. That least integer is obviously itself a prime. Yet that integer cannot be 2 or 3 or 5 . . . or p. That integer is therefore a prime greater than p. Since this statement contradicts the earlier statement about p, the conclusion that the number of primes is infinite follows.

Do you find yourself wondering about hidden assumptions in this proof? The assumptions are:

If n is divisible by bc, then n is divisible by b.

If m has the form $de + 1$, and d is not the number 1, then m is not divisible by d.

There is nothing in the proof to prevent q from being a prime; we simply do not know, one way or the other. But it does not matter. If q should be prime, the theorem is established at once, though the proof given in the second paragraph still holds.

EXERCISES

1. Investigate $(2 \cdot 3 \cdot 5 \cdot 7 \cdot 11) + 1$. Is this number a prime? Is $(2 \cdot 3 \cdot 5 \cdot 7 \cdot 11) - 1$ a prime?

2. Prove the existence of an infinitude of primes by using a negative sign instead of a positive sign in defining q.

▶ Non-Euclidean Geometers

The postulates of Euclidean geometry were regarded by practically every mathematician and philosopher, up to the early part of the nineteenth century, as fundamental truths. One eighteenth-century scholar had such admiration and respect for Euclid that he wrote a book having the title, *Euclid Vindicated From Every Flaw*. Little did he realize that in setting out to defend Euclid's work he was laying the foundations of the first non-Euclidean geometry.

He tried, as men had tried for over two thousand years, to prove the Parallel Postulate. His approach was to deny the Parallel Postulate and then to look for a contradiction in the set of theorems which would follow. While he succeeded in proving many theorems different from those of Euclid, the theorems did not contradict each other. Finally, however, he convinced himself that there was a contradiction. Actually he had unknowingly discovered a new kind of geometry.

Nicolai Lobachevski was one of three men who did consciously develop non-Euclidean geometry a century later. How he found time to do this is a marvel. Promoted to a professorship when in his early twenties, he was soon made — although he kept his position in the mathematics department — curator of his university's museum and head of its library. He did — and did well — whatever needed doing. Even after being made head of the university he still worked, on occasion, in the museum and library. In the meantime he did highly original work in mathematics. He assumed the existence of two parallels to a given line through a point outside the line and developed the system of geometry that follows from this startling postulate.

Janos Bolyai was creating the same new kind of mathematics at much the same time. Neither he, in Hungary, nor Lobachevski, in Russia, knew of the work of the other man. Bolyai assumed the existence of many parallels to a line through a point not on the line. You may think that it takes a bold man to hold such a belief. Well, Bolyai was brave. One story of his early manhood tells that he was provoked and challenged by thirteen fellow officers in the Hungarian cavalry. He accepted the challenges on the condition that he could play his violin between duels. Either dueling skill or cold war strategy paid off, for Bolyai was the victor in all thirteen duels.

6 Congruent Triangles

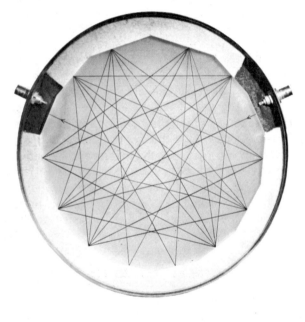

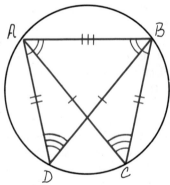

Several pairs of congruent triangles are formed by these delay lines of fused silica which are used in one small part of the nation's radar warning system.

Engineers of the space age use triangles in their constructions just as builders of the past did. The triangle will always play a basic role in making things strong because the triangle is a rigid figure.

Take the three sticks shown.

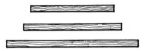

Fasten them together at their ends and you can get a figure of only one size and shape. The lengths of the three sticks determine the triangle: they determine its area; the measure of its angles; in fact, all its mathematical properties.

In our present age of mass production, a manufacturer must produce an item by the thousands and still guarantee that any two samples of that item are alike. For example, a plant turns out thousands of one-inch bolts in a day. Where one bolt fits, the others must fit also. Ideally, all the bolts have the same size and shape. Figures, whether plane or solid, which have the same size and shape are described as congruent.

This chapter will deal with the congruence of geometrical figures. Although geometrical figures are abstract, they help us to describe what we see in the physical world. You expect a study of the triangles of geometry to take into account such facts about concrete objects as the fact that the three sticks pictured above can form just one triangular object. The postulates are chosen so that there is agreement with physical facts.

■ Proving That Triangles Are Congruent

6–1   Congruence of Triangles

Suppose you are asked if triangle *ABC* and triangle *XNT* appear to be congruent. To decide whether the triangles have the same size and shape, you can mentally slide △*ABC* to the right until point *A* falls on point *X* and then rotate △*ABC* until $\overline{AB}$ is lined up with $\overline{XN}$.

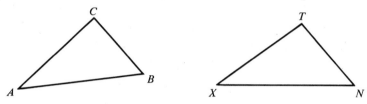

Clearly you wouldn't pair vertex *A* with either vertex *N* or vertex *T*. You want the following pairing:

$$A \leftrightarrow X \qquad\qquad B \leftrightarrow N \qquad\qquad C \leftrightarrow T$$

When this 1–1 correspondence is set up between the vertices of the triangles, ∠*A* and ∠*X* are called **corresponding angles.** Other corresponding angles are ∠*B* and ∠*N*, ∠*C* and ∠*T*. $\overline{AB}$ and $\overline{XN}$ are **corresponding sides.** Other corresponding sides are $\overline{BC}$ and $\overline{NT}$, $\overline{AC}$ and $\overline{XT}$. For each *part* (side or angle) of one triangle there is a corresponding part of the other triangle.

Return to the problem of deciding whether triangles *ABC* and *XNT* are congruent. For the triangles to be congruent, you can see that corresponding angles must have equal measures. You must have:

$$\angle A \cong \angle X \qquad \angle B \cong \angle N \qquad \angle C \cong \angle T$$

Also, for the triangles to be congruent, they must be the same size and you must have:

$$\overline{AB} \cong \overline{XN} \qquad \overline{BC} \cong \overline{NT} \qquad \overline{AC} \cong \overline{XT}$$

The informal thinking outlined above suggests the following exact definition.

> If a correspondence between the vertices of two triangles is such that each side and each angle of one triangle is congruent to the corresponding part of the other triangle, then the correspondence is called a **congruence** between the triangles.

To show what parts correspond to each other you write the letters that name the vertices in order. Name one triangle as you wish, say triangle *ABC*. Then name the second triangle so that

X, the vertex corresponding to *A*, is named first,

N, the vertex corresponding to *B*, is named second,

T, the vertex corresponding to *C*, is named last.

You indicate the correspondence by writing

$$\triangle ABC \leftrightarrow \triangle XNT$$

If this particular correspondence is a congruence you write

$$\triangle ABC \cong \triangle XNT$$

and say the $\triangle ABC$ **is congruent to** $\triangle XNT$ or that $\triangle ABC$ and $\triangle XNT$ are **congruent triangles.**

Notice how much information the notation $\triangle ABC \cong \triangle XNT$ gives. From it you see, first of all, that there is a particular correspondence between the vertices of the two triangles. Then you see that each side and each angle of one triangle is congruent to the corresponding part of the other triangle.

You can mark figures, as shown here, to indicate corresponding sides and angles. When side $\overline{AB}$ is given one mark, corresponding side $\overline{XN}$ is also given one mark. $\angle C$ and $\angle T$, the angles *opposite* these sides, are also given one mark each.

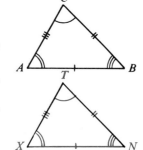

$\angle X$ is said to be **included** between sides $\overline{XN}$ and $\overline{XT}$. Side $\overline{XN}$ is said to be **included** between $\angle X$ and $\angle N$.

You can use the definition of congruent triangles, and theorems about the congruence of segments and angles, to establish the following theorem.

THEOREM 6–1   Congruence of triangles is reflexive, symmetric, and transitive.

Proofs of the parts of the theorem are left as exercises.

ORAL
EXERCISES

In Exercises 1–10 use the meaning of congruence developed informally on page 192.

1. Can two triangles be congruent without being coplanar?

2. Can a quadrilateral be congruent to a pentagon?

3. Must two regular hexagons be congruent?

4. Can two manufactured articles properly be called congruent in the strictest mathematical sense of the word?

5. A side of one square is congruent to a side of another square. Are the squares necessarily congruent?

6. An edge of one cube is congruent to an edge of another cube. Are the cubes congruent?

7. Is a side wall of your classroom congruent to the ceiling?

8. Two figures are each congruent to a third figure. Are they congruent to each other?

9. How many triangles are shown in the figure?

10. Each triangle in the figure is equilateral. In how many ways can you set up a correspondence between the vertices of △1 and △2 and establish congruence of the triangles?

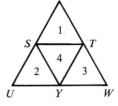

Exs. 9, 10

Complete the correspondence table in such a way that a congruence could be established.

11.

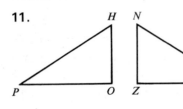

$P \leftrightarrow$?

$O \leftrightarrow$?

$H \leftrightarrow$?

12.

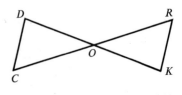

$C \leftrightarrow$?

$O \leftrightarrow$?

$D \leftrightarrow$?

Basing your decision upon the appearance
of the figure, tell whether the
statement is correct *as written.*

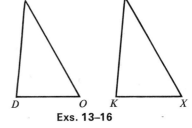

13. $\triangle DOT \cong \triangle KXV$

14. $\triangle DOT \cong \triangle XKV$

15. $\triangle ODT \cong \triangle VXK$

16. $\triangle TDO \cong \triangle VKX$

Exs. 13–16

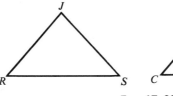 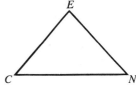

17. $\triangle RJS \cong \triangle CEN$

18. $\triangle RJS \cong \triangle NEC$

19. $\triangle JSR \cong \triangle CEN$

20. $\triangle RJS \cong \triangle SJR$

Exs. 17–20

Answer the question by noting the order in which vertices of the scalene triangles
are named.

21. If $\triangle ABC \cong \triangle XYZ$, is $\triangle ABC \cong \triangle YZX$?

22. If $\triangle ABC \cong \triangle XYZ$, is $\triangle BAC \cong \triangle YXZ$?

23. If $\triangle RST \cong \triangle NOK$, is $\triangle RTS \cong \triangle KNO$?

24. If $\triangle RST \cong \triangle NOK$, is $\triangle SRT \cong \triangle ONK$?

25. Restate the congruence $\triangle ABC \cong \triangle XYZ$ in some other correct ways.

26. Restate the congruence $\triangle LID \cong \triangle RST$ in some other correct ways.

WRITTEN EXERCISES

A

1. Use your ruler and protractor to draw two triangles each having a
side 4 inches long, a side 3 inches long, and an angle with measure 40
included between those two sides. Does it appear that the two triangles
you have drawn are congruent?

2. Repeat Exercise 1 using lengths of 5 inches and 2 inches and an angle
with measure 130.

3. Use your ruler and protractor to draw two right triangles, each such
that a side whose endpoint is the vertex of the right angle is 5 cm. long,
and the side opposite the right angle is 11 cm. long. Does it appear that
the two triangles you have drawn are congruent?

4. Repeat Exercise 3 using sides 6 cm. and 9 cm. long.

In each exercise it is given that two triangles are congruent. Judging from the appearance of the figure, list by pairs the sides and 'angles that are corresponding parts.

EXAMPLE.

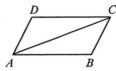

Solution: $\overline{AB}$ and $\overline{CD}$; $\overline{BC}$ and $\overline{DA}$; $\overline{CA}$ and $\overline{AC}$. $\angle ACB$ and $\angle CAD$; $\angle BAC$ and $\angle DCA$; $\angle B$ and $\angle D$.

5.

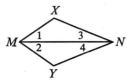

6.

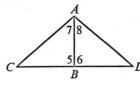

9. If vertices J and J correspond.

7.

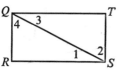

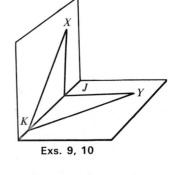

Exs. 9, 10

8.

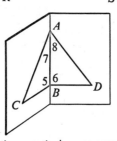

10. If vertices J and K correspond

Given the particular congruence shown, list the corresponding parts of the two triangles named.

B **11.** $\triangle DXB \cong \triangle EXC$
12. $\triangle ABE \cong \triangle ACD$

13. $\triangle RKS \cong \triangle TJS$
14. $\triangle RTJ \cong \triangle TRK$

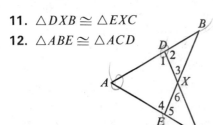

Exs. 11, 12

Exs. 13, 14

15. Prove: For any triangle ABC, $\triangle ABC \cong \triangle ABC$. (Reflexive Property)

16. Prove: If $\triangle ABC \cong \triangle XYZ$, then $\triangle XYZ \cong \triangle ABC$. (Symmetric Property)

C **17.** Prove: If $\triangle ABC \cong \triangle XYZ$ and $\triangle XYZ \cong \triangle PQR$ then $\triangle ABC \cong \triangle PQR$. (Transitive Property)

18. Think of a pair of shoes. You buy them as mates because your feet are mates. But the shoes are different. Just one of them fits your left foot. The shoes illustrate solid figures which are called oppositely congruent, not directly congruent. Copy this three-dimensional figure and extend $\overline{AV}$, $\overline{BV}$, and $\overline{CV}$ through V to R, S, and T in such a way that $RV = AV$, $SV = BV$, $TV = CV$. Is pyramid V-RST directly congruent or oppositely congruent to pyramid V-ABC?

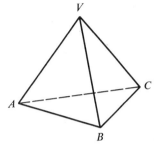

6–2 Some Ways to Prove Triangles Congruent

Experience suggests that we accept the postulates which follow.

P12   If three sides of one triangle are congruent to three sides of another triangle, the triangles are congruent. (SSS Postulate)

The statement above is a somewhat informal statement of the idea expressed more formally and precisely below.

P12   If a correspondence between two triangles is such that the three sides of one triangle are congruent to the corresponding sides of the other triangle, then the correspondence is a congruence.

To apply the SSS postulate to establish a congruence between particular triangles you must first identify corresponding vertices. Suppose, in the figure at the top of the next page, you are given the statements shown.

Given: $\overline{AB} \cong \overline{DE}$

$\overline{BC} \cong \overline{EF}$

$\overline{AC} \cong \overline{DF}$

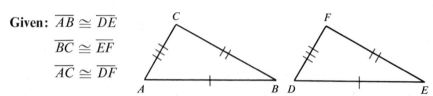

You need to pair the vertices in such a way that $\overline{AB}$ and $\overline{DE}$, known to be congruent sides, will also be corresponding sides. Do the same for the other pairs of congruent segments. The correspondence that works is: $\triangle ABC \leftrightarrow \triangle DEF$. In other words, if you have a triangle with vertices A, B, C and a triangle with vertices D, E, F for which it is known that $\overline{AB} \cong \overline{DE}$, $\overline{BC} \cong \overline{EF}$, and $\overline{AC} \cong \overline{DF}$, then you can use the SSS postulate to deduce: $\triangle ABC \cong \triangle DEF$. From the definition of congruence between triangles you then have:

$$\angle A \cong \angle D, \ \angle B \cong \angle E \ \text{ and } \ \angle C \cong \angle F.$$

Notice that Postulate 12 is the geometric formulation of the statement (p. 191) that, when the lengths of three sticks permit the formation of any triangle at all, the three sticks rigidly determine a single triangle. The congruence postulates that follow also reflect physical reality.

P₁₃   If two sides and the included angle of one triangle are congruent to two sides and the included angle of another triangle, the triangles are congruent. (SAS Postulate)

For a more formal statement of Postulate 13 see Exercise 11.

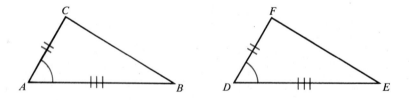

When you have $\overline{AB} \cong \overline{DE}$, $\overline{AC} \cong \overline{DF}$, and $\angle A \cong \angle D$ you take the correspondence: $\triangle ABC \leftrightarrow \triangle DEF$, and have $\triangle ABC \cong \triangle DEF$ from the postulate. Do you see that you can apply the definition of congruence between triangles and make three more assertions about congruence between parts of the triangles?

Some special terms are convenient to use in discussing the congruence of right triangles. In any right triangle the two sides that intersect at the vertex of the right angle are called **legs.** The other side, which lies opposite the right angle, is the **hypotenuse.**

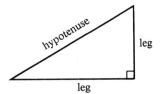

THEOREM 6–2   If the legs of one right triangle are congruent to the legs of another right triangle, the triangles are congruent. (LL Theorem)

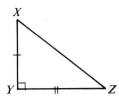   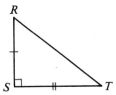

Since the right angles are congruent, Postulate 13 provides an immediate proof.

P14   If the hypotenuse and a leg of one right triangle are congruent to the hypotenuse and a leg of another right triangle, the triangles are congruent. (HL Postulate)

For a more formal statement of Postulate 14 see Exercise 12.

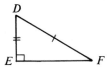   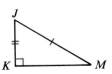

If $\angle E$ and $\angle K$ are right angles, $\overline{DF} \cong \overline{JM}$, and $\overline{DE} \cong \overline{JK}$, you take the correspondence: $\triangle DEF \leftrightarrow \triangle JKM$ and have $\triangle DEF \cong \triangle JKM$ from the postulate. What statements about congruence between parts of the triangles can you write?

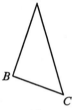

1. What angle is included between sides $\overline{AC}$ and $\overline{BC}$?
2. Between what two sides is $\angle A$ included?
3. If $\angle B$ is a right angle, what side is the hypotenuse?
4. Name two angles not included between the sides $\overline{AC}$ and $\overline{BC}$.

Exs. 1–4

5. Examine the triangles shown. Do you believe that there will ever be a triangle-congruence theorem or postulate given information only about the angles of the triangles?

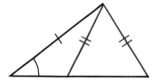

6. Examine the triangles shown. Do you believe that there will ever be a triangle-congruence theorem or postulate given information only about two sides and an angle not included between those sides?

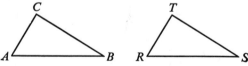

7. State the postulate:
   a. SSS Postulate   **b.** SAS Postulate   **c.** HL Postulate

8. State the LL Theorem.

In Exs. 9–16 state the postulate or theorem that supports the conclusion that $\triangle ABC \cong \triangle RST$.

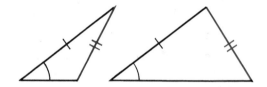

9. Given: $\angle A \cong \angle R$; $\overline{AC} \cong \overline{RT}$; $\overline{AB} \cong \overline{RS}$.
10. Given: $\triangle ABC$ and $\triangle RST$ are rt. $\triangle$ with $\angle C$ and $\angle T$ rt. $\triangle$; $\overline{AC} \cong \overline{RT}$; $\overline{CB} \cong \overline{TS}$.
11. Given: $\angle B \cong \angle S$; $\overline{AB} \cong \overline{RS}$; $\overline{BC} \cong \overline{ST}$.
12. Given: $\overline{BC} \cong \overline{ST}$; $\overline{AB} \cong \overline{RS}$; $\angle C$ and $\angle T$ are rt. $\triangle$.

13. Given: $\overline{BC} \cong \overline{ST}$; $\overline{AC} \cong \overline{RT}$; $\angle C \cong \angle T$.

14. Given: $\overline{CA} \cong \overline{TR}$; $\angle ACB \cong \angle RTS$; $\overline{CB} \cong \overline{TS}$.

15. Given: $\overline{AC} \perp \overline{BC}$; $\overline{RT} \perp \overline{ST}$; $\overline{AB} \cong \overline{RS}$; $\overline{AC} \cong \overline{RT}$.

16. Given: $\overline{AC} \cong \overline{RT}$; $\overline{AB} \cong \overline{RS}$; $\overline{CB} \cong \overline{TS}$.

WRITTEN EXERCISES

EXAMPLE 1.

Given: $\overline{AB}$ and $\overline{CD}$ bisect each other at M.

Prove: $\triangle ACM \cong \triangle BDM$.

Proof

STATEMENT	REASON
1. $\overline{AB}$ and $\overline{CD}$ bisect each other.	1. Given.
2. $\overline{AM} \cong \overline{BM}$.	2. Definition of bisect.
3. $\overline{CM} \cong \overline{DM}$.	3. Definition of bisect.
4. $\angle 1 \cong \angle 2$.	4. If two lines intersect, vert. $\angle\!\!\!\angle$ are $\cong$.
5. $\triangle ACM \cong \triangle BDM$.	5. SAS postulate.

EXAMPLE 2.

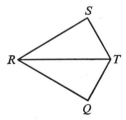

Given: $\overline{RS} \cong \overline{RQ}$; $\overline{ST} \cong \overline{QT}$.

Prove: $\triangle RST \cong \triangle RQT$.

Proof

STATEMENT	REASON
1. $\overline{RT} \cong \overline{RT}$.	1. Reflexive property of congruence.
2. $\overline{RS} \cong \overline{RQ}$.	2. Given.
3. $\overline{ST} \cong \overline{QT}$.	3. Given.
4. $\triangle RST \cong \triangle RQT$.	4. SSS postulate.

In Exs. 1–6 prove that △ACX ≅ △BCX.

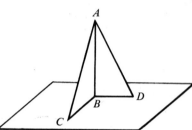

Exs. 1–6

A   1. Given: $\overline{AX} \cong \overline{BX}$; $\overline{AC} \cong \overline{BC}$.

2. Given: $\overline{AC} \cong \overline{BC}$; $\angle 1 \cong \angle 2$.

3. Given: $\angle 3$ and $\angle 4$ are rt. $\angle$s; $\overline{AC} \cong \overline{BC}$.

4. Given: $\angle 3$ and $\angle 4$ are rt. $\angle$s; $\overline{AX} \cong \overline{BX}$.

5. Given: $\overline{CX} \perp \overline{AB}$; $\overline{AC} \cong \overline{BC}$.

6. Given: $\overline{CX}$ is $\perp$ bisector of $\overline{AB}$.

7. Given: $\overline{AB} \perp \overline{BC}$; $\overline{AB} \perp \overline{BD}$;
$\overline{BC} \cong \overline{BD}$.

Prove: △ABC ≅ △ABD.

8. Given: $\overline{AB} \perp \overline{BC}$; $\overline{AB} \perp \overline{BD}$;
$\overline{AC} \cong \overline{AD}$.

Prove: △ABC ≅ △ABD.

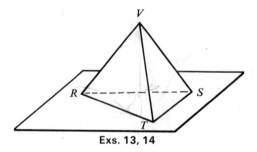

Exs. 7, 8

9. Use your ruler and protractor to draw two triangles each having an angle with measure 70, an angle with measure 50, and a side of length 4 included between these angles. What seems to be true about the triangles?

10. Repeat Exercise 9, using angle measures of 40 and 100 and a length of 3.

11. Using the formal statement of Postulate 12 as a guide, write a formal statement of Postulate 13.

12. Write formal statements of Theorem 6–2 and Postulate 14.

B   13. Given: $\overline{RT} \cong \overline{RS}$;
$\overline{VT} \cong \overline{VS}$.

Prove: △VRT ≅ △VRS.

14. Given: $\angle VTR \cong \angle VTS$;
$\overline{TR} \cong \overline{TS}$.

Prove: △VTR ≅ △VTS.

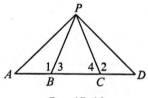

Exs. 13, 14

15. Given: △ADP; $\angle 3 \cong \angle 4$;
$\overline{AB} \cong \overline{DC}$; $\overline{PB} \cong \overline{PC}$.

Prove: △ABP ≅ △DCP

16. Given: △ADP; $m\angle 1 + m\angle 4 = 180$;
$\overline{AB} \cong \overline{DC}$; $\overline{PB} \cong \overline{PC}$.

Prove: △ABP ≅ △DCP.

Exs. 15, 16

17. Given: $\overline{EF} \parallel \overline{KJ}$; $\overline{EF} \cong \overline{JK}$.

    Prove: $\triangle EFJ \cong \triangle JKE$.

18. Given: $\overline{JF} \parallel \overline{KE}$; $\overline{JF} \cong \overline{EK}$.

    Prove: $\triangle EFJ \cong \triangle JKE$.

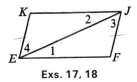

Exs. 17, 18

19. Prove: If $\overline{QX}$ is perpendicular to $\overline{AB}$ at X, the midpoint of $\overline{AB}$, then $\triangle AXQ \cong \triangle BXQ$.

20. Prove: If P is a point on $\overrightarrow{OQ}$ in the interior of $\angle RON$, $\overline{PX} \perp \overrightarrow{OR}$ at X, $\overline{PY} \perp \overrightarrow{ON}$ at Y, and $\overline{OX} \cong \overline{OY}$, then $\triangle POX \cong \triangle POY$.

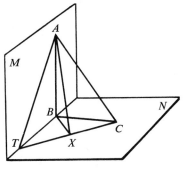

C 21. Given: $\overleftrightarrow{BX}$ is $\perp$ bisector of $\overline{TC}$; $\overline{AT} \cong \overline{AC}$.

    Prove: $\triangle AXT \cong \triangle AXC$.

22. Given: $\overline{AB} \perp$ plane N; $\overline{AT} \cong \overline{AC}$.

    Prove: $\triangle ABT \cong \triangle ABC$.

Exs. 21, 22

6–3 More Ways to Prove Triangles Congruent

Do you think that the particular measures given in Exercises 9 and 10 of the last set were responsible for the triangles appearing to be congruent? More test drawings, using any measures you like, suggest that we accept the following statement:

P 15 If two angles and the included side of one triangle are congruent to two angles and the included side of another triangle, the triangles are congruent. (ASA Postulate)

For a more formal statement of Postulate 15 see Exercise 13.

If $\angle A \cong \angle D$, $\angle B \cong \angle E$, and $\overline{AB} \cong \overline{DE}$, you take the correspondence $ABC \leftrightarrow DEF$ and have $\triangle ABC \cong \triangle DEF$ from the postulate. What state-

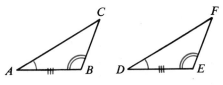

ments about congruence between parts of the triangles can you write?

THEOREM 6–3 If two angles and a not-included side of one triangle are congruent to the corresponding parts of another triangle, the triangles are congruent. (AAS Theorem)

Given: $\triangle ABC$ and $\triangle RST$ with $\angle A \cong \angle R$; $\angle B \cong \angle S$; $\overline{BC} \cong \overline{ST}$.

To Prove: $\triangle ABC \cong \triangle RST$.

Analysis: Show $\angle C \cong \angle T$ and then apply the ASA postulate.

Proof

The proof is left for you.

COROLLARY 1 If the hypotenuse and an acute angle of one right triangle are congruent to the hypotenuse and an acute angle of another right triangle, the triangles are congruent. (HA corollary)

COROLLARY 2 If a leg and an acute angle of one right triangle are congruent to the corresponding parts of another right triangle, the triangles are congruent. (LA corollary)

Ways to Prove Two Triangles Congruent	
Any triangles	*Right triangles*
SSS	HL
SAS	LL
ASA	HA
AAS	LA

ORAL EXERCISES

1. State the postulate, theorem, or corollary abbreviated by:
   a. SSS   **b.** SAS   **c.** ASA   **d.** AAS

2. State the postulate, theorem, or corollary abbreviated by:
   a. HL   **b.** LL   **c.** HA   **d.** LA

3. Parts of the triangles are congruent as indicated. You wish to prove △ *DEF* ≅ △ *XYZ* by the ASA postulate. What parts not marked in the figures must you know are congruent?

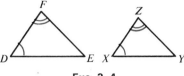

Exs. 3, 4

4. Parts of the triangles are congruent as indicated. You wish to prove △ *DEF* ≅ △ *XYZ* by the AAS theorem. Can you complete the proof if given that $\overline{FE} \cong \overline{ZY}$? $\overline{DE} \cong \overline{XY}$? $\overline{FE} \cong \overline{XY}$? $\overline{DE} \cong \overline{ZY}$?

5. You wish to prove the right triangles congruent. You are given that $\overline{RS} \cong \overline{JK}$. Can you apply the HA corollary if also given that $\angle S \cong \angle K$? $\angle R \cong \angle J$? $\overline{RT} \cong \overline{JM}$? $\angle S \cong \angle J$?

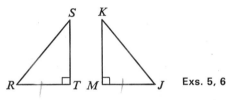

Exs. 5, 6

6. You wish to prove the right triangles congruent. You are given that $\overline{RT} \cong \overline{JM}$. Can you apply the LA corollary if also given that $\angle R \cong \angle J$? $\angle T \cong \angle M$? $\angle S \cong \angle K$? $\angle S \cong \angle J$?

In Exs. 7–16 state the postulate, theorem, or corollary you would use to prove △ABC ≅ △DEF.

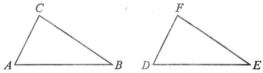

7. Given: $\angle C$ and $\angle F$ are rt. △; $\overline{AB} \cong \overline{DE}$; $\angle A \cong \angle D$.

8. Given: $\angle C$ and $\angle F$ are rt. △; $\overline{AC} \cong \overline{DF}$; $\angle B \cong \angle E$.

9. Given: $\angle C \cong \angle F$; $\angle B \cong \angle E$; $\overline{BC} \cong \overline{EF}$.

10. Given: $\angle C \cong \angle F$; $\angle B \cong \angle E$; $\overline{AC} \cong \overline{DF}$.

11. Given: $\angle C$ and $\angle F$ are rt. △; $\angle B \cong \angle E$; $\overline{BC} \cong \overline{EF}$.

12. Given: $\angle A \cong \angle D$; $\overline{AB} \cong \overline{DE}$; $\angle B \cong \angle E$.

13. Given: $\angle A \cong \angle D$; $\angle C \cong \angle F$; $\overline{BC} \cong \overline{EF}$.

14. Given: $\overline{BC} \perp \overline{AC}$; $\overline{EF} \perp \overline{DF}$; $\overline{AB} \cong \overline{DE}$; $\angle B \cong \angle E$.

15. Given: $\overline{AB} \cong \overline{DE}$; $\overline{BC} \cong \overline{EF}$; $\overline{AC} \cong \overline{DF}$.

16. Given: $\angle C \cong \angle F$; $\overline{AC} \cong \overline{DF}$; $\overline{BC} \cong \overline{EF}$.

WRITTEN EXERCISES

In Exs. 1–6 prove that △RZS ≅ △RZT.

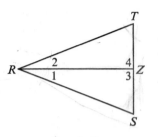

Exs. 1–6

 1. Given: ∠1 ≅ ∠2; ∠3 ≅ ∠4.

2. Given: ∠1 ≅ ∠2; ∠S ≅ ∠T.

3. Given: ∠3 and ∠4 are rt. ∡; $\overline{RS} \cong \overline{RT}$.

4. Given: ∠3 and ∠4 are rt. ∡; ∠1 ≅ ∠2.

5. Given: ∠3 ≅ ∠4; ∠S ≅ ∠T.

6. Given: ∠1 ≅ ∠2; $\overline{RS} \cong \overline{RT}$.

7. Given: ∠1 ≅ ∠2; ∠3 ≅ ∠4.
    Prove: △ABX ≅ △ACX.

8. Given: ∠3 and ∠4 are rt. ∡;
    ∠B ≅ ∠C.
    Prove: △ABX ≅ △ACX.

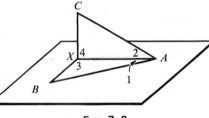

Exs. 7, 8

9. Given: ∠RST ≅ ∠RSQ;
    ∠RTS ≅ ∠RQS.
    Prove: △RST ≅ △RSQ.

10. Given: $\overline{RS} \perp \overline{ST}$; $\overline{RS} \perp \overline{SQ}$;
    ∠SRT ≅ ∠SRQ.
    Prove: △RST ≅ △RSQ.

11. Given: $\overline{RS} \perp \overline{ST}$; $\overline{RS} \perp \overline{SQ}$;
    ∠STR ≅ ∠SQR.
    Prove: △RST ≅ △RSQ.

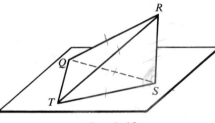

Exs. 9–12

12. Given: $\overline{RT} \cong \overline{RQ}$; $\overline{ST} \cong \overline{SQ}$.
    Prove: △RST ≅ △RSQ.

13. Write formal statements of Postulate 15 and Theorem 6–3.

14. Write formal statements of the two corollaries of Theorem 6–3.

B **15.** Given: $\overline{AB} \parallel \overline{DC}$; $\overline{AD} \parallel \overline{BC}$.
    Prove: △ABC ≅ △CDA.

16. Given: $\overline{AB} \parallel \overline{DC}$; ∠B ≅ ∠D.
    Prove: △ABC ≅ △CDA.

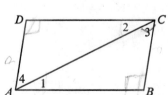

Exs. 15–18

17. Given: $\angle B$ and $\angle D$ are·rt. $\angle$s;
$\qquad \angle 1 \cong \angle 2$.
$\qquad$ Prove: $\triangle ABC \cong \triangle CDA$.

18. Given: $\overline{AD} \perp \overline{DC}$; $\overline{CB} \perp \overline{AB}$;
$\qquad \overline{AD} \parallel \overline{BC}$.
$\qquad$ Prove: $\triangle ABC \cong \triangle CDA$.

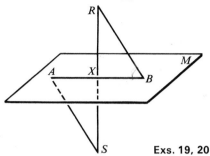

C **19.** Given: $\overleftrightarrow{AB}$ lies in plane M;
$\qquad \overleftrightarrow{RB} \parallel \overleftrightarrow{AS}$;
$\qquad \overline{RS}$ bisects $\overline{AB}$.
$\qquad$ Prove: $\triangle RXB \cong \triangle SXA$.

20. Given: $\overleftrightarrow{AB}$ lies in plane M;
$\qquad \overline{RS} \perp M$ at X;
$\qquad \overline{RX} \cong \overline{SX}$; $\angle A \cong \angle B$.
$\qquad$ Prove: $\triangle XRB \cong \triangle XSA$.

Exs. 19, 20

6–4 Overlapping Triangles

Suppose you have $\overline{RS} \cong \overline{TQ}$ in the figure, but need to have $\overline{RT} \cong \overline{SQ}$ in order to prove that overlapping triangles RJT and SKQ are congruent. You can prove $\overline{RT} \cong \overline{SQ}$ as follows.

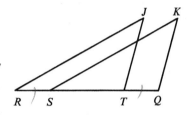

1. $\overline{RS} \cong \overline{TQ}$.	1. Given.
2. $RS = TQ$.	2. Def. of congruence of segments.
3. $RS + ST = ST + TQ$.	3. Addition property of equality.
4. But $RS + ST = RT$, and $ST + TQ = SQ$.	4. Betweenness property.
5. $RT = SQ$.	5. Substitution principle.
6. $\overline{RT} \cong \overline{SQ}$.	6. Def. of congruence of segments.

Steps 2 and 6 in the proof seem trivial. Knowing the definition of congruent segments, you know that the statements $\overline{RS} \cong \overline{TQ}$ and $RS = TQ$ are logically equivalent. When one statement is true, the other is true. From now on it will be permissible to replace steps 1 and 2 by the single step:

$$RS = TQ. \qquad \text{Given.}$$

It will be permissible to replace steps 5 and 6 by the single step:

$$RT = SQ, \text{ and } \overline{RT} \cong \overline{SQ}. \qquad \text{Substitution principle.}$$

Similarly such statements as $\angle A \cong \angle X$ and $m\angle A = m\angle X$ are logically equivalent, and interchangeable. Notice steps 1 and 6 in the example that follows.

Agreement

Since $\overline{AB} \cong \overline{XY}$ if and only if $AB = XY$,
you can replace $\overline{AB} \cong \overline{XY}$ with $AB = XY$ and vice versa.
Since $\angle A \cong \angle X$ if and only if $m\angle A = m\angle X$,
you can replace $\angle A \cong \angle X$ with $m\angle A = m\angle X$ and vice versa.

When you have a figure in which two triangles you wish to prove congruent overlap, you should redraw the two triangles as separate figures. After gaining experience you will be able to see the triangles well enough without redrawing.

EXAMPLE.

Given: $\angle XRO \cong \angle YTO$;
$\angle ORT \cong \angle OTR$

Prove: $\triangle XRT \cong \triangle YTR$

Proof

STATEMENT	REASON
1. $m\angle XRO = m\angle YTO$, $m\angle ORT = m\angle OTR$.	1. Given.
2. $m\angle XRO + m\angle ORT = m\angle YTO + m\angle OTR$.	2. Addition property of equality.
3. But $m\angle XRO + m\angle ORT = m\angle XRT$, and $m\angle YTO + m\angle OTR = m\angle YTR$.	3. Angle addition theorem.
4. $m\angle XRT = m\angle YTR$.	4. Substitution principle.
5. $RT = TR$.	5. Reflexive property of equality.
6. $m\angle XTR = m\angle YRT$.	6. Given.
7. $\triangle XRT \cong \triangle YTR$.	7. ASA postulate.

Though step 6 is not necessary in the preceding proof, for it is essentially a repetition of the second part of step 1, it makes the proof easier to follow.

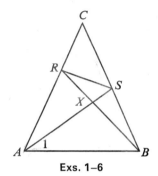

Exs. 1–6

1. In $\triangle ABC$ what angles include side $\overline{AC}$?
2. In $\triangle RSX$ what sides include $\angle SRX$?
3. In $\triangle BRC$ what angles include side $\overline{RC}$?
4. In $\triangle XAB$ what sides include $\angle 1$?
5. Name four triangles with a vertex at C.
6. Name four triangles with a vertex at X.

7. In $\triangle XYK$ and $\triangle WZK$, what side corresponds to side $\overline{XY}$? what angle to $\angle XKY$?
8. In $\triangle XZK$ and $\triangle WYK$, what angle corresponds to $\angle KZX$? what side to side $\overline{XZ}$?
9. $XY + YZ = \underline{\quad?\quad}$.
10. $m\angle YKZ + m\angle ZKW = \underline{\quad?\quad}$.
11. Given $XY = ZW$, what other equality can you deduce?
12. Given $m\angle XKY = m\angle WKZ$, what other equality can you deduce?
13. Given $XZ = YW$, what other equality can you deduce?
14. Name three triangles with a vertex at Y.

Exs. 7–18

15. Name six triangles shown in the figure.
16. Name two triangles in the figure that appear to be isosceles.
17. Name two nonoverlapping triangles that appear to be congruent.
18. Name two overlapping triangles that appear to be congruent.

210 *Chapter 6*

In Exs. 1–10 prove $\triangle DEF \cong \triangle XYZ$.

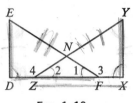

Exs. 1–10

A **1.** Given: $\overline{DE} \cong \overline{XY}$; $\overline{DF} \cong \overline{XZ}$; $\overline{EF} \cong \overline{YZ}$.

2. Given: $\angle E \cong \angle Y$; $\angle 1 \cong \angle 2$; $\overline{DF} \cong \overline{XZ}$.

3. Given: $\angle D$ and $\angle X$ are rt. $\angle$s; $\overline{EF} \cong \overline{YZ}$; $\angle E \cong \angle Y$.

4. Given: $\angle D$ and $\angle X$ are rt. $\angle$s; $\overline{EF} \cong \overline{YZ}$; $\angle 1 \cong \angle 2$.

5. Given: $\overline{ED} \perp \overline{DF}$; $\overline{YX} \perp \overline{XZ}$; $\overline{EF} \cong \overline{YZ}$; $\overline{DE} \cong \overline{XY}$.

6. Given: $\overline{ED} \perp \overline{DF}$; $\overline{YX} \perp \overline{XZ}$; $\overline{DF} \cong \overline{XZ}$; $\angle E \cong \angle Y$.

B **7.** Given: $DZ = XF$; $ED = YX$; $m\angle D = m\angle X$.

8. Given: $EN = YN$; $NF = NZ$; $m\angle D = m\angle X$; $m\angle E = m\angle Y$.

9. Given: $\overline{ED} \parallel \overline{YX}$; $\overline{ED} \perp \overline{DX}$; $DE = XY$; $m\angle E = m\angle Y$.

10. Given: $\overline{YX} \perp \overline{DX}$; $\overline{YX} \parallel \overline{ED}$; $YX = ED$; $m\angle 1 = m\angle 2$.

In Exercises 11–14, $\triangle ABK$ and $\triangle BAJ$ lie in a plane.

Exs. 11–14

11. Given: $\angle JAB \cong \angle KBA$; $\angle 1 \cong \angle 2$.

Prove: $\triangle ABK \cong \triangle BAJ$.

12. Given: $\angle 1 \cong \angle 2$; $\angle AJB \cong \angle BKA$.

Prove: $\triangle ABK \cong \triangle BAJ$.

13. Given: $AK = BJ$; $AC = BC$.

Prove: $\triangle ACJ \cong \triangle BCK$.

14. Given: $m\angle JAB = m\angle KBA$; $\overrightarrow{AK}$ bisects $\angle JAB$; $\overrightarrow{BJ}$ bisects $\angle KBA$.

Prove: $\triangle ABK \cong \triangle BAJ$.

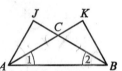

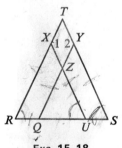

Exs. 15–18

C **15.** Given: $\overline{XU} \parallel \overline{TS}$; $\overline{YQ} \parallel \overline{TR}$; $m\angle R = m\angle S$; $RQ = US$.

Prove: $\triangle RUX \cong \triangle SQY$.

16. Given: $\angle 1 \cong \angle 2$; $\overline{QZ} \cong \overline{UZ}$; $\overline{ZX} \cong \overline{ZY}$; $\overline{RT} \cong \overline{ST}$; $\overline{XT} \cong \overline{YT}$.

Prove: $\triangle RUX \cong \triangle SQY$.

17. Given: $\angle T \cong \angle XZY$; $\angle RUX \cong \angle S$; $\overline{RQ} \cong \overline{US}$.

Prove: $\triangle RUX \cong \triangle QSY$.

18. Given: $\overline{XU} \parallel \overline{TS}$; $\angle YQS$ supplementary to $\angle XUS$; $RU = QS$; $\angle R \cong \angle S$.

Prove: $\triangle RUX \cong \triangle QSY$.

■ Using Congruent Triangles to Prove Segments Congruent and Angles Congruent

6–5 Proving Corresponding Parts Congruent

Once you know that two triangles are congruent, you know that each side and each angle of one triangle is congruent to the corresponding part of the other triangle. This is simply what the definition specifies. Thus, to prove that two angles or segments are congruent, try to find congruent triangles of which they are corresponding parts.

> **A way to prove that segments or angles are congruent**
>
> Show that they are corresponding parts of congruent triangles. Use the reason: Corresponding parts of congruent triangles are congruent. (Corr. parts of ≅ △ are ≅.)

WRITTEN EXERCISES

EXAMPLE.

Given: $\triangle ABC$; $\overline{AC} \cong \overline{BC}$; $\overline{AX} \cong \overline{BX}$.

Prove: $\angle 1 \cong \angle 2$; $\overline{CX} \perp \overline{AB}$.

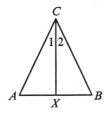

Proof

STATEMENT	REASON
1. $\overline{AC} \cong \overline{BC}$.	1. Given.
2. $\overline{AX} \cong \overline{BX}$.	2. Given.
3. $\overline{CX} \cong \overline{CX}$.	3. Reflexive property of congruence.
4. $\triangle ACX \cong \triangle BCX$.	4. SSS postulate.
5. $\angle 1 \cong \angle 2$.	5. Corr. parts of ≅ △ are ≅.
6. $\angle AXC \cong \angle BXC$.	6. Same as (5).
7. $\overline{CX} \perp \overline{AB}$.	7. If two lines meet to form ≅ adj. ∡, the lines are ⊥.

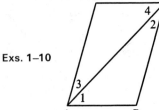

A **1.** Given: $\overline{AB} \cong \overline{CD}$; $\overline{BC} \cong \overline{DA}$.
　　Prove: $\angle B \cong \angle D$.
2. Given: $\overline{AB} \cong \overline{CD}$; $\angle 1 \cong \angle 4$.
　　Prove: $\overline{AD} \cong \overline{CB}$.   **Exs. 1–10**
3. Given: $\angle 1 \cong \angle 4$; $\angle 2 \cong \angle 3$.
　　Prove: $\overline{AB} \cong \overline{CD}$.
4. Given: $\angle 1 \cong \angle 4$; $\angle B \cong \angle D$.
　　Prove: $\overline{AD} \cong \overline{CB}$.

5. Given: $\overline{AB} \parallel \overline{DC}$; $\overline{AD} \parallel \overline{BC}$.   **8.** Given: $AB = CD$; $AD = CB$.
　　Prove: $AD = CB$.   Prove: $m\angle 2 = m\angle 3$.
6. Given: $\overline{AB} \parallel \overline{DC}$; $AB = CD$.   **9.** Given: $AB = CD$; $AD = CB$.
　　Prove: $m\angle 2 = m\angle 3$.   Prove: $\overline{DC} \parallel \overline{AB}$.
7. Given: $\overline{AD} \parallel \overline{BC}$; $AD = CB$.   **10.** Given: $\overline{AD} \parallel \overline{BC}$; $AD = CB$.
　　Prove: $AB = CD$.   Prove: $\overline{AB} \parallel \overline{DC}$.

11. Given: $\overline{TQ}$ bisects $\angle RTS$; $\angle R \cong \angle S$.
　　Prove: $\overline{TQ} \perp \overline{RS}$.
12. Given: $\overline{TQ}$ bisects $\overline{RS}$; $\overline{RT} \cong \overline{ST}$.
　　Prove: $\overline{TQ} \perp \overline{RS}$.
13. Given: $\overline{TQ} \perp \overline{RS}$; $\overline{TQ}$ bisects $\angle RTS$.
　　Prove: $RT = ST$.
14. Given: $\overline{TQ}$ is the $\perp$ bisector of $\overline{RS}$.
　　Prove: $m\angle R = m\angle S$.

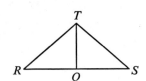

Exs. 11–14

B **15.** Given: $\angle 3 \cong \angle 5$;
　　　　$\angle 4 \cong \angle 6$;
　　　　$\overline{JK} \cong \overline{JM}$;
　　　　$\overline{NK} \cong \overline{NM}$.
　　Prove: $r \parallel s$.
16. Given: $\angle 3 \cong \angle 5$;
　　　　$\angle 4 \cong \angle 6$;
　　　　$\angle 1 \cong \angle 2$; $r \parallel s$.
　　Prove: $\overline{JK} \cong \overline{JM}$.

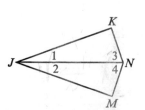
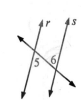

Exs. 15, 16

17. Given: $\angle 2 \cong \angle 3$; $\angle 4 \cong \angle 5$.
　　Prove: $\overline{RS} \cong \overline{RT}$.
18. Given: $\angle 4 \cong \angle 5$; $\overline{RS} \cong \overline{RT}$.
　　Prove: $\angle 2 \cong \angle 3$.

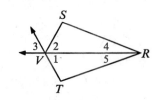

Exs. 17, 18

19. Prove: If P is a point on the bisector of $\angle ABC$ with $\overrightarrow{PX} \perp \overrightarrow{BA}$ at X and $\overrightarrow{PY} \perp \overrightarrow{BC}$ at Y, then $\overline{PX} \cong \overline{PY}$.

20. Prove: Any point on the perpendicular bisector of a segment is equidistant from the endpoints of the segment.

21. Given: $\overline{AD} \cong \overline{BE}$; $\angle DAB \cong \angle EBA$.

Prove: $\overline{BD} \cong \overline{AE}$.

22. Given: $\overline{AD} \cong \overline{BE}$; $\overline{BD} \cong \overline{AE}$.

Prove: $\angle ADB \cong \angle BEA$.

23. Given: $\overline{AC} \cong \overline{BC}$; $\overline{DC} \cong \overline{EC}$.

Prove: $\angle AEC \cong \angle BDC$.

24. Given: $\overline{AD} \cong \overline{BE}$; $\overline{CD} \cong \overline{CE}$.

Prove: $\overline{AE} \cong \overline{BD}$.

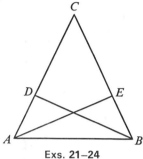

Exs. 21–24

25. Given: $\overline{RS} \cong \overline{TQ}$; $\overline{ST} \cong \overline{QR}$;
$\angle 7 \cong \angle 8$.

Prove: $\overline{QX} \cong \overline{SY}$.

Analysis: Prove $\triangle RST \cong \triangle TQR$
to get $\angle 1 \cong \angle 2$.

Then prove

$\triangle RSY \cong \triangle TQX$.

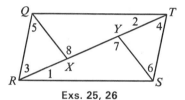

Exs. 25, 26

You write the proof.

26. Given: $\overline{RS} \cong \overline{TQ}$; $\overline{RS} \parallel \overline{QT}$;
$\angle 5 \cong \angle 6$.

Prove: $\overline{QX} \cong \overline{SY}$.

Analysis: Prove $\triangle RST \cong \triangle TQR$
to get $\angle 3 \cong \angle 4$ and $\overline{RQ} \cong \overline{TS}$.
Prove $\triangle RXQ \cong \triangle TYS$.

You write the proof.

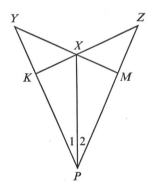

27. Given: $\overline{PK} \cong \overline{PM}$; $\overline{KY} \cong \overline{MZ}$.

Prove: $\angle 1 \cong \angle 2$.

28. Given: $\angle 1 \cong \angle 2$; $\overline{KP} \cong \overline{MP}$.

Prove: $\overline{YX} \cong \overline{ZX}$.

Exs. 27, 28

29. Given: $\angle ABC \cong \angle ACB$; $\overline{BX} \cong \overline{CX}$;
$\angle PXB \cong \angle QXC$.

Prove: $\overline{BQ} \cong \overline{CP}$.

30. Given: $\overline{AP} \cong \overline{AQ}$; $\overline{PB} \cong \overline{QC}$.

Prove: $m\angle QBC = m\angle PCB$.

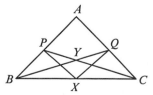

Exs. 29, 30

31. Given: $\overline{VD} \cong \overline{VE} \cong \overline{VF}$; $\overline{DE} \cong \overline{DF} \cong \overline{EF}$; R, S, T and Q are midpoints of $\overline{DF}$, $\overline{VE}$, $\overline{DE}$, and $\overline{VF}$.

Prove: $\overline{RS} \cong \overline{TQ}$.

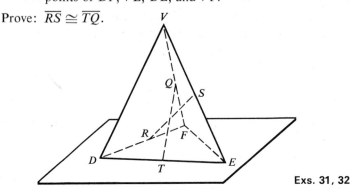

Exs. 31, 32

32. Given: $\overline{VD}$, $\overline{VE}$, $\overline{VF}$, $\overline{DE}$, $\overline{DF}$, and $\overline{EF}$ are $\cong$; Q is the midpoint of $\overline{VF}$;
T is the midpoint of $\overline{DE}$.

Prove: $\overline{QT} \perp \overline{DE}$ and $\overline{QT} \perp \overline{VF}$.

6–6   Isosceles Triangles

You will recall that an isosceles triangle is a triangle with two congruent sides. The congruent sides are called **legs,** and the third side is called the **base.** The angles that include the base are called **base angles;** the third angle is

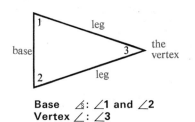

Base ∡: ∠1 and ∠2
Vertex ∠: ∠3

called the **vertex angle,** and its vertex is often referred to as *the* vertex of the triangle.

Two words often used in discussions of isosceles triangles but applicable to other triangles too, are the words *altitude* and *median.*

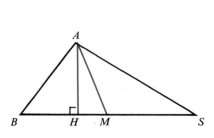

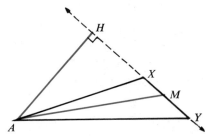

In each of the figures shown, $\overline{AH}$ is an altitude and $\overline{AM}$ is a median of the triangle. An **altitude** of a triangle is the perpendicular segment from any vertex to the line that contains the opposite side. A **median** of a triangle is the segment from any vertex to the midpoint of the opposite side. Do you see that every triangle has three altitudes and three medians?

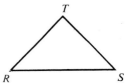

The appearance of triangle *RST* suggests that the altitude from vertex *T* and the median from vertex *T* may be the same segment. Unless you are given some facts about the triangle, however, you cannot assert that the altitude and median are the same segment.

A general word of caution about mistakes commonly made when auxiliary lines are used is in order. Although nobody would be so careless as to say, when using the figure at the right: "Draw $\overleftrightarrow{XY}$ through point *Z*," some people, when they deal with more complicated figures, reach incorrect conclusions that they base upon the mere appearance of the figures.

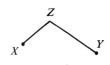

For example, given the figure shown, you might be tempted to say: "Bisect $\angle M$ with a ray perpendicular to $\overline{JK}$." Angle *M* does have one bisector, as Theorem 4–4 states, and this bisector may happen to be perpendicular to $\overline{JK}$. On the other hand, the bisector of angle *M* may happen not to be perpendicular to $\overline{JK}$. You must not place too many *conditions* upon an auxiliary line. If you do, the line is said to be *overdetermined*.

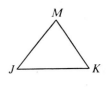

On the other hand, if you do not place enough conditions on a line, it is *underdetermined*. For example, referring to the triangle above, it would not be definite enough to say, "Draw the line through *M*."

An auxiliary line is *determined* if exactly one line can be drawn to meet the conditions. Referring again to $\triangle JKM$, you can properly say:

Draw a line through *M* perpendicular to $\overleftrightarrow{JK}$.

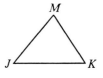

Or: Draw a line bisecting $\angle M$.

Or: Draw a line through *M* and the midpoint of $\overline{JK}$.

Each of these steps can be supported by an acceptable reason.

THEOREM 6–4 If two sides of a triangle are congruent, then the angles opposite those sides are congruent. (Base angles of an isosceles triangle are congruent.)

Given: △*ABC* with $\overline{AC} \cong \overline{BC}$.

To Prove: ∠*A* ≅ ∠*B*.

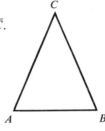

Analysis: Draw an auxiliary line to get two new triangles that can be proved congruent.

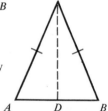

Proof

STATEMENT	REASON
1. Draw the bisector of ∠*C* and let *D* be the point where the bisector intersects $\overline{AB}$.	1. An angle has exactly one bisector.
2. ∠*ACD* ≅ ∠*BCD*.	2. By definition of angle bisector.
3. $\overline{AC} \cong \overline{BC}$.	3. Given.
4. $\overline{CD} \cong \overline{CD}$.	4. Reflexive property of congruence.
5. △*ACD* ≅ △*BCD*.	5. SAS postulate.
6. ∠*A* ≅ ∠*B*.	6. Corr. parts of ≅ △ are ≅.

COROLLARY 1 An equilateral triangle is also equiangular.

COROLLARY 2 Each angle of an equilateral triangle has measure 60.

In the proof of Theorem 6–4, and again in the proof of Theorem 6–5, the statement that the bisector of ∠*C* intersects $\overline{AB}$ could be supported by this statement: *The bisector of an angle of a triangle intersects the opposite side.* Although this statement could be proved, we will accept it as an assumption in this section.

Theorem 6–5, the converse of Theorem 6–4, has a proof much like the proof of Theorem 6–4.

THEOREM 6–5 If two angles of a triangle are congruent, then the sides opposite those angles are congruent.

Given: △*ABC* with ∠*A* ≅ ∠*B*.

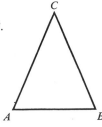

To Prove: $\overline{AC} \cong \overline{BC}$.

Analysis: Draw an auxiliary line to get two new triangles that can be proved congruent.

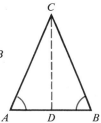

Proof

STATEMENT	REASON
1. Draw the bisector of ∠*C* and let *D* be the point where the bisector intersects $\overline{AB}$.	1. An angle has exactly one bisector.
2. ∠*ACD* ≅ ∠*BCD*.	2. By definition of angle bisector.
3. ∠*A* ≅ ∠*B*.	3. Given.
4. $\overline{CD} \cong \overline{CD}$.	4. Reflexive property of congruence.
5. △*ACD* ≅ △*BCD*.	5. AAS Corollary.
6. $\overline{AC} \cong \overline{BC}$.	6. Corr. parts of ≅ △ are ≅.

COROLLARY An equiangular triangle is also equilateral.

ORAL EXERCISES

1. In an exercise you are given that $\overline{RS} \cong \overline{TS}$. What angles must be congruent? Do you need to draw an auxiliary line to make your deduction?

2. In an exercise you are given that ∠*R* ≅ ∠*T*. What statement of congruence can you deduce? Quote a theorem to support your deduction.

Exs. 1, 2

3. State the three corollaries of this section in *If-Then* form.

4. State the measure of:

    a. Each angle of an equiangular triangle.

    b. Each angle of an equilateral triangle.

    c. A base angle of an isosceles triangle whose vertex angle has measure 40.

    d. A base angle of an isosceles right triangle.

In Exercises 5–10 you need not make any drawings. If you wish to make drawings, do so on your own paper — not in this book. You are to treat the directions as if they were steps in proofs. In each case tell whether the line or segment is determined, underdetermined, or overdetermined.

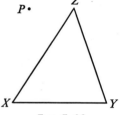

5. Draw $\overleftrightarrow{PZ}$.

6. Draw $\overleftrightarrow{PZ} \parallel \overline{XY}$.

7. Draw $\overrightarrow{PY} \parallel \overline{XZ}$.

8. Draw a perpendicular segment from P to $\overleftrightarrow{XY}$.

9. Draw a segment from X to the midpoint of $\overline{YZ}$.

10. Draw a line through Y parallel to $\overline{XZ}$.

Exs. 5–10

WRITTEN EXERCISES

 A

1. Given: $\triangle ABC$ with $\overrightarrow{AB}$ and $\overrightarrow{CB}$;
        $\overline{AC} \cong \overline{BC}$.

    Prove: $\angle 3 \cong \angle 1$.

2. Given: $\triangle ABC$ with $\overrightarrow{AB}$ and $\overrightarrow{CB}$;
        $\angle 3 \cong \angle 1$.

    Prove: $\overline{AC} \cong \overline{BC}$.

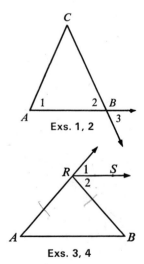

Exs. 1, 2

3. Given: $\triangle ABR$ with $\overrightarrow{AR}$; $\overrightarrow{RS} \parallel \overline{AB}$;
        $\angle 1 \cong \angle 2$.

    Prove: $\overline{RA} \cong \overline{RB}$.

4. Given: $\triangle ABR$ with $\overrightarrow{AR}$; $\overline{RA} \cong \overline{RB}$;
        $\overrightarrow{RS} \parallel \overline{AB}$.

    Prove: $\angle 1 \cong \angle 2$.

Exs. 3, 4

5. Given: $\triangle DEF$ and $\overleftrightarrow{DE}$; $\overline{DF} \cong \overline{EF}$.

Prove: $\angle 3 \cong \angle 4$.

6. Given: $\triangle DEF$ and $\overleftrightarrow{DE}$; $\angle 3 \cong \angle 4$.

Prove: $\overline{DF} \cong \overline{EF}$.

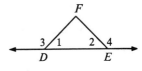

Exs. 5, 6

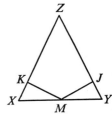

7. Given: $\triangle XYZ$; $\overline{XZ} \cong \overline{YZ}$; M is midpoint of $\overline{XY}$; $\overline{MK} \perp \overline{XZ}$; $\overline{MJ} \perp \overline{YZ}$.

Prove: $\overline{MK} \cong \overline{MJ}$.

8. Given: $\triangle XYZ$; $\overline{MK} \perp \overline{XZ}$; $\overline{MJ} \perp \overline{YZ}$; $\overline{XK} \cong \overline{YJ}$; $\overline{MK} \cong \overline{MJ}$.

Prove: $\triangle XYZ$ is isosceles.

Exs. 7, 8

B

9. Prove Theorem 6–4 by using the perpendicular from the vertex to the base line as your auxiliary line. You may assume that the perpendicular intersects the base segment.

10. Prove Theorem 6–5 by drawing an auxiliary line as in Exercise 9.

11. Given: $\triangle ARQ$; $\overline{AR} \cong \overline{AQ}$; $\overline{RS} \cong \overline{QT}$.

Prove: $\overline{AS} \cong \overline{AT}$.

12. Given: $\triangle ARQ$; $\overline{AR} \cong \overline{AQ}$; $\angle 1 \cong \angle 3$.

Prove: $\overline{AS} \cong \overline{AT}$.

13. Given: $\triangle ARQ$; $\angle R \cong \angle Q$; $\overline{AS} \cong \overline{AT}$.

Prove: $\overline{RS} \cong \overline{QT}$.

14. Given: $\triangle ARQ$; $\overline{AR} \cong \overline{AQ}$; $\overline{RS} \cong \overline{QT}$.

Prove: $\angle RAT \cong \angle QAS$.

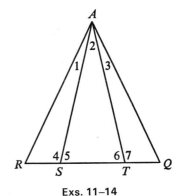

Exs. 11–14

Write complete demonstrations for each of the following statements:

15. The bisector of the vertex angle of an isosceles triangle is perpendicular to the base.

16. The median containing the vertex of an isosceles triangle bisects the vertex angle.

17. The line through the vertex of an isosceles triangle and perpendicular to the base bisects the base.

18. Segments drawn perpendicular to the base of an isosceles triangle from the midpoints of the legs are congruent.

C 19. Given: *B* lies on $\overrightarrow{AC}$;
        $\overline{BD} \cong \overline{BE}$; $\overline{AD} \cong \overline{AE}$.

    Prove: $\overline{DC} \cong \overline{EC}$.

20. Given: *B* lies on $\overrightarrow{AC}$;
        $\angle 1 \cong \angle 2$;
        $\overline{AD} \cong \overline{AE}$.

    Prove: $\angle 3 \cong \angle 4$.

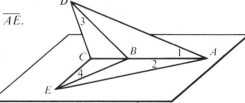

Exs. 19, 20

21. Given: $\overrightarrow{AD} \perp$ plane *P*; $\overline{AB} \cong \overline{AC}$.

    Prove: $\triangle BDC$ is isosceles.

22. Given: $\angle DBC \cong \angle DCB$;
        $\overrightarrow{AD} \perp$ plane *P*.

    Prove: $\angle ABC \cong \angle ACB$.

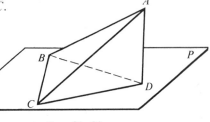

Exs. 21, 22

23. Given: $\triangle RST \cong \triangle QST$.

    Prove: $\triangle QKR$ is isosceles.

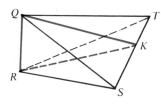

Ex. 23

24. Write a proof of the theorem that the base angles of an isosceles triangle are congruent, using this method:

Begin by taking points *X* and *Y* on $\overrightarrow{CA}$ and $\overrightarrow{CB}$, as shown, so that $AX = BY$. Draw $\overline{AY}$ and $\overline{BX}$. (You are writing Euclid's proof.)

25. The union of $\overrightarrow{OR}$ and $\overrightarrow{OS}$ is an acute angle. $\overrightarrow{OR} \cong \overrightarrow{OS}$. *T* lies on $\overrightarrow{OR}$. *Q* lies on $\overrightarrow{OS}$. $\overline{RQ} \cong \overline{ST}$. Can you prove that $\overline{OT} \cong \overline{OQ}$?

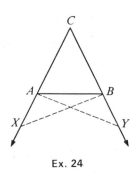

Ex. 24

26. Prove, treating the three possible cases: In a plane, two points each equidistant from the end points of a segment determine the perpendicular bisector of the segment.

Case 1. One point lies on the segment.

Case 2. The two points lie on opposite sides of the segment.

Case 3. The two points lie on the same side of the segment.

PRACTICAL APPLICATIONS

1. The distance between two points A and B can sometimes be found by this method: Drive a stake at a convenient point X. Sight along $\overrightarrow{AX}$ and measure off to get $XA' = XA$. Similarly, find B' on $\overrightarrow{BX}$. Tell why $A'B' = AB$.

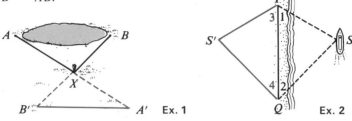

Ex. 1   Ex. 2

2. You can use an old method to learn the distance from point P on land to a ship S. Take a point Q. Measure $\angle 1$ and $\angle 2$. Make $\angle 3 \cong \angle 1$ and $\angle 4 \cong \angle 2$. Why does PS' give the desired distance?

3. Napoleon,.on a river bank, desired immediate knowledge of the width of the stream. A young soldier faced directly across the stream and adjusted the visor of his cap until the tip of the visor was in line with his eye and the opposite bank. Next he did an about-face and noted the spot on the ground now in line with his eye and visor-tip. He paced off the distance to this spot, made his report, and earned a pro-motion. Use a lettered diagram to tell why the method was correct.

4. A cross-staff had a vertical pole PQ and a horizontal crossbar RS which could be moved up and down on pole PQ. A man sighted from P to X and moved the crossbar until S lay on $\overrightarrow{PX}$. The tool was then revolved about pole PQ. Next the man sighted along $\overrightarrow{PS'}$ to determine X'. Why does $QX' = QX$?

Ex. 4

5. A pilot of a small coastal vessel can learn how close he comes to a lighthouse L by using *bow-and-beam* bearings. He checks the angle between the line c on which his course lies and the line of sight from his boat to L until he gets a measure of 45. At that instant he reads his distance indicator. When L is abeam, that is, at right angles to his course, he reads the distance indicator again. Subtracting, he finds AB. Why is this also BL?

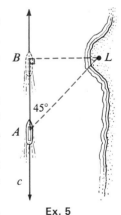

Ex. 5

6. You can bisect an angle quickly by using a carpenter's square. Take
$AX = AY$. Maneuver the square until point P is in such a position
that $PX = PY$. Why is $\angle XAP \cong \angle YAP$?

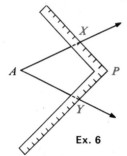

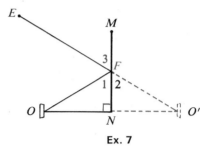

Ex. 6   Ex. 7

7. $\overline{MN}$ represents a side view of a mirror. To the eye at point E an object
at O seems to lie behind the mirror at O'. Physicists tell us that
$m\angle 3 = m\angle 1$ and that $\overline{OO'} \perp \overline{MN}$ at N. Why does $O'N = ON$?

CHAPTER SUMMARY

Inventory of Structure and Methods

1. Ways to prove triangles congruent:
   SSS postulate
   SAS postulate
   ASA postulate
   AAS theorem

2. Ways to prove right triangles congruent:
   HL postulate
   LL theorem
   HA corollary
   LA corollary

3. From the definition of congruent triangles, it follows that corresponding
   parts of congruent triangles are congruent. A common method of proving
   two angles or two segments congruent is to show that they are corresponding parts of congruent triangles. At times it is necessary to draw
   an auxiliary line in order to form triangles which can be proved congruent.
   You draw such a line to prove each of the theorems:

   > If two sides of a triangle are congruent, the angles opposite
   > those sides are congruent.
   > If two angles of a triangle are congruent, the sides opposite
   > those angles are congruent.

Vocabulary and Spelling

congruent (*p. 192*)
corresponding parts (corr. parts) (*p. 192*)
  corresponding sides (*p. 192*)
  corresponding angles (*p. 192*)
congruence between
  two triangles (*p. 192*)
congruent triangles (≅ △) (*p. 193*)
included side (*p. 193*)
included angle (*p. 193*)
leg of a right triangle (*p. 199*)
hypotenuse (*p. 199*)

overlapping triangles (*p. 207*)
isosceles triangle
  legs (*p. 214*)
  base (*p. 214*)
  base angles (*p. 214*)
  vertex angle (*p. 214*)
altitude (*p. 215*)
median (*p. 215*)
determine (*p. 215*)
  underdetermine (*p. 215*)
  overdetermine (*p. 215*)

CHAPTER TEST

6–1
1. Two triangles, to be tested for congruence, are named in such a way that the order of the letters indicates corresponding vertices. In △*JKM* and △*YZU*, side $\overline{JK}$ corresponds to __?__ and ∠*Z* corresponds to __?__.

2. In △*RST*, sides $\overline{RS}$ and $\overline{RT}$ include angle __?__.

3. In △*JKM*, side $\overline{JM}$ is included between angles __?__.

4. How many pairs of triangles that look congruent can you find in the figure?

Ex. 4

6–2 Write the postulate or theorem you would use to prove △PYZ ≅ △QYZ.

5. Given: $\overline{PY} \cong \overline{QY}$; ∠*PYZ* ≅ ∠*QYZ*.

6. Given: ∠*P* and ∠*Q* are rt. ∡; $\overline{PY} \cong \overline{QY}$.

7. Given: $\overline{PZ} \cong \overline{QZ}$; $\overline{PY} \cong \overline{QY}$.

8. Given: $\overline{PY} \perp \overline{PZ}$; $\overline{QY} \perp \overline{QZ}$; $\overline{PY} \cong \overline{QY}$; $\overline{PZ} \cong \overline{QZ}$. (Do not use $\overline{YZ} \cong \overline{YZ}$ in this exercise.)

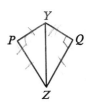

Exs. 5–8

6–3   Write the postulate, theorem, or corollary you would use to prove
△DEF ≅ △JUM.

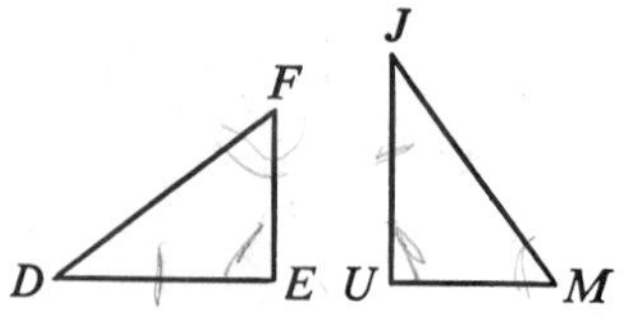

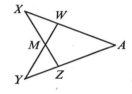

9. Given: ∠D ≅ ∠J; ∠F ≅ ∠M;
$\overline{DF} \cong \overline{JM}$.

10. Given: ∠E and ∠U are rt. ∡;
$\overline{FD} \cong \overline{MJ}$; ∠F ≅ ∠M.

11. Given: △DEF and △JUM are rt. ∡; ∠F ≅ ∠M; $\overline{DE} \cong \overline{JU}$.

12. Given: $\overline{DE} \cong \overline{JU}$; ∠E ≅ ∠U; ∠F ≅ ∠M.

6–4   **13.** In the figure shown, what pairs of
triangles appear to be congruent?

14. a. What two sides of △AWY appear
to be congruent to side $\overline{XZ}$?

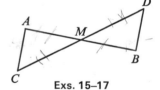

b. You would pair vertices so that
side __?__ of △AWY would correspond to side $\overline{XZ}$ of △AZX.

6–5   **15.** Given: $\overline{AB}$ and $\overline{CD}$ bisect each other.
Prove: AC = BD.

16. Given: ∠A and ∠B are rt. ∡;
AC = BD.
Prove: MC = MD.

17. Given: AM = BM; CM = DM; $\overline{CA} \perp \overline{AB}$.
Prove: $\overline{DB} \perp \overline{AB}$.

Exs. 15–17

6–6   Exercises 18–21 refer to the theorem: Base angles of an isosceles triangle are congruent.

18. Write the *Given* and the *To Prove*.

19. Name two correct ways to draw an auxiliary
line to prove the theorem.

20. Name a way that is incorrect, because of over-
determining, to draw an auxiliary line in the
figure.

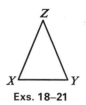

21. Write the statement of the converse theorem.

Exs. 18–21

CHAPTER REVIEW

6–1 Corresponding Parts of Two Triangles   *Pages 192–197*

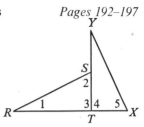

1. In $\triangle RTS$, side $\overline{RS}$ is said to be included between __?__ and __?__ and is said to lie __?__ $\angle 3$.

2. In $\triangle XTY$, the angle included between $\overline{XT}$ and $\overline{YT}$ is __?__, and the angle opposite $\overline{YT}$ is __?__.

3. When $\angle 3$ of $\triangle RTS$ corresponds to $\angle 4$ of $\triangle XTY$, then $\overline{RS}$ corresponds to __?__.

Exs. 2–4

6–2 Formal Treatments of Congruent Triangles   *Pages 197–203*

4. Write the statement abbreviated by SSS; by SAS; by HL.

5. Which of the postulates named in Exercise 4 is used to prove the LL theorem?

6. Draw figures to show that though three angles of one triangle are congruent to three angles of another triangle, the triangles need not be congruent.

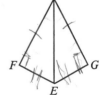

7. Given: $\overline{DF} \cong \overline{DG}$; $\overline{EF} \cong \overline{EG}$.
   Prove: $\triangle DEF \cong \triangle DEG$.

8. Given: $\angle FDE \cong \angle GDE$; $\overline{DF} \cong \overline{DG}$.
   Prove: $\triangle DFE \cong \triangle DGE$.

9. Given: $\angle F$ and $\angle G$ are rt. $\angle$s; $\overline{FE} \cong \overline{GE}$.
   Prove: $\triangle DEF \cong \triangle DEG$.

10. Given: $\angle F$ and $\angle G$ are rt. $\angle$s; $\overline{DF} \cong \overline{DG}$; $\overline{EF} \cong \overline{EG}$. Name four methods that you could use to prove that $\triangle DEF \cong \triangle DEG$. You need not write the proofs.

6–3 More Ways to Prove Triangles Congruent   *Pages 203–207*

11. Write the statement abbreviated ASA; AAS; HA; LA.

12. Given: $\angle Q \cong \angle T$; $\overline{RX} \cong \overline{SX}$.
    Prove: $\triangle RXQ \cong \triangle SXT$.

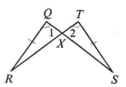

13. Given: $\angle Q$ and $\angle T$ are rt. $\angle$s; $\overline{RX} \cong \overline{SX}$.
    Prove: $\triangle RXQ \cong \triangle SXT$.

14. Given: $\overline{XQ} \perp \overline{RQ}$; $\overline{XT} \perp \overline{ST}$; $\overline{RQ} \cong \overline{ST}$.
    Prove: $\triangle RXQ \cong \triangle SXT$.

Exs. 12–14

6–4 Overlapping Triangles

Pages 207–210

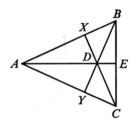

15. What side of $\triangle ADC$ would you have correspond to side $\overline{AD}$ of $\triangle ADB$?

16. What angle of $\triangle CYB$ would you have correspond to $\angle XCB$ of $\triangle BXC$?

17. $\overline{AY}$ in $\triangle ABY$ corresponds to __?__ in $\triangle ACX$.

18. Given: $AX = AY$; $XB = YC$.
    Prove: $AB = AC$.

19. Given: $AX = AY$; $AB = AC$.
    Prove: $\triangle ABY \cong \triangle ACX$.

6–5 Proving Corresponding Parts Congruent

Pages 211–214

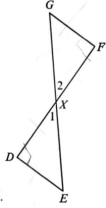

20. In statements about triangles, the word *parts* refer to both __?__ and __?__.

21. When two triangles are congruent, the number of pairs of congruent parts is __?__.

22. Given: $\overline{GX} \cong \overline{EX}$; $\angle F \cong \angle D$.
    Prove: $\overline{FX} \cong \overline{DX}$.

23. Given: $\overline{FX} \cong \overline{DX}$; $\angle F \cong \angle D$.
    Prove: $\overline{FG} \cong \overline{DE}$.

24. Given: $\overline{GF} \parallel \overline{DE}$; $FG = DE$.
    Prove: $XF = XD$.

25. Given: $\overline{GF} \perp \overline{FD}$; $\overline{ED} \perp \overline{DF}$; $\overline{DF}$ bisects $\overline{EG}$.
    Prove: $\overline{EG}$ bisects $\overline{DF}$.

6–6 Isosceles Triangles

Pages 214–220

26. This figure shows that two isosceles triangles can have the same base without being __?__.

27. This figure shows that isosceles triangles need not be congruent even though they have congruent __?__.

28. Given: $\overline{XZ} \cong \overline{YZ}$; $\overline{XW} \cong \overline{YW}$.
　　Prove: $\angle WXZ \cong \angle WYZ$.

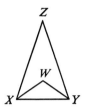

29. Given: $\overline{WX} \cong \overline{WY}$; $\angle WXZ \cong \angle WYZ$.
　　Prove: $\overline{XZ} \cong \overline{YZ}$.

● EXTRA FOR EXPERTS

An IBM 704 computer, programmed to prove theorems in Euclidean geometry, produced the following proof of the theorem: Base angles of an isosceles triangle are congruent. Actually, other mathematicians had known the proof for some time, and some inventive students had even discovered the proof for themselves. The argument is based upon a one-to-one correspondence in which point A corresponds to point A, M to T, and T to M.

Given:　A triangle with $MA = TA$.

To Prove:　$m\angle M = m\angle T$.

Analysis:　Prove $\triangle MAT \cong \triangle TAM$.

Proof

STATEMENT	REASON
1. $MA = TA$.	1. Given.
2. $TA = MA$.	2. Symmetric property of equality.
3. $TM = MT$.	3. Reflexive property of equality.
4. $\triangle MAT \cong \triangle TAM$.	4. SSS theorem.
5. $m\angle M = m\angle T$.	5. Corr. parts of $\cong$ ⧌ are $\cong$.

The following proof is another one "discovered" by the machine mentioned above. It is reprinted here by courtesy of Dr. H. L. Gelernter, who designed the computer program, and of the IBM Research Laboratory, where the work was performed. The machine was able to find the proof, which requires the construction of an auxiliary segment, in less than five minutes.

THEOREM In a quadrilateral with one pair of opposite sides equal and parallel, the other sides are equal.

```
**PREMISES**

QUAD-LATERAL ABCD
SEGMENT BC PARALLEL SEGMENT AD
SEGMENT BC EQUALS SEGMENT AD
```

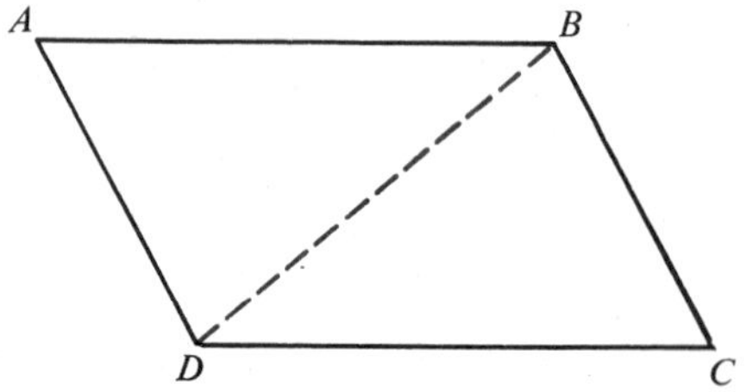

```
   **SYNTACTIC SYMMETRIES**

   ****        ****        ****
   CA          BA          DA
   DB          AB          CB
   AC          DC          BC
   BD          CD          AD
   ****        ****        ****


   **GOALS**

SEGMENT AB EQUALS SEGMENT CD


   I AM STUCK, ELAPSED TIME   0.88
****
CONSTRUCT SEGMENT DB
ADD PREMISE SEGMENT DB
RESTART PROBLEM


   **SOLUTION**

SEGMENT BC PARALLEL SEGMENT AD
         **PREMISE**
OPP-SIDE CADB
         **ASSUMPTION BASED ON DIAGRAM**
SEGMENT DB
         **PREMISE**
ANGLE ADB EQUALS ANGLE CBD
         **ALTERNATE-INTERIOR ANGLES OF PARALLEL LINES**
SEGMENT BC EQUALS SEGMENT AD
         **PREMISE**
SEGMENT BD EQUALS SEGMENT DB
         **IDENTITY**
TRIANGLE CDB
         **ASSUMPTION BASED ON DIAGRAM**
TRIANGLE ABD
         **ASSUMPTION BASED ON DIAGRAM**
TRIANGLE ABD CONGRUENT TRIANGLE CDB
         **SIDE-ANGLE-SIDE**
SEGMENT AB EQUALS SEGMENT CD
         **CORRESPONDING ELEMENTS OF CONGRUENT TRIANGLES**


   TOTAL ELAPSED TIME =  4.06
```

The machine has succeeded in finding proofs for a number of more complicated theorems, some of which the average high-school student would find difficult, or impossible, to prove.

▶ Archimedes

Is the number of grains of sand in the world finite or infinite? In *The Sand Reckoner* Archimedes showed that the number is finite. He also devised a system of numeration convenient for dealing with the large numbers in such questions. *The Sand Reckoner* reveals that some astronomers of Archimedes' time conceived of the universe with the sun in its center and the other planets, including the earth, revolving around it. This view was abandoned until the time of Copernicus, nearly 1800 years later.

Archimedes, the son of an astronomer, was born in Syracuse, Sicily, in 287 B.C. Some historians believe he was related to the King. After studying at the famous library in Alexandria, Egypt, he returned to Syracuse.

Although he was best known in his own time for many mechanical inventions, Archimedes looked upon mathematics as his real work. One of his achievements is a method for calculating a value for π, which he used to solve many problems involving areas of circles and volumes of cylinders. Some of Archimedes' methods are similar to those used in a branch of mathematics called calculus, which Newton and Leibniz developed in the eighteenth century. Archimedes discovered that levers could be used to move very heavy objects with a slight amount of effort and said, "Give me a place to stand and I will move the earth."

One well-known anecdote about Archimedes concerns a gold crown which was made for the King. The King suspected that some of the gold had been replaced with silver by the goldsmith and asked Archimedes to investigate. As Archimedes bathed, he discovered a way of using water to solve the problem. He immediately jumped up and ran through the streets of Syracuse shouting "Eureka, eureka!" ("I have found it, I have found it!")

When Syracuse was attacked by the Romans, catapults and other war machines designed by Archimedes were used to defend the city. The siege lasted three years, and the Romans finally entered the city in 212 B.C. Although the Roman commander gave orders not to harm Archimedes, a soldier killed him as he contemplated mathematical figures drawn in the sand. Legend has it that the soldier became incensed when Archimedes told him, "Don't step on my circles."

7

Applying
Congruent Triangles

The interior triangular design of these rectangular shapes etched on glass show the congruence of standardized, manufactured parts.

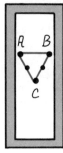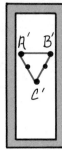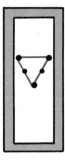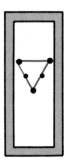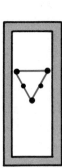

Perhaps you have heard some person make the statement: "A straight line is the shortest distance between two points." Technically, the statement is meaningless, for a line is a set of points and not a distance. You know what the person means, however. The shortest route from *P* to *Q* is along the line that passes through *P* and *Q*. In this chapter you will use postulates and theorems to prove such statements as: $PN + NQ > PQ$. First, however, you will prove some relationships between distances and angle measures that are associated with quadrilaterals.

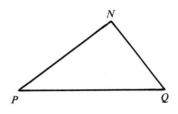

■ Quadrilaterals

7-1 Properties of Parallelograms

A **parallelogram** (□) is a quadrilateral in which both pairs of opposite sides are parallel. From this definition it follows that a parallelogram is a plane figure, for every quadrilateral is a polygon and the term polygon refers only to plane figures. Actually if, in the figure shown, you are given only the fact that $\overline{RS}$ and $\overline{QT}$ are parallel, you can prove that figure *RSTQ* is a plane figure. (How?)

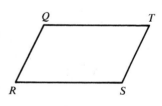

Here you see a four-sided figure that does not lie in a plane. Figure *ABCD* is a *skew quadrilateral*. A **skew quadrilateral** is a four-sided figure whose sides are not all contained in any one plane. A quadrilateral is a plane figure, while a skew quadrilateral is not.

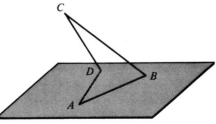

This book has so far used the term **distance** in just one sense: the distance between two points. The word is used in other senses, too.

231

The **distance between a point and a line** (or a plane) is the length of the perpendicular segment from the point to the line (or plane).

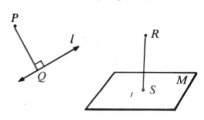

Here PQ is the distance between point P and line l, and, where $\overline{RS}$ is perpendicular to plane M, RS is the distance between point R and plane M. We shall prove later that $\overline{PQ}$ is the shortest segment joining point P to line l and that $\overline{RS}$ is the shortest segment joining point R to plane M.

In general, the **distance from a point to a figure** is the length of the shortest segment that can be drawn from the given point to any point of the figure. Here the distance from point P to circle O is PX, and the distance from point R to circle O is RZ.

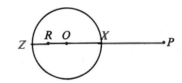

THEOREM 7–1   A diagonal of a parallelogram separates the parallelogram into two congruent triangles.

Given: $\square ABCD$ with diagonal $\overline{AC}$.

To Prove: $\triangle ABC \cong \triangle CDA$.

Analysis: Use parallel lines to prove angles congruent. Then use the ASA postulate.

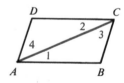

Proof

STATEMENT	REASON
1. $ABCD$ is a $\square$.	1. Given.
2. $\overline{AB} \parallel \overline{DC}$, and $\overline{BC} \parallel \overline{AD}$.	2. Definition of $\square$.
3. $\angle 1 \cong \angle 2$, and $\angle 3 \cong \angle 4$.	3. If 2 $\parallel$ lines __?__.
You are to complete the proof.	

COROLLARY 1   Opposite angles of a parallelogram are congruent.

COROLLARY 2   Opposite sides of a parallelogram are congruent.

COROLLARY 3   If two lines are parallel, all points of each line are equidistant from the other line.

Outline of Proof of Corollary 3:

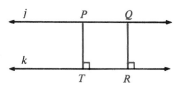

Let P and Q be any two points of j. $\overline{PT}$ and $\overline{QR}$ are parallel, and quadrilateral $PQRT$ is a parallelogram. $PT = QR$ by Corollary 2.

Corollary 3 is sometimes stated: Parallel lines are everywhere equidistant. Since the corollary shows that the number is unique, you can define the **distance between two parallel lines** to be the length of the perpendicular segment drawn from any point in one line to the other line.

THEOREM 7–2   The diagonals of a parallelogram bisect each other.

For a demonstration, see Written Exercise 2.

| ORAL
| EXERCISES

1. What characteristic does a quadrilateral have that a skew quadrilateral cannot have?

2. Is it possible for a skew quadrilateral to have four congruent sides?

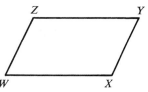

In Exercises 3 and 4 quadrilateral WXYZ is a parallelogram.

3. State the definition, postulate, theorem or corollary that supports the statement:

   a. $\overline{ZY} \parallel \overline{WX}$ **b.** $\overline{ZY} \cong \overline{WX}$ **c.** $\angle W \cong \angle Y$

4. What relation exists between $\angle W$ and $\angle X$? Between $\angle W$ and $\angle Z$?

In Exercises 5 and 6, quadrilateral ABCD is a parallelogram.

5. What reason can you give to support the assertion that $\angle 1 \cong \angle 2$? that $AK = CK$?

6. How many pairs of congruent triangles does the figure show?

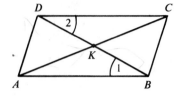

Exs. 5, 6

7. In the figure, line *l* in plane *M* contains points *A*, *B*, and *C*. $\overrightarrow{PA} \perp M$, and $\overline{AD} \perp \overline{DE}$. Name a segment whose length is equal to the distance from

   a. Point *P* to plane *M*.
                    c. Point *P* to $\overline{BC}$.

   b. Point *P* to line *l*.
                     d. Point *A* to $\overrightarrow{DE}$.

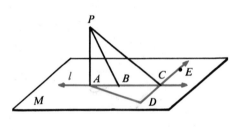

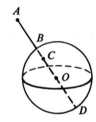

Ex. 7   Ex. 8

8. What represents the distance to sphere *O* from point *A*? from point *C*?

9. Suppose you know that $\overline{AB} \parallel \overline{CD}$ and that $\overline{AB} \cong \overline{CD}$. Draw $\overline{AC}$ and $\overline{BD}$ *in your mind.* State a theorem, not yet proved, beginning: If two sides of a quadrilateral are . . . .

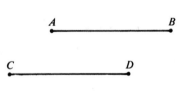

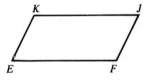

Ex. 9   Ex. 10

10. Suppose you know that $\overline{EF} \cong \overline{KJ}$ and that $\overline{EK} \cong \overline{FJ}$. The figure suggests that quadrilateral *EFJK* is a parallelogram. State a theorem, not yet proved, beginning: If both pairs of . . . .

WRITTEN
EXERCISES

A **1.** Write a demonstration of Theorem 7–1.
Hint: The diagonal is congruent to itself. Apply the ASA postulate.

2. Write a demonstration of Theorem 7–2.
Hint: Apply the ASA postulate to two triangles that have, as sides, the segments you wish to prove congruent.

In Exercises 3–6 quadrilateral *JKPQ* is a parallelogram with vertex *J* opposite vertex *P*.

3. Given: $m\angle J = 2x + 10$; $m\angle P = 3x - 20$. Determine the value of x.

4. Given: $m\angle Q = 5y$; $m\angle P = 2y + 19$.   Determine the value of y.

5. Express $m\angle K$ in terms of n, given: $m\angle J = 2n + 15$.

6. Given: $JK = x + 5$; $KP = 2x$; $PQ = y - 5$; $QJ = y$. Determine the numerical value of JK.

B **7.** Write a demonstration of Corollary 3 of Theorem 7–1.

8. Given: $\square RSTQ$; $\overline{XY}$ contains point O.
Prove: $\overline{XO} \cong \overline{YO}$.

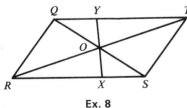   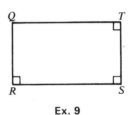

Ex. 8   Ex. 9

9. Given: $\angle R$, $\angle S$, and $\angle T$ are right angles.
Prove: Quadrilateral *RSTQ* is a parallelogram.

10. Given: Quadrilateral *ABCD* is a parallelogram;
Quadrilateral *ABJK* is a parallelogram.

Prove: $JK = CD$.

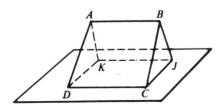

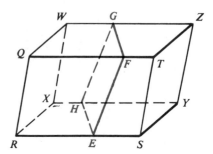

C **11.** Given: Plane $RT \parallel$ plane XZ;
Plane $RW \parallel$ plane SZ;
Plane $QZ \parallel$ plane RY;
Points E, F, G, and H
are coplanar.

Prove: $\angle FGH \cong \angle HEF$.

12. Prove: The sum of the lengths of the perpendicular segments drawn from any point in the base of an isosceles triangle to the legs is equal to the length of the altitude drawn to one of the legs.
Hint: Draw a perpendicular segment from the given point to the altitude.

7–2   Proving that Quadrilaterals are Parallelograms

One way to prove that a quadrilateral is a parallelogram is to show that the requirements of the definition are met, that is, to show that that both pairs of opposite sides are parallel. Two other methods were suggested by Oral Exercises 9 and 10 of Section 7–1.

THEOREM 7–3   If two sides of a quadrilateral are congruent and parallel, the quadrilateral is a parallelogram.

Given: $\overline{AB} \cong \overline{CD}$; $\overline{AB} \parallel \overline{CD}$.

To Prove: Quad. $ABCD$ is a $\square$.

Analysis: If a diagonal is drawn, the two triangles formed can be proved congruent. One pair of corresponding $\angle$ of these triangles can be used as alternate interior angles to prove that $\overline{AD}$ and $\overline{BC}$ are parallel. The proof is left for you.

THEOREM 7–4   If both pairs of opposite sides of a quadrilateral are congruent, the quadrilateral is a parallelogram.

To prove the theorem, you can draw a diagonal, show that two triangles are congruent, and use either Theorem 7–3 or the definition of parallelogram.

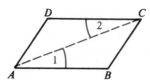

THEOREM 7–5 If the diagonals of a quadrilateral bisect each other, the quadrilateral is a parallelogram.

One way to prove the theorem is to prove that $\triangle AOB$ and $\triangle COD$ are congruent and then apply Theorem 7–3.

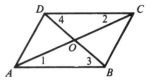

THEOREM 7–6 The segment joining the midpoints of two sides of a triangle is parallel to the third side and its length is half the length of the third side.

Given: $\overline{RM} \cong \overline{MT}; \overline{SX} \cong \overline{XT}.$

To Prove: $\overline{MX} \parallel \overline{RS}; MX = \frac{1}{2}RS.$

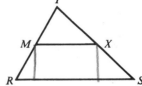

Outline of Proof:

Let Y be the point on $\overrightarrow{MX}$, with X between M and Y, such that $XY = MX$. Draw $\overline{YS}$.   Because $\triangle SXY \cong \triangle TXM$ (SAS), $\angle 1 \cong \angle 2$ and $YS = MT$.   But $MT = MR$. Then $YS = MR$. Also, since $\angle 1 \cong \angle 2$, $\overline{YS} \parallel \overline{MR}$.   Therefore, quad. $RSYM$ is a $\square$ and $\overline{MX} \parallel \overline{RS}$.   Since $MY = RS$ and $MX = \frac{1}{2}MY$, $MX = \frac{1}{2}RS$.

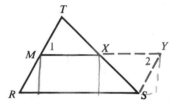

THEOREM 7–7 If three parallel lines cut off congruent segments on one transversal, they cut congruent segments on every transversal.

The theorem says that if lines h, j, and k are parallel, and if $\overline{AB}$ is congruent to $\overline{BC}$, then $\overline{A'B'}$ is congruent to $\overline{B'C'}$. For a proof see Exercises 17 and 18.

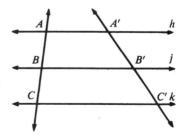

ORAL EXERCISES

State the definition, postulate, theorem, or corollary you would use to support the statement that quadrilateral *XYZW* is a parallelogram, given the information shown.

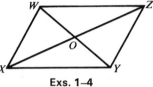

1. $\overline{XY} \parallel \overline{WZ}$; $\overline{XW} \parallel \overline{YZ}$.
2. $\overline{WO} \cong \overline{YO}$; $\overline{XO} \cong \overline{ZO}$.
3. $\overline{WZ} \cong \overline{XY}$; $\overline{XW} \cong \overline{YZ}$.
4. $\overline{WZ} \parallel \overline{XY}$; $\overline{WZ} \cong \overline{XY}$.

Exs. 1–4

In Exercises 5 and 6 it is given that points *X* and *Y* are the midpoints of $\overline{RS}$ and $\overline{RT}$.

5. State the length of $\overline{XY}$ if $ST = 8$. If $ST = 29$. If $ST = k$.

6. State the length of $\overline{ST}$ if $XY = 5$. If $XY = \frac{3}{7}$. If $XY = j$.

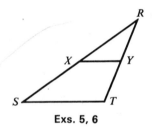

Exs. 5, 6

In the figure lines *h*, *j*, and *k* are parallel.

7. If $AB = BC = 4$ and $A'B' = 6$, then $B'C' = \underline{\ ?\ }$.

8. If $AB = BC = 10$, $A'B' = 12$, and $B'C' = 13$, can lines *h*, *j*, and *k* be parallel?

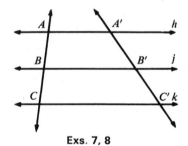

Exs. 7, 8

WRITTEN EXERCISES

A

1. Write a demonstration of Theorem 7–3.
2. Write a proof of Theorem 7–4 that does not use Theorem 7–3.
3. Write a proof of Theorem 7–4 that uses Theorem 7–3.
4. Write a demonstration of Theorem 7–5.

In Exercises 5–8, points X and Y are the midpoints of $\overline{RT}$ and $\overline{ST}$.

5. If $XY = 13\frac{6}{7}$, $RS = $ __?__. $27\frac{5}{7}$

6. If $RS = 3k + \frac{j}{2}$, then, expressed by a single fraction, $XY = $ __?__. $\frac{6k+j}{4}$

7. Suppose a line g is drawn through point Y and parallel to $\overline{RT}$. Describe the intersection of g and $\overline{RS}$.

8. Copy the figure shown. Where Z is the midpoint of $\overline{RS}$, draw $\overline{YZ}$.

   Given: $RT < RS$, compare YZ and XY.

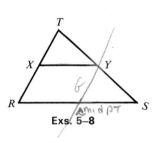

Exs. 5–8

B

9. Given: Points A, A', B, B' are coplanar;
   Plane $M \parallel$ Plane N;
   $\overline{AB} \cong \overline{A'B'}$
   Prove: Quad. $AA'B'B$ is a $\square$.

10. Given: $\overline{BC} \parallel \overline{B'C'}$;
    $\angle 1 \cong \angle 2$;
    Quad. $AA'B'B$ is a $\square$.
    Quad. $AA'C'C$ is a $\square$.
    Prove: Quad. $BB'C'C$ is a $\square$.

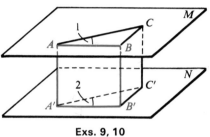

Exs. 9, 10

11. Given: $\square ABDC$; $\overline{CD} \parallel \overline{EF}$.
    Prove: Quad. $ABFE$ is a $\square$.

12. Given: $AC = BD$; $CE = DF$;
    $\overline{AE} \parallel \overline{BF}$.
    Prove: Quad. $ABFE$ is a $\square$.

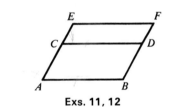

Exs. 11, 12

13. Given: $\square GHJK$; $\overrightarrow{KP}$ bisects $\angle GKJ$;
    $\overrightarrow{HQ}$ bisects $\angle JHG$.
    Prove: Quad. $KPHQ$ is a $\square$.

14. Given: $\square PHQK$; $\overline{GP} \cong \overline{GK}$;
    $m\angle GPK = t$;
    $m\angle HJL = 2t$.
    Prove: Quad. $GHJK$ is a $\square$.

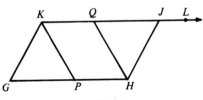

Exs. 13, 14

15. Prove: The figure formed by joining, in order, the midpoints of the sides of a quadrilateral is a parallelogram.
    Hint: Draw a diagonal of the quadrilateral.

16. Draw a lettered diagram and write a short paragraph to support the statement: A line that contains the midpoint of one side of a triangle and is parallel to a second side bisects the third side.

C **17.** Prove Theorem 7–7 for the case shown. *Hint:* Through A' and B' draw lines parallel to $\overleftrightarrow{AC}$. Show that quadrilaterals $ABXA'$ and $BCYB'$ are parallelograms. Use a property of parallelograms and the fact that $\overline{AB} \cong \overline{BC}$ to show that $\overline{A'X} \cong \overline{B'Y}$. Then prove that $\triangle A'XB'$ and $\triangle B'YC'$ are congruent.

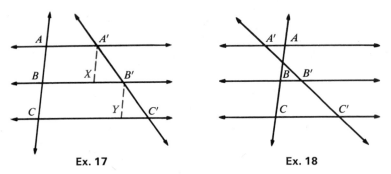

Ex. 17   Ex. 18

18. Prove Theorem 7–7 for the case shown. *Hint:* Try the same auxiliary segments as you used in Exercise 17.

19. Given: $\square XYZW$; $\overline{XA} \perp \overline{WY}$;
$\qquad \overline{ZB} \perp \overline{WY}$.
Prove: $\overline{XB} \cong \overline{ZA}$.

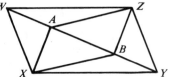

20. Assuming that the union of the segments that join the midpoints of the sides (taken in order) of a skew quadrilateral is a plane figure, prove that the union is a parallelogram.

7–3 Rectangles and Rhombuses

A **rectangle** (rect.) is a parallelogram with four right angles. Using this definition and facts about the congruence of angles in a parallelogram, you can deduce a statement that you may use as a theorem:

A parallelogram with one right angle is a rectangle. (See Oral Exercises 1 and 2.)

Do you observe something about the diagonals of a rectangle that could be expressed as a theorem?

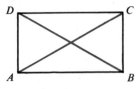

A **rhombus** is a parallelogram with four congruent sides. Using this definition and the fact that opposite sides of a parallelogram are congruent, you can deduce a statement that you may use as a theorem:

A parallelogram with two consecutive sides congruent is a rhombus.
(See Oral Exercises 3 and 4.)

Notice how effectively the figure in the middle, below, suggests some special properties of a rhombus. It suggests that the diagonals are perpendicular and that they bisect the angles of the rhombus.

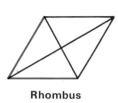   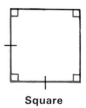

Rhombus   **Rhombus**   **Square**

A **square** (sq.) is a rectangle with two consecutive sides congruent. A square, being a rhombus as well as a rectangle, has all the special properties of both rhombuses and rectangles.

The proofs of three theorems are left for you. See Written Exercises 1, 2, and 3.

THEOREM 7–8   The diagonals of a rectangle are congruent.

THEOREM 7–9   The diagonals of a rhombus are perpendicular.

THEOREM 7–10   Each diagonal of a rhombus bisects two angles of the rhombus.

ORAL EXERCISES

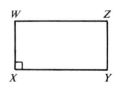

In the parallelogram shown, $\angle X$ is a right angle.

1. Explain why $\angle Z$ must be a right angle.

2. Explain why $\angle W$ and $\angle Y$ must be right angles.

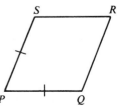

In the parallelogram shown, $\overline{PQ} \cong \overline{PS}$.

3. Why are $\overline{PQ}$ and $\overline{SR}$ congruent? $\overline{PS}$ and $\overline{SR}$?

4. Why are $\overline{PS}$ and $\overline{QR}$ congruent? $\overline{PQ}$ and $\overline{QR}$?

Quadrilateral *ABCD* is a square.

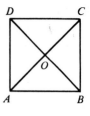

5. Is square *ABCD* a quadrilateral? Is it a parallelo-gram? A rhombus? A rectangle?

6. How many right angles does the figure show?

7. How many angles with measure 45 does the figure show?

8. What is the total number of triangles shown?

Exs. 5–8

9. State two properties of a rectangle that are not properties of all parallel-ograms.

Ex. 9

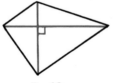

Ex. 10

10. State two properties of a rhombus that are not properties of all parallel-ograms.

11. Suppose the diagonals of a quadrilateral are congruent. Is the quadri-lateral necessarily a rectangle?

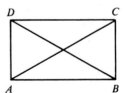

Ex. 11

Ex. 12

12. Suppose the diagonals of a quadrilateral are perpendicular. Is the quadrilateral necessarily a rhombus?

WRITTEN EXERCISES

Ａ   1. Prove Theorem 7–8.
   Hint: Show △*ABC* ≅ △*BAD*.

2. Prove Theorem 7–9.
   Hint: Show $\triangle RXQ \cong \triangle TXQ$. Use the congruence of $\angle 1$ and $\angle 2$ to establish perpendicularity.

3. Prove Theorem 7–10.
   Hint: Prove $\triangle RST \cong \triangle RQT$.

4. Draw a quadrilateral that is not a rectangle even though it has two opposite angles that are right angles.

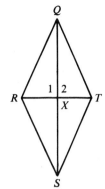

5. Prove: If the diagonals of a parallelogram are congruent, the parallelogram is a rectangle.

6. Prove: If the diagonals of a parallelogram are perpendicular, the parallelogram is a rhombus.

Exs. 2, 3

7. Prove: If a diagonal of a parallelogram bisects an angle of the parallelogram, the parallelogram is a rhombus.

8. Prove: If the four sides of a quadrilateral are congruent, the quadrilateral is a rhombus.

9. Prove: The quadrilateral formed by joining, in order, the midpoints of the sides of a rectangle is a rhombus.

10. Prove: The quadrilateral formed by joining, in order, the midpoints of the sides of a rhombus is a rectangle.

Indirect proofs are suggested for Exercises 11 and 12.

11. Prove: If a rectangle is not a square, a diagonal cannot bisect an angle of the rectangle.

12. Prove: If a rhombus is not a rectangle, its diagonals cannot be congruent.

13. Given: Square $RSTQ$; $RJ = SK = TL = QM = a$;
    $\qquad\qquad\quad JS = KT = LQ = MR = b$.

    Prove: Quad. *JKLM* is a square.

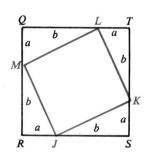

14. Given: $\overline{RS}$, $\overline{ST}$, $\overline{TR}$, $\overline{KR}$, $\overline{KS}$, and $\overline{KT}$ are congruent; Points W, X, Y, and Z are coplanar and are midpoints of $\overline{TR}$, $\overline{RS}$, $\overline{KS}$, and $\overline{KT}$.

Prove: Quad. $WXYZ$ is a square.

Ex. 14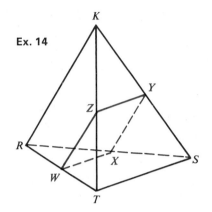

Exs. 15, 16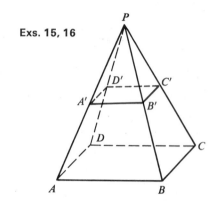

15. Given: The plane of quad. $A'B'C'D'$ is parallel to the plane of quad. $ABCD$; $BA = BC$; $PA = PC$.

Prove: $AA' = CC'$.

16. Given: Quad. $ABCD$ is a square; Points A', B', C', D' are coplanar; Points A', B', C', D' are the midpoints of $\overline{PA}$, $\overline{PB}$, $\overline{PC}$, and $\overline{PD}$.

Prove: Quad. $A'B'C'D'$ is a square.

7–4 Trapezoids

A **trapezoid** (trap.) is a quadrilateral with exactly two sides parallel. The parallel sides are **bases** and the other two sides are **legs.**

An **isosceles trapezoid** is a trapezoid with congruent legs.

The **median** of a trapezoid is the segment joining the midpoints of the legs.

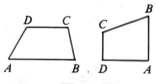

Bases: $\overline{AB}$ and $\overline{DC}$
Legs: $\overline{AD}$ and $\overline{BC}$

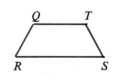

Isosceles Trapezoid
$\overline{RQ} \cong \overline{ST}$

Median
($\overline{XY}$ is a median.)

The median shown above appears to be parallel to the bases. Clearly the median is longer than one base and shorter than the other. A precise relationship is expressed in the following theorem.

THEOREM 7–11 The median of a trapezoid is parallel to the bases; it has a length equal to half the sum of the lengths of the bases.

Given: $\overline{DC} \parallel \overline{AB}$;
M is midpt. of $\overline{AD}$;
N is midpt. of $\overline{BC}$.

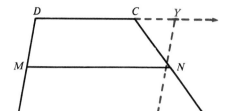

Prove:
(1) $\overleftrightarrow{MN} \parallel \overleftrightarrow{AB}$.
(2) $MN = \frac{1}{2}(AB + DC)$.

Outline of proof:
(1) Through N draw a line parallel to $\overline{AD}$. Let the intersections of that line with $\overleftrightarrow{DC}$ and $\overleftrightarrow{AB}$ be Y and X.
$\triangle BXN \cong \triangle CYN$ (ASA). Then $XN = YN$ and $XN = \frac{1}{2}XY$.
Quad. $AXYD$ is a $\square$, with $AD = XY$. Substituting AD for XY we get $XN = \frac{1}{2}AD = AM$. Since $\overline{XN}$ and $\overline{AM}$ are parallel and congruent, quad. $AXNM$ is a $\square$ and $\overline{MN} \parallel \overline{AB}$.

(2) $MN = AX = AB - XB$
$MN = DY = DC + CY$
$2MN = AB + DC + (CY - XB)$
$2MN = AB + DC + 0$
$MN = \frac{1}{2}(AB + DC)$

The proofs of the following two theorems are left for you. (Exercises 7 and 8, p. 247)

THEOREM 7–12 Base angles of an isosceles trapezoid are congruent.

THEOREM 7–13 The diagonals of an isosceles trapezoid are congruent.

It is now possible to show the various types of quadrilaterals in a Venn diagram.

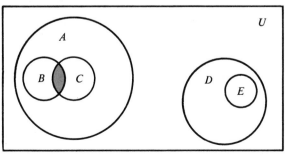

$U = \{$Quads.$\}$

$A = \{$parallelograms$\}$

$B = \{$rectangles$\}$

$C = \{$rhombuses$\}$

$D = \{$trapezoids$\}$

$E = \{$isos. trapezoids$\}$

Do you see that $B \cap C$ is the set of squares, and that $A \cap D = \emptyset$?

ORAL
EXERCISES

Quadrilateral ABCD is a trapezoid with median $\overline{MN}$.

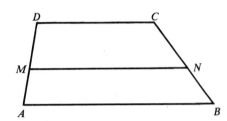

1. If $AB = 10$ and $DC = 6$,
   $MN = \underline{\quad?\quad}$.

2. If $AB = j$ and $DC = k$,
   $MN = \underline{\quad?\quad}$.

3. If $DC = 10$ and $MN = 13$,
   $AB = \underline{\quad?\quad}$.

4. If $MN = g$ and $AB = g + c$, $DC = \underline{\quad?\quad}$.

5. If $m\angle A = 80$ and $m\angle B = 50$, $m\angle D = \underline{\quad?\quad}$ and $m\angle C = \underline{\quad?\quad}$.

6. If $\overline{AD} \cong \overline{BC}$ and $m\angle A = k$, $m\angle B = \underline{\quad?\quad}$, $m\angle C = \underline{\quad?\quad}$, and $m\angle D = \underline{\quad?\quad}$.

WRITTEN
EXERCISES

A **1.** Draw a figure that shows clearly that a trapezoid can have two congruent sides, yet not be isosceles.

2. Draw a figure that shows clearly that a trapezoid can have two congruent angles, yet not be isosceles.

Quadrilateral RSTQ is a trapezoid with median $\overline{XY}$.

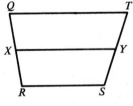

3. If $RS = 4.7$ and $TQ = 6.1$,
   $XY = \underline{\quad?\quad}$.

4. If $RS = n$ and $TQ = n + 6$,
   $XY = \underline{\quad?\quad}$ (in terms of n).

5. If $QT = n$ and $XY = j$, $RS = \underline{\quad?\quad}$
   (in terms of n and j).

6. If $XY = 2j + 5$ and $RS = 20 - j$, $TQ = \underline{\quad?\quad}$ (in terms of j).

7. Prove Theorem 7–12. *Hint:* Draw the auxiliary segments shown. Show that quad. *XYCD* is a ▱ and that $\overline{DX} \cong \overline{CY}$. Then use congruent triangles.

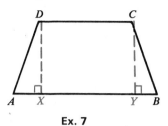

Ex. 7

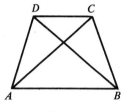

Ex. 8

8. Prove Theorem 7–13. *Hint:* Prove △*ABD* ≅ △*BAC*.

9. Prove: If points *R* and *S* are the midpoints of $\overline{PT}$ and $\overline{QT}$, then quad. *PQSR* is a trapezoid.

10. Using Exercise 9 explain in a sentence or two why trap. *PQSR* must be isosceles if △*RST* is isosceles.

B 11. Prove a converse of Theorem 7–12: If the base angles of a trapezoid are congruent, the trapezoid is isosceles.

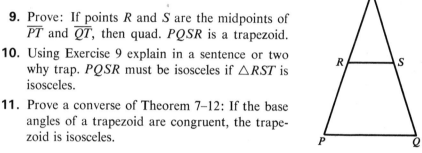

Exs. 9, 10

12. Prove a converse of Theorem 7–13: If diagonals of a trapezoid are congruent, the trapezoid is isosceles.

13. Prove: If trapezoid *ABCD* is isosceles, then △*AXB* is isosceles.

14. Prove: If △*DXC* is isosceles and $\overline{DC} \parallel \overline{AB}$, then quad. *ABCD* is an isosceles trapezoid.

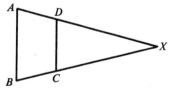

15. Prove: The quadrilateral formed by joining, in order, the midpoints of the sides of an isosceles trapezoid is a rhombus.

16. Prove: The diagonals of a trapezoid cannot bisect each other.
Hint: Use an indirect proof.

C 17. Given: $PX = \frac{1}{4}PB$;
$\quad\quad\quad PY = \frac{1}{4}PC.$

Prove: $XY = \frac{1}{4}BC.$

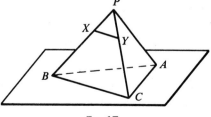

Ex. 17

18. Given: The square faces of the cube shown lie, in pairs, in parallel planes; a plane contains $\overline{AC}$ and the midpoints X and Y of $\overline{A'B'}$ and $\overline{B'C'}$.

   Prove: Quad. *ACYX* is an isosceles trapezoid.

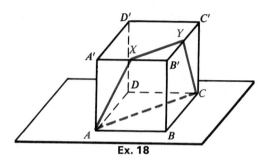

Ex. 18

■ Inequalities

7–5   Inequalities for One Triangle

The contrapositive of Theorem 6–5 is: If two sides of a triangle are not congruent, then the angles opposite those sides are not congruent. Since Theorem 6–5 has been proved, the contrapositive must be true. Applying the contrapositive to triangle *ABC*, we see that if $\overline{AC} \not\cong \overline{BC}$, then $\angle B \not\cong \angle A$. The figure suggests a more specific relationship, however.   It suggests that if $AC > BC$, then $m\angle B > m\angle A$. To prove this statement and other statements of inequality, we shall use the following algebraic theorem about real numbers *a*, *b*, *c*.

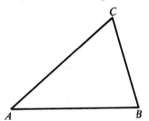

   If $a = b + c$, and *c* is a positive number, then $a > b$.

EXAMPLE 1. In the given figure prove: $RT > RS$.

Proof: $RT = RS + ST$ Betweenness property.

$\quad\quad\quad RT > RS$ If $a = b + c$ and *c* is a positive number, then $a > b$.

Here $a = RT$, $b = RS$, and $c = ST$. *ST*, a length, is a positive number.

   You should identify *a*, *b*, and *c* in Example 2 and check to see that *c* is a positive number.

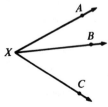

EXAMPLE 2. In the given figure, prove:
$\quad\quad m\angle AXC > m\angle BXC.$

Proof: $m\angle AXC = m\angle AXB + m\angle BXC$ Angle addition theorem.
             $m\angle AXC > m\angle BXC$ If $a = b + c$ and c is a
                                                  positive number, then
                                                  $a > b$.

In Example 2, $\angle AXC$ is **larger** than $\angle BXC$. Just as we call one segment **longer** than another when its length is greater, so we call one angle **larger** than another when its measure is greater.

THEOREM 7–14   If two sides of a triangle are not congruent, then the angles opposite those sides are not congruent and the angle opposite the longer side is the larger.

Given: $AC > BC$

To Prove: $m\angle B > m\angle A$

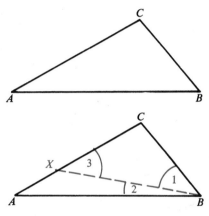

Analysis:

By taking pt. X on $\overrightarrow{CA}$ so that $CX = CB$, we can show $\angle 1 \cong \angle 3$. After showing $m\angle 3 > m\angle A$, we can show $m\angle 1 > m\angle A$. Since $m\angle ABC > m\angle 1$, we can reach the desired conclusion.

Proof

STATEMENT	REASON
1. On $\overrightarrow{CA}$ take point X so that $CX = CB$.	1. On a ray there is exactly one point at . . .
2. Draw $\overline{BX}$.	2. Through two . . .
3. $m\angle 1 = m\angle 3$.	3. If two sides of a $\triangle$ are . . .
4. $m\angle 3 = m\angle A + m\angle 2$.	4. The measure of an ext. . . .
5. $m\angle 3 > m\angle A$.	5. If $a = b + c$ and . . .
6. $m\angle 1 > m\angle A$.	6. Substitution principle.
7. $m\angle ABC = m\angle 1 + m\angle 2$.	7. Angle addition theorem.
8. $m\angle ABC > m\angle 1$.	8. If $a = b + c$ and . . .
9. $m\angle ABC > m\angle A$ or $m\angle B > m\angle A$.	9. Trans. prop. of inequality (Steps 6 and 8).

THEOREM 7–15   If two angles of a triangle are not congruent, then the sides opposite those angles are not congruent and the side opposite the larger angle is the longer side.

Given: $m\angle S > m\angle R$.

To Prove: $RT > ST$.

Analysis: Use an indirect proof, showing that neither of the statements
$$RT = ST, \qquad RT < ST$$
is correct.

Proof: Suppose $RT \not> ST$. Then either $RT = ST$ or $RT < ST$. But then either $m\angle S = m\angle R$ (base angles of an isosceles triangle) or $m\angle S < m\angle R$ (Theorem 7–14). Both of these statements contradict the given fact that $m\angle S > m\angle R$. Therefore, the assumed statement $RT \not> ST$ must be false, and it follows that $RT > ST$.

COROLLARY 1   The perpendicular segment from a point to a line is the shortest segment from the point to the line.

Since $\angle PTQ$ is an acute angle, $m\angle PTQ < m\angle PQT$. Then $PQ < PT$.

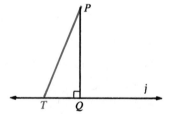

COROLLARY 2   The perpendicular segment from a point to a plane is the shortest segment from the point to the plane.

Where $\overline{RS}$ is the perpendicular segment and $\overline{RX}$ is any other segment from point R to plane M, draw $\overline{XS}$. $\overline{RS}$ must be $\perp$ to $\overline{SX}$, $\overline{RX}$ cannot be $\perp$ to $\overline{SX}$, and $RS < RX$.

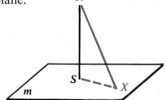

THEOREM 7–16 The sum of the lengths of any two sides of a triangle is greater than the length of the third side.

Given: $\triangle XYZ$

To Prove: $XZ + XY > ZY.$

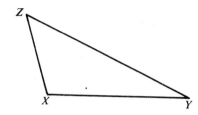

Analysis:

By locating point W as shown, with $XW = XZ$, you have
$$m\angle 2 = m\angle 1.$$
Since
$$m\angle 3 > m\angle 2,$$
$$m\angle 3 > m\angle 1.$$
Then $WY > ZY$, and
$$XW + XY > ZY.$$
Finally substitute XZ for XW.

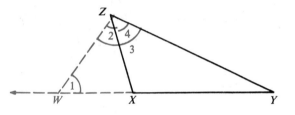

Proof

STATEMENT	REASON
1. On $\overrightarrow{YX}$ take point W, with X between Y and W, so that $XW = XZ$.	1. On a ray there is exactly one point at . . .
2. $m\angle 1 = m\angle 2.$	2. If two sides . . .
3. $m\angle 3 = m\angle 2 + m\angle 4.$	3. Angle addition theorem.
4. $m\angle 3 > m\angle 2.$	4. If $a = b + c$ and . . .
5. $m\angle 3 > m\angle 1.$	5. Substitution principle (Steps 2 and 4).
6. $WY > ZY.$	6. If two angles of one $\triangle$ are not . . .
7. $WY = WX + XY.$	7. Betweenness property.
8. $WX + XY > ZY.$	8. Substitution principle (Steps 6 and 7).
9. $XZ + XY > ZY.$	9. Substitution principle (Steps 1 and 8).

1. If $a = b + c$, and c is a positive number, then $a - b$ is a __?__ number.

2. If $a - b$ is a positive number, which of the following is correct?

$$a = b \qquad a > b \qquad a < b$$

3. State the largest angle in each triangle.

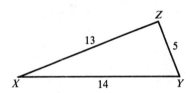 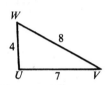 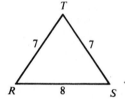

4. State the smallest angle in each triangle of Exercise 3.

5. State the longest side in each triangle.

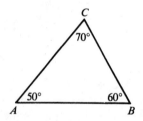 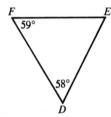 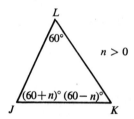

6. State the shortest side in each triangle of Exercise 5.

Which of the following could be used as the lengths of the sides of a triangle?
$(j > k > 0)$

7. 10, 11, 12

8. 3, 4, 5

9. 1, 2, 3

10. 7, 7, 13

11. $j, k, j + k$

12. $j, k, j - k$

13. $j, k, j + \frac{1}{2}k$

14. $j, k, j - \frac{1}{2}k$

15. If two sides of a triangle have lengths 3 and 7, then the length of the third side must be less than __?__.

16. If two sides of a triangle have lengths 4 and 6, then the length of the third side must be greater than __?__.

A **1.** The longest of the segments shown is __?__. The shortest is __?__.

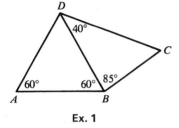

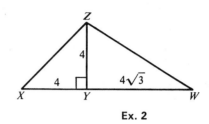

Ex. 1   **Ex. 2**

2. The largest acute angle shown is ∠__?__. The smallest is ∠__?__.

3. Given: $UV = ST$.
Prove: $RT > UV$.

4. Given: $m\angle 2 = m\angle 4$.
Prove: $m\angle 3 > m\angle 4$.

5. Prove: An exterior angle of a triangle is larger than each remote interior angle.
Hint: $m\angle 1 = m\angle 3 + m\angle 4$.

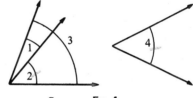

Ex. 4

6. Given: $TS > RS$.
Prove: $m\angle 1 > m\angle 2$.

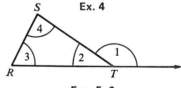

Exs. 5, 6

B **7.** Given: $JL = KL = 5$.
Prove: $LX < 5$.

8. Given: $AB > BD$;
$AC = CD$.

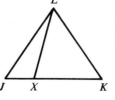

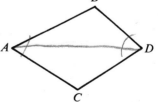

Prove: $m\angle D > m\angle A$.   **Ex. 7**   **Ex. 8**
Hint: Use an auxiliary segment, $\overline{AD}$.

9. Prove: The hypotenuse is the longest side of a right triangle.

10. Prove: If a triangle is isosceles, and the measure of the vertex angle is greater than 60, then the base of the triangle is longer than a leg.

11. Two sides of a triangle have lengths 10 and 15. Between what numbers does the length of the third side lie?

12. Each leg of an isosceles triangle has length 12. Between what numbers does the length of the base lie?

13. Three sides of a quadrilateral have lengths 5, 6, and 8. Between what values does the length of the fourth side lie?

14. Four sides of a pentagon have lengths 1, 2, 4, and 8. Between what values does the length of the fifth side lie?

C 15. Prove: The length of each median of a triangle is less than half the sum of the lengths of the sides.

16. Prove: The sum of the lengths of the altitudes of a triangle is less than the sum of the lengths of the sides.

17. Given: $XZ > YZ$;
   $\overrightarrow{XW}$ bisects $\angle ZXY$; $\overrightarrow{YW}$ bisects $\angle ZYX$.

   Prove: $XW > YW$.

18. Given: $XW > YW$;
   $\overrightarrow{XW}$ bisects $\angle ZXY$; $\overrightarrow{YW}$ bisects $\angle ZYX$.

   Prove: $XZ > YZ$.

19. Prove: The sum of the lengths of the two diagonals drawn from one vertex of a pentagon is less than the sum of the lengths of the five sides.

20. Prove: The sum of the lengths of any three sides of a quadrilateral is greater than the length of the fourth side.

21. Given: Segments of the plane figure have the lengths shown.

   Prove: $a + b + c > \frac{1}{2}(d + e + f)$

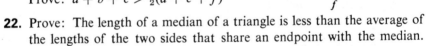

22. Prove: The length of a median of a triangle is less than the average of the lengths of the two sides that share an endpoint with the median.

7–6 Inequalities for Two Triangles

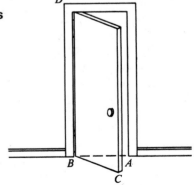

Here you see a partly open door. Open the door some more and these things happen: The dihedral angle becomes larger, $\angle ABC$ becomes larger, and the distance AC becomes greater. This physical situation suggests theorems that intuition tells you must be true. Yet the proofs are quite involved.

THEOREM 7–17 If two sides of one triangle are congruent to two sides of another triangle, but the included angle of the first triangle is larger than the included angle of the second, then the third side of the first triangle is longer than the third side of the second.

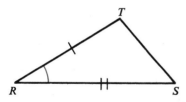

Given: $\overline{AC} \cong \overline{RT}$; $\overline{AB} \cong \overline{RS}$;
$\qquad m\angle A > m\angle R$.

To Prove: $BC > ST$.

Outline of proof:

Draw a ray $\overrightarrow{AZ}$ such that
$$\angle BAZ \cong \angle SRT.$$
On $\overrightarrow{AZ}$ take point X such that
$$AX = RT.$$

Case 1. If point X lies on $\overline{BC}$, we have
$CB = CX + XB$ and $CB > XB$.
But since
$\triangle ABX \cong \triangle RST$ (SAS), $ST = XB$.
Substituting, we have $CB > ST$.

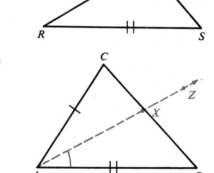

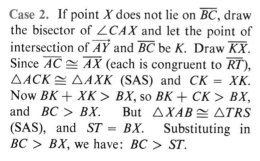

Case 2. If point X does not lie on $\overline{BC}$, draw the bisector of $\angle CAX$ and let the point of intersection of $\overrightarrow{AY}$ and $\overline{BC}$ be K. Draw $\overline{KX}$. Since $\overline{AC} \cong \overline{AX}$ (each is congruent to $\overline{RT}$), $\triangle ACK \cong \triangle AXK$ (SAS) and $CK = XK$. Now $BK + XK > BX$, so $BK + CK > BX$, and $BC > BX$. But $\triangle XAB \cong \triangle TRS$ (SAS), and $ST = BX$. Substituting in $BC > BX$, we have: $BC > ST$.

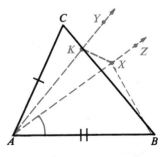

THEOREM 7–18   If two sides of one triangle are congruent to two sides of another triangle, but the third side of the first triangle is longer than the third side of the second, then the included angle of the first triangle is larger than the included angle of the second.

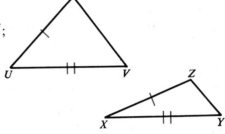

Given: $\overline{UW} \cong \overline{XZ}$; $\overline{UV} \cong \overline{XY}$;
$VW > YZ$.

To Prove: $m\angle U > m\angle X$

Outline of proof:

Suppose $m\angle U \not> m\angle X$. Then (1) $m\angle U = m\angle X$ or (2) $m\angle U < m\angle X$. If (1) is true, $\triangle UVW \cong XYZ$ (SAS) and $VW = YZ$.
If (2) is true, $VW < YZ$ (Theorem 7–17).
Since the assumption that $m\angle U \not> m\angle X$ leads to a contradiction of the given fact that $VW > YZ$, the assumed statement must be false, and it follows that $m\angle U > m\angle X$.

ORAL EXERCISES

Compare the sides of $\triangle I$ and $\triangle II$ that are shown in color. Is the length of the side in $\triangle I$ greater than, equal to, or less than the length of the side in $\triangle II$?

1.   **2.**

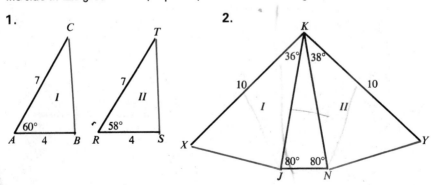

3.

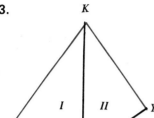

4.

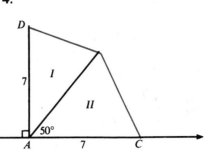

Compare the angles of △*I* and △*II* that are marked in color. Is the measure of the angle in △*I* greater than, equal to, or less than the measure of the angle in △*II*?

5.

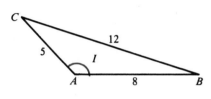

7.

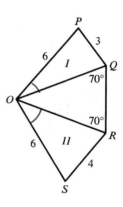

6.

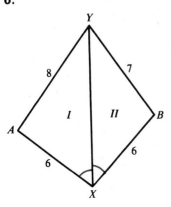

8.

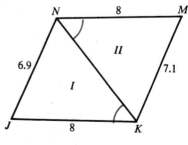

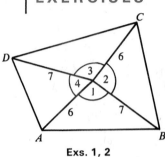

A   **1.** In the plane figure, $AB = 10$, $BC = 9$, $CD = 11$. Compare the measures of angles 1, 2, and 3.

2. In the plane figure $m\angle 1 = 100$, $m\angle 2 = 90$, $m\angle 3 = 102$. Compare the lengths AB, BC, CD and DA.

Exs. 1, 2

3. Given: $XP = XR$; $m\angle 1 > m\angle 2$.
    Prove: $PQ > RQ$.

4. Given: $PQ = RQ$; $PX < RX$.
    Prove: $m\angle 3 < m\angle 4$.

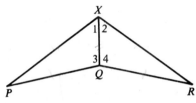

Exs. 3, 4

5. Given: $\triangle RST$ is an equilateral $\triangle$;
        $SQ = SR$; $m\angle 2 = 50$.
    Prove: $TQ < RT$.

6. Given: $SQ = TR$; $m\angle 3 > m\angle 2$.
    Prove: $RS > TQ$.

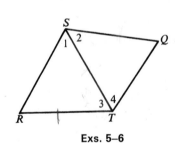

Exs. 5–6

B   **7.** Given: $AB = CB$; $m\angle 1 > 90$.
    Prove: $AD > DC$.

8. Given: $AB = DB = DC$.
    Prove: $AD > BC$.

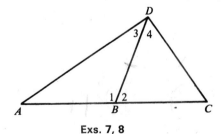

Exs. 7, 8

9. Given: $PD = PE = PF$;
   $m\angle DPE = m\angle DPF > m\angle EPF$.

Prove: $DE = DF > EF$.

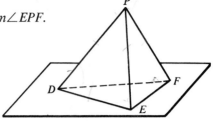

10. Given: $DP = DF$;
   $m\angle PDE < m\angle EDF$.

Prove: $PE < EF$.

Exs. 9, 10

11. Given: $WZ = XY$;
   Points X, Y, Z lie
   in M;
   $\overline{WZ} \perp M$;
   $\overline{YZ} \perp \overline{XZ}$.

Prove: $XW > YZ$.

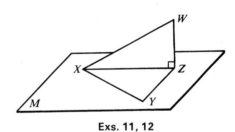

12. Given: Points X, Y, Z lie
   in M; $\overline{WZ} \perp M$;
   $\overline{XY} \perp \overline{ZY}$.

Prove: $XW > XY$.

Exs. 11, 12

13. Prove: The diagonal between the vertices of the smaller angles of a parallelogram is the longer diagonal.

14. Given: The square faces of the cube
   shown lie in parallel planes.

Prove: $\overline{A'C}$ is not perpendicular to
   $\overline{D'B}$.

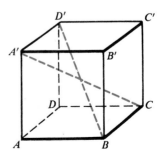

PRACTICAL APPLICATIONS

1. The parallel rulers shown are constructed with $AB = DC$ and $BC = AD$. Though the joints are such that $\overline{DC}$ can be moved with respect to $\overline{AB}$, $\overline{AB}$ is always parallel to $\overline{DC}$. Find a theorem in Section 7–2 which shows why $\overline{AB} \parallel \overline{DC}$.

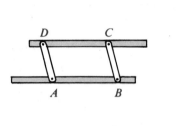

Ex. 1

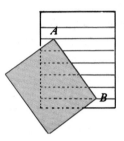

Ex. 2

2. You can use a sheet of lined notebook paper to divide a segment into a number of equal parts. Here a piece of cardboard with edge AB is placed so that $\overline{AB}$ is separated into five equal parts. Find a theorem in Section 7–2 which shows that the parts must be equal.

3. The gate shown is not rigid. A diagonal brace from A to B, bolted at four points, would strengthen the gate. How many triangles would then lend rigidity to the gate?

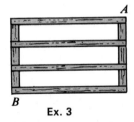

Ex. 3

Fold a piece of scrap paper with a little care and you get a good approximation of a line. Beginning with a piece of paper which need not have straight edges you can represent other figures, too.

4. Fold a piece of paper to form a right angle.
5. Draw $\overline{AB}$ on paper. Show, by folding, the perpendicular bisector of $\overline{AB}$.
6. Draw an angle COD. Find, by folding, the bisector of $\angle COD$.
7. Represent points P and Q by dots on a piece of paper. Find, by folding, point X such that $XP = XQ$.

CHAPTER SUMMARY

Inventory of Structure and Methods

1. In a parallelogram: opposite sides are congruent; opposite angles are congruent; diagonals bisect each other.

2. You can prove a quadrilateral is a parallelogram by showing: opposite sides are parallel; opposite sides are congruent; two sides are both congruent and parallel; diagonals bisect each other.

3. A segment joining the midpoints of two sides of a triangle is parallel to, and is half as long as, the third side. If parallel lines cut off congruent segments on one transversal, they cut off congruent segments on every transversal.

4. Rectangles, rhombuses, and squares have the properties of all parallelograms and special properties besides.

5. The median of a trapezoid is parallel to the bases; its length is half the sum of the lengths of the bases.

6. In triangle ABC, $AC > BC$ if and only if $m\angle B > m\angle A$. The sum of the lengths of any two sides is greater than the length of the third side.

7. In triangles ABC and $A'B'C'$ with $AB = A'B'$ and $AC = A'C'$, $BC > B'C'$ if and only if $m\angle A > m\angle A'$.

Vocabulary and Spelling

parallelogram (*p. 231*)
skew quadrilateral (*p. 231*)
distance between a point
  and line (or plane) (*p. 232*)
distance between parallel
  lines (*p. 233*)
rectangle (*p. 240*)

rhombus (*p. 240*)
square (*p. 241*)
trapezoid (*p. 244*)
median of trap. (*p. 244*)
isosceles trapezoid (*p. 244*)
longer segment (*p. 249*)
larger angle (*p. 249*)

CHAPTER TEST

7-1 **1.** Why is it impossible for a parallelogram to be a skew quadrilateral?

2. By definition, the opposite sides of a parallelogram are parallel. Name three additional properties of a parallelogram.

3. Given: $\overline{AC} \parallel \overline{DF} \parallel \overline{GK}$; $\overline{AG} \parallel \overline{BH} \parallel \overline{CK}$.
How many parallelograms are shown in the figure?

4. In parallelogram *ACKG*, $m\angle A = 2x - 23$ and $m\angle K = 3x - 81$. The value of x is __?__.

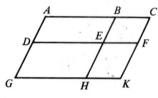

Exs. 3, 4

7-2 **5.** State three ways, not counting the definition, to prove that a quadrilateral is a parallelogram.

6. In triangle *RST*, *X* is the midpoint of $\overline{RT}$ and *Y* is the midpoint of $\overline{ST}$. How are lines $\overleftrightarrow{XY}$ and $\overleftrightarrow{RS}$ related?

7. Use the information given for Exercise 6. How are the lengths *XY* and *RS* related?

8. $\overline{AX} \parallel \overline{BY} \parallel \overline{CZ}$. Point *B* is the midpoint of $\overline{AC}$. $XZ = 14$. Then $XY = $ __?__.

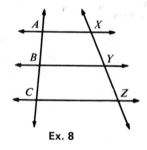

Ex. 8

7-3 Name the special kind of parallelogram for which it is true that

9. The diagonals are congruent, but not necessarily perpendicular.

10. The diagonals are perpendicular, but not necessarily congruent.

11. The diagonals are perpendicular bisectors of each other and are congruent.

12. A diagonal bisects an angle of the parallelogram, and that angle is not a right angle.

7-4 $\overline{EF}$ is the median of trapezoid *ABCD*, with point *E* on $\overline{AD}$.

13. If $CF = 6$, then $CB = $ __?__.

14. $EF = $ __?__. (Answer in terms of *AB* and *DC*.)

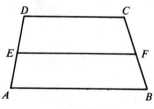

Exs. 13-16

15. Trapezoid *ABCD* is isosceles only if *CB* = ___?___.

16. If trapezoid *ABCD* is isosceles and $m\angle A = 99 - 2x$, and $m\angle C = 7x + 21$, then the value of *x* is ___?___.

7–5 For the given figure, RS = TS. State the reasons that support the following steps in a proof.

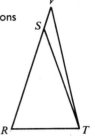

17. $m\angle VTR = m\angle STR + m\angle VTS$.

18. $m\angle VTR > m\angle STR$.

19. $m\angle STR = m\angle SRT$.

20. $m\angle VTR > m\angle SRT$.

21. $VR > VT$.

7–6 For the given figure, AM = MC and $m\angle 1 = 89$. Complete each statement below by writing "<", "=", or ">".

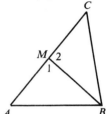

22. $m\angle 2$ ___?___ $m\angle 1$.

23. *CB* ___?___ *AB*.

24. $m\angle C$ ___?___ $m\angle A$.

CHAPTER REVIEW

7–1 **Properties of Parallelograms** *Pages 231–236*

Quadrilateral ABCD is a parallelogram.

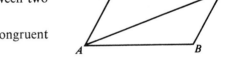

1. State a congruence between two triangles shown.

2. Name two pairs of congruent segments.

3. Name four pairs of congruent angles.

4. Suppose $AD = 5$. What can you say about the distance between $\overleftrightarrow{DC}$ and $\overleftrightarrow{AB}$?

7–2 **Proving that Quadrilaterals are Parallelograms** *Pages 236–240*

Given: $\overline{SR} \parallel \overline{PQ}$; *SR* = *PQ*. *Certain steps of the proof of the theorem that asserts that quadrilateral PQRS is a parallelogram are shown. State the reason that supports each step shown.*

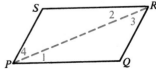

5. $\angle 1 \cong \angle 2$.

6. $\triangle PQR \cong \triangle RSP$.

7. $\angle 3 \cong \angle 4$.

8. $\overline{SP} \parallel \overline{RQ}$.

Exs. 5–8

9. Complete: The segment joining the midpoints of two sides of a triangle . . . .

10. Complete: If three parallel lines cut off congruent segments on . . . .

7–3 Rectangles and Rhombuses   *Pages 240–244*

Quadrilateral ABCD is a square.

11. Is the quadrilateral a parallelogram? A rectangle? A rhombus?

12. Every angle shown has measure __?__ or __?__.

13. Is the congruence a correct one?
$\triangle AXD \cong \triangle DXA$? $\triangle ABC \cong \triangle BDC$? $\triangle AXD \cong \triangle CXD$?

14. Can square *ABCD* be a skew quadrilateral?

7–4 Trapezoids   *Pages 244–248*

In quadrilateral RSTQ: $\overline{RQ} \parallel \overline{ST}$; $\overline{RS} \not\parallel \overline{QT}$.
Describe as true or false.

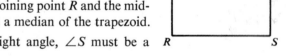

15. The legs of the trapezoid are $\overline{RQ}$ and $\overline{ST}$.

16. The segment joining point *R* and the midpoint of $\overline{ST}$ is a median of the trapezoid.

17. If $\angle R$ is a right angle, $\angle S$ must be a right angle.

18. If the trapezoid were isosceles, then $\angle S$ and $\angle T$ would be congruent angles.

7–5 Inequalities for One Triangle   *Pages 248–254*

19. If $a = b + c$ and c is a positive number, then a __?__ b. ($<, =, >$).

20. In triangle *XYZ*, $XZ > YZ$ if and only if $m\angle Y$ __?__.

21. If the lengths of two sides of a triangle are 17 and 22, then the length of the third side must be less than __?__ and greater than __?__.

22. Complete: The shortest segment from a point to a plane is __?__.

7–6 Inequalities for two triangles   *Pages 254–259*

23. Given: $JX = JY$
    $m\angle 1 > m\angle 2$.
    State the theorem that supports the deduction: $XK > YK$.

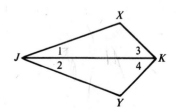

24. Given: $XK = YK$; $JX > JY$.
    State the theorem that supports the deduction: $m\angle 3 > m\angle 4$.

CUMULATIVE REVIEW: CHAPTERS 1–7

Completion Exercises

Write the correct word or set of words on your paper.

1. ∅ denotes the __?__ set, a set with __?__ elements.
2. The union of {1, 2, 3} and {2, 4} is __?__.
3. The intersection of {1, 2, 3} and {2, 4} is __?__.
4. Each element of set A is also an element of set B. Then A is a __?__ of B.
5. When to each element of set C there corresponds exactly one element of set D, and vice versa, sets C and D are said to be in __?__.
6. The distance between two points on the number line is __?__ of the difference of their __?__.
7. The sum of the measures of two supplementary angles is __?__.
8. A dihedral angle is the __?__ of two half-planes with the same __?__.
9. The midpoint of $\overline{CX}$ is R. Then $CR =$ __?__.
10. A rational number can be expressed as the __?__ of two __?__.
11. If the four sides of a quadrilateral are equal in length, the quadrilateral may be a square, but it must be a __?__.
12. A quadrilateral with exactly two parallel sides is called a __?__.
13. A radius which is perpendicular to a chord of a circle __?__ the chord.
14. The measure of each acute angle of an isosceles right triangle is __?__.
15. The longest possible chord in a certain circle has length 10. Then $r =$ __?__.
16. When two triangles are congruent, corresponding angles are __?__ and corresponding sides are __?__.
17. Two lines are said to be skew when __?__.
18. The sum of the measures of the exterior angles, one at each vertex, of an octagon is __?__.
19. Given $ax = ay$, we cannot deduce that $x = y$ unless it is known that __?__.
20. $|-5| - |2| =$ __?__.
21. The set of numbers between 0 and 180 inclusive is in one-to-one correspondence with the set of rays, in the union of a half-plane and its edge, with end point A in the edge of the half-plane. $\overrightarrow{AJ}$ corresponds to 30 and $\overrightarrow{AM}$ corresponds to 70. $\overrightarrow{AK}$, which bisects $\angle JAM$, corresponds to __?__.

22. When the statement p is true and the statement q is false, the compound statement $p \wedge q$ is __?__.

23. In the figure shown:
    Points T, R, and __?__ are collinear.
    Points S, T, B, and __?__ are coplanar.
    Points T, R, and A are __?__, but are not __?__.

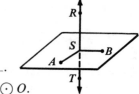

Ex. 23

24. $\overline{JK}$ is a chord of $\odot O$. Then $\overleftrightarrow{JK}$ is a __?__ of $\odot O$.

25. The SAS postulate is to be applied, and side $\overline{BC}$ and $\angle C$ of $\triangle ABC$ are to be used. The other side of $\triangle ABC$ needed is __?__.

26. The ASA postulate is to be applied, and $\angle ABD$ and $\angle DAB$ of $\triangle ABD$ are to be used. The side of $\triangle ABD$ needed is __?__.

27. The radius of circle P is 5. Point A lies in the interior. $AB = 11$. Point B must lie __?__.

28. One endpoint of a median of a triangle is a __?__ of the triangle, while the other endpoint is the __?__ of a side.

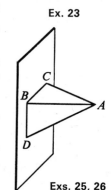

Exs. 25, 26

29. When the statements p and q are both true, the compound statement $p \vee q$ is __?__.

30. Two tangents to a circle from an outside point are __?__.

31. If $a < b$, then $a - c$ __?__ $b - c$.

B 32. Two distinct lines perpendicular to a third line may be __?__, __?__, or __?__.

33. Points X, O, and B are collinear. O lies on $\overrightarrow{XB}$. B does not lie on $\overrightarrow{OX}$. Then __?__ lies between __?__ and __?__.

34. Points R, S, and T are not collinear. The intersection of $\overrightarrow{RS}$ and $\overrightarrow{ST}$ is __?__.

35. Points X, Y, and Z are not collinear. The union of $\overrightarrow{XY}$ and $\overrightarrow{XZ}$ is __?__.

36. If the diagonals of a quadrilateral bisect each other and are not congruent, the quadrilateral must be a __?__ but cannot be a __?__.

37. If the diagonals of a quadrilateral are perpendicular bisectors of each other and are congruent, the quadrilateral must be a __?__.

38. M, the midpoint of $\overline{AB}$, corresponds to $6\frac{1}{3}$ on the number line. A corresponds to $8\frac{2}{3}$. B corresponds to __?__.

39. A correct negation of the statement: *All students like sports* is the statement: __?__ students do not like sports.

40. $\overline{AP}$, $\overline{BP}$, and $\overline{CP}$ are perpendicular to each other at P. $\overline{PD} \perp \overline{BC}$. Then $\overline{AD}$ __?__ $\overline{BC}$.

Always, Sometimes, or Never Exercises

Write A, S, or N on your paper to denote the correct choice.

1. An equilateral triangle is __?__ isosceles.
2. An angle __?__ has a complement.
3. A ray __?__ has two endpoints.
4. If n is a number, the $|n|$ is __?__ equal to n.
5. A subset of a nonempty set S __?__ contains all the elements of S.
6. $\overrightarrow{AB}$ is a side of an angle. B is __?__ the vertex of that angle.
7. The negation of a false statement is __?__ false.
8. Two triangles are __?__ congruent if two sides and an angle of one triangle are congruent to two sides and an angle of the other triangle.
9. An irrational number expressed in decimal form is __?__ non-ending.
10. The measure of an angle is __?__ equal to the measure of the supplement.
11. A square is __?__ a rectangle.
12. A right triangle is __?__ isosceles.
13. Two skew lines __?__ lie in one plane.
14. A conclusion based upon inductive thinking is __?__ a correct statement.
15. The complement of an acute angle is __?__ an obtuse angle.
16. $|a - b|$ is __?__ equal to $|b - a|$.
17. If the diagonals of a quadrilateral are perpendicular, the quadrilateral is __?__ a rhombus.
18. A segment __?__ has a length.
19. The diagonals of a rectangle __?__ bisect each other.
20. Two perpendicular lines are __?__ both parallel to a third line.
21. If $m\angle A < m\angle B$, then the measure of the supplement of $\angle A$ is __?__ less than the measure of the supplement of $\angle B$.
22. The diagonals of a skew quadrilateral __?__ intersect.
23. Two lines perpendicular to a third line are __?__ skew.
24. A conditional and its converse are __?__ both true.
25. The diagonals of a trapezoid are __?__ perpendicular.
26. The altitudes of an acute triangle __?__ intersect at a point in the exterior of the triangle.
27. If the compound statement $p \vee q$ is a true statement, then q is __?__ a true statement.
28. Lines, j, k, and m are perpendicular to each other at point P. When another line intersects both j and k, that other line is __?__ parallel to m.

In Exercises 29–32, line *m* is the edge of a half-plane. The half-plane contains points *A* and *B*.

29. $\overleftrightarrow{AB}$ ___?___ intersects *m*.

31. $\overrightarrow{AB}$ ___?___ intersects *m*.

30. $\overrightarrow{AB}$ ___?___ intersects *m*.

32. *A*, *B*, and *m* are ___?___ coplanar.

Multiple-Choice Exercises

Indicate the best answer by writing the appropriate letter.

1. The angle determined by $\overrightarrow{XZ}$ and $\overrightarrow{XY}$ is (**a**) $\angle RXZ$, (**b**) $\angle Y$, (**c**) $\angle Z$, (**d**) $\angle XYZ$, (**e**) none of these.

2. A point in the exterior of $\triangle XYZ$ is (**a**) *X*, (**b**) *Z*, (**c**) *Q*, (**d**) *R*, (**e**) none of these.

3. A point not on any angle shown is (**a**) *R*, (**b**) *Q*, (**c**) *T*, (**d**) *Z*, (**e**) none of these.

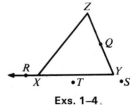

Exs. 1–4

4. The point that is interior to exactly two of the angles shown is (**a**) *S*, (**b**) *Q*, (**c**) *R*, (**d**) *T*, (**e**) none of these.

5. A figure that has *H* and *K* as end points is (**a**) *HK*, (**b**) $\overrightarrow{HK}$, (**c**) $\overleftrightarrow{HK}$, (**d**) $\overline{HK}$, (**e**) none of these.

6. The conjunction of statements *p* and *q* is (**a**) $p \rightarrow q$ (**b**) $p \vee q$ (**c**) $p \wedge q$ (**d**) $\sim p \wedge \sim q$ (**e**) none of these.

7. Two lines tangent to a sphere at the opposite ends of a diameter are (**a**) parallel, (**b**) perpendicular, (**c**) coplanar, (**d**) skew, (**e**) cannot tell from the information given.

8. No postulate or theorem in this geometry is abbreviated by (**a**) SSS, (**b**) SSA, (**c**) HL, (**d**) LA, (**e**) HA.

9. The contrapositive of the conditional $p \rightarrow q$ is (**a**) $\sim p \rightarrow q$ (**b**) $\sim q \rightarrow \sim p$ (**c**) $q \rightarrow p$ (**d**) $\sim p \rightarrow \sim q$ (**e**) $\sim q \rightarrow p$.

10. The number of diagonals in a hexagon is (**a**) 3, (**b**) 6, (**c**) 9, (**d**) $6 \cdot 5$, (**e**) $\dfrac{6 \cdot 5}{2}$.

11. When two circles are tangent externally, the number of possible common tangents in their plane is (**a**) 0, (**b**) 1, (**c**) 2, (**d**) 3, (**e**) 4.

12. At 1:15 the hands of a clock determine an angle whose measure is (**a**) 15, (**b**) 30, (**c**) 45, (**d**) 60, (**e**) none of these.

13. If point *Q* lies between points *P* and *R*, then (**a**) *R* lies on $\overrightarrow{QP}$, (**b**) *P* lies on $\overrightarrow{QR}$, (**c**) $PQ + PR = QR$, (**d**) $PQ = QR$, (**e**) *Q* lies on $\overrightarrow{PR}$.

14. The fact that corresponding parts of congruent triangles are congruent comes directly from a(n) (**a**) definition, (**b**) postulate, (**c**) theorem, (**d**) inductive argument, (**e**) none of these.

15. In acute triangle ABC, $m\angle A < m\angle B < m\angle C$. The shortest of the three altitudes of the triangle is the one containing (**a**) A, (**b**) B, (**c**) C, (**d**) cannot tell.

16. If $\triangle TOX \cong \triangle JNU$, then it is also true that (**a**) $\triangle XTO \cong \triangle UJN$, (**b**) $\triangle TXO \cong \triangle NJU$, (**c**) $\triangle XOT \cong \triangle UJN$, (**d**) $\triangle TOX \cong \triangle UNJ$, (**e**) $\triangle OTX \cong \triangle NUJ$.

17. The five planes which are the perpendicular bisectors of the five sides of a regular pentagon intersect in (**a**) a pyramid, (**b**) a point, (**c**) a line, (**d**) 5 points, (**e**) none of these.

18. The Law of Detachment can be stated:

   a. If q and $p \rightarrow q$ are both true, then p is true.
   b. If $p \lor q$ is true, then q is true.
   c. If p is true or $p \rightarrow q$ is true, then q is true.
   d. If p and $p \rightarrow q$ are both true, then q is true.
   e. If p and $q \rightarrow p$ are both true, then q is true.

19. The number of planes which can be passed tangent to a sphere from an outside point is, (**a**) 0, (**b**) 1, (**c**) 2, (**d**) 4, (**e**) infinitely great.

20. The converse of the inverse of the converse of the conditional $p \rightarrow q$ is: (**a**) $p \rightarrow \sim q$, (**b**) $q \rightarrow \sim p$, (**c**) $\sim p \rightarrow q$, (**d**) $\sim q \rightarrow p$, (**e**) none of these.

Algebraic Exercises

A

1. Two vertical angles have measures $3x$ and $x + 50$. Find x.

2. Alternate interior angles of parallel lines have measures x^2 and $7x$. Find x.

3. The measures of the exterior angles of a pentagon are in the ratio $1:2:3:4:5$. Find the measure of the largest exterior angle.

4. Two complementary angles have measures $4x$ and $6x - 20$. Find the measure of the smaller angle.

5. $x \in \{-3, -2, -1, 0, 1\}$ and $x^2 > 8$. Find x.

6. Two interior angles on one side of a transversal that cuts two parallel lines have measures $3x - 4$ and $[6 - (7 - 2x)]$. Find x.

7. The perimeter of an isosceles triangle is 47. The length of the base is 3 greater than one-fifth the length of a leg. Find the length of the base.

8. Each base angle of an isosceles triangle has a measure which is 20 more than three times the measure of the vertex angle. Find the measure of a base angle.

9. Express as a single fraction the measure of an angle whose complement has measure $\dfrac{k}{3}$.

10. The measures of two supplementary angles are in the ratio 5:7. Find the measure of the larger angle.

B 11. Two vertical angles have measures $3x$ and $x^2 - 28$. Find x.

12. Make a deduction about an angle whose measure is 5 greater than twice the measure of its complement.

13. An exterior angle of a triangle has measure $7x - 13$. The remote interior angles have measures $2x$ and $3x$. Find the measure of the largest of the three interior angles of the triangle.

14. The interior angles of a pentagon have measures in the ratio 4:5:5:5:8. Find the measure of the largest angle.

15. Two parallel lines are cut by a transversal. Corresponding angles have measures x^2 and $30 - x$. Find two values of x.

16. The measure of an exterior angle of a triangle lies between 100 and 120. The measure of a remote interior angle lies between 30 and 40. Between what values must the measure of the other remote interior angle lie?

17. Find the greatest number that belongs to $\{x: x^2 - 81 = 0\} \cup \{y: y^2 - 2y = 80\}$.

18. One angle of a quadrilateral has a measure which is twice that of a second angle and half that of a third angle. The fourth angle has measure 80. Find the measure of each angle.

19. The measure of one angle of a parallelogram is three-fourths that of another. Find the smaller angle correct to the nearest minute.

20. Express as a single fraction the measure of the third angle of a triangle in which two angles have measures $\dfrac{n}{2}$ and $\dfrac{t}{5}$ respectively.

True-False Exercises

Write + for a statement that is always true and 0 for a statement that is not always true.

A 1. In a regular polygon the sides must be congruent.

2. Through a point outside a line, infinitely many lines can be drawn parallel to the given line.

3. If point P lies between points J and K, then $PJ + JK = PK$.

4. A line parallel to the base of a triangle must bisect the other two sides.

5. Two planes tangent to a sphere at the ends of a diameter must be parallel.

6. When a plane is parallel to a line, every line in that plane is parallel to the original line.

 7. A nonempty set must contain more elements than each one of its subsets.

 8. The intersection of two sets must contain at least as many elements as one of the sets does.

 9. The union of two rays must be an angle.

10. If $\overrightarrow{AB}$ is a side of each of two angles, those angles must be adjacent.

B 11. A conditional and its contrapositive are equivalent statements.

12. Given that $xy > zy$, you can conclude that $x > z$.

13. If two planes are cut by a third plane so that the lines of intersection are parallel, then the two planes must be parallel.

14. A line and an outside point lie in exactly one plane.

15. Two planes can intersect in exactly one point.

16. If $|a| > 3$, then $2a > 6$.

17. The inverse of a true conditional must be true.

18. The angle bisectors of a scalene triangle meet at a point which is equidistant from the three vertices.

19. A line which is perpendicular to one of two perpendicular lines must be perpendicular to the other line also.

20. Each interior angle of a regular n-gon has measure $(n - 2)180$.

Miscellaneous Exercises

A 1. List all the subsets of $\{x, y\}$.

 2. A certain polygon has exactly five diagonals. How many sides does that polygon have?

 3. $\overrightarrow{OB}$ bisects $\angle AOC$, and $m\angle AOB = 25\frac{2}{3}$. Find $m\angle AOC$.

 4. The diagonals of a parallelogram are drawn. How many pairs of congruent triangles are formed?

 5. No three of a particular set of four points are collinear. How many lines are determined by pairs of those points?

 6. Four particular points are not coplanar and no three are collinear. How many planes are determined by triples of those points?

 7. Write the contrapositive of: *If p, then q.*

 8. The average of the measures of the exterior angles of a polygon is 36. How many sides does the polygon have?

 9. Write the inverse of: *If not-r, then s.*

10. Given: $p \lor q$ is false. What can you say about the truth of p and of q?

B 11. In $\triangle ABC$, $AB > BC$ and $m\angle B = 60$. What angle of $\triangle ABC$ has the greatest measure?

12. The lengths of two sides of a triangle are 20 and 25. Between what values does the length of the third side lie?

13. In $\triangle RST$, $m\angle R = 48$ and $m\angle S = 73$. Which side of $\triangle RST$ is the longest side?

14. Three sides of a quadrilateral have lengths 10, 12, and 14. Between what values must the length of the fourth side lie?

15. Points A, R, X, and Y are collinear in some order. $RX + XY = RY$, $YX + XA = YA$, and $RX > AX$. Find the order.

16. Let $U = \{$quadrilaterals$\}$. Draw a Venn diagram showing regions that represent $J = \{$parallelograms$\}$, $K = \{$rectangles$\}$, $M = \{$rhombuses$\}$.

17. A point lies on a sphere. That point is contained in how many radii? How many chords? How many tangent lines? How many tangent planes?

18. Use the roster method to show two sets whose intersection has exactly two elements and whose union has exactly six elements.

19. Write the converse of the inverse of the conditional: *If t, then q.*

20. In $\triangle RST$, point X is the midpoint of $\overline{ST}$ and $RT > RS$. Make a deduction about the measure of $\angle RXT$.

Proof Exercises

1. Given: $\overline{AC} \cong \overline{BC}$; $\angle 1 \cong \angle A$.
   Prove: $\angle 1 \cong \angle B$.

2. Given: $\angle 1 \cong \angle 2$; $\overline{DE} \parallel \overline{AB}$.
   Prove: $\angle A \cong \angle B$.

3. Given: $CD = CE$; $DA = EB$.
   Prove: $\triangle ABC$ is isosceles.

4. Given: $DC = EC$; $\angle 1 \cong \angle A$; $\angle 2 \cong \angle B$.
   Prove: $\triangle ABC$ is isosceles.

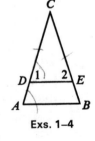

Exs. 1–4

5. Given: $\angle ATB \cong \angle CTB$; $\angle A \cong \angle C$.
   Prove: $\triangle ATB \cong \triangle CTB$.

6. Given: $\overline{BT} \perp \overline{AC}$; $\overline{AB} \cong \overline{CB}$;
   Prove: $\overline{AT} \cong \overline{CT}$.

7. Given: $\angle ATB \cong \angle CTB$; $\overline{AT} \cong \overline{CT}$;
   Points A, B, C are collinear.
   Prove: $\overline{TB} \perp \overline{AC}$.

8. Given: $\overline{AC} \perp$ plane M; $\overline{AB} \cong \overline{CB}$;
   $\overline{BT}$ lies in M.
   Prove: $\overline{AT} \cong \overline{CT}$.

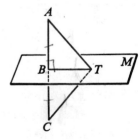

Exs. 5–8

9. Given: The plane figure shown.

Prove: $m\angle AOB + m\angle BOC + m\angle COD$
$= m\angle AOD.$

10. Given: The plane figure shown.

Prove: $m\angle AOC - m\angle BOC = m\angle AOB.$

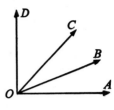

Exs. 9, 10

11. Given: $AR = XY;\ BT = XY;\ RY = TX;$
$m\angle R = m\angle T.$

Prove: $\triangle ARY \cong \triangle BTX.$

12. Given: $AX = BY;\ AR = BT;$
$m\angle A = m\angle B.$

Prove: $m\angle R = m\angle T.$

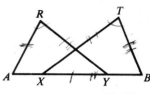

Exs. 11, 12

13. Given: $\overrightarrow{XA},\ \overrightarrow{XB},\ \overrightarrow{XC}$ are coplanar.

Prove: $m\angle AXC > m\angle AXB.$

14. Given: $\overrightarrow{XA},\ \overrightarrow{XB},\ \overrightarrow{XC}$ are coplanar;
$m\angle BXC = j.$

Prove: $m\angle AXC > j.$

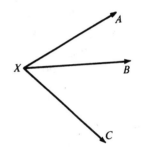

Exs. 13, 14

15. Given: $l \parallel m;\ a \parallel b.$

Prove: $\angle 4 \cong \angle 13.$

16. Given: $l \parallel m;\ \angle 10 \cong \angle 4.$

Prove: $a \parallel b.$

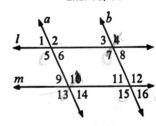

Exs. 15, 16

17. Given: $\overline{AX} \cong \overline{BX};\ \angle 1 \cong \angle 2;\ \overline{DC} \parallel \overline{AB}.$

Prove: $\angle A \cong \angle B.$

18. Given: $\angle ADC \cong \angle BCD;\ \overline{XD} \cong \overline{XC};$
$\overline{DC} \parallel \overline{AB}.$

Prove: $\overline{AX} \cong \overline{BX}.$

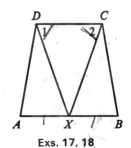

Exs. 17, 18

19. Given: $\overline{AB} \parallel \overline{DC}$; $\overline{DX} \parallel \overline{YB}$; $AB = CD$.

Prove: $AY = CX$.

20. Given: $\overline{AB} \parallel \overline{DC}$; $\overline{AD} \parallel \overline{BC}$; $AX = CY$.

Prove: $DX = BY$.

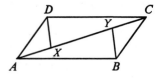

Exs. 19, 20

21. Given: $\overline{AX} \perp \overline{XY}$; $\overline{BY} \perp \overline{XY}$;
$\overline{XM} \cong \overline{YM}$; $\overline{AX} \cong \overline{BY}$.

Prove: $\angle 3 \cong \angle 4$.

22. Given: $\overline{AX} \perp \overline{XY}$; $\overline{BY} \perp \overline{XY}$;
$\overline{XM} \cong \overline{YM}$; $\angle 1 \cong \angle 2$;
$\angle 3 \cong \angle 4$.

Prove: $\overline{AR} \cong \overline{BS}$.

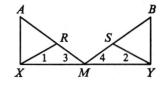

Exs. 21, 22

C **23.** Given: Square $ABCD$;
$\overline{AX} \perp \overline{BY}$.

Prove: $\overline{AX} \cong \overline{BY}$.

24. Given: Rhombus $ABCD$;
$\overline{AX} \cong \overline{BY}$; $\overline{XC} \cong \overline{YD}$.

Prove: Quad. $ABCD$ is a square.

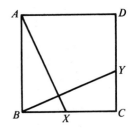

Exs. 23, 24

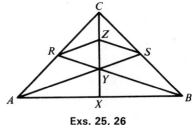

25. Given: $AX = BX$; $AY = BY$.

Prove: $RZ = SZ$.

26. Given: $\overline{RC} \cong \overline{SC}$; $\overline{RZ} \cong \overline{SZ}$.

Prove: $\angle XAY \cong \angle XBY$.

Exs. 25, 26

27. Given: $\overline{RS}$ and $\overline{JK}$ bisect each other at point X; $\overline{RK}$ and $\overline{JZ}$ bisect each other at point M.

Prove: $\overline{ZK}$ lies on $\overleftrightarrow{KS}$.

28. A line is parallel to a plane. Prove that a line drawn perpendicular to the plane from a point in the original line is perpendicular to the original line.

▶ A 20th Century Mathematician

The present century has produced several outstanding mathematicians both in America and abroad. Their names are seldom mentioned in high-school texts since their research has been in mathematical areas not taught at the high-school level. However, some of their contributions to mathematics have been most significant.

George D. Birkhoff (1884–1944), a Harvard professor, was one of the leading mathematicians of the first half of the present century. He is today recognized for his contributions in several areas of mathematics: point-set theory, differential equations, dynamics, ergodic theory, and relativity.

In the early thirties, Professor Birkhoff became vitally concerned with both the content and approach to high-school geometry. In 1932 he proposed a set of postulates for plane geometry based on ruler and protractor. He later became the co-author of a text for high schools, *Basic Geometry*. His postulates, designed to correct shortcomings of the traditional Euclidean postulates, have become increasingly popular and have been adopted, in part, in this text.

While studying the mathematical principles of dynamics, Professor Birkhoff established his celebrated ergodic theorem. This asserts, for example, that a billiard ball, moving under ideal conditions for an unlimited period of time, tends to lie in any given area of the table a definite proportion of the time. This theorem has important applications in the problems of celestial mechanics.

Perhaps some day you will have an opportunity to study in the areas of mathematics to which Professor Birkhoff contributed so much. There is no guarantee that such study will make you a billiard expert, but it will convince you that not all great mathematicians lived centuries ago.

8

Similar Polygons

Each snowflake differs from the others, but each reveals a pattern based on a regular hexagon. All regular hexagons are similar to each other.

In everyday life you learn to recognize objects more on the basis of their shapes than on the basis of their actual sizes. All of you could glance at a photograph of your school building and readily recognize the building because of its familiar shape. While many of you have never actually seen the White House in Washington, you could quickly identify it from a distance on a first visit to Washington because you are acquainted with its characteristics as shown in pictures. No doubt some of you are adept at naming types of airplanes passing overhead on the basis of their similarity to scale models you have collected.

This chapter will be concerned with a study of the properties of geometric figures having the same shape but not necessarily the same size. Many of these properties are used daily in industries where models and scale drawings play key roles. Conclusions about a proposed product can be reached at a considerable saving in both time and money on the basis of experimentation with small scale models.

■ Some Principles of Algebra

8–1   Ratio and Proportion

In your previous work in algebra you were introduced to the terms "ratio" and "proportion." Since these terms will be used extensively in the study of similar figures, you should refresh your memory of their meaning.

Finding the ratio of one number to another is a method of comparing those two numbers by division. Thus, if a and b are numbers and $b \neq 0$, **the ratio of a to b is the number** $\dfrac{a}{b}$. Keep in mind that you cannot find the ratio of one object to another. You can find the ratio of two numbers that are measures, in terms of the same unit, of the objects. A ratio is a number!

EXAMPLE 1. If $\overline{AB}$ is 15 in. long and $\overline{CD}$ is 2 ft. long, find the ratio of AB to CD.

Solution: $\dfrac{AB}{CD} = \dfrac{15}{24} = \dfrac{5}{8}$. (*Inch* is the common unit.)

EXAMPLE 2. If $\angle A$ has measure 20 and $\angle B$ is a right angle, find the ratio of $m\angle A$ to $m\angle B$.

Solution: $\dfrac{m\angle A}{m\angle B} = \dfrac{20}{90} = \dfrac{2}{9}$. (*Degree* is the common unit.)

EXAMPLE 3. Find the ratio of 3 gal. to 7 yd.

Solution: Since these measures cannot be expressed in terms of a common unit, you cannot write a ratio.

The ratio of a to b is often written in the form $a:b$. This form has an advantage; it can be used to express the comparison between three or more numbers. The statement that three numbers are in the ratio $2:3:5$ means that the ratio of the first to the second is 2 to 3, the second to the third is 3 to 5, and the first to the third is 2 to 5. It does **not** mean that the numbers must be 2, 3, and 5. The following sets of numbers all have the ratio $2:3:5$.

24, 36, 60	(12 is a common factor.)
$2x, 3x, 5x \ (x \neq 0)$	(x is a common factor.)
$8k^2, 12k^2, 20k^2 \ (k \neq 0)$	($4k^2$ is a common factor.)

For nonzero numbers a, b, c, d, an equation written in the form $\dfrac{a}{b} = \dfrac{c}{d}$, or $a:b = c:d$, is called a **proportion.**

The proportion $\dfrac{a}{b} = \dfrac{c}{d}$ tells you that the ratio of a to b equals the ratio of c to d. It can be read either "a is to b as c is to d" or "the quotient of a and b equals the quotient of c and d."

Each of the numbers a, b, c, d in the proportion $\dfrac{a}{b} = \dfrac{c}{d}$ is called a **term** of the proportion: a is the **first term,** b is the **second term,** c is the **third term,** and d is the **fourth term.**

The fact that more than two ratios are equal is often expressed in the form of an **extended proportion:**

$\dfrac{a}{b} = \dfrac{c}{d} = \dfrac{e}{f} = \dfrac{g}{h}$ states that all four ratios are the same number.

Since a proportion is an equation, properties of equality can be used to transform a proportion. For example, the proportion $\dfrac{a}{b} = \dfrac{c}{d}$ can be transformed into the equivalent equation $ad = bc$ by using the *multiplication property of equality* (multiply each member by bd).

1. State the ratio of x to y in simplest form when:

   a. $x = 4$ and $y = 6$ **c.** $x = 3a$ and $y = 5a$ ($a \neq 0$)

   b. $x = 10$ and $y = 26$ **d.** $x = 5a^2$ and $y = 20a^2$ ($a \neq 0$)

2. When the numerator and denominator of a fraction are multiplied by the same nonzero number, is the new ratio equal to the given ratio? if the numerator and denominator are divided by the same number?

3. When the same number is added to the numerator and denominator of a fraction, is the new ratio equal to the given ratio? if the same number is subtracted from numerator and denominator?

4. The ratio of the lengths of two segments measured in inches is $3:5$. What is the ratio of their lengths when measured in feet?

5. Given $AB = 8$ in. and $AC = 2$ in. State the value of the following ratios.

   a. $AC:CB$ **c.** $CB:AC$ **e.** $CB:AB$

   b. $AC:AB$ **d.** $AB:AC$ **f.** $AB:CB$

6. Which of the following are correct statements?

   a. $\dfrac{2}{5} = \dfrac{4}{10}$ **b.** $\dfrac{4}{7} = \dfrac{3}{5}$ **c.** $\dfrac{2x}{3y} = \dfrac{4x}{6y}$ ($y \neq 0$)

7. On the given line segment, X is located so that $\dfrac{AX}{XB} = \dfrac{4}{3}$. State the following

   ratios: **a.** $AX:AB$ **c.** $XB:AX$ **e.** If $AX = 12$, find XB.

               b. $XB:AB$ **d.** $AB:XB$ **f.** If $XB = 15$, find AX.

A

1. Express in simplest fractional form the ratio $r : t$ when:

   a. $r = 6$ and $t = 15$ **d.** $r = 3$ days and $t = 2$ wk.

   b. $r = 4x$ and $t = 10x$ $(x \neq 0)$ **e.** $r = 5$ ft. and $t = 2$ yd.

   c. $r = 2$ in. and $t = 2$ ft.   **f.** $r = 1$ degree and $t = 40$ min.

2. Point X is located on $\overline{CD}$ so that $CD = 12$ in. and $CX = 4$ in. Find the following ratios:

   a. $CX:XD$ **c.** $CD:XD$ **e.** $XD:CX$

   b. $CX:CD$ **d.** $CD:CX$ **f.** $XD:CD$

3. Determine the following ratios:

   a. The measure of a right angle to the measure of a 120° angle.

   b. The perimeter of a square to the length of one of its sides.

   c. The sum of the measures of the angles of a triangle to the sum of the measures of the angles of a quadrilateral.

   d. The measure of the complement of an angle with measure 40 to the measure of the supplement of the same angle.

4. Which of the following are true statements?

   a. $\dfrac{3}{5} = \dfrac{6}{10}$
   b. $\dfrac{5}{7} = \dfrac{7}{10}$
   c. $\dfrac{2}{3} = \dfrac{2^2}{3^2}$
   d. $\dfrac{1^{\frac{1}{2}}}{2^2} = \dfrac{1}{4}$

EXAMPLE. Find the value of x: $\dfrac{5}{3} = \dfrac{4}{x}$.

Solution: $3x\left(\dfrac{5}{3}\right) = 3x\left(\dfrac{4}{x}\right)$ (multiplication property of equality)

$\qquad\qquad 5x = 12$ (simplifying each member)

$\qquad\qquad\ \ x = \tfrac{12}{5}$

Check: $\dfrac{5}{3} \overset{?}{=} \dfrac{4}{\frac{12}{5}}$ $\dfrac{5}{3} \overset{?}{=} \dfrac{20}{12}$ $\dfrac{5}{3} = \dfrac{5}{3}$ ✔ $\dfrac{12}{5}$, **Answer.**

5. Find the value of x in each of the following proportions:

   a. $\dfrac{x}{2} = \dfrac{5}{3}$
   b. $\dfrac{4}{x} = \dfrac{2}{5}$
   c. $\dfrac{3}{2} = \dfrac{x}{4}$
   d. $\dfrac{x+1}{x+2} = \dfrac{2}{3}$

6. Find the ratio of r to s if $s \neq 0$ and

   a. $2r = 3s$
   b. $5r = 7s$
   c. $\dfrac{r}{3} = \dfrac{s}{2}$
   d. $2r - 3s = 0$

EXAMPLE. Two complementary angles have measures in the ratio 4:5. Find the measure of each angle.

Solution: Let $4x =$ the measure of the smaller angle,

$\qquad\qquad\ \ 5x =$ the measure of the larger angle.

$\qquad\qquad\ \ \overline{9x = 90}$

$\qquad\qquad\ \ \ x = 10.$ Therefore, $4x = 40$ and $5x = 50.$ **Answer.**

Check: 40 and 50 are in the ratio 4 to 5 and their sum is 90.

7. Two complementary angles have measures in the ratio 1:5. Find the measure of each angle.

8. The ratio of the measures of two supplementary angles is 3:7. Find the measure of each angle.

9. The angles of a triangle have measures in the ratio 1:2:3. Find the measure of each angle.

10. A 30-inch segment is divided into two parts whose lengths have the ratio 3 to 5. Find the length of each segment.

11. The perimeter of a triangle is 48 in. and the lengths of the sides have the ratio 3:4:5. Find the length of each side.

12. A triangle with perimeter 18 in. has one 8-inch side. Find the lengths of the remaining two sides if their ratio is 2:3.

13. Express each of the following ratios in lowest terms. No denominator is zero.

a. $\dfrac{2x - 6y}{x^2 - 9y^2}$ b. $\dfrac{6x^2 - 7x - 3}{2x^2 + x - 6}$ c. $\dfrac{x^3 - 8}{2x - 4}$

14. Find the ratio of x to y given that:

a. $\dfrac{x - y}{x + y} = \dfrac{2}{3}$ b. $\dfrac{1}{x - 2y} = \dfrac{3}{x + y}$ c. $\begin{array}{l}2x - y = 7 \\ x + 2y = 11\end{array}$

8–2 Properties of Proportions

You will frequently find it necessary to transform a proportion into some equivalent equation. Although you can do this by applying basic properties of equality, you can save steps by using special properties of proportions. In the following statements, zero is not included in the replacement set of any variable.

1. $\dfrac{a}{b} = \dfrac{c}{d}$ and $ad = bc$ **are equivalent.**

To get one equation from the other multiply (or divide) each member by bd.

2. $\dfrac{a}{b} = \dfrac{c}{d}, \dfrac{a}{c} = \dfrac{b}{d}, \dfrac{b}{a} = \dfrac{d}{c}, \dfrac{c}{a} = \dfrac{d}{b}$ **are equivalent.**

Each is equivalent to the equation $ad = bc$.

3. $\dfrac{a}{b} = \dfrac{c}{d}$ **is equivalent to** $\dfrac{a + b}{b} = \dfrac{c + d}{d}$.

If $\dfrac{a}{b} = \dfrac{c}{d}, \dfrac{a}{b} + 1 = \dfrac{c}{d} + 1, \dfrac{a}{b} + \dfrac{b}{b} = \dfrac{c}{d} + \dfrac{d}{d}$, and $\dfrac{a + b}{b} = \dfrac{c + d}{d}$.

4. $\dfrac{a}{b} = \dfrac{c}{d}$ **is equivalent to** $\dfrac{a - b}{b} = \dfrac{c - d}{d}$.

Use subtraction instead of addition in the steps supporting number 3.

5. If $\dfrac{a}{b} = \dfrac{c}{d} = \dfrac{e}{f} = \dots$, **then** $\dfrac{a + c + e + \dots}{b + d + f + \dots} = \dfrac{a}{b} = \dfrac{c}{d} = \dots$

Let r be the number each ratio represents. (See page 281.)

Then
$$\frac{a}{b} = r \qquad \frac{c}{d} = r \qquad \frac{e}{f} = r$$

and
$$a = br \qquad c = dr \qquad e = fr$$

Therefore
$$\frac{a + c + e + \cdots}{b + d + f + \cdots} = \frac{br + dr + fr + \cdots}{b + d + f + \cdots}$$
$$= \frac{(b + d + f + \cdots)r}{b + d + f + \cdots}$$
$$= r, \quad \text{or} \quad \frac{a}{b}, \quad \text{or} \quad \frac{c}{d}, \quad \cdots$$

Each of the proportion properties is, of course, an algebraic property. When you use any one of them in a proof, a satisfactory reason to use is *A property of proportions.*

ORAL EXERCISES

In the following exercises zero is not included in the replacement set of any variable.

1. Given: $rs = xy$.

    a. State two proportions each having r as the first term.

    b. State two proportions each having y as the first term.

2. State the ratio of x to y if:

    a. $3x = 4y$ **b.** $7x = 5y$ **c.** $x = 3y$ **d.** $3y = 2x$

Complete each statement:

3. If $\dfrac{x}{2} = \dfrac{y}{3}$, then $\dfrac{x + 2}{2} = \dfrac{y + 3}{?}$.

4. If $\dfrac{x + 1}{3} = \dfrac{y}{5}$, then $5(x + 1) = \underline{\ ?\ }$.

5. If $\dfrac{p}{q} = \dfrac{r}{s} = \dfrac{2}{3}$, then $\dfrac{p + r + 2}{q + s + 3} = \dfrac{?}{?}$.

6. If $\dfrac{x}{4} = \dfrac{y}{3}$, then $\dfrac{x}{y} = \dfrac{?}{?}$.

7. If $\dfrac{a}{b} = \dfrac{7}{3}$, then $\dfrac{a - b}{b} = \dfrac{4}{?}$.

8. If $5j = 6k$, then $\dfrac{j}{k} = \dfrac{?}{?}$

    and $\dfrac{?}{k} = \dfrac{?}{j}$.

In Exercises 9–12, $\dfrac{CX}{XA} = \dfrac{CY}{YB}$.

Complete each statement.

9. $\dfrac{XA}{CX} = \dfrac{?}{?}$.

10. $\dfrac{CX + XA}{XA} = \dfrac{?}{YB}$.

11. $\dfrac{CX}{CY} = \dfrac{XA}{?}$.

12. $\dfrac{XA}{YB} = \dfrac{CX}{?}$.

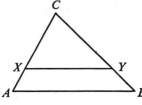

In the following exercises zero is not included in the replacement set of any variable.

A

1. Given: $xy = pq$. Form a proportion in which

 a. x is the first term. **c.** p is the first term.

 b. x is the second term. **d.** p is the last term.

2. Find the value of x in each proportion.

 a. $\dfrac{x}{6} = \dfrac{1}{2}$ **b.** $\dfrac{9}{x} = \dfrac{3}{5}$ **c.** $3:5 = x:4$ **d.** $12:x = 3:2$

3. Determine the values of x and y.

 a. $\dfrac{2}{x} = \dfrac{5}{y} = \dfrac{3}{5}$ **b.** $\dfrac{2}{x} = \dfrac{y}{8} = \dfrac{1}{4}$

4. The numbers, listed in order, are the first three terms of a proportion. Find the fourth term.

 a. 2, 3, 4 **b.** 6, 2, 8 **c.** $\frac{1}{2}, \frac{2}{3}, \frac{3}{4}$ **d.** $2a, 3b, 5a$

5. Given $\dfrac{CX}{XA} = \dfrac{CY}{YB}$ in $\triangle ABC$. In each row below, certain lengths are given. Find the length asked for in each exercise.

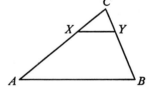

	CX	XA	CY	YB
a.	3	4	6	?
b.	5	4	?	6
c.	2	?	3	5
d.	?	4	4	8

6. Given $\dfrac{SX}{XT} = \dfrac{SR}{TR}$ in $\triangle RST$. Complete the indicated proportions.

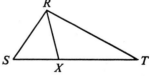

 a. $\dfrac{SX}{SR} = \dfrac{?}{?}$.   **c.** $\dfrac{TR}{XT} = \dfrac{?}{?}$.

 b. $\dfrac{SX + XT}{XT} = \dfrac{?}{?}$. **d.** $\dfrac{TR}{SR} = \dfrac{?}{?}$.

B

7. Find the value of x in each proportion.

 a. $\dfrac{x+1}{4} = \dfrac{2}{3}$ **b.** $\dfrac{x-2}{3} = \dfrac{x}{4}$ **c.** $\dfrac{x}{4} = \dfrac{9}{x}$ **d.** $\dfrac{x-3}{1} = \dfrac{7}{x+3}$

EXAMPLE. Find the ratio of a to b if $5a - 2b = 3a + 5b$.

Solution: $2a = 7b$ (addition and subtraction properties of equality)

   $\dfrac{a}{b} = \dfrac{7}{2}$, **Answer.** (a property of proportions)

8. Find the ratio of a to b.

a. $\dfrac{a}{3} = \dfrac{b}{2}$

c. $\dfrac{a+b}{a-b} = \dfrac{5}{2}$

b. $2a - 3b = 4b - 3a$

d. $2a - 3b = 0$

In Exs. 9 and 10, what is the ratio x:y?

9. $\dfrac{2a}{b} = \dfrac{c}{x}$ and $\dfrac{a}{b} = \dfrac{c}{y}$

10. $\dfrac{3a}{2b} = \dfrac{6}{x}$ and $\dfrac{y}{c} = \dfrac{b}{a}$

11. For what values of x is the expression $\dfrac{8}{x^2 - 2x - 3}$ not defined?

12. What positive value of x satisfies the proportion $\dfrac{x-1}{3} = \dfrac{2}{x-2}$?

■ What Similarity Means

8–3 Similar Polygons

Pictured are two scale drawings of the same plot of ground. The drawings differ in size but are alike in shape. Note that corresponding angles have equal measures but that each segment in drawing B is twice as long as the corresponding segment in drawing A. The second drawing can be described as an enlargement of the first. In fact, similar plane figures have the characteristic that it is possible to make an enlarged picture of the smaller that will be congruent to the larger.

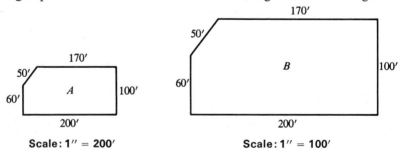

Scale: 1″ = 200′   Scale: 1″ = 100′

To get an idea of what similarity means for solid figures think about blowing up a toy balloon: the size changes, but the shape does not. Whenever two three-dimensional figures are such that the smaller can be blown up (mentally) until it is congruent to the larger, the original figures are said to be similar.

While there are certain like-
nesses between the two cylinders
pictured, they are *not* similar
solids. It would not be possible
to "blow up" the one with the
smaller height without enlarging
its top and bottom as well.

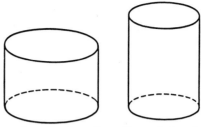

Thus far, similar figures have been described rather than defined.
A definition of similar polygons involves the terms **correspondence**,
corresponding angles, and **corresponding sides**.

Consider two *n*-gons, one with vertices A,
B, C, D, ... and the other with vertices P, Q,
R, S, ... A one-to-one correspondence can
be set up between the n vertices of one polygon and the n vertices of the other polygon.
One such correspondence pairs vertices A and
P, B and Q, C and R, D and S, ... Then,
pairs of **corresponding angles** are $\angle A$ and
$\angle P$, $\angle B$ and $\angle Q$, $\angle C$ and $\angle R$, $\angle D$ and
$\angle S$, ... Pairs of **corresponding sides** are
$\overline{AB}$ and $\overline{PQ}$, $\overline{BC}$ and $\overline{QR}$, $\overline{CD}$ and $\overline{RS}$, ...

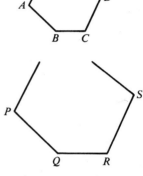

Now an exact definition can be given. If a correspondence between
the vertices of two convex polygons is such that the *measures of corresponding angles are equal* and *the lengths of corresponding sides are in
proportion*, then the correspondence is called a **similarity between the
polygons**.

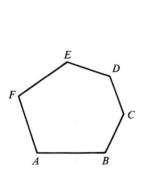

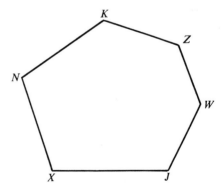

To show what parts of two polygons correspond to each other, first
write in order the letters that name the vertices of one polygon, say
hexagon *ABCDEF*. Then you state a correspondence by writing the

letters of the second hexagon so that

> *X*, the vertex corresponding to *A*, is named first,
> *J*, the vertex corresponding to *B*, is named second,
> *W*, the vertex corresponding to *C*, is named third,
> *Z*, the vertex corresponding to *D*, is named fourth,
> *K*, the vertex corresponding to *E*, is named fifth,
> *N*, the vertex corresponding to *F*, is named sixth.

You indicate the correspondence by writing

$$\text{Hexagon } ABCDEF \leftrightarrow \text{hexagon } XJWZKN$$

If this particular correspondence is a similarity you write

$$\text{Hexagon } ABCDEF \sim \text{hexagon } XJWZKN$$

and say that **hexagon *ABCDEF* is similar to hexagon *XJWZKN*** or that hexagons *ABCDEF* and *XJWZKN* are **similar hexagons.**

Notice how much information the notation "hexagon *ABCDEF* ∼ hexagon *XJWZKN*" gives. From it you see first that there is a particular correspondence between the vertices of the two hexagons. Then you see that

$$\angle A \cong \angle X, \qquad \angle B \cong \angle J, \qquad \angle C \cong \angle W$$
$$\angle D \cong \angle Z, \qquad \angle E \cong \angle K, \qquad \angle F \cong \angle N$$

and that

$$\frac{AB}{XJ} = \frac{BC}{JW} = \frac{CD}{WZ} = \frac{DE}{ZK} = \frac{EF}{KN} = \frac{FA}{NX}.$$

The figures below show that two polygons can have congruent angles without being similar polygons. Furthermore, two polygons can have sides with proportional lengths and still not be similar figures.

When the corresponding angles of two polygons are congruent, it does not follow that the lengths of the corresponding sides must be in proportion.

When the lengths of the corresponding sides of two polygons are in proportion, it does not follow that the corresponding angles must be congruent.

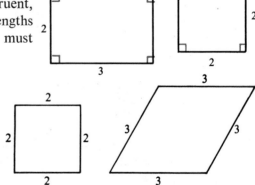

The first theorem about similarity is very much like a theorem about congruence (Theorem 6–1).

THEOREM 8–1 Similarity of convex polygons is reflexive, symmetric, and transitive.

Transitive Part

Given: Polygon $ABC \ldots \sim$ Polygon $RST \ldots$;
Polygon $RST \ldots \sim$ Polygon $XYZ \ldots$.

To Prove: Polygon $ABC \ldots \sim$ Polygon $XYZ \ldots$

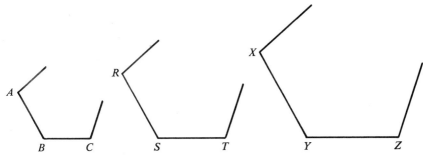

Analysis: Use the facts that corresponding angles of similar polygons are congruent and that congruence of angles is transitive to establish the congruence of angles that is needed. Use the fact that lengths of corresponding sides of similar polygons are in proportion and properties of proportions and of equality to establish the proportions needed.

Proof

STATEMENT	REASON
1. $\angle A \cong \angle R$; $\angle R \cong \angle X$.	1. Corr. $\angle$ of $\sim$ polygons are $\cong$.
2. $\angle A \cong \angle X$.	2. Congruence of $\angle$ is transitive.
3. $\dfrac{AB}{RS} = \dfrac{BC}{ST}$; $\dfrac{RS}{XY} = \dfrac{ST}{YZ}$.	3. Lengths of corr. sides of $\sim$ polygons are in proportion.
4. $\dfrac{AB}{BC} = \dfrac{RS}{ST}$; $\dfrac{RS}{ST} = \dfrac{XY}{YZ}$.	4. A property of proportions.
5. $\dfrac{AB}{BC} = \dfrac{XY}{YZ}$.	5. Transitive property of equality.
6. Polygon $ABC \ldots \sim$ Polygon $XYZ \ldots$	6. Two polygons are $\sim$ if corr. $\angle$ are $\cong$ and lengths of corr. sides are in proportion.

Proofs of the other two parts of the theorem are left for you. (Exercises 23 and 24.)

Recalling that the **perimeter of a polygon** is the sum of the lengths of its sides, consider the two similar quadrilaterals *ABCD* and *RSTU* pictured below.

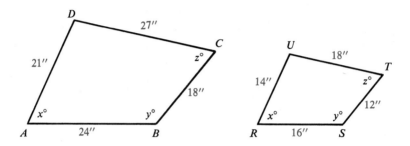

What is the ratio of the length of a side of *ABCD* to the length of the corresponding side of *RSTU*? What is the ratio of the perimeter of *ABCD* to the perimeter of *RSTU*? In this pair of quadrilaterals, how is the ratio of the perimeters related to the ratio of the lengths of any pair of corresponding sides?

THEOREM 8–2   If two polygons are similar, the ratio of their perimeters equals the ratio of the lengths of any pair of corresponding sides.

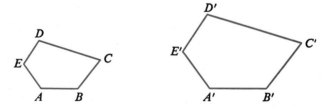

Given: Polygon *ABCDE* ~ polygon *A'B'C'D'E'*, with perimeters p and p' respectively.

To Prove: $\dfrac{p}{p'} = \dfrac{AB}{A'B'}$.

Analysis: Write a series of equal ratios based on similarity. Then use a property of proportions.

Proof

STATEMENT	REASON
1. $ABCDE \sim A'B'C'D'E'$.	1. Given.
2. $\dfrac{AB}{A'B'} = \dfrac{BC}{B'C'} = \dfrac{CD}{C'D'} = \cdots$.	2. Lengths of corr. sides of $\sim$ polygons are in proportion.
3. $\dfrac{AB + BC + CD + \cdots}{A'B' + B'C' + C'D' \cdots} = \dfrac{AB}{A'B'}$	3. A property of proportions.
4. $\dfrac{p}{p'} = \dfrac{AB}{A'B'}$.	4. Substitution principle.

ORAL EXERCISES

1. Must any two squares be similar? any two rectangles?

2. Must any two equilateral triangles be similar? any two isosceles triangles?

3. If two triangles are congruent, are they also similar? What is the ratio of the lengths of two corresponding sides?

4. If two similar convex polygons have sides with lengths in the ratio 1:1, what word might you reasonably use to describe the polygons?

5. Suggest a definition of congruent polygons.

6. The dimensions of one rectangle are 4 in. and 6 in. A second rectangle has dimensions of 6 in. and 9 in. Are the rectangles similar?

7. What is the ratio of the measures of two corresponding angles of two similar convex polygons?

8. What is the ratio of the perimeters of two squares which have sides t inches and k inches long respectively?

9. Must two rhombuses be similar if one angle of the first is congruent to one angle of the second?

10. Are two regular polygons with the same number of sides similar?

11. If two convex polygons are similar, must they be regular polygons?

12. The sum of the perimeters of two similar convex polygons is 18 in. The ratio of the lengths of two corresponding sides is 1:2. State the perimeter of each polygon.

> # WRITTEN
> # EXERCISES

The polygons in the exercises are all convex polygons.

EXAMPLE. The sides of a polygon are 2, 3, 4, 5, and 6 in. long. Find the perimeter of a similar polygon whose longest side is 15 in. long.

Solution: Let p = perimeter of the larger polygon, in inches.

1st polygon: perimeter is 20 in., length of longest side is 6 in.
2nd polygon: perimeter is p in.; length of longest side is 15 in.

Therefore: $\dfrac{20}{p} = \dfrac{6}{15}$ or $\begin{aligned} 6p &= 300 \\ p &= 50 \text{ in.} \end{aligned}$ **Answer.**

$$Check: \frac{20}{50} \stackrel{?}{=} \frac{6}{15} \qquad \frac{2}{5} = \frac{2}{5} \checkmark$$

A

1. The sides of the smaller of two similar triangles are 3, 4, and 5 cm. long. The shortest side of the larger triangle is 9 cm. long. Find the lengths of the remaining two sides of the larger triangle.

2. The smaller of two similar rectangles has dimensions 4 in. and 6 in. Find the dimensions of the larger rectangle if the ratio of the lengths of a pair of corresponding sides of the rectangles is 2 to 5.

3. The perimeters of two similar polygons are 20 in. and 28 in. One side of the smaller polygon is 4 in. long. Find the length of the corresponding side of the larger polygon.

4. Given two similar polygons. One pair of corresponding sides has lengths 12 in. and 15 in. The perimeter of the smaller polygon is 30 in. Find the perimeter of the larger polygon.

5. If polygon A is similar to polygon B, and polygon B is similar to polygon C, must polygon A be similar to polygon C?

6. If two polygons with the same number of sides are not similar, can you conclude that the corresponding angles are not congruent?

7. The sides of a polygon are 3, 5, 6, 8, and 10 in. long. The perimeter of a similar polygon is 40 in. Find the lengths of the sides of the second polygon.

8. The sides of a quadrilateral are 3, 5, 4, and 6 in. long. The shortest side of a similar quadrilateral is 9 in. long. Find the lengths of the sides of the larger quadrilateral.

9. A rectangular-shaped snapshot has dimensions $2\frac{1}{2}$ in. and $1\frac{1}{2}$ in. It is to be enlarged so that the longer dimension will be 10 in. What will the perimeter of the enlarged picture be?

10. A rectangular plot of ground 30 ft. by 80 ft. is represented on a map, with a scale of $\frac{1}{4}$ of an inch to the foot. What are the dimensions of the drawing?

11. Given quadrilateral *ABCD* ~ quadrilateral *RSTU*. Find the following measures.

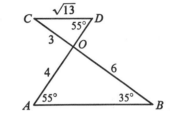

  a. *UT* = ? DC
  b. *UR* = ? DA
  c. *BC* = ? ST
  d. *m∠R* = ? A   80°

12. Given △*AOB* ~ △*DOC*. Find the following measures.

  a. *m∠C* = ?
  b. *OD* = ?
  c. *AB* = ?
  d. *m∠AOB* = ?

13. The base of an isosceles triangle is 8 in. long and one of the congruent sides is 10 in. long. Find the lengths of the sides of a similar triangle whose shortest side is 12 in. long.

14. The sides of a polygon are 4, 5, 8, 10, and 12 in. long respectively. Find the lengths of the sides of a similar polygon whose longest side is 15 in. long.

Given △*ABC* ~ △*XYC*.

15. If *BY* = 4, *YC* = 7, *XC* = 10, then *AC* = ?

16. If *BY* = 6, *YC* = 10, *AX* = 3, then *XC* = ?

17. If *BY* = 5, *BC* = 20, *AC* = 18, then *XC* = ?

18. If *YC* = 4, *BC* = 6, *XY* = 5, then *AB* = ?

Given similar rectangles *ABCD* and *AXYZ*.

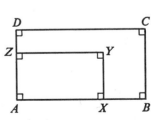

19. If *AB* = 10, *AX* = 6, *XY* = 4, then *BC* = ?

20. If *AX* = 5, *BX* = 3, *BC* = 4, then *XY* = ?

21. If *ZY* = 8, *AZ* = 3, *BC* = 5, then *XB* = ?

22. If *AZ* = 3, *AD* = 8, *AB* = 12, then *AX* = ?

C **23.** Prove, using two quadrilaterals: Similarity of polygons is symmetric.

24. Prove, using one pentagon: Similarity of polygons is reflexive.

8–4   Similar Triangles

At present you have no method of proving that two triangles are similar other than to show that the two triangles meet all the requirements named in the definition of similar polygons. You will recall that you were able to prove two triangles congruent without having to appeal directly to the definition of congruent triangles. ⁄ Your first proofs were based upon certain congruence postulates, such as the SSS postulate. At least one initial postulate about similar triangles is needed to provide you with a more direct method of proving two triangles similar.

AN EXPERIMENT:

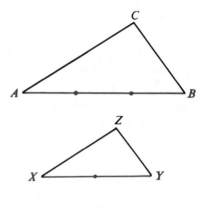

1. On a piece of paper draw two line segments $\overline{AB}$ and $\overline{XY}$ such that $XY = \frac{2}{3}AB$.

2. Pick some point C not on $\overline{AB}$ and draw $\overline{AC}$ and $\overline{BC}$ so as to form $\triangle ABC$.

3. Using a protractor, make angles at X and Y congruent to $\angle A$ and $\angle B$ respectively and on the same side of $\overleftrightarrow{XY}$. Call the vertex of the triangle formed Z.

   How do $m\angle C$ and $m\angle Z$ compare? Measure $\overline{XZ}$ and $\overline{AC}$. Is XZ approximately two-thirds AC? Is YZ approximately two-thirds BC? Does it appear that $\triangle ABC$ and $\triangle XYZ$ are similar?

Vary this experiment by drawing any two triangles such that two angles of one triangle are congruent to two angles of the other. You will find that the lengths of corresponding sides are approximately in proportion.

The relationship suggested by your experiment is taken as a postulate.

> **P₁₆**   If two angles of one triangle are congruent to two angles of another triangle, the triangles are similar. (AA Postulate)

We shall classify the statements which follow as corollaries even though they are directly related to a postulate rather than a theorem.

COROLLARY 1 If two right triangles have an acute angle of one triangle congruent to an acute angle of the other, the triangles are similar.

COROLLARY 2 If two isosceles triangles have congruent vertex angles, the triangles are similar.

When you were called upon to prove the lengths of two segments equal, you often were able to do so by showing that the segments were corresponding sides of congruent triangles. Similarly, to prove that the lengths of four segments are in proportion you can often do so by showing that the segments are corresponding sides of similar triangles. When given a similarity between two triangles, for example

$$\triangle ABC \sim \triangle XYZ$$

you simply note the order in which the letters are written. Then you can write the extended proportion: $\dfrac{AB}{XY} = \dfrac{AC}{XZ} = \dfrac{BC}{YZ}$.

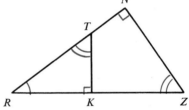

Stating an extended proportion for the adjacent figure requires greater care. Since $\angle R \cong \angle R$, you pair vertex R with vertex R. Since $\angle K \cong \angle N$, you pair vertex N with vertex K. Then, of course, you pair vertex Z with vertex T. You can draw the two triangles as separate figures if you find this helpful.

You state the similarity between these triangles:

$$\triangle RKT \sim \triangle RNZ.$$

Then write the extended proportion: $\dfrac{RK}{RN} = \dfrac{RT}{RZ} = \dfrac{KT}{NZ}$.

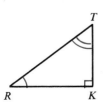

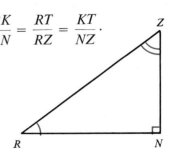

A common method of proving that the lengths of four segments are in proportion is to prove that two triangles which contain those segments as sides are similar.

On occasion you may be called upon to prove that the product of the lengths of two segments is equal to the product of the lengths of two other segments. To do this, you can often prove that two triangles are similar, write a proportion, and then apply a property of proportions. The following example illustrates this type of proof.

EXAMPLE.

Given: $AX \perp BC$; $CY \perp AB$.

To Prove: $AY \cdot TX = CX \cdot TY$.

Analysis: Two proportions equivalent to $AY \cdot TX = CX \cdot TY$ are:

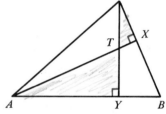

$$\frac{AY}{TY} = \frac{CX}{TX} \text{ and } \frac{AY}{CX} = \frac{TY}{TX}.$$

In the second proportion, but not in the first, the numerators are lengths of sides of one triangle and the denominators are lengths of sides of another triangle. Therefore, prove $\triangle AYT \sim \triangle CXT$.

Proof

STATEMENT	REASON
1. $AX \perp BC$; $CY \perp AB$.	1. Given.
2. $\angle AYT \cong \angle CXT$.	2. $\perp$ lines form rt. $\angle$, and all rt. $\angle$ are congruent.
3. $\angle ATY \cong \angle CTX$.	3. Vertical angles are congruent.
4. $\triangle AYT \sim \triangle CXT$.	4. AA postulate.
5. $\dfrac{AY}{CX} = \dfrac{TY}{TX}$.	5. Lengths of corr. sides of similar $\angle$ are in proportion.
6. $AY \cdot TX = CX \cdot TY$.	6. A property of proportions.

A common method of proving that the product of the lengths of two segments is equal to the product of the lengths of two other segments is to prove triangles similar, write a proportion, and then apply a property of proportions.

ORAL
EXERCISES

1. Are all isosceles right triangles similar?
2. Can a quadrilateral and a triangle be called similar figures?
3. Express $AB \cdot RS = CD \cdot TW$ in the form of a proportion.
4. Express $(XY)^2 = AB \cdot CD$ in the form of a proportion.

5. If $\triangle ABC \sim \triangle XBY$, complete the extended proportion

$$\frac{AC}{?} = \frac{BC}{?} = \frac{AB}{?}.$$

$$XY \quad BY \quad XB$$

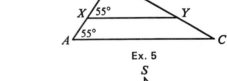

Ex. 5

6. If $\triangle ABC \sim \triangle RST$, complete the extended proportion

$$\frac{AB}{?} = \frac{BC}{?} = \frac{CA}{?}.$$

$$RS \quad ST \quad TR$$

7. If $\triangle ADC \sim \triangle CDB$, complete the extended proportion

$$\frac{AD}{AD} = \frac{BC}{DC} = \frac{?}{AC}.$$

$$AB \quad BC \quad AC$$

8. If $\triangle ABC \sim \triangle ACD$, complete the extended proportion

$$\frac{AB}{?} = \frac{BC}{?} = \frac{AC}{?}.$$

$$AD \quad DC \quad AC$$

Ex. 6

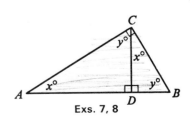

Exs. 7, 8

WRITTEN EXERCISES

A 1. If two similar triangles have one pair of corresponding sides congruent, are the triangles congruent?

2. What is the ratio of the lengths of the sides of two squares with perimeters 8 in. and 12 in. respectively?

3. If $\dfrac{AB}{XY} = \dfrac{BC}{YZ} = \dfrac{CA}{ZX}$, must it be true that $\dfrac{XY}{AB} = \dfrac{YZ}{BC} = \dfrac{ZX}{CA}$?

4. If $RS \cdot VW = TQ \cdot NJ$, must it be true that $\dfrac{RS}{TQ} = \dfrac{VW}{NJ}$?

In Exercises 5–8, ABZ is a triangle, and $\angle 1 \cong \angle 2$.

5. Name two triangles that are similar.

6. Complete this proportion:

$$\frac{XY}{?} = \frac{ZY}{?} = \frac{XZ}{?}.$$

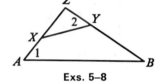

7. If $XY = 4$, $BA = 10$, and $ZY = 2$, find ZA.

Exs. 5–8

8. If $ZX = 3$, $ZB = 5$, and $ZY = 2$, find ZA.

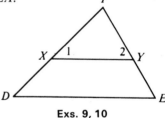

9. Given: $\angle 1 \cong \angle D$.
   Prove: $\triangle FXY \sim \triangle FDE$.

10. Given: $m\angle 2 = j$; $m\angle E = j$.
    Prove: $\triangle FXY \sim \triangle FDE$.

Exs. 9, 10

11. Prove: If two triangles are congruent, they are similar.

12. Prove: If a base angle of one isosceles triangle is congruent to a base angle of another isosceles triangle, the triangles are similar.

13. Given: $\angle JNK \cong \angle JKM$.
    Prove: $\triangle KNJ \sim \triangle MKJ$.

14. Given: $MJ = MK$; $KN = KJ$.
    Prove: $\triangle NKJ \sim \triangle KMJ$.

Exs. 13, 14

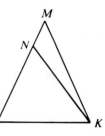

15. Given: $\angle G \cong \angle F$.

Prove: $\dfrac{GE}{FH} = \dfrac{ME}{MH}$.

16. Given: $m\angle E = x; m\angle H = x$.

Prove: $\dfrac{GM}{FM} = \dfrac{GE}{FH}$.

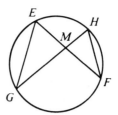

Exs. 15, 16

17. Given: $\overline{RS} \parallel \overline{AC}$.

Prove: $\triangle ABC \sim \triangle RBS$. **Ex. 17**

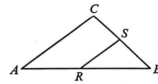

18. Given: $\angle 1 \cong \angle 2$.

Prove: $\triangle AOB \sim \triangle DOC$.

19. Given: $\overline{BC} \perp \overline{AC}, \overline{RS} \perp \overline{AB}$.

Prove: $\dfrac{AS}{AC} = \dfrac{AR}{AB}$.

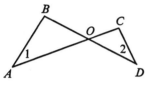

Ex. 18

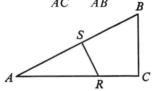

Ex. 19

20. Given: $\overline{CD} \parallel \overline{AB}$.

Prove: $OB \cdot OD = OA \cdot OC$.

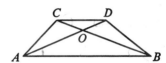

In Exercises 21–24 it is given that $\triangle ADE \sim \triangle ABC$.

EXAMPLE. $AB = 6$, $AD = 2$, and $EC = 2\frac{1}{2}$.
Find AE.

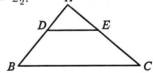

Solution: Since $\triangle ADE \sim \triangle ABC$,

$$\frac{AD}{AB} = \frac{AE}{AC}.$$

Let $x = AE$.

Then, $\dfrac{2}{6} = \dfrac{x}{x + 2\frac{1}{2}}$ 　　 *Check:* $\dfrac{2}{6} \overset{?}{=} \dfrac{\frac{5}{4}}{\frac{5}{4} + 2\frac{1}{2}}$

$\qquad\quad 6x = 2x + 5$

$\qquad\qquad x = \frac{5}{4}$ 　　 $\dfrac{2}{6} \overset{?}{=} \dfrac{\frac{5}{4}}{\frac{15}{4}} = \dfrac{5}{15}$

$\qquad AE = \frac{5}{4}$, **Answer.** 　　 $\dfrac{1}{3} = \dfrac{1}{3}$

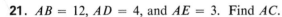

B **21.** $AB = 12$, $AD = 4$, and $AE = 3$. Find AC.

22. $AB = 8$, $AD = 6$, and $DE = 5$. Find BC.

23. $AD = 3$, $DB = 2$, $AE = 4$. Find EC.

24. $AD = a$, $AB = 3a$ and $AC = 5a$. Find AE.

Exs. 21–24

25. If $\triangle AYB \sim \triangle CXB$, complete the extended proportion: $\dfrac{AY}{?} = \dfrac{YB}{?} = \dfrac{AB}{?}$.

26. If $\triangle AOX \sim \triangle COY$, complete the extended proportion: $\dfrac{?}{AX} = \dfrac{?}{XO} = \dfrac{?}{OA}$.

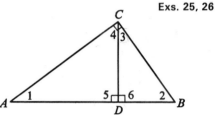

Exs. 25, 26

27. Given: $\overline{AC} \perp \overline{BC}$, $\overline{CD} \perp \overline{AB}$.

Prove: $\dfrac{AC}{CB} = \dfrac{CD}{BD}$.

28. Given: $\overline{AC} \perp \overline{BC}$, $\overline{CD} \perp \overline{AB}$.

Prove: $AB \cdot AD = AC \cdot AC$.

29. Prove Corollary 1, page 293.

30. Prove Corollary 2, page 293.

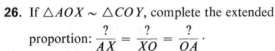

Exs. 27, 28

C **31.** Prove: The lengths of the bisectors of any two corresponding angles of two similar triangles have the same ratio as the lengths of any two corresponding sides.

32. Given: the adjacent figure with $\angle 1 \cong \angle 2$.

Prove: $(AB)^2 = AD \cdot AC$.

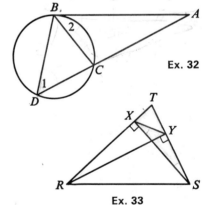

Ex. 32

33. Given: $\overline{XS}$ and $\overline{RY}$ are altitudes of $\triangle RST$.

Prove: $TY \cdot TS = TR \cdot TX$.

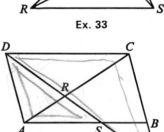

Ex. 33

34. Given: Parallelogram $ABCD$; D, R, S, and T collinear; C, B, and T collinear.

Prove: $(DR)^2 = RS \cdot RT$.

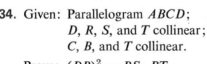

Ex. 34

8-5 Properties of Special Segments in a Triangle

The proportions you have been writing have to do with the lengths of segments that are corresponding sides of similar triangles. Proportions may also be written that have to do with the lengths of two parts of one segment and the corresponding parts of a second segment. For example:

Let X and Y be points located on segments $\overline{AB}$ and $\overline{CD}$. Each point divides the segment on which it lies into two parts. The segments $\overline{AB}$ and $\overline{CD}$ are said to be **divided proportionally** if

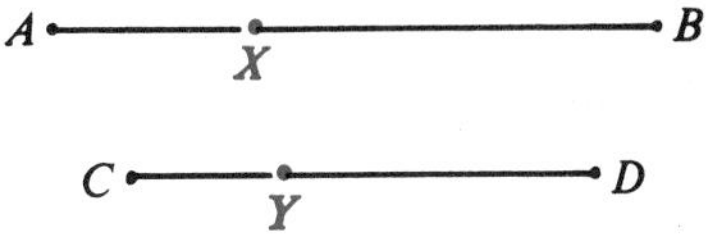

$$\frac{AX}{XB} = \frac{CY}{YD}, \quad \text{or} \quad \frac{AX}{AB} = \frac{CY}{CD}.$$

THEOREM 8-3 If a line is parallel to one side of a triangle and intersects the other two sides, it divides them proportionally.

Given: $\overleftrightarrow{XY} \parallel \overleftrightarrow{AB}$.

To Prove: $\dfrac{AX}{XC} = \dfrac{BY}{YC}$.

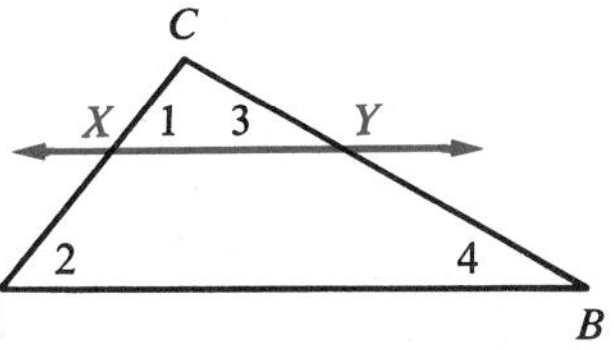

Analysis: Form a proportion on the basis of $\sim\triangle$. Then transform the proportion by using a property of proportions.

Proof

STATEMENT	REASON
1. $\overleftrightarrow{XY} \parallel \overleftrightarrow{AB}$.	1. ?
2. $\angle 1 \cong \angle 2;\ \angle 3 \cong \angle 4$.	2. ?
3. $\triangle ACB \sim \triangle XCY$.	3. ?
4. $\dfrac{AC}{XC} = \dfrac{BC}{YC}$.	4. Lengths of corr. sides of $\sim\triangle$ are in proportion.
5. $\dfrac{AC - XC}{XC} = \dfrac{BC - YC}{YC}$.	5. A property of proportions.
6. $AC - XC = AX$, $BC - YC = BY$.	6. Betweenness property and subtraction property of equality.
7. $\dfrac{AX}{XC} = \dfrac{BY}{YC}$.	7. Substitution principle.

Two equivalent forms of the proportion in step 7 of the proof of Theorem 8–3 are:

$$\frac{AC}{XC} = \frac{BC}{YC}. \quad \text{Step 4 in the proof.}$$

$$\frac{AC}{AX} = \frac{BC}{BY}. \quad \text{First obtain } \frac{XC}{AX} = \frac{YC}{BY} \text{ from } \frac{AX}{XC} = \frac{BY}{YC}. \quad \text{Then use}$$

another property of proportions.

These equivalent proportions tell you that the parallel line also divides the sides so that the length of either side is to the length of one of its segments as the length of the other side is to the length of its corresponding segment. Since these relationships can also be considered as expressing the fact that the sides of the triangle are *divided proportionally*, we shall agree to the following meaning of that phrase.

The sides of a triangle are said to be **divided proportionally** when either

1. The lengths of corresponding segments of the sides are in proportion, or

2. The length of either side is to the length of one of its segments as the length of the other side is to the length of its corresponding segment.

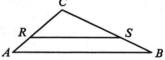

The basic properties of proportion can be used to show that each statement implies the other. If $\overline{AC}$ and $\overline{BC}$ are divided proportionally, by R and S respectively, then

$$\frac{AR}{RC} = \frac{BS}{SC}; \quad \frac{AC}{AR} = \frac{BC}{BS}; \quad \frac{AC}{RC} = \frac{BC}{SC}.$$

COROLLARY If three parallel lines intersect two transversals, they divide them proportionally.

Designate lengths of segments by lower-case letters. You are to prove that

$$\frac{a}{a'} = \frac{b}{b'}.$$

Outline of Proof:

Draw the indicated auxiliary line.

From Theorem 8–3

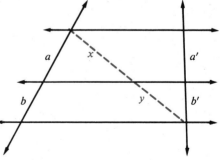

$$\frac{a}{b} = \frac{x}{y} \text{ and } \frac{x}{y} = \frac{a'}{b'}. \quad \text{Therefore } \frac{a}{b} = \frac{a'}{b'} \text{ or } \frac{a}{a'} = \frac{b}{b'}.$$

The proof of the next theorem is based upon auxiliary lines first drawn by some ingenious person. We cannot know just what thinking and experimenting he did before he discovered a proof. In a sense our analysis merely tells us to follow a certain well-worn path.

THEOREM 8–4   If a ray bisects an angle of a triangle, it divides the opposite side into segments whose lengths are proportional to the lengths of the other two sides.

Given: $\triangle ABC$ with $\angle 1 \cong \angle 2$.

To Prove: $\dfrac{AD}{DC} = \dfrac{BA}{BC}$.

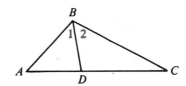

Analysis: Draw auxiliary lines which will make the use of Theorem 8–3 possible.

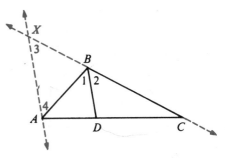

Proof

STATEMENT	REASON
1. Draw $\overleftrightarrow{CB}$ through B and C.	1. Two points determine a line.
2. Through A draw $\overleftrightarrow{AX} \parallel \overleftrightarrow{BD}$.	2. Through a point outside a line ___?___.
3. $\overleftrightarrow{BC}$ and $\overleftrightarrow{AX}$ must meet in a point (X).	3. They lie in a plane and cannot be $\parallel$ since $\overleftrightarrow{BD}$ and $\overleftrightarrow{BC}$ intersect.
4. $\dfrac{AD}{DC} = \dfrac{XB}{BC}$.	4. A line parallel to one side of a $\triangle$ ___?___.
5. $\angle 3 \cong \angle 2$.	5. ?
6. $\angle 2 \cong \angle 1$.	6. Given.
7. $\angle 1 \cong \angle 4$.	7. ?
8. $\angle 3 \cong \angle 4$.	8. ?
9. $XB = BA$.	9. ?
10. $\dfrac{AD}{DC} = \dfrac{BA}{BC}$.	10. ?

THEOREM 8–5   If two triangles are similar, the lengths of corresponding altitudes have the same ratio as the lengths of any pair of corresponding sides.

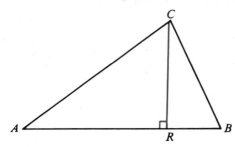
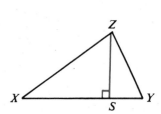

Given: $\triangle XYZ \sim \triangle ABC$ with altitudes $\overline{ZS}$ and $\overline{CR}$.

To Prove: $\dfrac{ZS}{CR} = \dfrac{XZ}{AC} = \dfrac{ZY}{CB} = \dfrac{XY}{AB}$.

Analysis: Since $\triangle XYZ \sim \triangle ABC$, $\dfrac{XZ}{AC} = \dfrac{ZY}{CB} = \dfrac{XY}{AB}$.

But $\triangle XSZ \sim \triangle ARC$; thus $\dfrac{ZS}{CR} = \dfrac{XZ}{AC}$.

Therefore, $\dfrac{ZS}{CR} = \dfrac{XZ}{AC} = \dfrac{ZY}{CB} = \dfrac{XY}{AB}$.

The proof is left for you. (Exercise 23)

ORAL
EXERCISES

Given: $\triangle ABC$ with $\overline{RS} \parallel \overline{BC}$.

1. State three proportions about the lengths of sides $\overline{AC}$ and $\overline{AB}$ and their segments.

2. If $\dfrac{AR}{RB} = \dfrac{2}{3}$, then $\dfrac{AR}{AB} = ?$

3. If $\dfrac{AS}{AC} = \dfrac{2}{7}$, then $\dfrac{AS}{SC} = ?$

4. If $\dfrac{AR}{RB} = \dfrac{3}{4}$, then $\dfrac{AS}{SC} = ?$

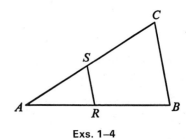

Exs. 1–4

Given: △*RST* with ∠1 ≅ ∠2.

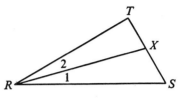

5. Complete this proportion: $\dfrac{TX}{XS} = \underline{}$

6. If $\dfrac{RT}{RS} = \dfrac{2}{3}$, then $\dfrac{TX}{XS} = ?$

7. What would be the ratio of *TX* to *XS* if △*RST* were isosceles, with *RS* = *RT*?

Exs. 5–8

8. If *XS* > *XT*, does it follow that *RS* > *RT*?

9. If two corresponding altitudes of two similar triangles are congruent, must the triangles be congruent?

10. Must a line parallel to one side of a triangle intersect the other two sides?

WRITTEN EXERCISES

1. A segment 15 in. long is divided into two segments having lengths in the ratio 2:3. Find the length of each segment.

2. A segment is divided into two segments having lengths in the ratio 5:3. If the difference between the lengths of the segments is 6 in., find the length of each.

Given $\overline{RS} \parallel \overline{AB}$ in △ ABC.

3. If *CR* = 3, *RA* = 5, and *CS* = 4, find *SB*.

4. If *CR* = 2, *RA* = 3, and *BC* = 10, find *CS*.

5. If *CR* = 4, *RA* = 6, and *RS* = 10, find *AB*.

6. If *CR* = *SB*, *RA* = 4, and *CS* = 9, find *CR*.

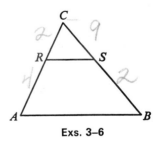

Exs. 3–6

7. Given: △*RST* with ∠1 ≅ ∠2.
Prove: $\dfrac{RX}{XS} = \dfrac{RY}{YT}$.

8. Given: △*RST* with $\overline{XY} \parallel \overline{ST}$.
Prove: *RX* · *RT* = *RS* · *RY*.

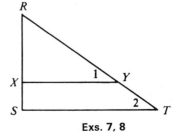

Exs. 7, 8

For Exs. 9–12, in the figure at the right $\overrightarrow{CD}$ bisects $\angle ACB$.

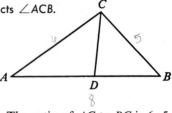

EXAMPLE. If $AC = 6$, $BC = 5$, and $AB = 8$, find AD and DB.

Solution: Either of two methods can be used.

Method 1: Let $AD = x$.
     Then $DB = 8 - x$.

Since $\dfrac{AD}{DB} = \dfrac{AC}{BC}$,

$$\dfrac{x}{8 - x} = \dfrac{6}{5}$$

$$5x = 48 - 6x$$
$$11x = 48$$

AD: $x = 4\tfrac{4}{11}$

DB: $8 - x = 3\tfrac{7}{11}$

Method 2: The ratio of AC to BC is $6 : 5$. Thus, the ratio of AD to DB is $6 : 5$.

Let $AD = 6x$. Then $DB = 5x$.

$$6x + 5x = 8$$
$$x = \tfrac{8}{11}$$

AD: $6x = 4\tfrac{4}{11}$

DB: $5x = 3\tfrac{7}{11}$

(Check $4\tfrac{4}{11}$ and $3\tfrac{7}{11}$ to see that they satisfy the requirements of the problem.)

9. If $AC = 3$, $BC = 5$, and $AB = 7$, find AD and DB.
10. If $AB = 10$, $AC = 6$, and $BC = 6$, find AD and DB.
11. If $AB = 10$, $AC = 4$, and $BC = 8$, find AD and DB.
12. If $AC : BC = 3 : 5$, and $AB = 12$, find AD and DB.

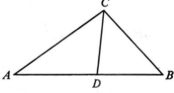

Exs. 9–12

B 13. The perimeter of a triangle is 30 in. The bisector of one angle divides the opposite side into segments 4 in. and 6 in. long. Find the lengths of the sides of the triangle.

14. One side of a triangle is 3 in. longer than another side. The ray bisecting the angle between these sides divides the opposite side into 5-inch and 3-inch segments. Find the perimeter of the triangle.

15. Given: $\triangle ABC$ with $\overline{RT} \parallel \overline{AB}$. Find x.

16. Given: $\angle 1 \cong \angle 2$. Find x.

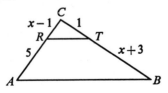

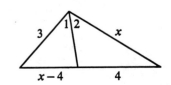

17. Given: Plane figure with
$\overline{XA} \perp \overleftrightarrow{ED}$; $\angle 1 \cong \angle 2$.

Prove: $\dfrac{BX}{XC} = \dfrac{AB}{AC}$.

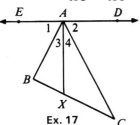

Ex. 17

18. Given: Plane figure with
$\overline{XZ} \parallel \overline{BC}$; $\angle 1 \cong \angle 2$.

Prove: $\dfrac{AX}{XB} = \dfrac{AY}{ZC}$.

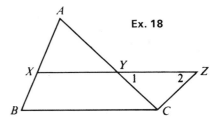

Ex. 18

19. Given: $\triangle ABC$ with $\angle 1 \cong \angle 2$;
$\overline{RS} \parallel \overline{BC}$.

Prove: $\dfrac{AS}{SC} = \dfrac{AR}{RS}$.

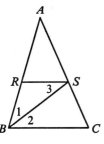

Ex. 19

20. Given: $\triangle YBC$ with $\angle 1 \cong \angle 2$;
$AC = CX$.

Prove: $\dfrac{AX}{YC} = \dfrac{BX}{BC}$.

Ex. 20

21. Given: $\overline{UZ} \parallel \overline{XB}$;
$\overline{ZV} \parallel \overline{AY}$.

Prove: $\dfrac{AU}{AX} = \dfrac{YV}{YB}$.

22. Given: $\overline{UZ} \parallel \overline{XB}$;
$\overline{ZV} \parallel \overline{AY}$.

Prove: $\dfrac{BY}{BV} = \dfrac{XA}{XU}$.

Exs. 21, 22

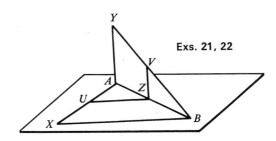

C **23.** Prove Theorem 8–5.

24. Given: $\triangle ABC$ with $\overline{XS} \perp \overline{BC}$,
$\overline{ZR} \perp \overline{AC}$, $\overline{YT} \perp \overline{AB}$;
X, Y, Z in plane of $\triangle ABC$.

Prove: $\triangle YXZ \sim \triangle ABC$.

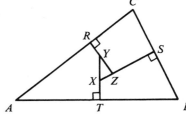

Ex. 24

25. In $\triangle ABC$, $\angle 1 \cong \angle 2 \cong \angle 3$.
$CA = 6$, $CX = 3\sqrt{3}$, $CY = 6$,
$CB = 6\sqrt{3}$, and $AB = 12$.
Find AX, XY, and YB.

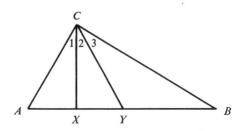

26. In the given diagram, $\overleftrightarrow{AC}$ and $\overleftrightarrow{DF}$
are skew lines intersecting three
parallel planes N, M, and L. Prove
that the lengths of corresponding
segments of the given skew lines are
in proportion.

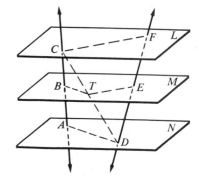

PRACTICAL APPLICATIONS

1. This diagram illustrates how a boy
5 ft. 4 in. tall determined the height
of a flagpole by measuring shadows.
If he found his shadow to be 4 ft.
long and that of the flagpole 30 ft.
long, what was his estimate of the
height of the pole?

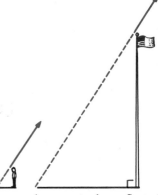

2. Light rays are known to be reflected
from a mirror at an angle congruent to
that at which they strike it. In the
given diagram a man 6 ft. tall finds
that if he places a mirror flat on the
ground at point X and backs up 4 ft.,
he can just see the reflection of the
top of a tree located 20 ft. from the
mirror. How high is the tree?

3. A *pantograph* is an instrument used to enlarge or reduce maps and drawings to scale. Four bars are joined so that *ABCD* is a parallelogram and points *P*, *D*, and *E* lie on a line. Point *P* is kept fixed. Drawing instruments can be inserted in holes at *D* and *E*. If *PA* is 3 units and *AB* is 2 units, what would be the ratio of the perimeters of the two similar figures traced at *D* and *E*?

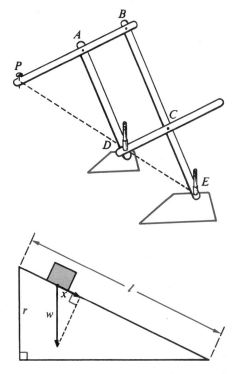

4. Inclined planes are sometimes used to raise heavy objects. By principles of physics, the force (*x*) with which the object tends to slide back down has the same ratio to the weight (*w*) as the rise (*r*) has to the length (*l*), assuming no friction.

a. Draw a figure in which *r* is 3 in. and *l* is 10 in. (This might be used to represent a 3-foot rise of a 10-foot plank.) Represent a 400-pound weight at some point on the plane by using 2 in. for *w*. Approximate the force *x* by completing your drawing and making measurements.

b. A person able to push with a force of 50 lb. uses a 12-foot plank. He wishes to push a 400-pound object along the plank. How much of a rise can be achieved?

CHAPTER SUMMARY

Inventory of Structure and Methods

1. For nonzero numbers *a*, *b*, *c*, *d*: The number $\dfrac{a}{b}$ or $a:b$ is the ratio of *a* to *b*.

   An equation written in the form $\dfrac{a}{b} = \dfrac{c}{d}$ is a proportion.

2. The proportion $\dfrac{a}{b} = \dfrac{c}{d}$ is equivalent to each of the following equations.

$$ad = bc$$

$$\frac{b}{a} = \frac{d}{c} ;\quad \frac{a}{c} = \frac{b}{d}$$

$$\frac{a+b}{b} = \frac{c+d}{d} ;\quad \frac{a-b}{b} = \frac{c-d}{d}$$

3. If $\dfrac{a}{b} = \dfrac{c}{d} = \dfrac{e}{f} = \cdots$, then $\dfrac{a+c+e+\cdots}{b+d+f+\cdots} = \dfrac{a}{b} = \dfrac{c}{d} = \cdots$.

4. In two similar convex polygons

Corresponding angles have equal measures.

The lengths of corresponding sides are in proportion.

The ratio of the perimeters equals the ratio of the lengths of any pair of corresponding sides.

5. Two triangles are similar if two angles of one triangle are congruent to two angles of the other triangle. In similar triangles the ratio of the lengths of two corresponding altitudes is equal to the ratio of the lengths of two corresponding sides.

6. In any triangle

A line parallel to one side and intersecting the other two sides divides them proportionally.

A ray that bisects an angle divides the opposite side into segments whose lengths are proportional to the lengths of the other two sides.

Vocabulary and Spelling

ratio of two numbers (*p. 277*)
proportion (*p. 278*)
terms of a proportion (*p. 278*)
extended proportion (*p. 278*)
properties of proportions (*p. 281*)
correspondence between
  vertices of two polygons (*p. 285*)

corresponding sides (*p. 285*)
corresponding angles (*p. 285*)
similar polygons (*p. 285*)
similar triangles (*p. 292*)
AA postulate (*p. 292*)
segments divided proportionally
  (*p. 299*)

CHAPTER TEST

8–1   Given: Point P lies on $\overline{JK}$; $JP = 4$; $PK = 5$. State the values of the following ratios.

    1. $JP:PK$ **3.** $PK:JP$

    2. $JP:JK$ **4.** $PK:JK$ J   P   K

8–2 Complete the statements. No letter represents zero.

5. If $\dfrac{n}{t} = \dfrac{r}{s}$, then $\dfrac{n}{r} = \dfrac{?}{?}$

6. If $\dfrac{n}{t} = \dfrac{r}{s}$, then $\dfrac{s}{r} = \dfrac{?}{?}$

7. If $\dfrac{n}{t} = \dfrac{r}{s}$, then $n \cdot \underline{\;?\;} = \underline{\;?\;} \cdot \underline{\;?\;}$

8. If $\dfrac{a}{b} = \dfrac{c}{d} = \dfrac{e}{f}$, then $\dfrac{a + c + e}{?} = \dfrac{?}{?}$

8–3 Which of the following polygons must be similar?

9. Any two squares.

10. Any two rectangles.

11. Any two regular polygons with the same number of sides.

12. Any two right triangles.

8–4 In the given figure $\overline{RS} \perp \overline{AB}$ and $\overline{BC} \perp \overline{AC}$.

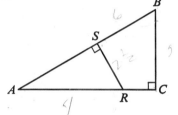

13. Is $\triangle ASR \sim \triangle ACB$?

14. $\dfrac{AR}{?} = \dfrac{RS}{?} = \dfrac{AS}{?}$.

15. If $AR = 4$, $AB = 6$, $BC = 5$, then $RS = \underline{\;?\;}$.

16. $m\angle SRC + m\angle SBC = \underline{\;?\;}$.

8–5 Given $\overline{XY} \parallel \overline{AB}$ in $\triangle ABC$.

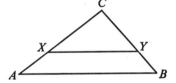

17. $\dfrac{XC}{AX} = \dfrac{YC}{?}$

18. $\dfrac{AC}{AX} = \dfrac{?}{BY}$

19. $\dfrac{?}{XC} = \dfrac{BC}{YC}$

20. $\dfrac{?}{AC} = \dfrac{XY}{AB}$

CHAPTER REVIEW

8–1 **Ratio and Proportion**   *Pages 277–281*

1. The ratio of the number a to the number b is $\underline{\;?\;}$ provided $\underline{\;?\;} \neq 0$.

2. The ratio of the measure of a right angle to that of a 36° angle is $\underline{\;?\;}$.

3. In the proportion $\dfrac{r}{s} = \dfrac{w}{t}$ the first term is $\underline{\;?\;}$, and the third term is $\underline{\;?\;}$.

4. If the ratio of a to b is 3 to 5, then b is $\underline{\;?\;}$ times a.

8–2 Properties of Proportions. *Pages 281–284*

5. If $\dfrac{a}{b} = \dfrac{2}{5}$ then $5a =$ __?__ .

6. Two proportions equivalent to $\dfrac{d}{k} = \dfrac{l}{m}$ are $\dfrac{?}{?} = \dfrac{?}{?}$ and $\dfrac{?}{?} = \dfrac{?}{?}$.

7. If $3x = 4y$, and $y \neq 0$, then the ratio of x to y is __?__ .

8. If $\dfrac{3}{x} = \dfrac{2}{5}$, then $x =$ __?__ .

8–3 Similar Polygons *Pages 284–292*

9. In similar polygons corresponding angles are __?__ and lengths of corresponding sides are __?__ .

10. The perimeters of two similar polygons have the ratio $3:5$. If the length of a side of the smaller polygon is 12, the length of the corresponding side of the larger polygon is __?__ .

11. If the lengths of corresponding sides of two similar triangles have the ratio $1:1$, then the triangles are __?__ as well as similar.

12. Similar figures which are not congruent have the same __?__ but not the same __?__ .

8–4 Similar Triangles *Pages 292–298*

13. If $\triangle ABC \sim \triangle RST$, then $\triangle BAC \sim \triangle$ __?__ .

14. If $\triangle ABC \sim \triangle RST$, then $\dfrac{AB}{?} = \dfrac{AC}{?}$.

15. Isosceles triangle NTX has vertex angle T and isosceles triangle JOC has vertex angle O. If $\angle T \cong \angle O$, then $\triangle XTN \sim \triangle$ __?__ .

16. If $\triangle DEF \sim \triangle RST$, then the assertion $\dfrac{DE}{RS} = \dfrac{EF}{ST}$ can be supported by the reason: __?__ .

8–5 Properties of Special Segments in a Triangle *Pages 299–306*

17. If $\angle 1 \cong \angle 2$, then $\dfrac{RK}{KS} = \dfrac{?}{?}$.

18. If $\angle 1 \cong \angle 2$, $RT = 6$, $TS = 9$, and $RS = 10$, then $RK =$ __?__ .

19. If $\overline{KL} \parallel \overline{RT}$, then $\triangle$ __?__ $\sim \triangle$ __?__ .

20. If $\overline{KL} \parallel \overline{RT}$, then $\overline{KL}$ divides the sides $\overline{SR}$ and $\overline{ST}$ of $\triangle RST$ __?__ .

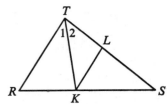

• EXTRA FOR EXPERTS

The Two-Pole Problem

Sometimes a problem catches your interest because it seems to be incomplete; you believe that the statement of the problem does not provide enough facts to permit a unique solution. Such a problem is the following.

> On a level plot of ground there stand two vertical posts, one rising six feet, the other ten feet, above ground level. From the top of each pole a rope is stretched to the foot of the other pole. How far above ground is the point where the ropes cross?

Obviously you are to ignore such refinements as the curvature of the earth and the slight sagging of the ropes. You may suspect, however, that you must be given one more thing, the distance between the poles. This belief turns out to be incorrect. Let the distance between the poles be *any* number n.

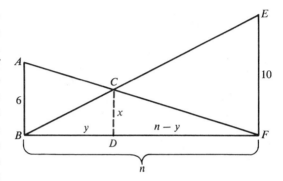

Using the similarity: $\triangle BDC \sim \triangle BFE$ you can write a proportion involving x, y, n and 10.

Using the similarity: $\triangle FDC \sim \triangle FBA$ you can write a proportion involving x, $n - y$, n, and 6.

From the *two* equations in *three* variables you can eliminate both n and y and express x in the easily-remembered form $\dfrac{1}{x} = \dfrac{1}{6} + \dfrac{1}{10}$.

EXERCISES

1. Write the complete solution outlined above.
2. Solve a problem like the one above except for these changes: Stretch each rope from the top of one pole to the middle of the other pole.

9 Similar Right Triangles

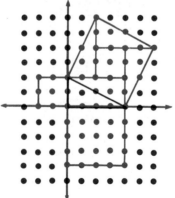

This rectangular array of holes in the surface of the Brookhaven Graphite Reactor suggests a grid where coordinate axes may be placed. A model for a proof of the Pythagorean Theorem can be seen on this grid.

We shall never know when man first conceived the idea now called the Pythagorean Theorem. It is interesting to speculate about how he may have made the discovery and even more interesting to wonder what chance you might have to make the discovery all by yourself. One thing is certain: The right triangle fact would first be observed in a special case. Since the simplest special case is an isosceles right triangle, the floor tile pattern shown below may provide a hint. Each individual tile pattern is the shape of an isosceles right triangle.

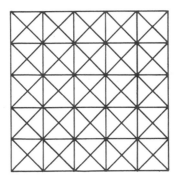

In the second figure you can concentrate on part of the floor. Some of the segments are drawn heavily to help you see relationships. Each of the small squares contains two tiles, while the large square contains four tiles. You see physical support for the statement: The area of the square drawn on the hypotenuse of an isosceles right triangle is equal to the sum of the areas of the squares drawn on the legs. Expressed algebraically, $c^2 = a^2 + b^2$. Could you have discovered this special theorem by yourself?

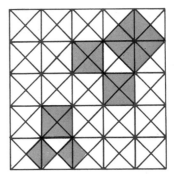

■ Similar Triangles and the Pythagorean Theorem

9–1   The Altitude to the Hypotenuse of a Right Triangle

Two of the altitudes of a right triangle are legs of the triangle. The third altitude, from the vertex of the right angle to the hypotenuse, has interesting properties. Two new terms will be convenient to use in investigating these properties.

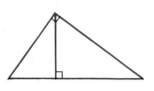

For any positive numbers a, b, and x, if $\dfrac{a}{x} = \dfrac{x}{b}$, then x is called the **geometric mean** between a and b. Note that $x = \sqrt{ab}$.

The **projection of a point on a line** is the point of intersection of the line and the perpendicular from the point to the line. When a point lies on a line it is considered to be its own projection on that line.

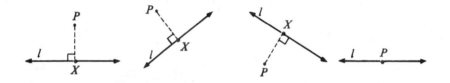

In the first three illustrations above, X is the projection of P on l. In the fourth illustration, point P is itself the projection of P on l.

The **projection of a segment on a line** in the same plane is the segment whose endpoints are the projections of the endpoints of the given segment.

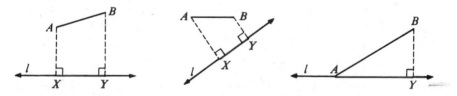

In the first two illustrations just above, $\overline{XY}$ is the projection of $\overline{AB}$ on l. In the third illustration, $\overline{AY}$ is the projection of $\overline{AB}$ on l. We shall use the idea of projection in stating corollaries of Theorem 9–1.

THEOREM 9–1   If the altitude is drawn to the hypotenuse of a right triangle, the two triangles formed are similar to the given triangle and to each other.

Given: $\triangle ACB$ with $\angle ACB$ a rt. $\angle$; $\overline{CD} \perp \overline{AB}$.

To Prove: $\triangle ADC \sim \triangle ACB$;
$\triangle CDB \sim \triangle ACB$;
$\triangle ADC \sim \triangle CDB$.

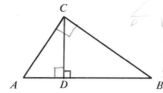

Analysis: Rt. $\triangle$ with one pair of acute $\angle$ congruent are $\sim$.

Proof

STATEMENT	REASON
1. $\angle ACB$ is a rt. $\angle$; $\overline{CD} \perp \overline{AB}$.	**1.** Given.
2. $\angle ADC$ and $\angle BDC$ are rt. $\angle$.	**2.** $\perp$ lines form rt. $\angle$.
3. In rt. $\triangle$ ADC and ACB, $\angle A \cong \angle A$.	**3.** Reflexive property of congruence.
4. Rt. $\triangle ADC \sim$ rt. $\triangle ACB$.	**4.** If two rt. $\triangle$ have an acute $\angle$ of . . . .
5. In rt. $\triangle$ CDB and ACB, $\angle B \cong \angle B$.	**5.** Same as reason 3.
6. Rt. $\triangle CDB \sim$ rt. $\triangle ACB$.	**6.** Same as reason 4.
7. $\triangle ADC \sim \triangle CDB$.	**7.** Similarity of $\triangle$ is transitive.

COROLLARY 1   The length of a leg of a right triangle is the geometric mean between the length of the hypotenuse and the length of the projection of that leg on the hypotenuse.

By Theorem 9–1, $\triangle ADC \sim \triangle ACB$; therefore $\dfrac{AD}{AC} = \dfrac{AC}{AB}$.

By Theorem 9–1, $\triangle CDB \sim \triangle ACB$; therefore $\dfrac{BD}{BC} = \dfrac{BC}{BA}$.

COROLLARY 2   The length of the altitude drawn to the hypotenuse of a right triangle is the geometric mean between the lengths of the segments of the hypotenuse.

By Theorem 9–1, $\triangle ADC \sim \triangle CDB$; therefore $\dfrac{AD}{CD} = \dfrac{CD}{DB}$.

COROLLARY 3 In a right triangle the product of the lengths of the hypotenuse and the altitude drawn to the hypotenuse is equal to the product of the lengths of the legs.

Since $\triangle ACB \sim \triangle ADC$, $\dfrac{AB}{AC} = \dfrac{BC}{CD}$ and $AB \cdot CD = AC \cdot BC$.

A figure in which a single letter designates the length of a segment will help you remember these three corollaries.

COROLLARY 1 $\dfrac{x}{a} = \dfrac{a}{c}, \dfrac{y}{b} = \dfrac{b}{c}$.

COROLLARY 2 $\dfrac{x}{h} = \dfrac{h}{y}$.

COROLLARY 3 $hc = ab$.

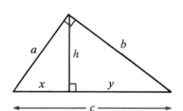

In applying the corollaries, you will often find irrational numbers represented in radical form. We remind you of some properties of radicals that you should keep in mind.

1. A **radical** is an indicated root of a number.

$$\sqrt{3}, \ \sqrt[3]{2}, \ \sqrt[4]{5} \text{ are radicals.}$$

2. The **radical sign,** $\sqrt{\ }$, indicates the positive square root.

3. The **radicand** is the number appearing under the radical sign.

4. An expression having a square-root radical is in **simplest form** when

   a) no integral radicand has a square factor other than 1,
   b) no fraction appears as a radicand, and
   c) no radical is in a denominator.

5. If $x > 0$ and $y > 0$, then $\sqrt{xy} = \sqrt{x} \cdot \sqrt{y}$.

EXAMPLE. Simplify: $\sqrt{20}$. *Solution:* $\sqrt{20} = \sqrt{4} \cdot \sqrt{5} = 2\sqrt{5}$

6. If $x > 0$ and $y > 0$, then $\sqrt{\dfrac{x}{y}} = \dfrac{\sqrt{x}}{\sqrt{y}} = \dfrac{\sqrt{xy}}{y}$.

EXAMPLE. Simplify: $\sqrt{\dfrac{2}{3}}$.   *Solution:* $\sqrt{\dfrac{2}{3}} = \sqrt{\dfrac{6}{9}} = \dfrac{\sqrt{6}}{\sqrt{9}} = \dfrac{\sqrt{6}}{3}$

7. When the variable in a quadratic equation represents a length, disregard negative roots as possible answers, since distance is > 0.

1. Name the geometric mean in each proportion.

a. $\dfrac{2}{4} = \dfrac{4}{8}$ **b.** $\dfrac{c}{d} = \dfrac{d}{t}$ **c.** $\dfrac{6}{4} = \dfrac{9}{6}$ **d.** $\dfrac{a}{s} = \dfrac{t}{a}$

2. Express each of the following numbers in simplest form.

a. $\sqrt{8}$ **b.** $\sqrt{49}$ **c.** $2\sqrt{12}$ **d.** $\dfrac{1}{\sqrt{5}}$ **e.** $\sqrt{\dfrac{1}{3}}$

3. If x represents the length of a segment, what are the acceptable values for x in each of the following?

a. $\dfrac{x}{4} = \dfrac{9}{x}$ **b.** $x^2 = 25$ **c.** $x = \pm\sqrt{9}$ **d.** $\dfrac{1}{x} = \dfrac{4x}{1}$

4. Which of these numbers are possible lengths of a segment?

a. $-\sqrt{7}$ **b.** $2 + \sqrt{12}$ **c.** $2 - \sqrt{12}$ **d.** $\sqrt{2} + \sqrt{3}$

5. In $\triangle RST$, $\overline{RS} \perp \overline{ST}$ and $\overline{SX} \perp \overline{RT}$. State the theorem or corollary which supports the conclusion that:

a. $\triangle RST \sim \triangle SXT$

b. $\dfrac{RT}{ST} = \dfrac{ST}{XT}$

c. $\dfrac{RX}{SX} = \dfrac{SX}{TX}$

d. $\dfrac{RX}{RS} = \dfrac{RS}{RT}$

e. $RT \cdot SX = RS \cdot ST$

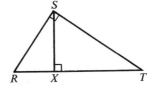

6. Refer to the adjacent figure and supply the missing terms:

a. $\dfrac{m}{?} = \dfrac{?}{n}$

b. $\dfrac{?}{r} = \dfrac{r}{m + n}$

c. $r \cdot s = (m + n) \cdot \underline{\ ?\ }$

d. $\dfrac{m + n}{s} = \dfrac{s}{?}$

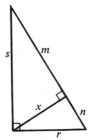

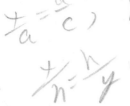

$$\frac{y}{a} = \frac{a}{c}, \quad \frac{y}{b} = \frac{b}{c}.$$

$$\frac{h}{n} = \frac{h}{y}$$

$$hc = ab$$

| **WRITTEN** |
| **EXERCISES** |

A **1.** Write the geometric mean between

    a. 4 and 8   **b.** 6 and 3   **c.** 8 and 5   **d.** $4k$ and k $(k \neq 0)$

2. Express in simplest form:

    a. $\sqrt{75}$ **b.** $2\sqrt{45}$ **c.** $\sqrt{\frac{2}{3}}$ **d.** $4\sqrt{\frac{5}{2}}$

3. Solve for all positive values of x:

    a. $\frac{2}{x} = \frac{x}{6}$ **b.** $\frac{x}{4} = \frac{5}{x}$ **c.** $x^2 + 3 = 12$ **d.** $x^2 - 2 = 6$

4. $\sqrt{6}$ is the geometric mean between

    a. 2 and ___?___   **b.** 12 and ___?___ **c.** 6 and ___?___   **d.** 4 and ___?___

In $\triangle ABC$, $\overline{AC} \perp \overline{BC}$ and $\overline{CD} \perp \overline{AB}$.

EXAMPLE. Find DB if $AD = 4$ and $CD = 6$.

Solution: Let $DB = x$.

(cord #) Then $\dfrac{4}{6} = \dfrac{6}{x}$

         $4x = 36$ *Check:* $\dfrac{4}{6} \overset{?}{=} \dfrac{6}{9}$

         $x = 9.$ **Answer.** $\dfrac{2}{3} = \dfrac{2}{3}.$

Exs. 5–10

5. If $AD = 2$ and $DB = 8$, find CD.

Cord # **6.** If $AD = 3$ and $DB = 6$, find AC.

7. Find DB if $BC = 6$ and $AD = 5$.

8. Find AD if $DC = 4$ and $DB = 6$.

9. If $AB = 12$ and $DB = 8$, find AC.

10. Find CD if $AC = 3$, $BC = 4$, and $AB = 5$.

In Exs. 11–14, it is given that $\angle RTS$ is a rt. $\angle$ and that $\overline{TQ} \perp \overline{RS}$.

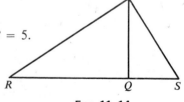

Exs. 11–14

11. Given: $TQ = n$.

    Prove: $RQ \cdot QS = n^2$.

12. Given: $RT = 5$.

    Prove: $RQ \cdot RS = 25$.

13. Given: $ST = \sqrt{13}$.

    Prove: $QS \cdot RS = 13$.

14. Given: $RS \cdot TQ = m^2$.

    Prove: $RT \cdot ST = m^2$.

In Exs. 15 and 16 the perpendicular segments are indicated. Find *x*, *y*, and *z*.

B **15.**

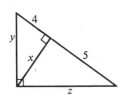

16.

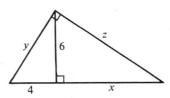

In the given right triangle ABC, $m\angle ACB = 90$ and $\overleftrightarrow{CD}$ is an altitude.

17. What segment is the projection of $\overline{BC}$ on $\overrightarrow{AB}$?

18. What segment is the projection of $\overline{AC}$ on $\overrightarrow{AB}$?

19. If $AD = 2$ and $DC = \sqrt{6}$, find BD.

20. If $BC = \sqrt{15}$ and $BD = 3$, find AD.

21. Find AD if $AC = 8$ and $BD = 12$.

22. Find BD if $DC = 8$ and $BD:AD = 2:1$.

23. Given: $m\angle ACB = 90$; $\overline{CX} \perp \overline{AB}$;
$AB \cdot CX = (AC)^2$.

Prove: $AC = BC$.

24. Given: $m\angle ACB = 90$; $\overline{CX} \perp \overline{AB}$;
$(AC)^2 = 2(AX)^2$.

Prove: $AX = \frac{1}{2}AB$.

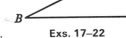

Exs. 17–22

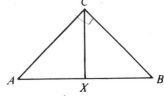

Exs. 23, 24

C **25.** Given right triangle ABC in which $m\angle ACB = 90$, $\overline{CY} \perp \overline{AB}$, and $\overline{CX}$ bisects $\overline{AB}$.

If $CY = 4\frac{4}{5}$ and $BC = 6$, find XY.

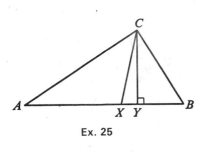

Ex. 25

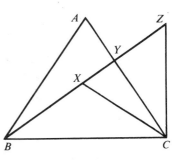

Ex. 26

26. Given the plane figure in which $AB = AC$, $CX = XZ$, $\overline{BZ} \perp \overline{AC}$ at Y, $\overline{ZC} \perp \overline{BC}$.

Prove: $\triangle ABC \sim \triangle XCZ$.

9–2 The Pythagorean Theorem

The theorem to be proved in this section is one of the best known and most useful theorems in all mathematics. It states an important relationship between the lengths of the legs and the length of the hypotenuse of a right triangle. Most of you are already familiar with the relationship, perhaps knowing it by such names as the "Right Triangle Principle" or the "Rule of Pythagoras."

THEOREM 9–2 In any right triangle the square of the length of the hypotenuse is equal to the sum of the squares of the lengths of the legs.

Given: Rt. $\triangle ABC$ with $m\angle C = 90$.

To Prove: $c^2 = a^2 + b^2$.

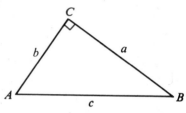

Analysis: Draw the altitude to the hypotenuse. Write proportions involving the length of each leg as a geometric mean. Transform each proportion to product form and add.

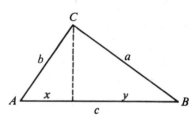

Proof

STATEMENT	REASON
1. Draw a perpendicular from C to $\overline{AB}$. Label segments of $\overline{AB}$ as shown.	1. Through a point outside a line there is exactly one perpendicular to the line.
2. $\dfrac{c}{a} = \dfrac{a}{y}$ and $\dfrac{c}{b} = \dfrac{b}{x}$.	2. The length of a leg of a right triangle is the geometric mean between __?__.
3. $cy = a^2$ and $cx = b^2$.	3. A property of proportions.
4. $cy + cx = a^2 + b^2$.	4. Addition property of equality.
5. $c(y + x) = a^2 + b^2$.	5. Distributive property.
6. $c^2 = a^2 + b^2$.	6. Substitution principle. ($c = x + y$)

The **Pythagorean Theorem** (pih-**thag**-o-**ree**-an) is so named because the first formal proof is attributed to the famous Greek philosopher Pythagoras (about 584–495 B.C.). It is believed that his method of proof was based on a comparison of areas. The proof presented on page 320 resembles a proof first used by Hindu mathematicians. Hundreds of different proofs for this theorem have been published over the years.

It is natural to consider the converse of this famous theorem.

THEOREM 9–3 If the sum of the squares of the lengths of two sides of a triangle is equal to the square of the length of the third side, the triangle is a right triangle. (Converse of the Pythagorean Theorem)

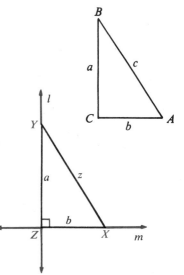

Given: $a^2 + b^2 = c^2$.
To Prove: $m\angle C = 90$.

Outline of proof:
At a point Z on a line l, draw a line $m \perp l$.
On l mark off $ZY = a$ and on m mark off
$\quad ZX = b$.
Draw $\overline{XY}$.
In right $\triangle XYZ$, $a^2 + b^2 = z^2$.
But $a^2 + b^2 = c^2$.
Therefore $c^2 = z^2$ and $c = z$.
$\triangle ABC \cong \triangle XYZ$, and $\angle C \cong \angle Z$.
$m\angle C = 90$.

ORAL EXERCISES

1. Can the three sides of a right triangle have lengths 2, 2, and 3?

2. Is the hypotenuse of a right triangle always longer than the altitude drawn to the hypotenuse?

3. Which of the following equations correctly express the relationship between a, b, and c in the given right triangle?

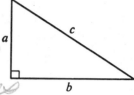

yes **a.** $a^2 + b^2 = c^2$

d. $b = \sqrt{c^2 - a^2}$ *yes*

yes **b.** $a = \pm\sqrt{c^2 - b^2}$

e. $a^2 = (c - b)(c + b)$ *yes*

no **c.** $b^2 + c^2 = a^2$

f. $\dfrac{1}{a^2} + \dfrac{1}{b^2} = \dfrac{1}{c^2}$ *no*

4. State the equation you would write to find x in each of the right triangles shown:

$3^2 + 4^2 = x^2$ $x^2 = 6^2 - 4^2$ $2\sqrt{2}$ ... $x^2 = \sqrt{9 + 3}^2$

a.

b.

c.

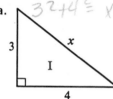

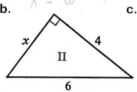

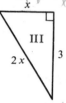

5. State the number which is the square of,
   a. $\sqrt{3}$ *3*   **b.** $2\sqrt{2}$ *8*   **c.** $\frac{1}{2}\sqrt{2}$ *½*   **d.** $3\sqrt{5}$ *45*   **e.** $\frac{1}{2}$ *¼*

6. State the exact number which is the positive square root of
   a. 9 *3*   **b.** 8 $2\sqrt{2}$ **c.** $12k^4$ $2k^2\sqrt{3}$ **d.** $\frac{1}{2}$ $\frac{\sqrt{2}}{2}$ **e.** 1 *1*

yes 7. If you are given the length of the hypotenuse of an isosceles right triangle, can you determine the length of a leg?

yes 8. If you are given the lengths of both diagonals of a rhombus, can you determine the length of a side?

WRITTEN EXERCISES

In the right triangle, a and b are the lengths of the legs and c is the length of the hypotenuse. In each exercise find the lengths of the sides not given. Express each radical answer in simplest form.

EXAMPLE. $a = 2\sqrt{3}$, $c = 6$

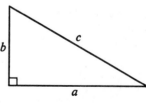

Solution: $(2\sqrt{3})^2 + b^2 = 36$
$$12 + b^2 = 36$$
$$b^2 = 24$$
$$b = \sqrt{24} = 2\sqrt{6}, \text{ Answer.}$$

Check: $12 + 24 \overset{?}{=} 36; \ 36 = 36$

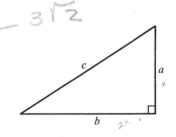

1. $a = 6, b = 8$ **5.** $a = 3\sqrt{2}, c = 6$
2. $a = 3, b = 3$ **6.** $b = \sqrt{3}, c = \sqrt{5}$
3. $b = 8, c = 12$ **7.** $a{:}b = 1{:}2, c = 5$
4. $b = \frac{1}{2}, c = 1$ **8.** $b{:}c = 1{:}2, a = 6$

9. Find the length of a diagonal of a square whose side has length
a. 4 in.   **b.** 6 cm.   **c.** $6\sqrt{2}$ ft.   **d.** $2t$ units

10. Find the length of a side of a square whose diagonal has length
a. 6 in.   **b.** 4 cm.   **c.** $\sqrt{2}$ ft.   **d.** $2t$ units

11. A rectangle 6 in. wide has a diagonal 10 in. long. Find the perimeter.

12. Find the length of a diagonal of a rectangle whose perimeter is 20 in. and whose width is 4 in.

13. Given: $\triangle RST$ with $\overline{SX} \perp \overline{RT}$.
   Prove: $a^2 - b^2 = c^2 - d^2$.

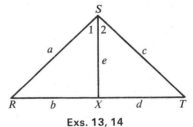

14. Given: $\triangle RST$ with $a = c$ and $\angle 1 \cong \angle 2$.
   Prove: $b^2 + e^2 = a^2$.

Exs. 13, 14

15. A man walks 7 mi. due north, 6 mi. due east, and then 4 mi. due north. How far is he from his starting point?

16. A man travels 5 mi. north, 2 mi. east, 1 mi. north, and then 4 mi. east. How far is he from his starting point?

17. The legs of an isosceles triangle are each 6 in. long. If the base is 8 in. long, find the length of the altitude to the base.

18. In an isosceles triangle the altitude to the base is 8 in. long. The legs are each 10 in. long. Find the length of the base.

19. Find the length of an altitude of an equilateral triangle with a side 6 in. long.

20. Find the length of an altitude of an equilateral triangle with a side $2\sqrt{3}$ in. long.

21. An isosceles right triangle has a 6-inch hypotenuse. Find the length of a leg.

22. Each leg of an isosceles right triangle is $5\sqrt{2}$ ft. long. Find the length of the hypotenuse.

23. The diagonals of a rhombus are 12 in. and 16 in. long. Find the perimeter of the rhombus.

24. The lengths of the diagonals of a rhombus have the ratio 2:1. If the perimeter of the rhombus is 40 in., find the length of each diagonal.

25. The legs of a right triangle are 9 in. and 12 in. long. Find the length of the projection of the longer leg upon the hypotenuse.

26. The hypotenuse of a right triangle is 8 ft. long and the projection of the shorter leg upon the hypotenuse is 2 ft. long. Find the lengths of the legs.

27. Given: $\overline{AB} \perp$ plane M; $\overline{BC} \perp \overline{CD}$.

   Prove: $(AD)^2 = (AB)^2 + (BC)^2 + (CD)^2$.

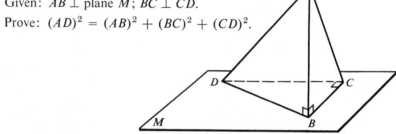

Exs. 27, 28

28. Given: $\overline{AB} \perp$ plane M; $\overline{BC} \perp \overline{CD}$.

   Prove: $(AC)^2 = (AB)^2 + (BD)^2 - (CD)^2$.

C **29.** Determine x and y in the figure shown.

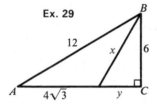

Ex. 29

30. The sides of a triangle are 10, 17, and 21 in. long. Find the length of the altitude to the 21-inch side. *Hint:* Use two variables.

Ex. 30

31. The sides of a right triangle are 3, 4, and 5 ft. long. A point is taken on the hypotenuse and at a distance of 2 ft. from the vertex where the hypotenuse and longer leg meet. Find the distance between the point and the vertex of the right angle.

32. Given: rectangle $ABCD$ with X any interior point.

   Prove: $(XA)^2 + (XC)^2 = (XB)^2 + (XD)^2$.

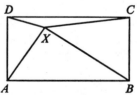

Ex. 32

9–3 Special Right Triangles: 30°–60°–90° and 45°–45°–90°

There are two special right triangles in which you can readily find the lengths of the other two sides when given the length of any one side. The relationships existing between the lengths of the sides in these two special right triangles follow from the Pythagorean Theorem.

THEOREM 9–4 If the acute angles of a right triangle have measures 30 and 60, the hypotenuse is twice as long as the shorter leg and the longer leg is $\sqrt{3}$ times as long as the shorter leg. (30°–60°–90° theorem.)

Given: Rt. $\triangle ACB$; $m\angle A = 60$; $m\angle B = 30$; $AC = t$.

To Prove: $AB = 2t$; $BC = t\sqrt{3}$.

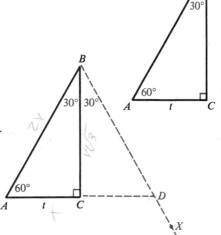

Outline of proof:

Draw $\overrightarrow{BX}$ so that $m\angle CBX = 30$.
$\overrightarrow{BX}$ and $\overrightarrow{AC}$ intersect at a point D.
$\triangle ABD$ is an equilateral $\triangle$; $CD = t$.
$AB = AD = 2t$.
Since $(AB)^2 = (AC)^2 + (BC)^2$,
$(2t)^2 = t^2 + (BC)^2$, $3t^2 = (BC)^2$,
and $BC = t\sqrt{3}$.

THEOREM 9–5 If each acute angle of a right triangle has measure 45, the hypotenuse is $\sqrt{2}$ times as long as a leg. (45°–45°–90° theorem.)

Given: Rt. $\triangle ACB$; $m\angle A = m\angle B = 45$; $AC = t$.

To Prove: $AB = t\sqrt{2}$.

Outline of proof:

If $AC = t$, $BC = t$. $(AB)^2 = (AC)^2 + (BC)^2$.
$(AB)^2 = t^2 + t^2$, $(AB)^2 = 2t^2$, and $AB = t\sqrt{2}$.

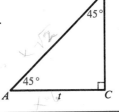

In working with special right triangles, you will sometimes write an expression that shows a radical in a denominator. Recall that you can simplify such a fraction by multiplying numerator and denominator by the same number. Choose a number that makes the resulting denominator a rational number.

EXAMPLE 1. $6 \div \sqrt{2} = \dfrac{6}{\sqrt{2}} = \dfrac{6\sqrt{2}}{\sqrt{2} \cdot \sqrt{2}} = \dfrac{6\sqrt{2}}{\sqrt{4}} = \dfrac{6\sqrt{2}}{2} = 3\sqrt{2}$

EXAMPLE 2. $5 \div \sqrt{12} = \dfrac{5}{\sqrt{12}} = \dfrac{5\sqrt{3}}{\sqrt{12} \cdot \sqrt{3}} = \dfrac{5\sqrt{3}}{\sqrt{36}} = \dfrac{5\sqrt{3}}{6}$

EXAMPLE 3. $2\sqrt{3} \div 3\sqrt{2} = \dfrac{2\sqrt{3}}{3\sqrt{2}} = \dfrac{2\sqrt{3} \cdot \sqrt{2}}{3\sqrt{2} \cdot \sqrt{2}} = \dfrac{2\sqrt{6}}{3\sqrt{4}} = \dfrac{2\sqrt{6}}{6} = \dfrac{\sqrt{6}}{3}$

Two typical right-triangle problems whose solutions involve division by an irrational number in radical form follow.

EXAMPLE 4. Find the length of a side of an equilateral triangle whose altitude is 6 in. long.

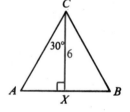

Solution: By the 30°–60°–90° theorem,

$$AX = \frac{6}{\sqrt{3}} = 2\sqrt{3} \text{ (in.)}$$

$$AC = 2(2\sqrt{3}) = 4\sqrt{3} \text{ (in.)}.$$

EXAMPLE 5. Find the length of a side of an isosceles right triangle whose hypotenuse is 5 in. long.

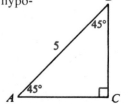

Solution: $AB = 5$ in.
By the 45°–45°–90° theorem,

$$AC = \frac{5}{\sqrt{2}} = \frac{5\sqrt{2}}{2} \text{ (in.)}.$$

ORAL EXERCISES

1. Opposite which angle of a 30°–60°–90° triangle is the shorter leg? *30°*

2. State the length of each leg of a 30°–60°–90° triangle in which the hypotenuse has length 6*t*.

3. If you know the length of the longer leg in a 30°–60°–90° triangle, how do you find the length of the shorter leg?

4. Each leg of an isosceles right triangle is 6 in. long. What is the length of the hypotenuse?

5. When you know the length of the hypotenuse of an isosceles right triangle, how do you find the length of a leg?

6. When a diagonal is drawn in a square, will a 45°–45°–90° triangle be formed?

7. When any altitude is drawn in an equilateral triangle, is a 30°–60°–90° triangle formed?

8. What is the ratio of the length of the longer leg to the length of the hypotenuse in a 30°–60°–90° triangle?

WRITTEN EXERCISES

A

1. Find the length of the hypotenuse of an isosceles right triangle whose legs each have length

   a. 6 in.   **b.** 8 in.   **c.** $3\sqrt{2}$ in.   **d.** $2a\sqrt{2}$ in.

2. Find the length of a leg of an isosceles right triangle whose hypotenuse has length

   a. 12 in.   **b.** 8 in.   **c.** $6\sqrt{2}$ in.   **d.** $10a\sqrt{2}$ in.

3. Find the length of the hypotenuse of a 30°–60°–90° triangle whose shorter leg has length

   a. 8 cm.   **b.** $4\frac{1}{2}$ cm.   **c.** $2\sqrt{3}$ cm.   **d.** $4t\sqrt{5}$ cm.

4. Find the length of the hypotenuse of a 30°–60°–90° triangle whose longer leg has length

   a. $10\sqrt{3}$ ft.   **b.** $6\sqrt{3}$ ft.   **c.** 6 ft.   **d.** *t* ft.

5. Find the length of the altitude of an equliateral triangle whose side has length

    a. 6 cm.   **b.** 8 cm.   **c.** $2\sqrt{3}$ cm.   **d.** t cm.

6. Find the length of a side of an equilateral triangle whose altitude has length

    a. 6 m.   **b.** 12 m.   **c.** $6\sqrt{3}$ m.   **d.** $t\sqrt{3}$ m.

In each exercise the length of one segment of the plane figure is given. Find the lengths of the remaining segments.

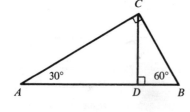

	AB	BC	CD	AD	DB	AC
7.	8	?	?	?	?	?
8.	?	2	?	?	?	?
9.	?	?	$4\sqrt{3}$	?	?	?
10.	?	?	?	9	?	?
11.	?	?	?	?	$10\sqrt{3}$	?
12.	?	?	?	?	?	$8\sqrt{3}$

13. The perimeters of two 30°–60°–90° triangles are in the ratio 1:2. If the hypotenuse of the larger triangle is 12 in. long, find the lengths of the sides of the smaller triangle.

14. The side of one square is equal in length to the diagonal of a second square. What is the ratio of the perimeter of the larger square to that of the smaller square?

15. The length of a side of one equilateral triangle is equal to the length of an altitude of a second equilateral triangle. What is the ratio of the perimeter of the larger triangle to that of the smaller?

16. Prove that in a 30°–60°–90° triangle the altitude on the hypotenuse divides the hypotenuse into segments with lengths in the ratio 1:3.

17. Prove that in a 30°–60°–90° triangle the ray which bisects the larger acute angle divides the opposite leg into segments with lengths in the ratio 1 to 2.

18. Prove that if one angle of a rhombus has a measure of 60, the diagonals have lengths in the ratio $\sqrt{3}$ to 1.

19. Express the perimeter of trapezoid $ABCD$ in simplest exact form.

20. Given trapezoid *RSTQ*. Express the length of $\overline{QT}$ in terms of *k*.

Ex. 20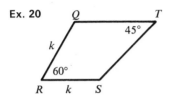

Ex. 21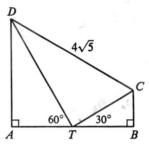

21. Find the length of $\overline{AB}$ if the ratio of the perimeter of △*TBC* to that of △*DAT* is 1:2.

22. Find the ratio of the perimeters of the following pairs of triangles.

  a. △*ACX* and △*BCA*

  b. △*ACX* and △*BAX*

  c. △*ACB* and △*ABY*

  d. △*XAB* and △*ABY*

  e. △*ABY* and △*BCY*

  f. △*ACX* and △*YCB*

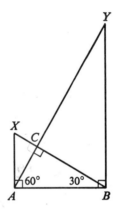

■ Applying the Pythagorean Theorem

9–4   Right Triangles in Three-Dimensional Figures

The Pythagorean Theorem has many applications in finding lengths of segments in three-dimensional figures. Your success in working with three-dimensional figures will depend to a great extent upon your ability to recognize right triangles in two-dimensional drawings where the legs do not "appear" to meet at right angles. You may understand relationships between lines and planes better if you hold sticks or pencils in appropriate positions as you look at drawings of three-dimensional figures.

Two line-plane relationships resulting in the formation of right triangles are shown.

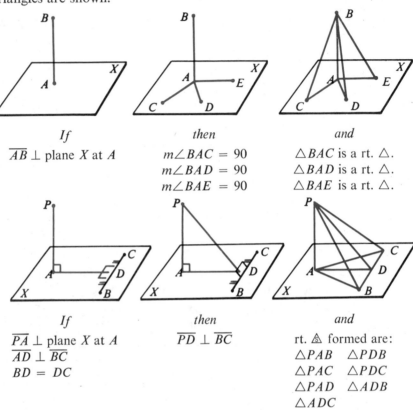

If	then	and
$\overline{AB} \perp$ plane X at A	$m\angle BAC = 90$	$\triangle BAC$ is a rt. $\triangle$.
	$m\angle BAD = 90$	$\triangle BAD$ is a rt. $\triangle$.
	$m\angle BAE = 90$	$\triangle BAE$ is a rt. $\triangle$.

If	then	and
$\overline{PA} \perp$ plane X at A	$\overline{PD} \perp \overline{BC}$	rt. $\triangle$ formed are:
$\overline{AD} \perp \overline{BC}$		$\triangle PAB$ $\triangle PDB$
$BD = DC$		$\triangle PAC$ $\triangle PDC$
		$\triangle PAD$ $\triangle ADB$
		$\triangle ADC$

Two common solids are pictured below. Each is an enclosed region of space bounded by planes. Any solid so formed is called a **polyhedron.**

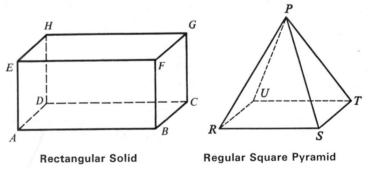

Rectangular Solid   **Regular Square Pyramid**

You will not be held responsible for the exact definitions of terms used in describing these solids. However, you should be familiar with these terms and be able to associate them with the appropriate points, segments, or planes in figures.

Face: The rectangular solid has six rectangular faces. The opposite faces are parallel; adjacent faces are perpendicular. Take face *ABCD* to be the base. Then the faces that intersect base *ABCD* are called **lateral faces.** The regular square pyramid has a square face as its base. The other faces are **lateral faces,** which intersect in a point that lies on a line perpendicular to the plane of the base at the center of the base.

Edge: Any segment formed by the intersection of two faces. The rectangular solid has twelve edges. The regular square pyramid has eight edges.

Vertex: Any point which is the intersection of two edges. The rectangular solid has eight vertices, and the regular square pyramid has five vertices.

Diagonal of a rectangular solid: A segment whose endpoints are vertices not in the same face. In the rectangular solid shown, $\overline{HB}$ is one of four congruent diagonals. Name the others.

By successive applications of the Pythagorean Theorem, the length of the diagonal of a rectangular solid can be expressed in terms of the lengths of the edges.

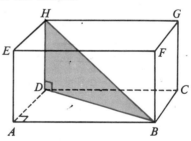

In right $\triangle DAB$, $(DB)^2 = (AD)^2 + (AB)^2$
In right $\triangle HDB$, $(HB)^2 = (DB)^2 + (DH)^2$
By the substitution principle, $(HB)^2 = (AD)^2 + (AB)^2 + (DH)^2$
      or $HB = \sqrt{(AD)^2 + (AB)^2 + (DH)^2}$

On the basis of the foregoing you should be able to write a formula for the length of a diagonal d of a rectangular solid with dimensions l, w, and h.

The following terms are used to name special segments in a regular square pyramid.

Altitude: The segment perpendicular to the base from the vertex common to the triangular faces.

Slant height: The length of the altitude of any one of the four congruent triangular faces (isosceles triangles).

Lateral edge: A segment joining the vertex common to the triangular faces to any vertex in the base.

In the figure at the right,

   altitude: $\overline{XY}$

   slant height: XZ

   lateral edges: $\overline{XR}$, $\overline{XS}$, $\overline{XT}$, $\overline{XV}$

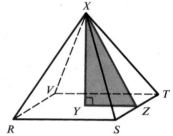

EXAMPLE. Find the slant height and the length of a lateral edge of a regular square pyramid with a 4-in. altitude and a 6-in. base.

Solution: Let l denote the slant height, in inches.

$$l^2 = (4)^2 + (3)^2 = 25$$
$$l = 5 \text{ (in.)}$$

Let k denote the length of the lateral edge, in inches.

$$k^2 = (l)^2 + (3)^2 = 25 + 9$$
$$k = \sqrt{34} \text{ (in.)}$$

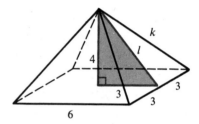

ORAL EXERCISES

Given the adjacent rectangular solid.

1. How many faces does the solid have?

2. Name four segments which are perpendicular to $\overline{BS}$.

3. Name four pairs of points which could serve as endpoints of a diagonal of the solid.

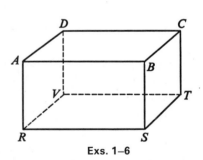

Exs. 1–6

4. Name three edges which have the same length as $\overline{AD}$.

5. If $\overline{VS}$ is drawn, what is the measure of $\angle DVS$?

6. Name three edges which are parallel to $\overline{DC}$.

Given the adjacent regular square pyramid.

7. Name the lateral edges.

8. Is $\triangle PXY \cong \triangle PXZ$?

9. Does $PY = PZ$?

10. Is $PB > PY$?

11. Must the slant height of a square pyramid be greater than the length of the altitude?

12. Can all eight edges of a regular square pyramid have equal lengths?

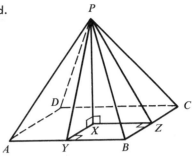

Exs. 7–12

WRITTEN EXERCISES

In the given rectangular solid, $AB = 6''$, $BC = 3''$ and $BM = 4''$. Find the following lengths.

1. OD	**5.** BN
2. CD	**6.** AM
3. LO	**7.** OB
4. DB	**8.** LC

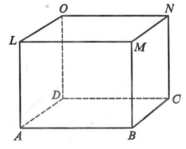

In the given regular square pyramid, $AB = 6''$ and $PX = 4''$. Find the following lengths.

9. XY	**13.** PB
10. PY	**14.** PC
11. BY	**15.** DB
12. BC	**16.** BX

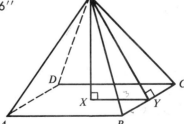

17. Find the length of a diagonal of a rectangular solid with length 6 in., width 2 in., and height 4 in.

18. Find the length of a diagonal of a rectangular solid with length 8 in., width 4 in., and height 5 in.

19. The base of a rectangular solid is a square with a $6\sqrt{2}$-cm. diagonal. The height of the solid is 4 cm. Find the length of a diagonal of the solid.

20. The bottom of a rectangular box is a rectangle with a $4\sqrt{3}$ in. diagonal. Find the length of a diagonal of the box if the height is 3 in.

21. A rectangular solid with all edges congruent is a **cube.** Find the length of a diagonal of a cube with a 4-inch edge.

22. Find the length of a diagonal of a cube with an edge 3 cm. long.

23. Find the length of a diagonal of a cube whose edge is t feet long.

24. Find the length of an edge of a cube whose diagonal is $4\sqrt{3}$ in. long.

25. A regular square pyramid has a base with a 6-in. edge and has a 4-in. altitude. Find the slant height and the length of a lateral edge of the pyramid.

26. All edges of a regular square pyramid are 4 in. long. Find the slant height and the length of the altitude of the pyramid.

C 27. The length, width, and height of a rectangular solid are in the ratio $3:4:12$. If the diagonal is 26 in. long, find the three dimensions.

28. The base of a rectangular solid is a rectangle 4 units wide and 6 units long. Find the height of the solid if its diagonal is $\sqrt{61}$ units long.

29. If you wished to pack a 3-foot rifle in a cubical box, what would be the minimum interior length of a suitable box?

30. If the diagonal of a face of a cube is 4 in. long, find the length of a diagonal of the cube.

31. The diagonal of one face of a cube is t inches long. Find the length of a diagonal of the cube.

32. In the given rectangular solid, Y is the midpoint of $\overline{AB}$. Write an argument in paragraph form showing that $\overline{HB}$ and $\overline{GY}$ must intersect. Then, find HX if $AB = 6$, $AD = 4$, $HD = 3$.

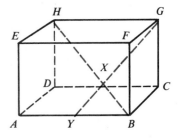

9–5 Projections into a Plane

Many interesting applications of the Pythagorean Theorem involve projections in three-dimensional situations.

The **projection of a point into a plane** is the point of intersection of the plane and the perpendicular segment from the point to the plane. When a point lies in a plane, the projection of that point into the plane is the point itself. The **projection of a set of points** X **into a plane** Y is the set of points in Y which are the projections of the points in X.

In the figure at the right:

$\overline{AB}$ is the set of points being projected.

$\overline{MN}$ is the projection of $\overline{AB}$ into plane Y.

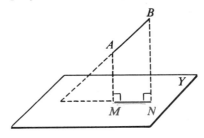

In the second figure:

planes M and Y are not parallel.

$\triangle ABC$ is the set of points being projected.

$\triangle RST$ is the projection of $\triangle ABC$ into Y.

$\triangle RST$ is not $\cong \triangle ABC$.

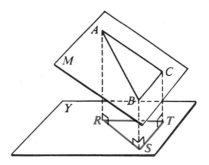

In this figure, plane $X \perp$ plane Y:

$\triangle ABC$, contained in plane X, is the set of points being projected.

$\overline{MN}$ is the projection of $\triangle ABC$ into Y.

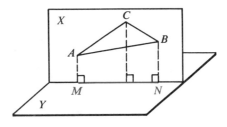

ORAL
EXERCISES

1. Is the projection of a segment into a plane always a segment? No

2. Can the projection of a segment into a plane be longer than the given segment? No

3. Can a rectangle be placed so that its projection into a plane is a segment? Yes

4. Can a rectangle be placed so that its projection into a plane is a point? No

5. Can the projection of an angle into a plane be a ray? a line? Yes

WRITTEN EXERCISES

1. Draw a diagram which illustrates a placement of $\triangle ABC$ with respect to plane K so that its projection $\triangle XYZ$ is congruent to $\triangle ABC$.

2. Draw a diagram which illustrates a placement of two skew segments l and m with respect to plane K such that their projections into K intersect.

3. If a segment is parallel to a plane, what will be true of the length of its projection into that plane?

4. The projection of a rectangle into a particular plane is a segment. What can you say about the plane of the rectangle and the given plane?

In the given diagram, $\angle A$ has measure 30.

5. If $AB = 6$, find AC.

6. If $AB = 4\sqrt{3}$, find AC.

7. If $AC = 9$, find AB.

8. If $AC = 6\sqrt{3}$, find AB.

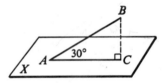

Exs. 5–8

9. What is the length of the projection of a 10-inch segment into a plane if the segment and its projection into the plane determine an angle with measure

   a. 30?   **b.** 45?   **c.** 60?   **d.** 90?

10. What is the measure of the angle determined by a 14-inch segment and its projection into a plane if the length, in inches, of the projection into the plane is

   a. 7?   **b.** $7\sqrt{2}$?   **c.** $7\sqrt{3}$?   **d.** 14?

In the given diagram $\overline{AB}$ is contained in plane T, and $ABCD$ is a rectangle. Segments $\overline{CR}$ and $\overline{DS}$ are perpendicular to plane T. $\angle CBR$ and $\angle DAS$ have measure n.

11. For $n < 90$, is the projection of $ABCD$ into plane T necessarily a rectangle?

12. For what value of n is $AS = \frac{1}{2}AD$?

13. Is the length of the projection of $\overline{DC}$ dependent upon the number n?

14. If $n = 45$ and $BC = 12$, find RB.

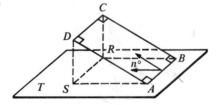

15. If $AD = 8$ and $AB = 4$, for what value of n is the projection of $ABCD$ a square?

16. If $n = 30$, $AB = 4$, and $AS = 6\sqrt{3}$, what are the dimensions of rectangle $ABCD$?

17. A square with 6-inch side can be placed in position with respect to a plane so that its projection into the plane is a segment. How long can the projection be? How short?

18. Repeat Ex. 17, substituting a 3-inch by 4-inch rectangle for the square.

In the given diagram, $\triangle ABC$ is an equilateral triangle with altitude $\overline{CP}$. $\overline{PC}$ and its projection into the plane determine a 30° angle.

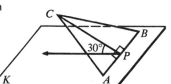

19. If $AB = 6$, find the perimeter of the projection of $\triangle ABC$ into plane K.

20. Repeat Ex. 19 if $AB = t$ units.

■ Trigonometry

9–6   The Tangent Ratio

The word *Trigonometry* literally means triangle measurement. The study of this branch of mathematics began before the Christian era when astronomers and surveyors used properties of similar triangles to determine distances that they could not measure directly. The brief discussion of trigonometry to be found here is limited to the trigonometry of right triangles.

The lengths of the sides of right triangle ABC are commonly denoted by small letters as shown. The tangent of angle A, usually shortened to *tangent A* (tan A) is defined by the equation:

$$\tan A = \frac{a}{b}$$

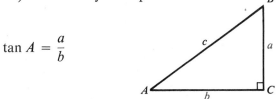

You may find it easy to remember the definition in the form

$$\tan A = \frac{\text{length of opposite side}}{\text{length of adjacent side}}.$$

Because any two right triangles, $\triangle ABC$ and $\triangle AB'C'$, having angle A as an acute angle are similar by the AA postulate, the lengths of corresponding sides are in proportion, $\dfrac{a}{b} = \dfrac{a'}{b'}$, and it does not matter what triangle is used. Note that tan A is a number, the ratio of two lengths.

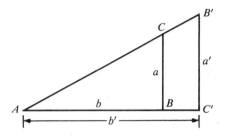

The number tan A is often referred to as the **tangent ratio.**

You could get an approximation for the tangent of angle A by measuring the legs of any right triangle containing angle A and performing a division. However, you will find it both simpler and more accurate to use values that have been recorded in tables.

The values printed in tables are put in decimal form. Since most tangents are irrational numbers, the decimal representations are only approximate. The tangent of angle X, in the figure, is exactly $\dfrac{1}{\sqrt{5}}$, or $\dfrac{\sqrt{5}}{5}$. The tangent of angle X is approximately equal to .44721.

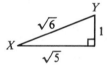

The symbol $\doteq$ will be used for the words **is approximately equal to.** Thus, for the angle shown above, all these statements are true:

$$\tan X = \frac{1}{\sqrt{5}}, \quad \tan X = \frac{\sqrt{5}}{5}, \quad \tan X \doteq .44721, \quad \tan X \doteq .447$$

For the tangent of Y you can write:

$$\tan Y = \frac{\sqrt{5}}{1}, \quad \tan Y \doteq 2.2366, \quad \tan Y \doteq 2.24$$

Suppose you are given an angle measure j, $0 < j < 90$. Take any two angles U and V that have measure j and you can show that the tangent of angle U is equal to the tangent of angle V. (Exercise 20, p. 341) Consequently, with given measure j there is associated a unique tangent value. For this reason you can write *tan $j°$* instead of tan U or tan V.

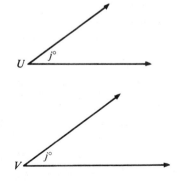

1. Tan $k°$ is equal to the tangent of $\angle$ __?__

Tan $k° = \dfrac{?}{?}$

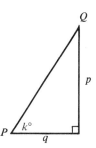

2. Tan $(90 - k)°$ is equal to the tangent of $\angle$ __?__

Tan $(90 - k)° = \dfrac{?}{?}$

3. State the tangent of each of the labeled angles.

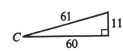
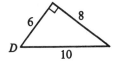

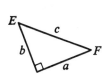

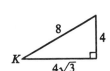

4. Tell whether the ratio named is the tangent of A, the tangent of B, or neither.

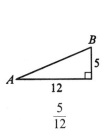

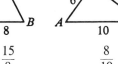
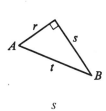

$\dfrac{5}{12}$ $\dfrac{15}{8}$ $\dfrac{8}{10}$ $\dfrac{s}{r}$

WRITTEN EXERCISES

Use the table of tangents printed on this page. In Exercises 1–6 find x. Since the given length is a two-digit number, you should round your answer off to two digits.

Angle	Tangent
5°	.087
10°	.176
15°	.268
20°	.364
25°	.466
30°	.577
35°	.700
40°	.839
45°	1.000
50°	1.192
55°	1.428
60°	1.732
65°	2.145
70°	2.747
75°	3.732
80°	5.671
85°	11.430

EXAMPLE.

$A = \frac{a}{p}$

Solution: $\tan 40° = \dfrac{x}{21}$

$.839 \doteq \dfrac{x}{21}$

$TAN = \dfrac{opp}{adj}$

$x \doteq 21 \times .839$

$x \doteq 17.619$, or 18

A 1.

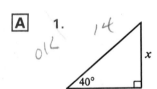

2.

3.

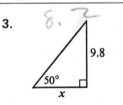

4.

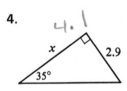

5.

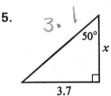

6.

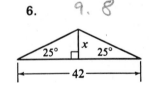

In Exercises 7–10, find x correct to the nearest five degrees.

EXAMPLE.

Solution: $\tan x° = \frac{108}{50}$

$\tan x° = 2.160.$ This number is clearly closer to 2.145 than to any other number in the table.

$x° \doteq 65°.$

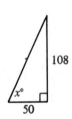

ok

35 o   55 o   60 o   40 o

7.

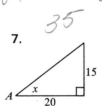

15
x
A 20

8.

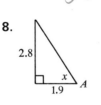

2.8
x
A
1.9

9.

44 75
x
A

10.

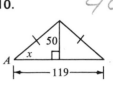

50
x
A
|←— 119 —→|

B

11. Use your ruler and protractor to draw a right triangle with an angle of measure 40 having an adjacent leg of length 5. Measure the opposite leg. Use your measurements to compute tan 40°.   . 84

12. Repeat Exercise 11 using an angle of measure 60. 1. 7

13. Compute the exact value of tan 30° × tan 60° by using the lengths shown in the figure at the right.

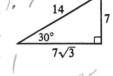

14   7
30°
$7\sqrt{3}$

3577=

C

14. Compute the value of tan n° × tan (90 − n)° by using the lengths of the legs in the right triangle shown.   )

(90-n)° r
n° s

15. $MN = 12$ in the plane figure. 3 1
Find JK.

16. $JN = 25$ in the plane figure.
Find NK.   30

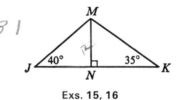

M
40°   35°
J K
N
Exs. 15, 16

17. $QT = 50$ in the plane figure.   7 3
Find RS.

18. $ST = 100$ in the plane figure.
Find RS.   4 5

19. $RS = 10$ in the plane figure.
Find QT and ST.   19, 22

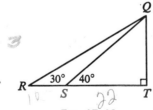

Q
30° 40°
R S T
Exs. 17–19

20. Given: $m\angle U = j$; $m\angle V = j$; $0 < j < 90$.
Prove: tan U = tan V.

Hint: From any point on one side of $\angle U$ draw the segment perpendicular to the other side of the angle. Do the same for $\angle V$.

9–7 The Sine and Cosine Ratios

The tangent ratio is useful in situations involving an acute angle and the legs of a right triangle. Suppose, however, that you know only the length of the hypotenuse and the measure of an acute angle. You need some ratio other than the tangent, for the tangent ratio does not involve the hypotenuse. The sine (sin) and cosine (cos) ratios are defined below.

$$\sin A = \frac{a}{c} \qquad \cos A = \frac{b}{c}$$

For an acute angle of given measure j, the sine and cosine are unique numbers. (See Exercise 16.) Hence, if $m\angle A = j$, you can write $\sin j°$ in place of $\sin A$ and $\cos j°$ in place of $\cos A$.

You may find it easy to remember the definitions of $\sin j°$ and $\cos j°$ in the form:

$$\sin j° = \frac{\text{length of opposite side}}{\text{length of hypotenuse}} \qquad \cos j° = \frac{\text{length of adjacent side}}{\text{length of hypotenuse}}$$

In the diagram shown above, $\sin B = \dfrac{b}{c}$ and $\cos B = \dfrac{a}{c}$.

ORAL EXERCISES

1. State the sine of each of the labeled angles.

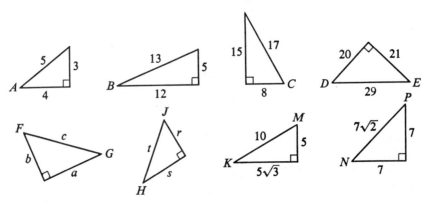

2. State the cosine of each of the labeled angles shown in the triangles for Exercise 1.

3. State an equation you can use to determine x in the diagrams below.

EXAMPLE. *Solution:* $\cos 40° = \dfrac{x}{13}$

a. **b.** **c.** **d.**

4. State an equation you can use to determine y.

EXAMPLE.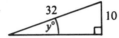

Solution: $\sin y° = \frac{10}{32}$

a. **b.** **c.** **d.**

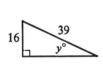   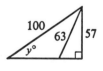

5. Read from the table on page 628
$\cos 72°$; $\sin 72°$; $\cos 15°$; $\tan 58°$.

6. Find from the table on page 628 the measure of x for which
$\sin x° \doteq .2419$; $\cos x° \doteq .1392$; $\tan x° \doteq 1.1106$; $\cos x° \doteq .9511$.

7. The numerator of the sine ratio is the length of a __?__, while the denominator is the length of the __?__. Since the hypotenuse of a right triangle is longer than a leg, the value of the sine of an acute angle is always __?__ than one.

8. The value of the cosine of an acute angle is always __?__ than __?__.

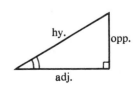

Exs. 7, 8

Point O is the center of a circle of radius 10.

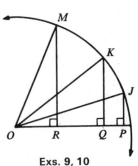

9. $\sin \angle JOP = \dfrac{?}{10}$, $\sin \angle KOQ = \dfrac{?}{10}$,   and

$\sin \angle MOR = \dfrac{?}{10}$· Since $JP < KQ < MR$,

$\sin \angle JOP \underline{\ \ ?\ \ } \sin \angle KOQ \underline{\ \ ?\ \ } \sin \angle MOR$.

In general, where x is the measure of an acute angle, as x increases, $\sin x° \underline{\ \ ?\ \ }$.

Exs. 9, 10

10. $\cos \angle JOP = \dfrac{?}{10}$, $\cos \angle KOQ = \dfrac{?}{10}$,

$\cos \angle MOR = \dfrac{?}{10}$· In general, where x is the measure of an acute

angle, as x increases, $\cos x° \underline{\ \ ?\ \ }$.

$cos = \dfrac{adj}{hypo}$

$sin = \dfrac{opp}{hypo}$

P. 628

WRITTEN EXERCISES

Use the table on page 628. Find x, expressing computed lengths to the same number of digits as are found in given lengths.

EXAMPLE.

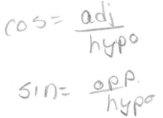

6.71

28°

x   5.92

Solution: $\cos 28° = \dfrac{x}{6.71}$

$.8829 \doteq \dfrac{x}{6.71}$

$x \doteq 6.71 \times .8829 = 5.924259$

$x \doteq 5.92$, **Answer.**

A

1.

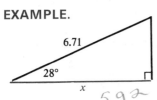

223

x

55°

122

2.

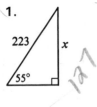

1.2

x

33°

2.2

3.

73.3

x

52°

119

4.

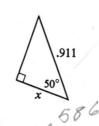

.911

50°

x

.586

5.

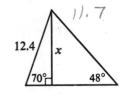

11.7

12.4

x

70°   48°

6.

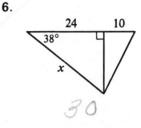

24   10

38°

x

30

In Exs. 7–10, find the measure of angle A to the nearest degree.

7. 33°
26 14

8. 49°
.91 1.2
A

9. 41°
100
A 75.5

10. 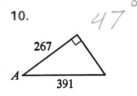 47°
267
A 391

11. Use your ruler and compass to draw a right triangle with an angle of measure 35 and a hypotenuse of length 10. Measure the opposite leg. Use your measurements to compute sin 35°.   .57

12. Repeat Exercise 11 using an angle of measure 50.   .77

B

13. Compute the exact value of $(\sin 30°)^2 + (\cos 30°)^2$, using the lengths shown in the figure.

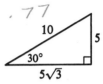
10   5
30°
$5\sqrt{3}$

14. Compute the exact value of $(\sin 60°)^2 + (\cos 60°)^2$, using the lengths shown in the figure.

Exs. 13, 14

15. Compute the exact value of $(\sin 45°)^2 + (\cos 45°)^2$. *Hint:* Keep Theorem 9–5 in mind when labeling a figure.

16. Explain why, for an acute angle A of given measure j, sin A has a unique value. *Hint:* See the discussion of tan j°, page 338.

17. A 12-inch segment and its projection into a plane determine a 20° angle. Find the length of the projection of the segment into the plane.   11 in

18. The projection of a segment on a line is 3.5 in. long. The segment and the line determine a 31° angle. Find the length of the segment.   4.1 in

19. The projection of a 20-in. segment on a certain line is 13 in. long. Find the measure of the angle determined by the segment and the line.

20. The ratio of the length of a segment to the length of its projection into a plane is 3 to 2. Find the measure of the angle determined by the segment and its projection.

 C

21.

22.

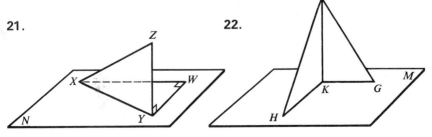

$\overline{ZY} \perp$ plane *N*. $\overline{XW} \perp \overline{WY}$.
$m\angle ZXY = 32$. $m\angle WXY = 43$.
$XW = 136$. Find XZ.

$\overline{JK} \perp$ plane *M*. $JG = 13.2$.
$m\angle JGK = 58$. $m\angle JHK = 50$.
Find HJ.

23. $m\angle AOB = m\angle BOC = m\angle COD = 20.$ $CD = 10.1.$
Segments OA, OB, OC, and OD are not coplanar.
Find AB.

24. $ST = 45$ in the plane figure.
Find UV and RV.

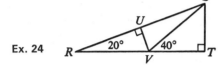

Ex. 24

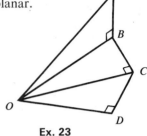

Ex. 23

9-8 Using the Sine, Cosine, and Tangent

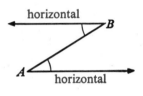

In practical applications one is often called upon to use an angle one side of which is a horizontal ray. When a person at A looks up at B, angle A is called the **angle of elevation.** When a person at B looks down at A, angle B is called the **angle of depression.** Notice that each of the angles named has one side in the line of sight and one side in a horizontal line.

ORAL
EXERCISES

1. Name the angle of elevation for a person looking from X to Z; from Y to Z.

2. Name the angle of depression for a person looking from Z to X; from Z to Y.

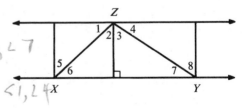

3. A person at a window 15 ft. above the sidewalk looks at a street light 12 ft. above the sidewalk. Is the angle at the person's eye an angle of elevation or an angle of depression?

WRITTEN EXERCISES

A   1. A vertical pole 6 ft. long casts a shadow 55 in. long. Find the measure *53*⁶ of the angle of elevation of the sun.

2. The angle of elevation of the sun has measure 70°. A flagpole casts a shadow 15 ft. long. Find the height of the flagpole.   *41 ft*

3. A man at the top of a watchtower knows that his eye is 86 ft. above ground. On the level plateau supporting the tower there is a rock known to be 500 ft. from the base of the tower. Find the measure of the angle *10⁶* of depression of the rock from the top of the tower.

4. A supporting wire stretches from the ground to the top of a television transmitting tower 200 ft. high. The angle the wire forms with its *207 ft* projection on the ground is a 75° angle. Find the length of the wire.

5. Sketch a 30°–60°–90° triangle, and label the sides with some correct set of lengths such as 4, 4√3, and 8. State the exact value of (**a**) sin 30°; (**b**) cos 30°; (**c**) tan 30°.   *½*   *√3/2*   *√3/3*

6. State the exact value of (**a**) sin 60°; (**b**) cos 60°; (**c**) tan 60°. *√3/2, ½, √3*

7. Compare the numbers (**a**) sin 30° and cos 60°; (**b**) sin 60° and cos 30°?   *equal, equal*

8. Compare the numbers (**a**) sin $n°$ and cos $(90 - n)°$; (**b**) sin $(90 - n)°$ and cos $n°$?   *sin (90-n) = cos n*   *sin n = cos(90-n)*

Ex. 8

9. Sketch an isosceles right triangle and label the sides with some correct set of lengths. State the exact value of
   a. sin 45° *√2/2*   **b.** cos 45° *√2/2*   **c.** tan 45°. *1*

10. Given: sin $x°$ is exactly $\dfrac{1}{\sqrt{2}}$, or $\dfrac{\sqrt{2}}{2}$. What is the exact value of x?

In Exercises 11–14, make a deduction about x, given

B   11. tan $x° > 1$ *x 745*   13. sin $x° > $ cos $x°$ *x 745*

12. sin $x° < \dfrac{\sqrt{3}}{2}$ *x L60*   14. tan $x° < $ tan $(90 - x)°$ *x L45*

15. Find the length of the altitude of an isosceles triangle with a 70° vertex angle and a base 246 units long.   *176*

16. Find the length of the base of an isosceles triangle with a 70° base angle and a leg 23.5 units long.   *16.1*

17. Find the approximate measure of the base angle of an isosceles triangle with a leg 28.2 units long and base 43.8 units long.   *39°*

18. Who gains altitude more quickly, a pilot traveling 400 m.p.h. and rising at an angle of 30°, or a pilot traveling 300 m.p.h. and rising at an angle of 40°? How much more quickly (in m.p.h.) does he gain altitude?

C 19. The 15-inch base of an isosceles triangle lies in a plane, and its 20-inch legs are both inclined at a 40° angle to the plane. The projection of the triangle into the plane is an isosceles triangle. Find:

    a. The length of the altitude of the original triangle.

    b. The length of a leg of the smaller isosceles triangle.

    c. The measure of the angle at which the altitude of the original triangle is inclined to the plane.

20. Find the measure of the acute angle formed at the point where two diagonals of a cube meet. (Since all cubes are similar, you can assign any length to the edge.)

21. Draw a general right triangle and use small letters to indicate the lengths of the sides. Let n be the measure of one of the acute angles. Show that $(\sin n°)^2 + (\cos n°)^2 = 1$.

22. Derive the **Law of Sines** for acute triangles. That is, show that

$$\frac{a}{\sin A} = \frac{b}{\sin B} = \frac{c}{\sin C}.$$

Hint: To prove that

$$\frac{a}{\sin A} = \frac{b}{\sin B},$$

draw the altitude from point C. Let h be its length.

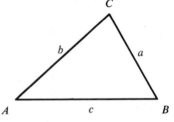

PRACTICAL APPLICATIONS

1. An extension ladder 65 ft. long is placed against a building so as to reach a window ledge 52 ft. above the ground. How far must the foot of the ladder be moved in toward the building so that the top of the ladder will reach a window ledge 8 ft. higher up?

2. The strongest rectangular beam that can be cut from a circular log is one in which the rectangular cross-section is such that perpendiculars from two opposite vertices trisect the diagonal joining the remaining two vertices. In the cross section shown, if $\overline{CX} \perp \overline{DB}$, $\overline{AY} \perp \overline{DB}$, and $DX = XY = YB$, show that the ratio of length to width in the cross section is $\sqrt{2}:1$.

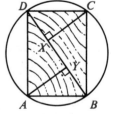

3. The diagram shows the measurements a man made so that he could find the distance between two points *J* and *K* on opposite sides of a river. Find *JK*.

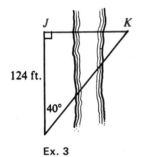

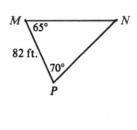

Ex. 3   Ex. 4

4. A triangular plot of ground *MNP* is shown. The only parts of the triangle that can be measured directly have the measures shown. Use the Law of Sines, stated in Exercise 22, page 348, to find *MN* and *PN*.

5. From a window *W* a man looks across a street at a building of height *RT*. He measures the angles shown at *W*. He knows the ground distance to be 50 ft. Find *RT*.

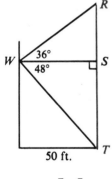

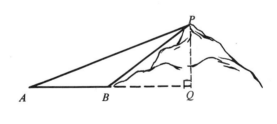

Ex. 5   Ex. 6

6. A team of surveyors finds the height of a mountain peak by using the figure shown. *A* is known to be 6500 feet above sea level, and *AB* is a stretch of level ground. *P* can be seen from both *A* and *B*. The angle of elevation at *A* is a 20° angle, and at *B* is a 35° angle. *AB* = 600 ft. How far above sea level is the peak *P*?

Hint: Draw a perpendicular *BJ* from *B* to *AP*. Label the various angle measures. Compute *BJ*, then *BP*, then *PQ*. Finally, find 6500 + *PQ*.

CHAPTER SUMMARY

Inventory of Structure and Methods

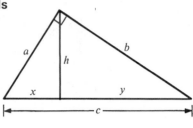

1. In the figure shown is a right triangle with the altitude drawn to the hypotenuse. Letters designate lengths of segments. a is the geometric mean between c and x, and b is the geometric mean between c and y. h is the geometric mean between x and y.
   The product of c and h is equal to the product of a and b.

2. In any right triangle the square of the length of the hypotenuse is equal to the sum of the squares of the lengths of the legs. The converse of the Pythagorean Theorem is also true.

3. The lengths of the sides of a 30°–60°–90° triangle are in the ratio $1:\sqrt{3}:2$. The lengths of the sides of a 45°–45°–90° triangle are in the ratio $1:1:\sqrt{2}$.

4. In the right triangle shown:

   The tangent of angle A is $\dfrac{a}{b}$

   The ratio is also called tan A or tan $j°$.

   The sine of angle A is $\dfrac{a}{c}$.

   The cosine of angle A is $\dfrac{b}{c}$.

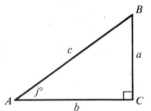

5. Given the lengths of two sides of a right triangle, or the length of one side and the measure of an acute angle, you can compute the measures of the other parts of the triangle by using tables that list approximations of the trigonometric ratios.

Vocabulary and Spelling

geometric mean (*p. 314*)
projection of a point
  on a line (*p. 314*)
projection of a segment
  on a line (*p. 314*)
radical (*p. 316*)
radicand (*p. 316*)
simplest form of a radical (*p. 316*)
Pythagorean Theorem (*p. 320*)
polyhedron (*p. 330*)
  face (*p. 330*)

polyhedron
  edge (*p. 330*)
  vertex (*p. 330*)
projection of a set of points
  into a plane (*p. 335*)
tangent (tan) (*p. 337*)
approximately equal to ($\doteq$) (*p. 338*)
sine (sin) (*p. 342*)
cosine (cos) (*p. 342*)
angle of elevation (*p. 346*)
angle of depression (*p. 346*)

CHAPTER TEST

In $\triangle ABC$, $m\angle ACB = 90$ and $\overline{CT} \perp \overline{AB}$.

9–1

1. $\triangle ACT$ is similar to $\triangle\underline{\ ?\ }$ and to $\triangle\underline{\ ?\ }$.

2. If $AT = 4$ and $TB = 9$, then $CT = \underline{\ ?\ }$.

3. If $AB = 8$ and $TB = 2$, then $BC = \underline{\ ?\ }$.

4. If $AC = 6$ and $AB = 9$, then $AT = \underline{\ ?\ }$.

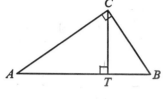

9–2 In the given right triangle a, b, and c are lengths of sides.

5. If $a = 4$ and $b = 6$, then $c = \underline{\ ?\ }$.

6. If $a = 3$ and $c = 6$, then $b = \underline{\ ?\ }$.

7. If $b = 2$ and $c = 3\sqrt{2}$, then $a = \underline{\ ?\ }$.

8. If $a:b = 1:2$ and $c = 2\sqrt{5}$, then $a = \underline{\ ?\ }$.

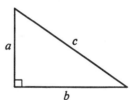

9–3 Given $\overline{BX} \perp \overline{AC}$ in equilateral triangle ABC.

9. If $AX = 3$, then $AB = \underline{\ ?\ }$.

10. If $AB = 8$, then $BX = \underline{\ ?\ }$.

11. If $AX = 2\sqrt{3}$, then $BX = \underline{\ ?\ }$.

12. If $BX = 9$, then $AX = \underline{\ ?\ }$.

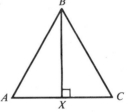

9–4 In the given rectangular solid $AB = 4$, $BC = 3$, $BF = 2$.

13. $m\angle DAB = \underline{\ ?\ }$.

14. $HD = \underline{\ ?\ }$.

15. $DB = \underline{\ ?\ }$.

16. $HB = \underline{\ ?\ }$.

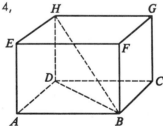

9–5 Find the length of the projection of $\overline{AB}$ into M if

17. $m\angle BAX = 30$ and $AB = 6$.

18. $m\angle BAX = 45$ and $AB = 4$.

19. $m\angle BAX = 60$ and $AB = 8$.

20. $AB = 10$ and $BX = 6$.

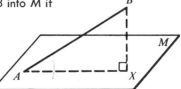

Use the table on page 628. Express computed lengths to the same number of digits as are found in given lengths, and angle measures to the closest integer.

9–6   In Exercises 21–24 find x.

21.

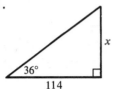

23.

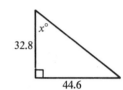

22.

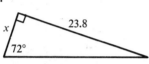

24.

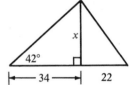

9–7   In Exercises 25–28 find y.

25.

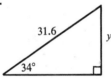

27.

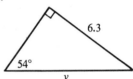

26.

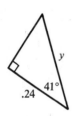

28.

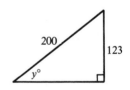

9–8   **29.** Find the angle of elevation of the sun when a vertical 10-foot pole casts a 6-foot shadow on level ground.

30. From the top of a tower the angle of depression of a spot on the ground is 38°. The spot and the foot of the tower are on level ground, with a distance of 126 ft. between them. Find the height of the tower.

31. Find the altitude of an isosceles triangle that has a 20-inch leg and a 12-inch base.

32. The length and width of a rectangle are 380 ft. and 152 ft. respectively. Find the measure of the angle between a diagonal and one of the longer sides.

B

33. $TQ = 13.2$
Find *RS*.

34. $RT = 127$
Find *ST*.

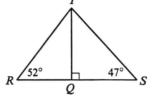

Exs. 33, 34

35. Find, without tables, the exact value of tan 30° × tan 60°.

36. Find, without tables, the exact value of (sin 30°)² + (cos 30°)².

CHAPTER REVIEW

9–1 The Altitude to the Hypotenuse of a Right Triangle.

Pages 314–319

Given: Segments perpendicular as shown.

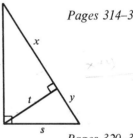

1. $\dfrac{?}{t} = \dfrac{t}{?}$ **2.** $\dfrac{?}{s} = \dfrac{s}{x+y}$

3. *r* is the __?__ between $x + y$ and *x*.

4. $(x + y) \cdot t = \underline{\quad?\quad} \cdot \underline{\quad?\quad}$.

9–2 The Pythagorean Theorem   *Pages 320–324*

5. Can the sides of a right triangle have lengths 3, 2, and 4 in.?

6. The simplified form of the number $\dfrac{6}{\sqrt{2}}$ is __?__.

7. A rectangle with length 6 in. and width 4 in. has a diagonal __?__ in. long.

8. If $a^2 + b^2 = c^2$, then $a^2 = \underline{\ ?\ } - \underline{\ ?\ }$ and $b^2 = \underline{\ ?\ } - \underline{\ ?\ }$.

9–3 Special Right Triangles: 30°–60°–90° and 45°–45°–90°

Pages 325–329

9. In a 30°–60°–90° triangle the hypotenuse has length 4*t*. Then the legs have lengths __?__ and __?__.

10. An equilateral triangle with a side 8 cm. long has an altitude __?__ cm. long.

11. A square with a 6-in. side has a __?__ in. diagonal.

12. A square with a 4-ft. diagonal has a __?__ ft. side.

9–4 Right Triangles in Three-Dimensional Figures *Pages 329–334*

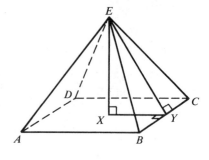

13. A rectangular solid and a regular square pyramid are types of __?__.

14. In the given regular square pyramid, $\overline{EX}$ is the __?__ and EY is the __?__.

15. The square $ABCD$ is called the __?__ of the pyramid and the four triangles are called __?__ faces.

16. If $AB = 4$, then $XY = $ __?__ and $BY = $ __?__.

9–5 Projections into a Plane *Pages 334–337*

17. If a segment is parallel to a plane, then its projection into the plane is a __?__ of equal __?__.

18. If the projection of a rectangle into a plane is a segment, then the rectangle must lie in a plane __?__ to the given plane.

19. If an 8-in. segment has a 4 in. projection into a plane, then the segment and its projection determine a __?__° angle.

20. If the projection of a segment into a plane is a point, then that segment must be __?__ to the plane.

9–6 The Tangent Ratio *Pages 337–341*

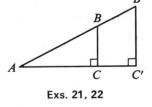

21. In the figure shown, the tangent of $\angle A = $ __?__ or __?__.

22. The fact that $\dfrac{BC}{AC} = \dfrac{B'C'}{AC'}$ shows that for a given acute angle the tangent is a __?__ positive number.

Exs. 21, 22

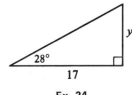

23. The tables on page 628 indicate that $\tan 73° \doteq$ __?__, and that $x \doteq$ __?__ when $\tan x° \doteq .466$.

24. To find y in the figure shown, you first write the equation $\tan$ __?__ $= \dfrac{?}{?}$.

Ex. 24

9–7 **The Sine and Cosine Ratios** *Pages 342–346*

25. In the figure shown, sin $n° =$ _?_ and cos $n° =$ _?_ .

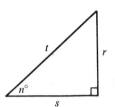

Ex. 25

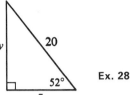

Ex. 28

26. For a given acute angle the sine is a _?_ positive number and the cosine is a _?_ positive number.

27. The tables on page 628 indicate that sin $23° \doteq$ _?_ , and that $x \doteq$ _?_ when cos $x° \doteq .326$.

28. To find y in the figure shown, you first write the equation _?_ . To find z, without using y, you first write the equation _?_ .

9–8 **Using the Sine, Cosine, and Tangent** *Pages 346–348*

29. When you look up to see an object, the angle between your line of sight and the horizontal is called the _?_ .

30. A person at P looks down at object O. The angle of depression is labeled _?_ in the figure.

31. To find n in the figure, you would use the _?_ ratio if given y and z, the _?_ ratio if given x and y, and the _?_ ratio if given x and z.

Ex. 30

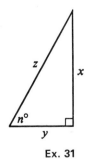

Ex. 31

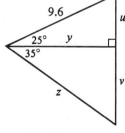

Ex. 32

32. To find v in the figure you would first use _?_ $25°$ to find _?_ , and then use _?_ $35°$ to find v.

• EXTRA FOR EXPERTS

Proofs of the Pythagorean Theorem

From the hundreds of known proofs of the Pythagorean Theorem two are selected for mention here. Historically, the theorem was stated in terms of area: *The area of the square on the hypotenuse of a right triangle is equal to the sum of the areas of the squares on the legs.* We assume the area formulas needed in the two proofs that follow.

The Oldest Known Proof of the Pythagorean Theorem

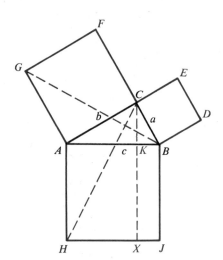

Given: $\triangle ABC$ with rt. $\angle C$; sqs. AJ, AF, and BE.

Prove: Area of sq. AJ = area of sq. AF + area of sq. BE.

Analysis: Divide square AJ into two rectangles, AX and BX. Show that area of rect. AX = area of sq. AF, and area of rect. BX = area of sq. BE.

Outline of Proof:
Draw $\overline{CX} \parallel \overline{AH}$, meeting $\overline{AB}$ in K and $\overline{HJ}$ in X.
Draw $\overline{BG}$ and $\overline{CH}$.
In $\triangle HAC$ and BAG: $\angle HAC \cong \angle BAG$, $\overline{AB} \cong \overline{AH}$, $\overline{AC} \cong \overline{AG}$.
$\triangle HAC$ and BAG are congruent; and their areas are equal.
Because sq. AF and $\triangle BAG$ both have base-length AG and alt.-length AC, area of sq. AF = 2 × area of $\triangle BAG$.
Because rect. AX and $\triangle HAC$ both have base-length AH and alt.-length AK, area of rect. AX = 2 × area of $\triangle HAC$.
Area of sq. AF = area of rect. AX.
By a similar proof, drawing $\overline{AD}$ and $\overline{CJ}$ and using $\triangle ABD$ and CBJ you can prove: Area of sq. BE = area of rect. BX.
Area of square AJ = area of rect. AX + area of rect. BX.
Area of square AJ = area of sq. AF + area of sq. BE.

The Shortest Known Proof of the Pythagorean Theorem

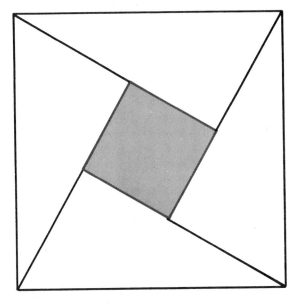

BEHOLD!

EXERCISES

Refer to the first proof above.

1. Explain why $\angle HAC \cong \angle BAG$.
2. Explain why AC can be taken as the length of an altitude of $\triangle BAG$.
3. Outline, in detail, the "similar proof" referred to near the end of the demonstration.
4. Using the adjacent figure, write an explanation that should enable any thinking person to grasp the proof that a Hindu mathematician believed, centuries ago, to be self-evident.

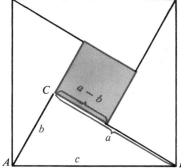

10 Circles

The face of the United Nations Building seen through this grill suggests concentric circles placed on a coordinate plane.

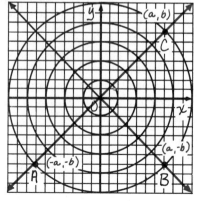

Have you ever stopped to consider the important part that objects of circular shape play in everyday life? If you disassemble a modern convenience such as an automobile or clock, you will find many parts of circular shape. In fact, it is sometimes said that man's greatest invention was the wheel.

Circles play an important part in nature, too. The earth takes an almost circular path around the sun. The earth itself has a circular cross section, as do most plants that grow on the earth.

In this chapter we shall be concerned with proving theorems about circles and certain related lines and segments. Many of the terms used are ones with which you have long been familiar. Some have already been defined earlier in this text. However, for convenience, as well as to increase your understanding, we shall sometimes repeat definitions.

■ Tangents, Arcs and Chords

10–1   Tangents

Recall that a **tangent** to a circle is a line that lies in the plane of the circle and intersects the circle in exactly one point. The point of intersection is called the **point of tangency** or **point of contact**. A ray or segment that contains the point of tangency and is a subset of a tangent line is also referred to as a tangent. Thus, $\overleftrightarrow{PR}$, $\overline{PR}$, $\overrightarrow{PR}$ are all tangents to $\odot O$ at point R.

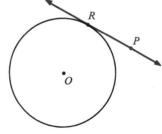

Intuition suggests the theorem stated at the top of the next page. However, a proof of this theorem is surprisingly difficult and will not be presented here. See Exercise 22, p. 364.

359

THEOREM 10–1   A line in the plane of a circle and containing an interior point of the circle intersects the circle in two points.

On the basis of this theorem you can assert that if line *l* contains an interior point *P* it must intersect ⊙*O* in two points. Also, since tangent line *m* by definition contains exactly one point of ⊙*O*, all other points of *m* must lie in the exterior of ⊙*O*. (For if *m* contained an interior point, *m* would intersect ⊙*O* in two points.)

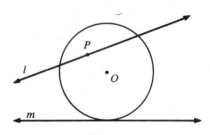

THEOREM 10–2   A tangent to a circle is perpendicular to the radius drawn to the point of tangency.

Given: Line *t* tangent to ⊙*O* at *A*.

To Prove: $\overline{OA} \perp t$.

Analysis: Use an indirect proof.

Proof:

Suppose $\overline{OA}$ is not ⊥ to *t*. Then there must be some other segment, $\overline{OB}$, through *O* that is ⊥ to *t* at *B*. (See p. 163.) Since $\overline{OB} \perp t$, $OB < OA$. But this contradicts the fact that $OB > OA$ (since *B* is in the exterior, and *A* lies on ⊙*O*.) Thus, the assumption that $\overline{OA}$ is not ⊥ to *t* must be false. Hence it follows that $\overline{OA} \perp t$.

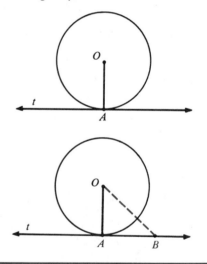

THEOREM 10–3   A line in the plane of a circle and perpendicular to a radius at its outer endpoint is tangent to the circle.

Given: Line *k* and ⊙*P* are coplanar; $k \perp \overline{PX}$.

To Prove: *k* is tangent to ⊙*P*.

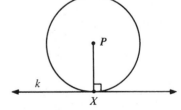

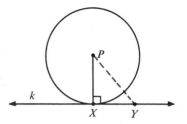

Outline of Proof:

Let Y be *any* point of k, other than point X. $\overline{PY}$ is the hypotenuse of rt $\triangle PXY$. Hence $PY > PX$. Thus, point Y lies in the exterior of $\odot P$. Since any point of k other than X lies in the exterior of $\odot P$, line k is tangent to $\odot P$ at point X.

A line that is tangent to each of two circles is called a **common tangent.** If a common tangent intersects the segment joining the centers, it is a **common internal tangent.** If it does not, it is a **common external tangent.**

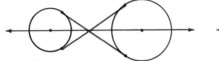 

Common Internal Tangent   **Common External Tangent**

Two coplanar circles are said to be **tangent** to each other if they are tangent to the same line at the same point. They are **externally tangent** if their centers lie on opposite sides of the common tangent and **internally tangent** if their centers lie on the same side of the common tangent.

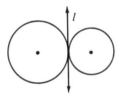

Externally   **Internally**
Tangent Circles   **Tangent Circles**
l is a common internal tangent   *l* is a common external tangent

A polygon each of whose sides is tangent to a circle is said to be **circumscribed** about the circle. The circle is **inscribed** in the polygon.

 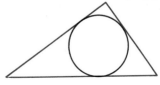

Circumscribed Quadrilateral   **Circumscribed Triangle**

Refer to the figure shown and state a theorem that supports the assertion made.

1. If *l* is tangent to ⊙*O*, $\overline{OP} \perp l$.

2. If $\overline{OP} \perp l$ at *P*, then *l* is a tangent.

In the plane figure shown

3. Name two internally tangent circles.

4. Name two externally tangent circles.

5. Of what two circles is *l* a common internal tangent?

6. Of what two circles is *l* a common external tangent?

Exs. 1, 2

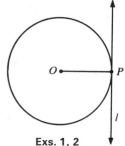

For each pair of coplanar circles shown below state

7. The number of common internal tangents that can be drawn.

8. The number of common external tangents that can be drawn.

Exs. 3–6

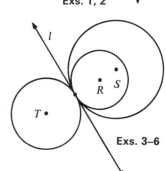

a.   **c.**   **e.**

b.   **d.**

Illustrate by a drawing.

 1. A right triangle circumscribed about a circle.

2. An obtuse triangle circumscribed about a circle.

3. An isosceles trapezoid circumscribed about a circle.

4. A nonisosceles trapezoid circumscribed about a circle.

5. A rhombus circumscribed about a circle.
   Is the rhombus necessarily a square?

6. A rectangle circumscribed about a circle. Is the rectangle necessarily a square?

7. Two circles for which no common tangents can be drawn.

8. Two circles for which two common external tangents but no common internal tangents can be drawn.

Draw two circles and all their common tangents such that the number of common tangents is

9. Four   **10.** Three   **11.** Two   **12.** One

For the points *P* and *Q* described, what is the greatest possible number, and what is the least possible number, of points in the intersection of $\overleftrightarrow{PQ}$ and circle *O*?

13. *P* lies on circle *O*, and *Q* lies in the interior.

14. *P* and *Q* both lie in the exterior of circle *O*.

15. *P* lies in the plane of circle *O* but *Q* does not.

16. Neither *P* nor *Q* lies in the plane of circle *O*.

17. Given: $\overline{AB}$ is a diameter of $\odot O$; $\overleftrightarrow{AC}$ and $\overleftrightarrow{BD}$ are tangents.

Prove: $\overleftrightarrow{AC} \parallel \overleftrightarrow{BD}$.

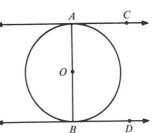

Ex. 17

18. Given: $\overleftrightarrow{RS}$ is tangent to $\odot O$ and $\odot P$ at points *R* and *S*.

Prove: $\overline{OR} \parallel \overline{PS}$.

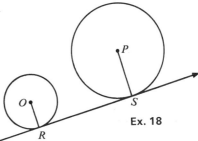

Ex. 18

19. Given: Line *k* is tangent to $\odot O$ at point *P*; $\overline{OT} \perp k$.

Consider $\overline{OP}$ (not drawn in the diagram).

a. What relationship do $\overline{OP}$ and line *k* have to each other?

b. In the plane, how many lines through point *O* and perpendicular to line *k* are possible?

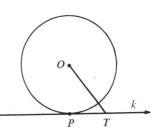

Ex. 19

c. Can $\overline{OP}$ and $\overline{OT}$ be different segments? *P* and *T* be different points?

d. Complete the statement: A line containing the center of a circle and perpendicular to a line tangent to the circle passes . . . .

20. Given: A plane figure with line *t*
tangent to ⊙*O* at point *X*;
j ⊥ *t* at *X*. Consider $\overleftrightarrow{OX}$
(not drawn in the diagram).

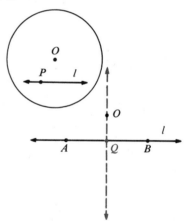

a. How is $\overleftrightarrow{OX}$ related, in position,
to line *t*?

b. In the plane, how many lines
perpendicular to line *t* at point
X are possible?

c. Can *j* and $\overleftrightarrow{OX}$ be different lines?

d. Complete the statement: A line in the plane of a circle and
perpendicular to a tangent line at the point of tangency . . . .

C **21.** Prove: A line joining the centers of two tangent circles passes through
the point of tangency.

22. Write a demonstration of Theorem 10–1.

Hints: Let the line through point *O*
and ⊥ to *l* intersect *l* at *Q*. Let
the radius of the circle be *r*.
On *l* there are two points, *A*
and *B*, on opposite sides of *Q*
and such that

$$QA = QB = \sqrt{r^2 - (OQ)^2}.$$

Show that points *A* and *B* lie
on ⊙*O* as well as on line *l*.

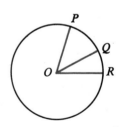

10–2 Arcs and Central Angles

From the definition of a circle it follows that
in ⊙*O*, *OP* = *OQ* = *OR* = ...   Hence,
$\overline{OP} \cong \overline{OQ} \cong \overline{OR} \cong$ . . . .   This property of a
circle is expressed by the following statement
which you can use as a reason in proofs. In this
statement the word "radii" refers to segments
rather than numbers.

Radii of a circle are congruent.

Congruent circles are circles that have congruent radii. When used
as a reason in proofs, this definition can be expressed in the form:

Radii of congruent circles are congruent.

A **central angle** of a circle is an angle whose vertex is the center of the circle. Angle 1 is a central angle of circle *O*.

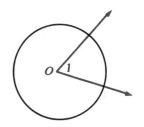

A **minor arc** of a circle is the union of two points of the circle, not the ends of a diameter, and all points of the circle that lie in the interior of the central angle whose sides contain the two points. The red part of circle *P* is minor arc *AB* ($\overarc{AB}$) or minor arc *AYB* ($\overarc{AYB}$).

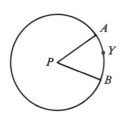

A **major arc** of a circle is the union of two points of the circle, not the ends of a diameter, and all points of the circle which lie in the exterior of the central angle whose sides contain the two points. In circle *Q*, point *W* lies on major arc *AWB* ($\overarc{AWB}$). Point *V* does not lie on $\overarc{AWB}$, but lies on $\overarc{AB}$. Always use at least three letters to name a major arc.

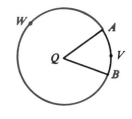

A **semicircle** is the union of the end points of a diameter and all points of the circle lying on one side of the diameter. Arc $\overarc{EJF}$ is one semicircle of circle *R*, and arc $\overarc{EKF}$ is another.

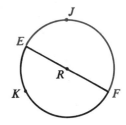

The **measure of a minor arc** is defined to be the measure of its central angle. The **measure of a major arc** $\overarc{AXB}$ is 360 minus the measure of minor arc $\overarc{AB}$. The **measure of a semicircle** is 180.

Suppose, in circle *O*, it is given that $m\angle 1 = 40$. Then the measure of $\overarc{AB}$ is 40, and the measure of $\overarc{AXB}$ is 320. Just as we write $m\angle 1 = 40$, so we write $m\overarc{AB} = 40$ and $m\overarc{AXB} = 320$. We can write $m\overarc{AB} = m\angle 1$, since the measure of $\overarc{AB}$ and the measure of $\angle 1$ are the same number.

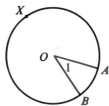

In the same circle or in congruent circles, arcs which have equal measures are called **congruent arcs.**

Figure 1

Figure 2

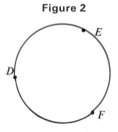

If you looked only at Figure 1 above, you might think it reasonable to say: "When point E lies between points D and F on a circle, then $m\widehat{DE} + m\widehat{EF} = m\widehat{DF}$." In Figure 2, however, point E lies between points D and F in a different way, and $m\widehat{DE} + m\widehat{EF} = m\widehat{DEF}$. Notice that only this second equation fits both figures.

P$_{17}$ If the intersection of arcs $\widehat{DE}$ and $\widehat{EF}$ of a circle is the single point E, then $m\widehat{DE} + m\widehat{EF} = m\widehat{DEF}$ (the Arc Addition Postulate).

THEOREM 10–4 If in the same circle or congruent circles two central angles are congruent, their arcs are congruent.

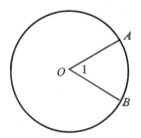
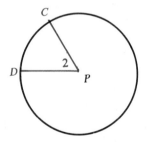

Given: Congruent circles O and P; $\angle 1 \cong \angle 2$.

To Prove: $m\widehat{AB} = m\widehat{CD}$.

Analysis: Use the fact that the measure of an arc equals the measure of its central angle. Then use the transitive property of equality.

Proof

The proof is left for you.

THEOREM 10–5 If in the same circle or congruent circles two minor arcs are congruent, their central angles are congruent.

The demonstration is left for you.

Point O is the center of the circle.

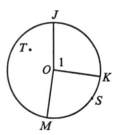

1. Is *T* a point of the circle? Is *O* a point of the circle?

2. Is point *S* on $\overgroup{MJK}$? on $\overgroup{MKJ}$?

3. Suppose that $\overline{OK} \perp \overline{OM}$. What is the measure of $\overgroup{MK}$? of $\overgroup{MJK}$?

4. Suppose that $m\overgroup{MJ} = 160$. $m\angle JOM = \underline{}$.

5. Name three central angles in the figure; three minor arcs; three major arcs.

6. Suppose that $m\angle 1 = 110$. Name an arc whose measure is 110; an arc whose measure is 250.

Ex. 1–6

Point Q is the center of the circle. Points X, Q, and W are collinear.

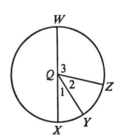

7. a. $m\overgroup{XY} + m\overgroup{YZ} = m\underline{}$.
   b. $m\overgroup{YZ} + m\overgroup{ZW} = m\underline{}$.
   c. State the postulate that supports your conclusions in Parts **a** and **b**.

8. a. $m\overgroup{WY} - m\overgroup{ZY} = m\underline{}$.
   b. $m\overgroup{XY} + m\overgroup{YZ} + m\overgroup{ZW} = m\underline{}$.

9. $m\angle 1 = 30$; $m\angle 2 = 45$; $m\overgroup{XZ} = \underline{}$.

10. $m\overgroup{WZ} = 100$; $m\overgroup{XZ} = \underline{}$.

Exs. 7–10

Point P is the center of a circle.

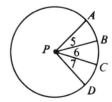

11. If $\angle 5 \cong \angle 6$, what nonoverlapping arcs must be congruent? State the theorem that supports your conclusion.

12. If $\overgroup{AB} \cong \overgroup{CD}$, what nonoverlapping angles must be congruent? State the theorem that supports your conclusion.

Exs. 11, 12

WRITTEN EXERCISES

1. In a circle of 6-in. radius a central angle has measure 60. How long is the chord joining the endpoints of the arc cut off by the angle?

2. In a circle of 10-in. diameter, a central angle has measure 90. A chord joins the endpoints of the arc cut off by the angle. Find the length of the chord.

3. A circle is divided into congruent arcs. Find the measure of each arc if there are 3 congruent arcs; 4 congruent arcs; 6 congruent arcs; 12 congruent arcs.

4. What is the measure of the angle determined by the hands of a clock at four o'clock?

Point O is the center of the circle shown, and $\overline{RS}$ is a diameter.

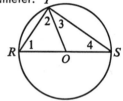

5. **a.** Why is $\overline{RO} \cong \overline{TO} \cong \overline{SO}$?
   b. Why does $m\angle 1 = m\angle 2$, and $m\angle 3 = m\angle 4$?
   c. Why does $m\angle 2 + m\angle 3 = m\angle RTS$?
   d. Why does $m\angle 1 + m\angle 4 = m\angle 2 + m\angle 3$?

6. What relationship holds between $m\angle 1 + m\angle 4$ and $m\angle RTS$? $m\angle RTS = $ __?__.

Exs. 5, 6

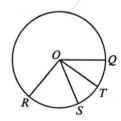

7. Given: Pts. R, S, T, and Q on $\odot O$.
   Prove: $m\widehat{RS} + m\widehat{ST} + m\widehat{TQ} = m\widehat{RQ}$.

8. Given: Pts. R, S, T, and Q on $\odot O$.
   Prove: $m\widehat{RT} - m\widehat{ST} = m\widehat{RS}$.

Exs. 7, 8

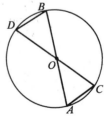

9. Given: $\overline{AB}$ and $\overline{CD}$ are diameters.
   Prove: $\widehat{AD} \cong \widehat{BC}$.

10. Given: $\overline{AB}$ and $\overline{CD}$ are diameters.
    Prove: $\widehat{BD} \cong \widehat{CA}$.

Exs. 9, 10

11. Given: $\odot O$; $m\angle XOY = m\angle WOV$;
$\qquad$ $m\widehat{YZ} = m\widehat{ZW}$.
$\qquad$ Prove: $m\widehat{XZ} = m\widehat{ZV}$.

12. Given: $\odot O$; $m\widehat{YZ} = m\widehat{ZW}$; $m\widehat{XY} = k$;
$\qquad$ $m\widehat{WV} = k$.
$\qquad$ Prove: $m\angle XOZ = m\angle ZOV$.

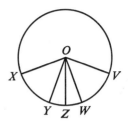

Exs. 11, 12

B **13.** Given: $\overline{AC}$ is a diameter of $\odot O$;
$\qquad$ $m\angle A = j$; $m\angle COD = 2j$.
$\qquad$ Prove: $\widehat{BC} \cong \widehat{CD}$.

14. Given: $\overline{AC}$ is a diameter of $\odot O$;
$\qquad$ $m\widehat{BC} = 50$.
$\qquad$ Prove: $m\angle A = 25$.

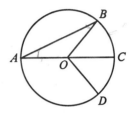

Exs. 13, 14

15. Given: $\overline{JN}$ is a diameter of $\odot O$;
$\qquad$ $\overline{OM} \parallel \overline{JK}$.
$\qquad$ Prove: $\widehat{KM} \cong \widehat{MN}$.

16. Given: $\overline{JN}$ is a diameter of $\odot O$;
$\qquad$ $\widehat{KM} \cong \widehat{MN}$.
$\qquad$ Prove: $\overline{OM} \parallel \overline{JK}$.

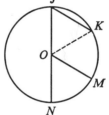

Exs. 15, 16

17. Prove: If point M, on $\widehat{AB}$ of $\odot O$, is such that $\widehat{AM} \cong \widehat{MB}$, then the perpendicular segments from M to $\overline{OA}$ and $\overline{OB}$ are congruent.

18. State and prove a converse of Exercise 17.

10-3 Arcs and Chords

Recall that a chord of a circle is a segment that joins two points of a circle. The endpoints of a chord that is not a diameter are the endpoints of two arcs of a circle, one a minor arc and the other a major arc. Unless otherwise specified, the expression *arc of a chord* refers to the minor arc.

THEOREM 10–6 In the same circle or in congruent circles, congruent chords have congruent arcs.

Given: ⊙O with $\overline{AB} \cong \overline{CD}$.

To Prove: $m\widehat{AB} = m\widehat{CD}$.

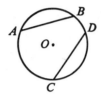

Analysis: Draw radii and use $\cong$ ⚠ to show that central ∡ are $\cong$.

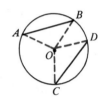

Proof

STATEMENT	REASON
1. Draw $\overline{OA}$, $\overline{OB}$, $\overline{OC}$, and $\overline{OD}$.	1. There is exactly __?__.
2. $\overline{OA} \cong \overline{OC}$; $\overline{OB} \cong \overline{OD}$.	2. Radii of __?__.
3. $\overline{AB} \cong \overline{CD}$.	3. ?
4. $\triangle AOB \cong \triangle COD$.	4. ?
5. $\angle AOB \cong \angle COD$.	5. ?
6. $m\widehat{AB} = m\widehat{CD}$.	6. Congruent central ∡ __?__.

(The proof where the chords lie in congruent circles is similar.)

The theorem stated below is the converse of theorem 10–6. Its proof is left as an exercise. (See Exercises 6 and 7, p. 374.)

THEOREM 10–7 In the same circle or in congruent circles, congruent arcs have congruent chords.

If point X lies on $\widehat{AB}$ and $\widehat{AX} \cong \widehat{XB}$, point X is said to **bisect** $\widehat{AB}$, and to be the **midpoint** of $\widehat{AB}$. Any line, segment or ray that contains X is a bisector of $\widehat{AB}$. The midpoint of an arc is *not* called the center of the arc. The **center of an arc** is the center of the circle that contains the arc. Thus in ⊙O if $\widehat{AX} \cong \widehat{XB}$, X is the midpoint of $\widehat{AB}$, $\overleftrightarrow{XT}$ is a bisector of $\widehat{AB}$, and point O is the center of $\widehat{AB}$.

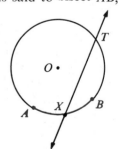

THEOREM 10–8   A diameter that is perpendicular to a chord bisects the chord and its two arcs.

Given: ⊙O with chord $\overline{CD}$ and diameter $\overline{AB}$; $\overline{AB} \perp \overline{CD}$.

To Prove: $\overline{CX} \cong \overline{DX}$; $\overset{\frown}{CB} \cong \overset{\frown}{DB}$; $\overset{\frown}{CA} \cong \overset{\frown}{DA}$.

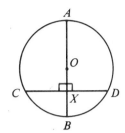

Analysis: Draw auxiliary segments and show $\triangle OXC \cong \triangle OXD$. Use congruent central angles to show that arcs are congruent.

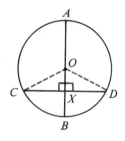

Proof

STATEMENT	REASON
1. $\overline{OX} \cong \overline{OX}$.	1. Reflexive property of congruence.
2. $\overline{OC} \cong \overline{OD}$.	2. Radii of a ⊙ are congruent.
3. $\overline{AB} \perp \overline{CD}$.	3. Given.
4. Rt. $\triangle OXC \cong$ rt. $\triangle OXD$.	4. HL postulate.
5. $\overline{CX} \cong \overline{DX}$; $\angle COX \cong \angle DOX$.	5. Corr. parts of $\cong \triangle$ are $\cong$.
6. $\angle COA \cong \angle DOA$.	6. If two $\angle$ are supplementary to __?__.
7. $\overset{\frown}{CB} \cong \overset{\frown}{DB}$; $\overset{\frown}{CA} \cong \overset{\frown}{DA}$.	7. If two central $\angle$ are $\cong$, their __?__.

Recall that the distance from a point to a line is the length of the perpendicular segment from the point to the line. In circle O, the distance of chord $\overline{XY}$ from the center O is OT (since OT is the length of $\overline{OT}$).

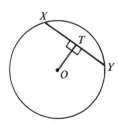

THEOREM 10–9   In the same circle or in congruent circles, chords that are equally distant from the center are congruent.

Given: Circle O with $\overline{OX} \perp \overline{AB}$; $\overline{OY} \perp \overline{CD}$; $OX = OY$.

To Prove: $\overline{AB} \cong \overline{CD}$.

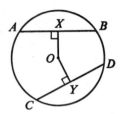

Analysis: Draw radii to A and C. Designate lengths of segments by lower case letters and use the Pythagorean Theorem.

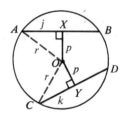

Proof

STATEMENT	REASON
1. Draw $\overline{OA}$ and $\overline{OC}$.	**1.** ?
2. $j^2 + p^2 = r^2$, or $j = \sqrt{r^2 - p^2}$.	**2.** In any rt. $\triangle$, __?__.
3. $k^2 + p^2 = r^2$, or $k = \sqrt{r^2 - p^2}$.	**3.** ?
4. $j = k$.	**4.** Transitive property of __?__.
5. $j = \frac{1}{2}AB$; $k = \frac{1}{2}CD$.	**5.** A diameter $\perp$ to __?__.
6. $\frac{1}{2}AB = \frac{1}{2}CD$.	**6.** ?
7. $AB = CD$ and $\overline{AB} \cong \overline{CD}$.	**7.** ?

Stated below is the converse of Theorem 10–9. Its proof is left as an exercise. (See Exercise 18, p. 375.)

THEOREM 10–10   In the same circle or in congruent circles, congruent chords are equally distant from the center.

A polygon is said to be **inscribed in a circle** and the circle to be **circumscribed about the polygon** when each vertex of the polygon is a point of the circle. Thus, the sides of an inscribed polygon are chords of the circle in which it is inscribed.

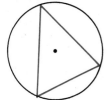 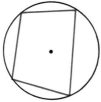 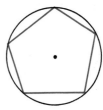

Inscribed Polygons

Refer to the circle shown and state the theorem that supports the assertion made.

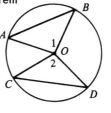

1. If $m\widehat{AB} = m\widehat{CD}$, then $\overline{AB} \cong \overline{CD}$.
2. If $\overline{AB} \cong \overline{CD}$, then $m\widehat{AB} = m\widehat{CD}$.
3. If $\angle 1 \cong \angle 2$, then $m\widehat{AB} = m\widehat{CD}$.
4. If $m\widehat{AB} = m\widehat{CD}$, then $\angle 1 \cong \angle 2$.

Exs. 1–4

Given $\odot O$ with $\overline{AB} \perp \overline{CD}$.

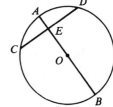

5. $\overline{CE} \cong$ __?__.
6. $\overline{AB}$ is a __?__ of $\overline{CD}$.
7. A is the __?__ of $\widehat{CD}$ and O is the __?__ of $\widehat{CD}$.
8. $m\widehat{BC} =$ __?__.

Exs. 5–8

When two circles intersect in exactly two points, the segment joining those two points is called a **common chord** of the circles. Shown are circles R and S with common chord $\overline{AB}$.

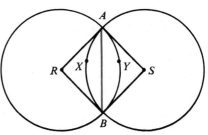

9. If $\overline{RA} \cong \overline{SA}$, then the circles are __?__.
10. If $\overline{RB} \cong \overline{SB}$, then $m\angle R = m\angle$?.
11. If the circles are congruent, name two minor arcs that are $\cong$.
12. Will $m\widehat{AXB} = m\widehat{AYB}$ if the circles are not congruent?

13. In each figure tell whether the triangle is inscribed in the circle, circumscribed about the circle, or neither.

    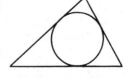

   a.   **b.**   **c.**   **d.**

Given ⊙O with $\overline{OX} \perp \overline{AB}$.

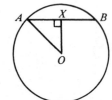

14. If $AO = 5$ and $OX = 3$, then $AB = $ __?__ .

15. If $AB = 6$, and $OX = 4$, then $AO = $ __?__ .

16. If $AB = 2\sqrt{2}$ and $AO = \sqrt{6}$, then $OX = $ __?__ .

WRITTEN EXERCISES

A

1. If a chord 10 inches long is 5 inches from the center of a circle, find the radius of the circle.

2. In a circle with a 12 inch radius, find the length of a segment joining the midpoint of a 20 inch chord and the center of the circle.

3. Find the radius of a circle in which the side of an inscribed square is 8.

4. Find the radius of a circle in which the perimeter of an inscribed square is $8k$.

5. Prove Theorem 10–6 for the case where the given congruent chords lie in congruent circles.

6. Prove Theorem 10–7 for the case where the given congruent arcs lie in the same circle.

7. Prove Theorem 10–7 for the case where the given congruent arcs lie in congruent circles.

8. Given: Pts. R, S, T, and Q on ⊙O; $\overset{\frown}{RS} \cong \overset{\frown}{TQ}$.
   Prove: $\overline{RT} \cong \overline{SQ}$.

9. Given: Pts. R, S, T, and Q on ⊙O; $\overline{RS} \cong \overline{TQ}$.
   Prove: $\overset{\frown}{RT} \cong \overset{\frown}{SQ}$.

Exs. 8, 9

10. Given: Pts. X, T, Y, and N on $\odot P$; $\overline{PT} \perp \overline{XY}$;
  $\overset{\frown}{NY} \cong \overset{\frown}{YT}$.

  Prove: $\overset{\frown}{NY} \cong \overset{\frown}{XT}$.

11. Given: Pts. X, T, Y, and N on $\odot P$; $\overline{PT} \perp \overline{XY}$.

  Prove: $\angle TXZ \cong \angle TYZ$.

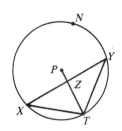

Exs. 10, 11

12. Given: $\odot O$ with diameter $\overline{JK} \perp \overline{EF}$.

  Prove: $\triangle EJF$ is an isosceles $\triangle$.

B **13.** Prove: If an equilateral pentagon is inscribed in a circle, then any two diagonals of that pentagon are congruent.

14. Prove: A radius that bisects a chord other than a diameter is perpendicular to the chord.

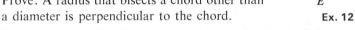

Ex. 12

15. Prove: A radius that bisects an arc bisects the chord of that arc.

16. Prove: If a line bisects each of the arcs of a chord, then that line bisects the chord.

17. Prove: If two circles are concentric, a chord of the larger circle that is tangent to the smaller circle is bisected at the point of tangency.

18. Prove Theorem 10–10. *Hint:* use an algebraic proof similar to that used in proving Theorem 10–9.

C **19.** Prove: If a plane intersects a sphere in more than one point, the intersection is a circle.

  Hint: Drop a perpendicular from O to the intersecting plane. Let A and B be any two points of the intersection. Show that $AP = BP$.

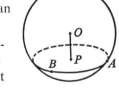

20. Given: $\odot O \cong \odot P$.

  Prove: $\angle JOK \cong \angle JPK$.

21. Given: $\odot O$ and $\odot P$; $m\overset{\frown}{JUK} = m\overset{\frown}{JVK}$.

  Prove: $\overline{OJ} \cong \overline{PJ}$.

22. Prove: If two chords of a circle have unequal lengths, then the minor arc of the longer chord has greater measure than the minor arc of the shorter chord.

Exs. 20, 21

23. Prove: If two minor arcs of a circle have unequal measures, then the chord of the arc with the greater measure is longer than the chord of the arc with the lesser measure.

24. Prove: If two chords are not equidistant from the center of a circle, then the chord at the greater distance is the shorter chord.

  Hint: Let p and q designate distances from the center. Use the Pythagorean Theorem. If $p > q$, where p and q are positive, then $p^2 > q^2$ and $r^2 - p^2 < r^2 - q^2$, by *algebraic theorems of inequality.*

25. Prove: If two chords of a circle have unequal lengths, then the shorter chord is at the greater distance from the center.

■ Angles and Segments Related to Circles

10–4 Angles Whose Measures Are Half Those of Their Intercepted Arcs

In each circle below, $\angle B$ is *inscribed* in the arc shown in red ($\overset{\frown}{ABC}$). In circle O, $\angle B$ is inscribed in a major arc; in circle P, $\angle B$ is inscribed in a minor arc; in circle R, $\angle B$ is inscribed in a semicircle.

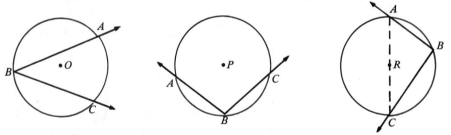

An angle is said to be **inscribed** in an arc and to be an **inscribed angle** if its sides contain the endpoints of the arc and its vertex is a point of the arc other than an endpoint. Thus, in the figures shown below only $\angle 1$ is an inscribed angle. Only $\angle 1$ is inscribed in an arc.

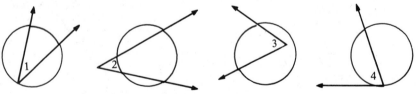

In each figure above, the numbered angle *intercepts* the arc or arcs shown in red. An angle is said to **intercept** an arc if

1. The endpoints of the arc lie on the sides of the angle with at least one endpoint on each side.

2. All points of the arc, other than the endpoints, lie in the interior of the angle.

In the figure shown at the right ∠*ABC* does not intercept $\overset{\frown}{CXD}$, since $\overrightarrow{BA}$ does not contain an endpoint of $\overset{\frown}{CXD}$.

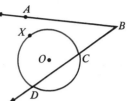

THEOREM 10–11   The measure of an inscribed angle is equal to half the measure of its intercepted arc.

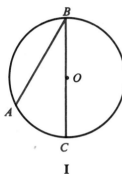 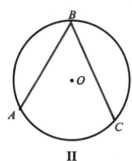 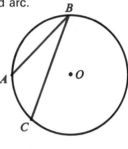

    I   **II**   **III**

Given: ∠*ABC* inscribed in ⊙*O*.   **To Prove:** $m\angle ABC = \frac{1}{2}m\overset{\frown}{AC}$.

Analysis: Consider three cases as suggested by the drawings above.

   Case I. When the center of the circle lies on one side of the angle, draw $\overline{OA}$ and compare $m\angle ABC$ with $m\angle AOC$.

  Case II. When the center of the circle lies in the interior of the angle, draw diameter $\overline{BX}$. Make use of Case I and the fact that $m\angle ABC = m\angle ABX + m\angle XBC$.

 Case III. When the center of the circle lies in the exterior of the angle, draw diameter $\overline{BX}$. Make use of Case I and the fact that $m\angle ABC = m\angle ABX - m\angle CBX$.

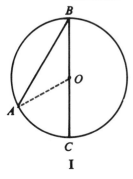 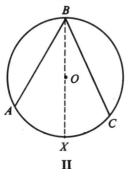 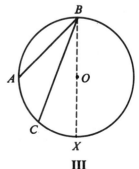

    I   **II**   **III**

Proof, Case I

STATEMENT	REASON
1. Draw $\overline{OA}$.	**1.** There is exactly one line through __?__.
2. $m\angle A + m\angle B = m\angle AOC$.	**2.** The measure of an ext. $\angle$ of a $\triangle$ __?__.
3. $\overline{OA} \cong \overline{OB}$.	**3.** Radii of a $\odot$ are $\cong$.
4. $m\angle A = m\angle B$.	**4.** Base $\angle\!\!\!\angle$ of an isos. $\triangle$ are $\cong$.
5. $m\angle B + m\angle B = m\angle AOC$.	**5.** Substitution principle.
6. $m\angle B = \frac{1}{2}m\angle AOC$.	**6.** Division property of equality.
7. $m\overset{\frown}{AC} = m\angle AOC$.	**7.** The measure of a minor arc is __?__.
8. $m\angle B = \frac{1}{2}m\overset{\frown}{AC}$.	**8.** Substitution principle.

Proof, Case II

STATEMENT	REASON
1. Draw diameter $\overline{BX}$.	**1.** There is exactly one line through __?__.
2. $m\angle ABX = \frac{1}{2}m\overset{\frown}{AX}$.	**2.** Case I.
3. $m\angle XBC = \frac{1}{2}m\overset{\frown}{XC}$.	**3.** Case I.
4. $m\angle ABX + m\angle XBC = \frac{1}{2}(m\overset{\frown}{AX} + m\overset{\frown}{XC})$.	**4.** Addition property of equality.
5. $m\angle ABC = \frac{1}{2}m\overset{\frown}{AC}$.	**5.** Angle addition postulate, arc addition theorem, and substitution principle.

Proof, Case III

STATEMENT	REASON
1. Draw diameter $\overline{BX}$.	**1.** There is exactly one line __?__.
2. $m\angle ABX = \frac{1}{2}m\overset{\frown}{AX}$.	**2.** Case I.
3. $m\angle XBC = \frac{1}{2}m\overset{\frown}{CX}$.	**3.** Case I.
4. $m\angle ABX - m\angle CBX = \frac{1}{2}(m\overset{\frown}{AX} - m\overset{\frown}{CX})$.	**4.** Subtraction property of equality.
5. $m\angle ABC = \frac{1}{2}m\overset{\frown}{AC}$.	**5.** Angle addition theorem, arc addition postulate, and substitution principle.

COROLLARY 1 An angle inscribed in a semicircle is a right angle.

COROLLARY 2 If a quadrilateral is inscribed in a circle, opposite angles are supplementary.

COROLLARY 3 If two inscribed angles intercept congruent arcs, the angles are congruent.

Shown below are figures illustrating the use of these corollaries.

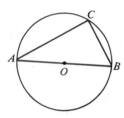
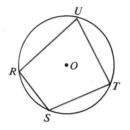
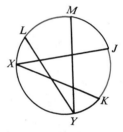

If $\overline{AB}$ is a diameter, $\angle C$ is a rt. $\angle$.

If *RSTU* is inscribed in $\odot O$, $\angle R$ and $\angle T$ are suppl., and $\angle S$ and $\angle U$ are suppl.

If $\overset{\frown}{JK} \cong \overset{\frown}{LM}$, $m\angle X = m\angle Y$.

In describing the positions of angles in relation to a circle, the terms *secant ray* and *tangent ray* are often used. A **secant ray** is a ray that lies on a secant line and contains both points of intersection with the circle. A **tangent ray** is a ray that lies on a tangent line and contains the point of tangency.

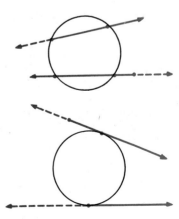

THEOREM 10–12   The measure of an angle formed by a secant ray and a tangent ray drawn from a point on a circle is equal to half the measure of the intercepted arc.

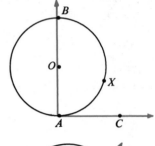

Given: Circle O with tangent ray $\overrightarrow{AC}$ and secant ray $\overrightarrow{AB}$.

To Prove: $m\angle BAC = \frac{1}{2}m\widehat{AXB}$.

Analysis:

Case I. $\overline{AB}$ is a diam.   Show that $m\angle BAC = 90$; $\frac{1}{2}m\widehat{AXB} = 90$.

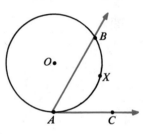

Case II. Draw $\overrightarrow{AO}$.   Apply the angle addition postulate, the arc addition postulate, Case I, and the inscribed angle theorem.

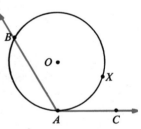

Case III. Quite similar to Case II.

The proofs of all three cases are left as exercises. (See Exs. 21, 22, 23, p. 383.)

ORAL EXERCISES

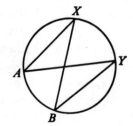

In Exercises 1 and 2, $\overline{XA}$, $\overline{XB}$, $\overline{YA}$, and $\overline{YB}$ are chords.

1. $m\widehat{AB} = 80$. $m\angle X = \underline{\ ?\ }$. $m\angle Y = \underline{\ ?\ }$.

2. $m\angle X = 35$. $m\widehat{AB} = \underline{\ ?\ }$. $m\angle Y = \underline{\ ?\ }$.

In Exercises 3 and 4, $\overline{UR}$, $\overline{US}$, and $\overline{UT}$ are chords.

3. $m\overset{\frown}{RS} = 40$, and $m\overset{\frown}{ST} = 80$. $m\angle 1 = \underline{\ ?\ }$;
$m\angle 2 = \underline{\ ?\ }$; $m\overset{\frown}{RST} = \underline{\ ?\ }$; $m\overset{\frown}{RUT} = \underline{\ ?\ }$.

4. $m\angle 1 = 15$, and $m\angle 2 = 50$.
$m\angle RUT = \underline{\ ?\ }$; $m\overset{\frown}{RT} = \underline{\ ?\ }$; $m\overset{\frown}{ST} = \underline{\ ?\ }$.

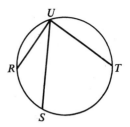

In Exercises 5–8, quadrilateral JKMN is inscribed in the circle. $\overleftrightarrow{QT}$ is a tangent at K.

5. $m\overset{\frown}{KM} = 60$. $m\angle TKM = \underline{\ ?\ }$.
$m\angle QKM = \underline{\ ?\ }$.

6. $m\angle QKJ = 45$. $m\overset{\frown}{JK} = \underline{\ ?\ }$.

7. $m\angle J = 80$, and $m\angle JKM = 110$.
$m\angle M = \underline{\ ?\ }$. $m\angle JNM = \underline{\ ?\ }$.

8. $m\angle J = 90$. $m\angle M = \underline{\ ?\ }$. $\overset{\frown}{KMN}$ is a $\underline{\ ?\ }$.
$\overline{KN}$ is a $\underline{\ ?\ }$. $m\angle JKM + m\angle JNM = \underline{\ ?\ }$.

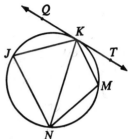

WRITTEN EXERCISES

$\overline{XA}$ and $\overline{XB}$ are chords of $\odot O$. $\overline{XC}$ is a diameter.

1. $m\overset{\frown}{BCX} = 260$. $m\overset{\frown}{AB} = 30$.
$m\overset{\frown}{AX} = \underline{\ ?\ }$. $m\overset{\frown}{BC} = \underline{\ ?\ }$.
$m\angle AXC = \underline{\ ?\ }$.

2. $m\angle AXC = 70$. $m\overset{\frown}{AB} = 50$.
$m\overset{\frown}{AC} = \underline{\ ?\ }$. $m\overset{\frown}{AX} = \underline{\ ?\ }$.
$m\angle BXC = \underline{\ ?\ }$.

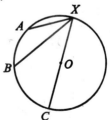

In Exercises 3 and 4, $\overline{DE}$, $\overline{EF}$, and $\overline{FD}$ are chords. $\overleftrightarrow{KG}$ is a tangent at E.

3. $m\angle D = 70$. $m\angle DEK = 50$.
$m\angle FEG = \underline{\ ?\ }$. $m\angle F = \underline{\ ?\ }$.

4. $m\angle KEF = 125$. $m\angle D = \underline{\ ?\ }$.

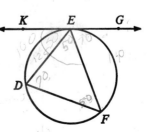

$\overline{RS}$, $\overline{ST}$, $\overline{TQ}$, $\overline{QR}$, and $\overline{RT}$ are chords. $\overline{QS}$ is a diameter. $\overleftrightarrow{TU}$ is a tangent at T.

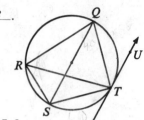

5. $m\angle QRS = \underline{\ ?\ }$, $m\angle SQT + m\angle QST = \underline{\ ?\ }$.

6. $m\overset{\frown}{RQ} = 120$. $m\angle RSQ = \underline{\ ?\ }$.
   $m\angle RTQ = \underline{\ ?\ }$.

7. $m\angle RSQ = 70$. $m\angle RQS = \underline{\ ?\ }$.
   $m\angle RTS = \underline{\ ?\ }$.

8. $m\angle SQT = 40$. $m\angle QRT = \underline{\ ?\ }$.
   $m\angle QTU = \underline{\ ?\ }$.

Exs. 5–8

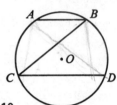

9. Given: $\odot O$ with $\overset{\frown}{AC} \cong \overset{\frown}{BD}$.
   Prove: $\overline{AB} \parallel \overline{CD}$.

10. Given: $\odot O$ with chord $\overline{AB} \parallel$ chord $\overline{CD}$.
    Prove: $\overset{\frown}{AC} \cong \overset{\frown}{BD}$.

Exs. 9, 10

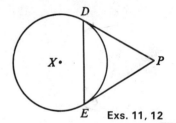

11. Given: $\overline{DP}$ and $\overline{EP}$ are tangent to $\odot X$
    at D and E.
    Prove: $\triangle DPE$ is isosceles.

12. Given: $\overline{DP}$ and $\overline{EP}$ are tangent to $\odot X$
    at D and E; $m\overset{\frown}{DE} = t$.
    Prove: $m\angle DPE = 180 - t$.

Exs. 11, 12

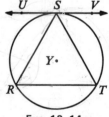

13. Given: $\triangle RST$ inscribed in $\odot Y$; $\overleftrightarrow{UV}$ tangent to
    $\odot Y$ at S; $\overleftrightarrow{UV} \parallel \overline{RT}$.
    Prove: $m\angle VST = \frac{1}{2}m\overset{\frown}{SR}$.

14. Given: $\triangle RST$ inscribed in $\odot Y$; $\overleftrightarrow{UV}$ tangent to
    $\odot Y$ at S; $\overline{RS} \cong \overline{TS}$.
    Prove: $\overleftrightarrow{UV} \parallel \overline{RT}$.

Exs. 13, 14

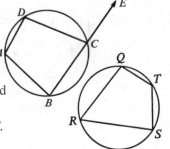

15. Given: Inscribed quadrilateral
    $ABCD$; points B, C, and
    E are collinear.
    Prove: $\angle A \cong \angle DCE$.

16. Given: Inscribed quadrilaterals $ABCD$ and
    $RSTQ$.
    Prove: $m\angle B + m\angle D = m\angle R + m\angle T$.

Exs. 15, 16

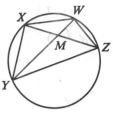

Exs. 17, 18

17. Given: $\overline{XY}$, $\overline{YZ}$, $\overline{ZW}$, $\overline{WX}$, $\overline{XZ}$, and $\overline{WY}$ are chords.

Prove: $\triangle XMY \sim \triangle WMZ$.

18. Given: $\overline{XY}$, $\overline{YZ}$, $\overline{ZW}$, $\overline{WX}$, $\overline{XZ}$, and $\overline{WY}$ are chords.

Prove: $\triangle XMW \sim \triangle YMZ$.

19. Prove: Tangents to a circle at the endpoints of a diameter are parallel.

20. Prove: The bisector of an inscribed angle separates the intercepted arc into two congruent arcs.

21. Prove Case I of Theorem 10–12.

22. Prove Case II of Theorem 10–12.

23. Prove Case III of Theorem 10–12.

24. Why is it impossible to circumscribe a circle about a quadrilateral whose consecutive angles have the measures 70, 80, 130, and 80?

25. Quadrilateral $ABCD$ is inscribed in a circle. $m\angle A = 7x + 20$, $m\angle B = 10x + 5$, and $m\angle C = 3x + 40$. Find $m\angle B$ as a number not involving x.

26. Quadrilateral $EFGH$ is inscribed in a circle. $m\angle E = x^2 + 20$ and $m\angle G = 160 - 10x$. What two measures can angle G have?

27. Given: $\overline{OA}$ and $\overline{OB}$ are radii of $\odot O$; $\overleftrightarrow{AC}$ is tangent to $\odot O$.

Prove: $m\angle BAC = \frac{1}{2}m\angle BOA$.

28. Given: $\overset{\frown}{RST}$ is a semicircle; $\overline{SV} \perp \overline{RT}$.

Prove: SV is the geometric mean between RV and VT.

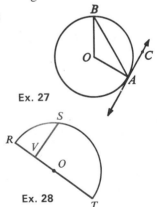

Ex. 27

Ex. 28

Points A, B, C, D, E, and F lie on the circles, as shown. Points A, B, and E are collinear. Points D, C, and F are collinear.

29. Prove: $m\angle F = \frac{1}{2}m\overset{\frown}{ADC}$.

30. Prove: $\overline{AD} \parallel \overline{EF}$.

31. Prove: If a tangent and a secant are parallel, they cut off congruent arcs on a circle.

32. Prove: If two tangents are parallel, they cut off congruent arcs on a circle.

33. Prove: An inscribed angle that intercepts a minor arc is an acute angle.

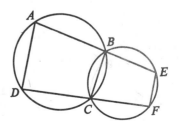

Exs. 29, 30

34. Prove: An inscribed angle that intercepts a major arc is an obtuse angle.

Use indirect proofs in Exercises 35 and 36.

C **35.** Given: $\triangle XYZ$ is inscribed in $\odot O$, $m\angle X = 30$, and $m\angle Y = 40$. Prove that points Z and O lie on opposite sides of $\overleftrightarrow{XY}$.

36. Given: Vertices A, B, and C of quadrilateral $ABCD$ lie on a circle; $m\angle A = m\angle B = m\angle C = 100$. Prove that point D cannot lie in the interior of the circle.

10–5 Other Angles Related to Circles

THEOREM 10–13 The measure of an angle formed by two secants intersecting inside a circle is equal to half the sum of the measures of the arcs intercepted by the angle and by its vertical angle.

Given: Secants $\overleftrightarrow{AB}$ and $\overleftrightarrow{CD}$ intersect at X.

To Prove: $m\angle 1 = \frac{1}{2}(m\widehat{AC} + m\widehat{BD})$.

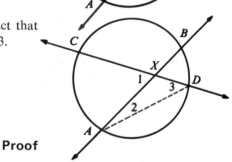

Analysis: Draw $\overline{AD}$. Use the fact that $m\angle 1 = m\angle 2 + m\angle 3$.

Proof

STATEMENT	REASON
1. Draw $\overline{AD}$.	1. There is exactly one line through __?__.
2. $m\angle 1 = m\angle 3 + m\angle 2$.	2. The measure of an ext. $\angle$ of a $\triangle$ __?__.
3. $m\angle 3 = \frac{1}{2}m\widehat{AC}$; $m\angle 2 = \frac{1}{2}m\widehat{BD}$.	3. The measure of an inscribed $\angle$ __?__.
4. $m\angle 1 = \frac{1}{2}m\widehat{AC} + \frac{1}{2}m\widehat{BD} = \frac{1}{2}(m\widehat{AC} + m\widehat{BD})$.	4. Substitution principle.

THEOREM 10–14   The measure of an angle formed by two secant rays with a common endpoint outside a circle equals one-half the difference of the measures of the intercepted arcs.

Given: Secant rays $\overrightarrow{UR}$ and $\overrightarrow{UT}$.

To Prove: $m\angle 1 = \frac{1}{2}(m\widehat{RT} - m\widehat{SQ})$.

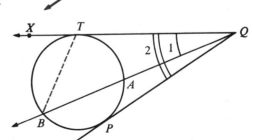

Analysis: Draw $\overline{ST}$. Use the fact that $m\angle RST = m\angle STU + m\angle 1$.

Proof: The proof is left for you.

THEOREM 10–15   The measure of an angle formed by a tangent ray and a secant ray, or by two tangent rays, with a common endpoint outside a circle is equal to half the difference of the measures of the intercepted arcs.

Given: Tangents $\overrightarrow{QT}$ and $\overrightarrow{QP}$ and secant $\overrightarrow{QB}$.

To Prove: I. $m\angle 1 = \frac{1}{2}(m\widehat{TB} - m\widehat{TA})$;

II. $m\angle 2 = \frac{1}{2}(m\widehat{TBP} - m\widehat{TAP})$.

Analysis:

Part I.   Draw $\overline{BT}$. Use the fact that $m\angle 1 + m\angle TBA = m\angle BTX$.

Part II. $m\angle 2 = m\angle BQT + m\angle BQP$.

Apply Part I to both terms of the right member.

The proofs are left for you. (Exercises 21 and 22, p. 387.)

ORAL EXERCISES

Points *J*, *K*, *N*, and *M* lie on the circle. Points *J*, *K*, and *Z* are collinear. Points *M*, *N*, and *Z* are collinear.

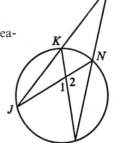

1. The measure of ∠1 is half the __?__ of the measures of $\widehat{JM}$ and $\widehat{KN}$.

2. The measure of ∠*Z* is half the __?__ of the measures of __?__ and __?__.

3. $\frac{1}{2}(m\widehat{JK} + m\widehat{MN}) = m\angle$ __?__.

4. If $m\widehat{JM} = 90$, and $m\widehat{KN} = 40$, then $m\angle 1 =$ __?__, and $m\angle Z =$ __?__.

Tangent $\overrightarrow{PA}$, secant $\overrightarrow{PB}$, and tangent $\overrightarrow{PC}$.

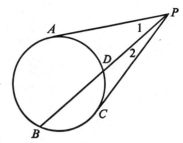

5. $m\angle 1 = \frac{1}{2}(m$ __?__ $- m$ __?__$).$

6. $\frac{1}{2}(m\widehat{BC} - m\widehat{DC}) = m\angle$ __?__.

7. $m\widehat{AC} = 100.$ Then $m\widehat{ABC} =$ __?__ and $m\angle APC =$ __?__.

8. If $m\widehat{AD} = 80$, and $m\widehat{BD} = 120$, then $m\widehat{AB} =$ __?__ and $m\angle 1 =$ __?__.

WRITTEN EXERCISES

A **1–10.** Points *A*, *B*, *C*, *D*, and *E* lie on circle *O*. $\overline{BE}$ is a diameter. $\overleftrightarrow{AT}$ is a tangent.

$$m\widehat{AB} = 80.$$
$$m\widehat{BC} = 20.$$
$$m\widehat{DE} = 50.$$

Copy the figure on your own paper so that you can label arcs and angles with their measures. Find the measure of each of the numbered angles.

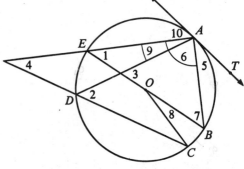

Exs. 1–10

EXAMPLE 1. $\overline{AB}$ and $\overline{CD}$ are chords. Find x.

Solution: $52 = \dfrac{x + 81}{2}$

$104 = x + 81$

$x = 23$

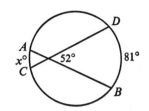

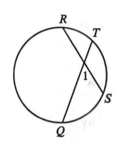

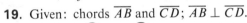

$\overline{RS}$ and $\overline{TQ}$ are chords of the circle.

11. $m\widehat{RT} = 20.\ m\widehat{QS} = 40.$ Find $m\angle 1.$
12. $m\widehat{RT} = a + 3c.\ m\widehat{QS} = c + d.$ Find $m\angle 1.$
13. $m\widehat{QS} = 50.\ m\angle 1 = 35.$ Find $m\widehat{RT}.$
14. $m\angle 1 = k.\ m\widehat{RT} = g.$ Find $m\widehat{QS}.$

Exs. 11–14

$\overline{TA}$ and $\overline{TB}$ are tangents.

15. $m\widehat{AXB} = 100.$ Find $m\angle 1.$
16. $m\widehat{AYB} = 204.$ Find $m\angle 1.$
17. $m\angle 1 = 60.$ Find $m\widehat{AXB}.$ **Exs. 15–18**
18. $m\angle 1 = j.$ Find $m\widehat{AXB}.$
19. Given: chords $\overline{AB}$ and $\overline{CD};\ \overline{AB} \perp \overline{CD}.$
   Prove: $m\widehat{AC} + m\widehat{BD} = 180.$
20. Given: chords $\overline{AB}$ and $\overline{CD};\ \overline{AB} \perp \overline{CD};$
   $m\widehat{BC} = k.$
   Prove: $m\widehat{AD} = 180 - k.$

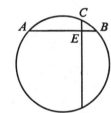

B **21.** Prove Part I of Theorem 10–15.
22. Prove Part II of Theorem 10–15.

Exs. 19, 20

$\overleftrightarrow{PQ}$ and $\overleftrightarrow{PR}$ are secants, and $\overleftrightarrow{PN}$ is a tangent of the circle shown.

23. Prove: $\triangle PQK \sim \triangle PRJ.$
24. Prove: $\triangle PNQ \sim \triangle PJN.$
25. Prove: The angle formed by two tangent rays from a point outside a circle is supplementary to the angle formed by rays drawn from the center of the circle through the points of contact.

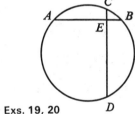

Exs. 23, 24

26. Prove: The angle formed by two rays drawn from a point in the interior of a circle through the endpoints of a diameter is obtuse.

EXAMPLE 2. $\overline{PK}$ and $\overline{PN}$ are tangents. $m\widehat{KN} > 100$. Make a deduction about $m\angle P$.

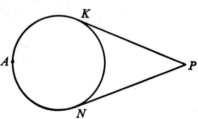

Solution: $m\widehat{KAN} + m\widehat{KN} = 360$

$$m\widehat{KN} > 100$$
$$m\widehat{KAN} < 260$$
$$m\widehat{KAN} - m\widehat{KN} < 160$$
$$\tfrac{1}{2}(m\widehat{KAN} - m\widehat{KN}) < 80$$
$$m\angle P < 80$$

$\overline{RS}$ and $\overline{TQ}$ are chords of the circle shown.

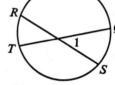

27. $m\angle 1 = 7x + 11.$ $m\widehat{RT} = 2x.$ $m\widehat{QS} = x + 88.$ Find x.

28. $m\angle 1 = x^2.$ $m\widehat{RT} = 3x.$ $m\widehat{QS} = x + 30.$ Find x.

29. $m\widehat{RT} < 40.$ $m\widehat{QS} < 60.$ Make a deduction about $m\angle 1$.

30. $m\widehat{RT} \le 30.$ $m\angle 1 > 40.$ Make a deduction about $m\widehat{QS}$.

$\overrightarrow{TA}$ and $\overrightarrow{TB}$ are tangent to the circle shown.

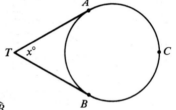

31. $m\widehat{AB} > 80.$ Make a deduction about x.

32. $m\widehat{ACB} > 225.$ Make a deduction about x.

33. $x \le 60.$ Make a deduction about $m\widehat{AB}$.

34. $x \ge 53.$ Make a deduction about $m\widehat{ACB}$.

$\overline{PX}$, $\overline{PY}$, and $\overline{RS}$ are chords of the circle shown.

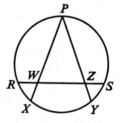

35. Given: $\widehat{RX} \cong \widehat{SY};$ $\widehat{PR} \cong \widehat{PS}.$
Prove: $\triangle WPZ$ is isosceles.

36. Given: $\overline{PW} \cong \overline{PZ};$ $\widehat{PR} \cong \widehat{PS}.$
Prove: $\widehat{XR} \cong \widehat{YS}.$

10–6 Theorems about Chords, Secant Segments, and Tangent Segments.

Many theorems proved in this book are statements you intuitively recognize as true. In this section, however, you will prove some facts that are not self-evident. In the figure shown, for example, $c \cdot d = a \cdot b$. Though this relation may seem unlikely, it can be established, by formal proof, for *any* two intersecting chords.

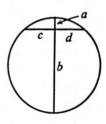

THEOREM 10–16 If two chords intersect within a circle, the product of the lengths of the segments of one chord equals the product of the lengths of the segments of the other.

Given: A circle with chords $\overline{RS}$ and $\overline{TQ}$ intersecting at X.

To Prove: $a \cdot b = c \cdot d$.

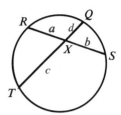

Analysis: Since $a \cdot b = c \cdot d$ is equivalent to $\dfrac{a}{d} = \dfrac{c}{b}$, establish this proportion by proving $\triangle RXT \sim \triangle QXS$. Draw $\overline{RT}$ and $\overline{QS}$.

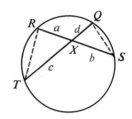

Proof

STATEMENT	REASON
1. Draw $\overline{RT}$ and $\overline{QS}$.	1. ?
2. $\angle T \cong \angle S$; $\angle R \cong \angle Q$.	2. If two inscribed $\angle$s intercept __?__.
3. $\triangle RXT \sim \triangle QXS$.	3. ?
4. $\dfrac{a}{d} = \dfrac{c}{b}$.	4. Lengths of corr. sides $\sim$ __?__.
5. $a \cdot b = c \cdot d$.	5. ?

The following theorems describe other relationships between the lengths of certain special segments associated with a circle.

If $\overleftrightarrow{AB}$ is tangent to circle O at point B, then segment $\overline{AB}$ is a **tangent segment** from A to circle O.

If $\overleftrightarrow{RT}$ is a secant intersecting circle O at S and T and R is in the exterior of circle O, then $\overline{RT}$ is a **secant segment** and $\overline{RS}$ an **external secant segment** to the circle from R.

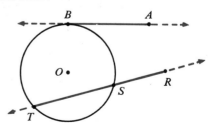

THEOREM 10–17   If two secant segments are drawn to a circle from an outside point, the product of the length of one secant segment and the length of its external secant segment is equal to the product of the length of the other secant segment and the length of the external secant segment.

Given: A circle with secant segments $\overline{PA}$ and $\overline{PC}$.

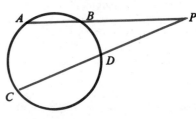

To Prove: $PA \cdot PB = PC \cdot PD$.

Analysis: Since $PA \cdot PB = PC \cdot PD$ is equivalent to $\dfrac{PA}{PC} = \dfrac{PD}{PB}$, establish this proportion by proving

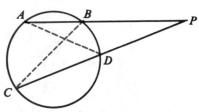

$$\triangle APD \sim \triangle CPB.$$

The proof is left for you.

THEOREM 10–18   If a tangent segment and a secant segment are drawn to a circle from an outside point, the length of the tangent segment is the geometric mean between the length of the secant segment and the length of the external secant segment.

Given: A circle with tangent $\overline{PT}$ and secant $\overline{PA}$.

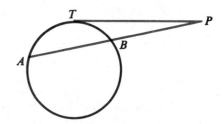

To Prove: $\dfrac{PA}{PT} = \dfrac{PT}{PB}$.   (See definition of geometric mean on p. 314.)

Analysis: A look at the required proportion suggests establishing that

$$\triangle PAT \sim \triangle PTB.$$

Hence draw chords $\overline{AT}$ and $\overline{BT}$.

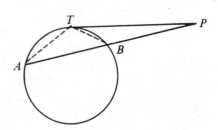

The proof is left for you.

The circles have chords, secant segments, and tangent segments as shown. In each exercise state the equation you can use to find x. Then state the theorem that supports the equation.

1.

2.

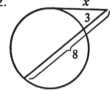

3.

4.

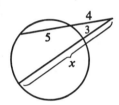

5.

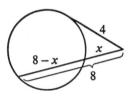

6.

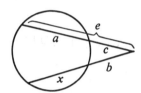

In Exercises 1–8 circles are shown with chords, tangent segments, or secant segments. In each exercise, find x.

A

1.

2.

3.

4.

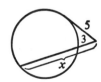

5.

6.

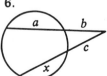

7.

8.

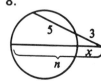

Chords $\overline{AB}$ and $\overline{CD}$ intersect at M.

EXAMPLE. $AM = 6$, $MB = 5$, $CD = 13$. Find MD.

Solution: Let $MD = x$. Then $CM = 13 - x$.
$$x(13 - x) = 6 \cdot 5$$
$$13x - x^2 = 30$$
$$x^2 - 13x + 30 = 0$$
$$(x - 3)(x - 10) = 0$$
$$x = 3, \ x = 10.$$
$$\therefore MD = 3 \text{ or } 10. \quad \textbf{Answer.}$$

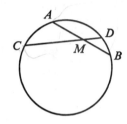

B   **9.** $AM = 7$, $MB = 6$, $CM = 8$. Find CD.
10. $CM = 8$, $DM = 6$, $AB = 16$. Find AM.
11. $AM = 8$, $AB = 16$, $CD = 20$. Find CM.
12. $AB = 15\frac{1}{11}$, $AM = 11$, $CD = 14$. Find MD.   Exs. 9–12

Secant segments $\overline{SO}$ and $\overline{QO}$ and tangent segment $\overline{RO}$ intersect at point O.

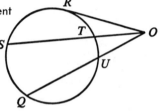

13. $OR = 6$, $OT = 4$. Find ST.
14. $OU = 5\sqrt{2}$, $UQ = 7\sqrt{2}$. Find OR.
15. $OQ = 6$, $OU = 4$, $ST = 5$. Find OT.
16. $RO = 10$, $ST = 21$. Find SO.   Exs. 13–16

17. Given: $PB = PD$.   Exs. 17, 18
        Prove: $PA = PC$.
18. Given: Secant segments $\overline{PB}$ and $\overline{PD}$;
        $PA = PC$.
        Prove: $AB = CD$.

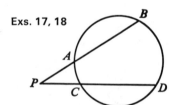

19. Prove: If two circles intersect, the line containing their common chord bisects a common external tangent segment.

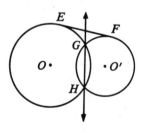

Ex. 19

20. Two circles are tangent externally. From any point in their common internal tangent, a secant is drawn to each circle. Prove that the product of the length of one secant segment and the length of its external secant segment is equal to the product of the length of the other secant segment and the length of its external secant segment.

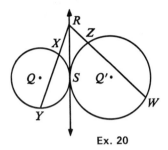

Ex. 20

21. Prove Theorem 10–17.

22. Prove Theorem 10–18.

23. Use Theorem 10–2 and congruent triangles to prove:
The two tangent segments to a circle from a given outside point are congruent.

24. Use Theorem 10–18 to prove:
The two tangent segments to a circle from a given outside point are congruent.

In proving Exercises 25 and 26, you may use the statement proved in Exercise 23.

25. Prove: If each of two circles lies in the exterior of the other circle, then their common internal tangent segments are congruent.

26. Prove: If part or all of each of two circles lies in the exterior of the other circle, then the common external tangent segments of the circles are congruent. (There are two cases: the tangents intersect; the tangents are parallel.)

PRACTICAL APPLICATIONS

1. You can find the center of a circular disk with the unmarked instrument shown. $\overline{AB} \cong \overline{AC}$, and $\angle BAD \cong \angle CAD$. When points B and C of the instrument are set against the rim of a disk, the center must lie on $\overleftrightarrow{AD}$. How many settings are needed to determine the center? Will the tool work on a disk so small that $\overline{AB}$ and $\overline{AC}$ are tangent to the circle?

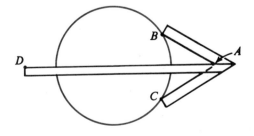

2. You can find a diameter of a circle with a carpenter's square. Set the square so that point *P* of the square lies on the circle. Mark intersection points *R* and *S*. Draw $\overline{RS}$. Can you find the center of a circle by using an unmarked carpenter's square?

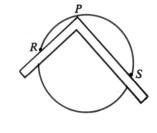

3. Suppose you wish to arrange a schedule so that on five consecutive days each team in a *six*-team league plays each of the other teams. Use a protractor to separate the circle into *five* congruent arcs. The pairings for the first day are shown: *A* plays *F*, *B* plays *E*, *C* plays *D*. To pair the teams for the second day draw $\overleftrightarrow{BF}$ instead of $\overleftrightarrow{AF}$.

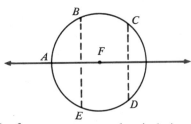

If a league has an odd number (*n*) of teams, separate the circle into *n* congruent arcs. Label the center *Y*, for bye.

Arrange a full schedule for six teams; for seven teams.

4. The top of a vertical tower is *h* feet above ground. Let the distance from the top of the tower to the horizon be *d* miles. (For the sake of clarity, an impossibly high tower is pictured.) Show that a good approximation for *d* is given by the formula: $d = \frac{5}{4}\sqrt{h}$. You will need to make your own drawing, showing a full circle. The earth's radius is approximately 4000 miles.

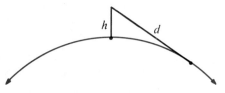

CHAPTER SUMMARY

Inventory of Structure and Method

1. Important circle relationships (Assume that any ray or segment that appears to be tangent is tangent to the circle.)

 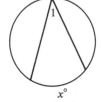 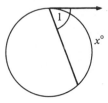 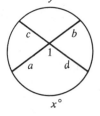

$m\angle 1 = x$ $m\angle 1 = \frac{1}{2}x$ $m\angle 1 = \frac{1}{2}x$ $m\angle 1 = \frac{1}{2}(x + y)$
$ab = cd$

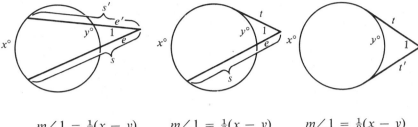

$$m\angle 1 = \tfrac{1}{2}(x - y)$$
$$s \cdot e = s' \cdot e'$$

$$m\angle 1 = \tfrac{1}{2}(x - y)$$
$$s \cdot e = t^2$$

$$m\angle 1 = \tfrac{1}{2}(x - y)$$
$$y = 360 - x$$
$$t = t'$$

2. Additional theorems and corollaries.

In the same circle or congruent circles, congruent central angles have congruent arcs, and conversely.

Inscribed angles that intercept the same or congruent arcs are congruent.

A diameter or radius drawn to the point of contact of a tangent is perpendicular to the tangent at that point.

An angle inscribed in a semicircle is a right angle.

A diameter perpendicular to a chord bisects the chord and its intercepted arcs.

Vocabulary and Spelling

tangent to a circle (*p. 359*)
    point of tangency (*p. 359*)
    (point of contact) (*p. 359*)
common tangents (*p. 361*)
    internal tangent (*p. 361*)
    external tangent (*p. 361*)
tangent circles (*p. 361*)
    internally tangent (*p. 361*)
    externally tangent (*p. 361*)
circumscribed polygon (*p. 361*)
inscribed circle (*p. 361*)
congruent circles (*p. 364*)
arc *AB* ($\overset{\frown}{AB}$) (*p. 365*)
    minor arc (*p. 365*)
    major arc (*p. 365*)
central angle (*p. 365*)

semicircle (*p. 365*)
measure of an arc (*p. 365*)
congruent arcs (*p. 366*)
bisect an arc (*p. 370*)
midpoint of an arc (*p. 370*)
center of an arc (*p. 370*)
inscribed polygon (*p. 372*)
circumscribed circle (*p. 372*)
common chord (*p. 373*)
inscribed angle (*p. 376*)
intercepted arc (*p. 376*)
secant ray (*p. 379*)
tangent ray (*p. 379*)
external secant segment (*p. 389*)

CHAPTER TEST

10–1 Given externally tangent circles M and N.

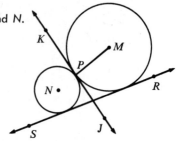

   1. $\overleftrightarrow{JK}$ is a common __?__.

   2. $\overleftrightarrow{RS}$ is a common __?__.

   3. $\overline{MP}$ is __?__ to $\overleftrightarrow{JK}$.

   4. Are all possible common tangents shown?

10–2 Given circle P with $\overline{AD}$ a diameter.

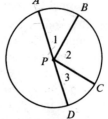

   5. If $m\angle 1 = 40$, $m\overset{\frown}{AB} = $ __?__.

   6. $m\overset{\frown}{BCD} - m\overset{\frown}{CD} = m$__?__.

   7. If $m\angle 1 = m\angle 3$, then m__?__ $= m$__?__.

   8. If $m\angle 3 = 30$, $m\overset{\frown}{ABC} = $ __?__.

10–3 State a theorem that supports the assertion made.

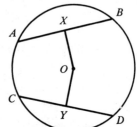

   9. If $\overline{AB} \cong \overline{CD}$, then $m\overset{\frown}{AB} = m\overset{\frown}{CD}$.

   10. If $m\overset{\frown}{AB} = m\overset{\frown}{CD}$, then $\overline{AB} \cong \overline{CD}$.

   11. If $\overline{OX} \perp \overline{AB}$, then $AX = XB$.

   12. If $\overline{OX} \perp \overline{AB}$, $\overline{OY} \perp \overline{CD}$, and $OX = OY$, then $\overline{AB} \cong \overline{CD}$.

10–4 Given circle O with tangent $\overrightarrow{MP}$.

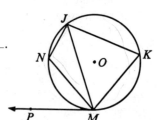

   13. If $m\overset{\frown}{JM} = 150$, then $m\angle N = $ __?__.

   14. If $m\angle K = 63$, then $m\angle JMP = $ __?__.

   15. If $m\angle NJK = x$, then $m\angle NMK = $ __?__.

10–5 Given tangent segment $\overline{PA}$ and secant segments $\overline{PB}$ and $\overline{PE}$.

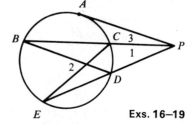

   16. If $m\overset{\frown}{BE} = 80$ and $m\overset{\frown}{CD} = 40$, $m\angle 1 = $ __?__.

   17. If $m\overset{\frown}{BE} = 70$ and $m\overset{\frown}{CD} = 30$, $m\angle 2 = $ __?__.

Exs. 16–19

18. If $m\overset{\frown}{AB} = 60$ and $m\overset{\frown}{AC} = 30$, $m\angle 3 = $ ___?___ .

19. If $m\angle 1 = 30$ and $m\overset{\frown}{CD} = 20$, $m\overset{\frown}{BE} = $ ___?___ .

10–6 In each circle shown find **x**. Assume a segment that appears to be tangent is tangent.

20.

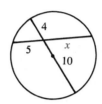

22.

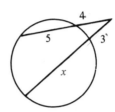

21.

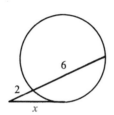

23.

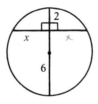

B

24. Given: Diameter $\overline{AB}$ and tangent segment $\overline{BC}$.

Prove: $\triangle AXB \sim \triangle ABC$.

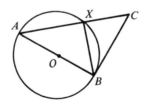

25. Given: Circle O with $m\overset{\frown}{AC} = m\overset{\frown}{BD}$.

Prove: $\overline{AB} \parallel \overline{CD}$.

26. In a circle a chord 18 inches long is parallel to a tangent and bisects the radius drawn to the point of tangency. How long is the radius?

CHAPTER REVIEW

10–1   Tangents   *Pages 359–364*

Given: △ABC is circum-
scribed about circle O.

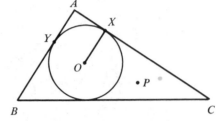

1. Circle *O* is __?__ in
   △*ABC*.

2. $\overline{AB}$ is __?__ to circle *O*
   at pt. __?__.

3. $m\angle OXC =$ __?__.

4. Point *P* lies in the __?__ of △*ABC* but in the exterior of __?__.

10–2   Arcs and Central Angles   *Pages 364–369*

5. Radii of congruent circles are __?__.

6. The measure of a minor arc is < __?__.

7. If points *R* and *S* are the endpoints of a diameter, then $\overset{\frown}{RS}$ is a
   __?__.

8. The measure of a minor arc is the same as the measure of its
   __?__ angle.

10–3   Arcs and Chords   *Pages 369–376*

9. A diameter that bisects a chord is __?__ to the chord and __?__
   the two __?__ of the chord.

10. A radius that bisects an arc __?__ the chord of that arc.

11. If two chords of a circle are unequal in length, the __?__ chord
    is nearer to the center of the circle.

12. In a circle of radius *k* a chord of length *k* intercepts a minor
    arc whose degree measure is __?__.

10–4   Angles Whose Measures Are Half   *Pages 376–384*
Those of Their Intercepted Arcs

Given: Inscribed quadrilateral *ABCD* and
tangent $\overrightarrow{DE}$.

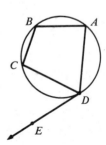

13. $m\angle CDE = \frac{1}{2}m$ __?__.

14. $m\angle A + m\angle C =$ __?__.

15. If $m\angle A = 90$, then $\overline{DB}$ is a __?__.

10–5   Other Angles Related to Circles   *Pages 384–388*

Given: $\overrightarrow{PD}$ and $\overrightarrow{PB}$ are secant rays
and $\overline{AB}$ a chord.

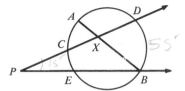

16. $m\angle AXC = \frac{1}{2}(m\underset{\frown}{\_?\_} + m\underset{\frown}{\_?\_}).$

17. $m\angle DPB = \frac{1}{2}(m\underset{\frown}{\_?\_} - m\underset{\frown}{\_?\_}).$

18. If $m\angle BXD = 40$ and
  $m\overset{\frown}{BD} = 55$, $m\overset{\frown}{AC} = \underline{\ ?\ }$.

19. If $m\angle P = 15$, and
  $m\overset{\frown}{BD} = 55$, $m\overset{\frown}{CE} = \underline{\ ?\ }$.

**10–6   Theorems about Chords, Secant Segments,   *Pages 388–393*
and Tangent Segments**

Given: Secant segments $\overline{RT}$ and $\overline{RS}$.

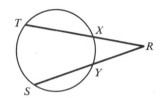

20. $(RT) \cdot (RX) = (?)(?).$

21. If $RX = 3$, $XT = 5$, and
  $RY = 2$, then $YS = \underline{\ ?\ }$.

22. If $RT = 2k$, $RX = k$ and
  $RS = 3k$, then $YR = \underline{\ ?\ }$.

Given: Tangent segment $\overline{PA}$ and secant
segment $\overline{PB}$.

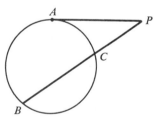

23. $(PA)^2 = (PB)(?).$

24. If $PB = 8$ and $PC = 2$,
  then $PA = \underline{\ ?\ }$.

25. If $PA = 6$ and $PB = 9$,
  then $PC = \underline{\ ?\ }$.

26. If $PC = CB$ and $PA = 3\sqrt{2}$, then $PC = \underline{\ ?\ }$.

CUMULATIVE REVIEW: CHAPTERS 8–10

COMPLETION EXERCISES

Write the correct word, phrase, or number on your paper.

1. An inscribed angle that intercepts a 70° arc has measure $\underline{\ ?\ }$.

2. An angle inscribed in a 160° arc has measure $\underline{\ ?\ }$.

3. When two distinct spheres have at least two points in common, the
  intersection of the spheres is a $\underline{\ ?\ }$.

4. When two polygons are similar, corresponding angles are $\underline{\ ?\ }$.

5. The length of the hypotenuse of a 30°–60°–90° triangle is 16. The length of the shorter leg is __?__. The length of the longer leg is __?__.

6. If $\dfrac{a}{b} = \dfrac{c}{d}$ and no letter represents zero, then $\dfrac{a+c}{c} = \dfrac{b+d}{?}$.

7. If $a = \dfrac{bx}{c}$ and $b \neq 0$, then $x =$ __?__.

8. A 2-by-3 rectangle is to be projected into a plane in such a way that the projection is a segment. That segment will be at least __?__ units long.

B 9. A 2-by-3 rectangle is to be projected into a plane in such a way that the projection is a segment. That segment will be at most __?__ units long.

10. $\triangle ABC \sim \triangle RST$. $m\angle A = m\angle R = 100$. In $\triangle ABC$ the longest side is twice as long as the shortest side. The shortest side of $\triangle RST$ has length 6. $ST =$ __?__.

11. The length of the hypotenuse of a right triangle is $x^2 + y^2$. The length of one leg is $2xy$. The length of the other leg is __?__.

12. The sides of a triangle have lengths 12, 16, and 21. The angle determined by the shorter sides is bisected. The length of the shorter of the two segments into which the third side is divided is __?__.

TRUE–FALSE EXERCISES

Write + for a statement that is always true and 0 for a statement that is not always true.

A 1. A circle can contain three collinear points.

2. A sphere can contain three coplanar points.

3. An angle inscribed in a major arc of a circle is obtuse.

4. All angles which intercept the same arc of a circle are congruent.

5. The perimeters of two similar polygons have the same ratio as the lengths of two corresponding sides.

6. To be concentric, two circles must lie in a plane.

7. Two concentric spheres have at least one point in common.

8. A segment joining the midpoints of the two arcs of a chord bisects the chord.

9. It is impossible to circumscribe a circle about an obtuse triangle.

10. If "$\triangle BXT \sim \triangle NRA$" is correct, then "$\triangle ANR \sim \triangle TBX$" is also correct.

B 11. If the measures of the angles of a triangle are in the ratio $1:2:3$, then the lengths of the sides are in the ratio $1:2:3$.

12. If three positive numbers g, h, n are such that $g = h + n$, then it is possible to have a right triangle whose sides have lengths $\sqrt{g}$, $\sqrt{h}$, $\sqrt{n}$.

13. The projection of a triangle into a plane must be a triangle.

14. If nonzero numbers a, b, c, d are such that $ab = cd$, then $\dfrac{a}{c} = \dfrac{d}{b}$.

15. If the lengths of the sides of a triangle are 12, 14, and 18, then that triangle is an obtuse triangle.

16. If two tangents to a circle determine a 40° angle, then those tangents intercept an arc of measure 140.

MISCELLANEOUS EXERCISES

In the figure shown, $\overline{OD}$ and $\overline{OE}$ are radii, $\overline{FD}$ is a tangent, $\overline{FB}$ is a secant, and $\overline{AC}$ is a chord.

$m\overarc{BC} = 60$, $m\overarc{DC} = 100$, $m\overarc{DE} = 80$, and $m\overarc{EA} = 40$.

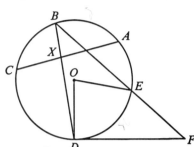

1. $m\overarc{AB} = $ ___?___
2. $m\angle EOD = $ ___?___
3. $m\angle ODF = $ ___?___
4. $m\angle BXC = $ ___?___
5. $m\angle DFB = $ ___?___
6. $m\angle BDF = $ ___?___

Exs. 1–6

7. Angle U of $\triangle NUX$ is a right angle. Altitude $\overline{UV}$ is drawn. List three pairs of similar triangles.

8. Two similar triangles have corresponding sides whose lengths are in the ratio 5:7. What is the ratio of the perimeters?

9. A ray bisects one angle of a triangle and separates the opposite side into segments with lengths 5 and 10. The shortest side of the triangle has length 8. Find the length of the remaining side.

10. The ratio of a to b is 5 to 1. The sum of a and b is 33. State the value of b.

In the figure shown, $\overline{AB}$ and $\overline{CD}$ are chords of the circle; $\overline{PA}$ and $\overline{PC}$ are secants, and $\overline{PT}$ is a tangent.

11. $PD = 4$ and $PA = 9$. Find PT.
12. $AX = 8$, $XB = 5$, and $CX = 10$. Find DX.
13. $PT = 10$ and $PB = 4$. Find BC.
14. $CD = 14$, $AX = 8$, and $XB = 5$. $CX > DX$. Find CX.
15. $AX = 2t$, $BX = 3n$, and $CX = 5k$. Find DX.
16. $PD = 6$, $DA = 5$, and $PB = 4$. Find PC.

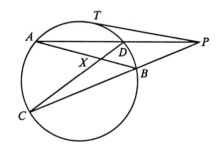

Exs. 11–16

17. The hypotenuse of a right triangle is 61 units long. One leg is 60 units long. Find the length of the other leg.

18. The altitude from the vertex of the right angle of a right triangle separates the hypotenuse into segments having lengths 9 and 4. Find the length of the altitude.

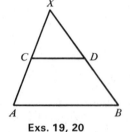

19. $\overline{CD} \parallel \overline{AB}$. $XC = 4$, $CA = 6$, and $XB = 15$. Find XD.

20. $\overline{CD} \parallel \overline{AB}$. $AX = 12$, $AC = 7$, and $DX = 6$. Find XB.

Exs. 19, 20

21. $\overleftrightarrow{OA}$ is perpendicular to the plane of circle O at O. Point X lies in the interior and point Y in the exterior of circle O. Compare AX with AY.

22. A man walks 100 ft. north, 250 ft. east, 50 ft. south, 50 ft. east, and finally 75 ft. north. How far is he from his starting point?

23. The altitude from the vertex of the right angle of a right triangle separates the hypotenuse into segments having lengths 7 and 21. Find the shorter leg of the triangle.

24. Find the length of a diagonal of a rectangular solid whose edges have lengths 8, 6, and 3.

25. Find the slant height of a regular square pyramid whose base is an 8 by 8 square and whose altitude has length 3.

26. Solve each proportion for x.

   a. $\dfrac{3}{5} = \dfrac{2x}{7}$

   b. $\dfrac{a}{b} = \dfrac{c}{x}$

   c. $\dfrac{x-3}{2} = \dfrac{x+5}{4}$

   d. $\dfrac{5}{x} = \dfrac{10}{x^2}$

   e. $\dfrac{x+3}{x-2} = \dfrac{x+7}{x-8}$

   f. $\dfrac{a-x}{b-x} = \dfrac{c+x}{d+x}$

27. A circular hole of radius 8 is cut in a flat board. A sphere of radius 10 fits against the rim of the hole. How far from the surface of the board is the most remote point of the sphere?

28. A wire bent to form a circular ring of radius $2a$ rests in a horizontal position on a sphere. Two horizontal planes are tangent to the sphere. The more remote of the planes is at distance $4a$ from the plane of the ring. How far from the plane of the ring is the other tangent plane?

PROOF EXERCISES

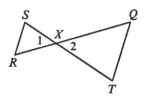

A

1. Given: $\overline{RS} \parallel \overline{TQ}$.
   Prove: $\triangle RXS \sim \triangle QXT$.
2. Given: $\angle R \cong \angle Q$.
   Prove: $\dfrac{RS}{QT} = \dfrac{RX}{QX}$.

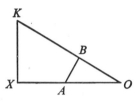

3. Given: $\angle OAB \cong \angle K$.
   Prove: $\dfrac{OA}{OK} = \dfrac{OB}{OX}$.
4. Given: $\overline{KX} \perp \overline{OX}$; $\overline{AB} \perp \overline{OK}$.
   Prove: $\dfrac{AB}{KX} = \dfrac{OB}{OX}$.

Exs. 3, 4

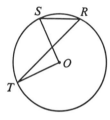

B

5. Given: $\overline{OT}$ and $\overline{OS}$ are radii of $\odot O$; $\overline{RS}$ and $\overline{RT}$ are chords; $m\angle R = 45$.
   Prove: $\overline{SO} \perp \overline{OT}$.
6. Given: $\overline{OT}$ and $\overline{OS}$ are radii of $\odot O$; $\overline{RS}$ and $\overline{RT}$ are chords; $\overline{OS} \perp \overline{OT}$.
   Prove: $m\angle R = 45$.

Exs. 5, 6

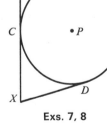

7. Given: $\overline{AB}$, $\overline{AX}$, and $\overline{XD}$ are tangent to $\odot P$.
   Prove: $AX = AB + XD$.
8. Given: $\overline{AB}$, $\overline{AX}$ and $\overline{XD}$ are tangent to $\odot P$.
   Prove: $AB + CX = AC + XD$.
9. Given: Line l intersects a circle in points R and S. Line k intersects the circle in T and Q. Lines l and k do not intersect in the interior of the circle. $\overset{\frown}{RT} \cong \overset{\frown}{SQ}$.
   Prove: $l \parallel k$.

Exs. 7, 8

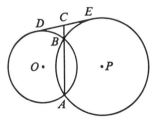

10. Given: $\overline{DE}$ is tangent to $\odot O$ and $\odot P$. $\overline{AB}$ is the common chord of $\odot O$ and $\odot P$. Point C is the intersection of $\overleftrightarrow{AB}$ and $\overline{DE}$.
    Prove: $DC = EC$.

C **11.** Given: $\odot P$ passes through the center of $\odot Q$ and is tangent to $\odot Q$ at point X; points Q, P, and X are collinear; $\overline{XY}$ is a chord of $\odot Q$.

Prove: $\odot P$ bisects $\overline{XY}$.

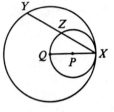

12. Given: Chords $\overline{AB}$ and $\overline{CD}$ of $\odot O$ intersect at point M.

Prove: AM, MB, CM, and MD cannot be the members of any set of four consecutive integers.

13. Given: $\odot O$ contains points R, S, and T such that $m\overset{\frown}{RS} = m\overset{\frown}{ST} = m\overset{\frown}{TR}$. Point P lies on $\overset{\frown}{ST}$.

Prove: $PS + PT = PR$.

14. Prove: A tangent to a circle at a midpoint of an arc is parallel to the chord of that arc.

15. Given: $\overline{PJ} \perp \overline{JK}$; $\overline{NK} \perp \overline{JK}$; $\overline{PR} \perp \overline{JN}$ at Q.

Prove: $\dfrac{PJ}{JK} = \dfrac{PR}{JN}$.

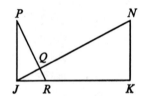

16. Given: $\overline{PJ} \perp \overline{JK}$; $\overline{NK} \perp \overline{JK}$; $\overline{PR} \perp \overline{JN}$ at Q.

Prove: $JQ \cdot JN = PJ \cdot NK$.

Exs. 15, 16

17. Given: Secant segments $\overline{PB}$ and $\overline{PD}$.

Prove: $\dfrac{BX}{BA} = \dfrac{DX}{DC}$.

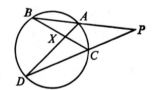

18. Given: Secant segments $\overline{PB}$ and $\overline{PD}$.

Prove: $BP \cdot AP = DP \cdot CP$.

Exs. 17, 18

19. In triangle RST, $m\angle R = m\angle S = 2 \cdot m\angle T$. The bisector of $\angle R$ meets $\overline{ST}$ at X. Prove that RS is the geometric mean between ST and SX.

20. Prove: If two chords of a sphere intersect in the interior of the sphere, the product of the lengths of the segments of one chord equals the product of the lengths of the segments of the other.

▶ A Child Prodigy

Perhaps you sometimes have a guilty conscience when you neglect your mathematics. Then think of Blaise Pascal, a seventeenth-century genius who often suffered pangs of conscience when he *was* working on the subject.

Pascal was denied an opportunity to study geometry in his early youth because of poor health. His father, knowing that his son would be intrigued by the subject, feared that the boy would over-exert himself. When Pascal was twelve, he insisted upon being told what geometry was about. His father described the subject. This was enough. Soon the lad proved — without the help of any book or teacher — that the sum of the measures of the angles of a triangle is equal to the sum of the measures of two right angles.

Given a copy of Euclid's geometry, Pascal quickly read the book for pleasure. By the time he was sixteen years old, he was discovering theorems that no man had thought of before. Two years later, he invented and made the world's first calculating machine. Already he had earned lasting fame in the fields of mathematics and physics.

Meanwhile Pascal was under pressure from members of his family to apply his energies to other matters. At the age of thirty-one, he yielded to their wishes and decided to devote his life to a study of philosophy and religion.

Several years later, however, during a period of illness, Pascal had one final fling with mathematics. While lying awake one day, he noticed that he forgot his pain when he thought about the cycloid, a type of geometric figure. Interpreting this as divine approval of mathematical activity, he spent a happy week making brilliant discoveries about the curve.

11 Constructions and Loci

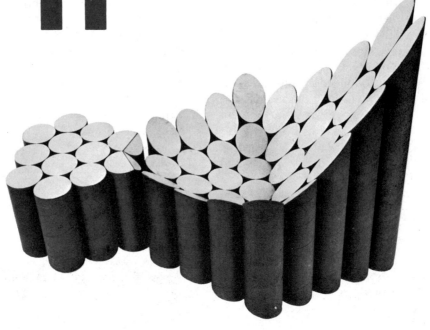

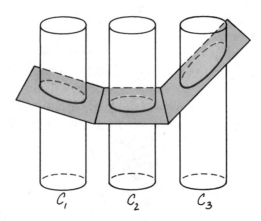

C_1 C_2 C_3

The unique design of this chair and ottoman comes from paperboard tubes cut by planes forming circles and ellipses.

Up to this point you have had no reason to be particularly concerned about the accuracy of your representations of various geometric figures on paper. You have made no formal deductions on the basis of measuring segments or angles in your drawings. About the only requirement has been that a drawing not represent a set of given conditions so inaccurately as to be misleading.

Many of you have taken pains to make accurate drawings using a ruler to measure distances and a protractor to measure angles. It may surprise you to learn that in many cases you could have attained the same, if not greater, accuracy using only a compass and straightedge. In this chapter you will learn how to construct a variety of plane figures using only a compass and straightedge. In addition you will become familiar with the technique used to locate and describe sets of points which satisfy one or more given conditions.

■ Constructions

11–1 What Construction Means: Permissible Instruments and Basic Angle Constructions

Since the days of the famous Greek philosopher and mathematician Plato (c. 380 B.C.), geometers have made a clear distinction between a drawing and a construction. A **drawing** is a representation made on paper using any suitable drawing instruments such as a protractor, T-square, marked ruler, compass, and straightedge. Theoretically, a **construction** is an imaginary drawing in which required points or lines are determined by use of just two idealized instruments, a compass and a straightedge. In practice, a *constructed figure* is made on paper when a compass and straightedge are used according to certain rules. No other instrument is used. Remember that the marks on a ruler cannot be used, for they are not part of a straightedge.

In this chapter we shall limit our consideration to constructions of plane figures. The rules governing the use of a straightedge and compass are given on the next page.

407

A straightedge is used only to

    1. Draw lines through a given point.

    2. Draw the unique line through two given points.

A compass is used only to

    1. Draw circles, or arcs of the circles, having a given center.

    2. Draw the unique circle, or arcs of that circle, having a given center and a given radius.

An illustration of an **incorrect** use of a straightedge in a construction follows.

Given: ⊙*O* and point *X*.   **To Construct:**   A line, through *X*, tangent to ⊙*O*.

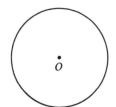

Steps: **NOT CORRECT:** Slide the straightedge until it passes through *X* and just touches ⊙*O*.

Notice that you do not have the two given points needed for the drawing of a specific line. Later (p. 418) you will see how to make this particular construction correctly.

In the following example a compass is used correctly.

EXAMPLE. Given $\overrightarrow{AB}$ and $\overrightarrow{OK}$. Mark off, on $\overrightarrow{OK}$, a segment congruent to $\overline{AB}$.

Solution: Using *O* as center, and *AB* as radius, draw an arc that intersects $\overrightarrow{OK}$. Call the intersection point *X*. $\overline{OX}$ is the required segment.

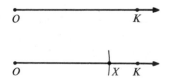

Do you see that drawing the complete circle would complicate the figure? On the other hand, if too short an arc were drawn, the drawing would be difficult for a reader to understand.

As in the example above, most constructions depend on intersection properties. A straightedge and compass can give these types of intersections.

1. Intersection of two coplanar lines. (Any two nonparallel lines that are coplanar intersect.)

2. Intersection of a coplanar line and circle. (By Theorem 10–1, when a line contains an interior point of a circle it intersects the circle in two points.)

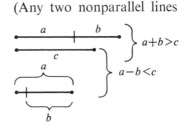

3. Intersection of two coplanar circles. Two coplanar circles intersect in two points if the distance between their centers is less than the sum of their radii but greater than the difference of their radii.   The two intersection points will lie on opposite sides of the line of centers. (See p. 412)

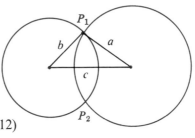

Two basic constructions follow. By studying them carefully you can become familiar with the form to use in presenting the solution to a construction problem.

CONSTRUCTION 1 Given an angle and a ray, construct an angle, with the given ray as a side, congruent to the given angle.

Given: $\angle ABC$ and $\overrightarrow{YZ}$.

To Construct: An angle with $\overrightarrow{YZ}$ as side and congruent to $\angle ABC$.

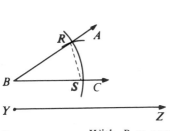

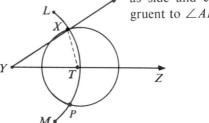

Steps: With B as center and a convenient radius construct an arc intersecting $\overrightarrow{BA}$ at R and $\overrightarrow{BC}$ at S. With the same radius and center Y, construct $\overarc{LM}$ intersecting $\overrightarrow{YZ}$ at T. With center T and radius SR construct a circle intersecting $\overarc{LM}$ at X and P. Draw $\overrightarrow{YX}$. $\angle XYT$ is congruent to $\angle RBS$. If $\overrightarrow{YP}$ is drawn, an alternate solution $\angle PYT$ is obtained.

Justification: If $\overline{RS}$ and $\overline{XT}$ are drawn, $\triangle RBS \cong \triangle XYT$ (SSS). Therefore, $\angle RBS \cong \angle XYT$. (Corr. $\angle$s of $\cong$ $\triangle$s are congruent.)

CONSTRUCTION 2 Given an angle, construct the ray that bisects the angle.

Given: ∠*ABC*.

To Construct: The ray bisecting ∠*ABC*.

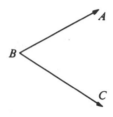

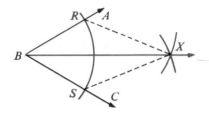

Steps: With *B* as center and any convenient radius, construct an arc intersecting $\overrightarrow{BA}$ in *R* and $\overrightarrow{BC}$ in *S*. With *R* and *S* as centers and a radius greater than $\frac{1}{2}RS$, construct arcs in the interior of ∠*ABC* intersecting at *X*. Draw $\overrightarrow{BX}$. **$\overrightarrow{BX}$ is the desired ray.**

Justification: If $\overline{XS}$ and $\overline{XR}$ are drawn, △*RBX* ≅ △*SBX* (SSS). Therefore, ∠*RBX* ≅ ∠*SBX*. (Corr. ∠s of ≅ △ are congruent.)

As illustrated by the two constructions shown, the complete solution to a construction problem consists of:

1. A *Statement:* a statement of the required construction in words.

2. The *Given:* all given data illustrated and expressed in terms of a lettered figure or figures.

3. The *To Construct:* the required construction expressed in terms of the given data.

4. The *Constructed Figure:* all essential points, arcs, and segments shown.

5. *Steps:* a description of all steps taken in the construction.

6. *Justification:* an argument in paragraph form supporting the validity of the construction.

1. Which one of the two preceding constructions can be used to construct an angle whose measure is double the measure of a given angle?

2. With the vertex of an angle as center, can you always construct an arc which intersects both sides of the angle?

3. If you are given two perpendicular lines, how can you construct an angle with measure 45?

4. If you construct two circles with the same center and different radii, will they intersect?

5. In a plane is there more than one point equidistant from two given points?

6. From the vertex of a given angle, how many rays are there that bisect the given angle?

Copy the two given segments on your paper. Then, without attempting to justify your procedure, construct a segment with length

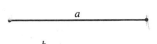

A

1. $a + b$ 3. $2b + a$

2. $a - b$ 4. $2b - a$ Exs. 1–4

For each of the following, show your construction but do not present a description or justification of it.

5. Draw an obtuse angle and bisect it.

6. Draw an acute triangle and bisect each of its angles.

7. Draw an obtuse triangle and bisect each of its angles.

8. Draw an obtuse angle A and a ray $\overrightarrow{OX}$. With O as vertex and $\overrightarrow{OX}$ as one side construct an angle congruent to angle A.

In Exercises 9–14 show only your construction. Be sure to show all essential arcs.

EXAMPLE. Given two angles, construct an angle with measure equal to the sum of the measures of the given angles.

Solution: **Given:** angles of measure x and y.

Answer. $\angle RST$

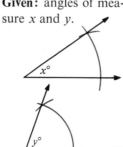

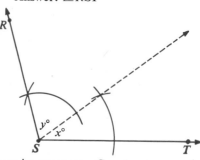

B **9.** Draw an acute angle. Let x represent its measure. Construct an angle with measure $2x$.

10. Given an obtuse angle and an acute angle, construct an angle whose measure is equal to the difference of the measures of the given angles.

11. Given two acute angles with measures a and b, construct an angle with measure $\frac{1}{2}(a + b)$.

12. Divide an obtuse angle into four angles with equal measures.

13. Draw an obtuse angle. At a point O on a given line l construct a supplement of the angle.

C Exercises 14 and 15 establish the assertion made on page 409 about intersecting circles.

Honors Problems

14. Given: $r > s; r - s < d < r + s$.

Prove: $s^2 - \left(\dfrac{d^2 - r^2 + s^2}{2d}\right)^2 > 0.$

Hint: $s^2 - \left(\dfrac{d^2 - r^2 + s^2}{2d}\right)^2 = \dfrac{4s^2 d^2 - (d^2 - r^2 + s^2)^2}{4d^2}.$ Factor

the numerator and show that each of the four factors is positive.

15. Given: $\odot O$ and $\odot Q$ are coplanar, with radii r and $s; r > s; OQ = d;$
    $r - s < d < r + s$.

Prove: $\odot O$ and $\odot Q$ intersect in two points.

Hint: Take point A as shown in the three cases.

(1) If $\dfrac{d^2 - r^2 + s^2}{2d} > 0$, on $\overline{OQ}$ take point A such that

$QA = \dfrac{d^2 - r^2 + s^2}{2d}.$

(2) If $\dfrac{d^2 - r^2 + s^2}{2d} < 0$, on $\overrightarrow{OQ}$ but not on $\overline{OQ}$ take

point A such that $QA = -\dfrac{d^2 - r^2 + s^2}{2d}$.

(3) If $\dfrac{d^2 - r^2 + s^2}{2d} = 0$, let point A be the same as point Q.

In each case draw line $j \perp$ to $\overleftrightarrow{OQ}$ at A.
On j take points X and Y such that

$$AX = AY = \sqrt{s^2 - \left(\dfrac{d^2 - r^2 + s^2}{2d}\right)^2}$$

Show that both QX and QY equal s and that both OX and OY equal r.

11–2   Constructing Parallel Lines and Perpendicular Lines

There are several ways in which you can construct parallel lines or perpendicular lines. The methods to be demonstrated in this section are not the only acceptable methods. You are free to use other methods provided you can justify their correctness.

CONSTRUCTION 3   Given a point on a line in a plane, construct a line perpendicular to the given line at the given point.

Given: Pt. P on line l.

To Construct: A line $\perp l$ through point P.

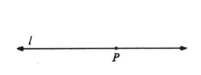

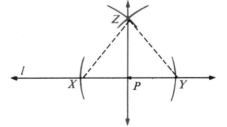

Steps: With P as center and a convenient radius, construct arcs intersecting l at points X and Y. With radius greater than $\frac{1}{2}XY$ construct arcs, with centers at X and Y, which intersect at Z. Draw $\overrightarrow{ZP}$. $\overrightarrow{ZP}$ **is the desired line.**

Justification: If $\overline{ZX}$ and $\overline{ZY}$ are drawn, $\triangle ZPX \cong \triangle ZPY$ (SSS). Therefore, $\angle ZPX \cong \angle ZPY$. $\overrightarrow{ZP} \perp l$ since the lines meet to form congruent adjacent angles at P.

CONSTRUCTION 4   Given a point outside a line, construct a per-pendicular to the line from the point.

Given: Pt. *P* not on line *l*.

To Construct: A line through *P* and ⊥ to *l*.

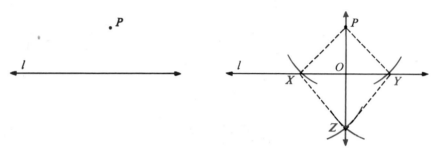

Steps:
Justification: } Complete these parts on the basis of the construction shown.

CONSTRUCTION 5   Given a segment, construct the perpendicular bisector of the segment.

Given: $\overline{AB}$.

To Construct: The perpendicular bisector of $\overline{AB}$.

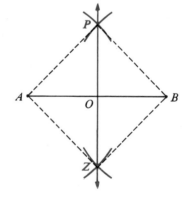

Steps: With radius greater than $\frac{1}{2}AB$ construct arcs with centers at *A* and *B* which intersect at *P* and *Z*. Draw $\overleftrightarrow{PZ}$. **$\overleftrightarrow{PZ}$ is the desired line.**

Justification: Write your own justification. *Hint*: show $\triangle APZ \cong \triangle BPZ$. Then use the fact that since $\angle APO \cong \angle BPO$, $\triangle APO \cong \triangle BPO$, and so $\angle AOP \cong \angle BOP$ and $\overline{AO} \cong \overline{BO}$.

CONSTRUCTION 6 Given a point outside a line, construct a line parallel to the given line through the given point.

Given: Point *P* not on *l*.

To Construct: A line through *P* parallel to *l*.

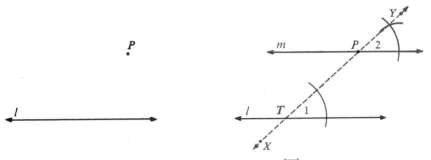

Steps: Through *P* draw any oblique line $\overleftrightarrow{XY}$ intersecting *l* at some point *T*. Let ∠1 be the acute angle having vertex *T* and $\overrightarrow{TY}$ as a side. With vertex *P* and $\overleftrightarrow{XY}$ as transversal, construct corresponding angle ∠2 congruent to ∠1. The side of ∠2 not lying in the transversal $\overleftrightarrow{XY}$ is a ray parallel to *l*. **Line *m*, containing this side, is the desired parallel.**

Justification: *l* and *m* are parallel lines because they form congruent corresponding angles with transversal $\overleftrightarrow{TP}$.

ORAL EXERCISES

1. Describe a method for constructing a segment whose length is one-fourth that of a given segment.

2. Describe a method based on a property of alternate interior angles for constructing a line parallel to a given line through a given point not on the line.

3. Describe a method based on constructing only perpendiculars for constructing a line parallel to a given line and passing through a given point not on the line.

4. Describe a method for constructing a line perpendicular to a segment at its endpoint.

WRITTEN EXERCISES

Begin each exercise by drawing a figure like the one shown, but larger. Then make the required construction showing all arcs clearly. You need not write a description or justification.

A

1. Construct a line ⊥ $\overline{AB}$ at point *P*.
2. Construct a line ⊥ $\overline{AC}$ and passing through *P*.
3. Construct a line ∥ $\overline{AB}$ and passing through *S*.
4. Construct a line through *P* ∥ $\overline{AC}$.

Exs. 1–4

5. Construct a line through *M* ⊥ $\overline{ZY}$.
6. Construct a line through *M* ∥ $\overline{ZY}$.
7. Construct a line through *M* ⊥ $\overline{XY}$.
8. Construct a line through *M* ∥ $\overline{XY}$.
9. At *M* construct a line ⊥ $\overrightarrow{YM}$.
10. At *Y* construct a line ⊥ $\overline{ZY}$.
11. Construct an angle with measure 45.
12. Construct an angle with measure 135.

Exs. 5–10

B

13. Draw an acute angle. Construct a complement.
14. Construct a square with sides of given length *t*.

In Exercises 15–18 make a separate drawing of △ABC for each exercise.

15. Through *C* construct a line ∥ $\overline{AB}$.
16. Construct a line through *C* ⊥ $\overline{AB}$.
17. Through the midpoint of $\overline{BC}$ construct a line ∥ $\overline{AC}$.
18. Through *B* construct a line ∥ $\overline{AC}$.

Exs. 15–18

19. Construct a rhombus with sides of given length *t* and having an angle with measure 45.
20. Construct a rhombus given the lengths *s* and *t* of its unequal diagonals.

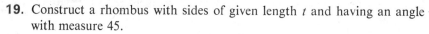

In Exercises 21–24 draw a large obtuse triangle roughly similar to the one shown. Remembering that it is possible to extend a segment in either direction with a straightedge, construct the following.

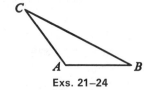

Exs. 21–24

C

21. The medians	23. The altitudes
22. The angle bisectors	24. The perpendicular bisectors of the sides

25. Construct an isosceles right triangle given only the length of its hypotenuse.

26. Given three segments of lengths *a*, *b*, and *c*, with $c > a > b$. What relations must exist between *a*, *b*, and *c* if a triangle can be constructed with sides of lengths *a*, *b*, and *c*?

11–3 Constructions Involving Circles

The construction problems presented in this section represent a small sampling of many interesting constructions dealing with circles. A knowledge of the basic constructions will enable you to handle more complex construction exercises whose solutions call for the combined use of two or more basic constructions.

CONSTRUCTION 7 Given an arc of a circle, construct a line that bisects the arc.

Given: $\overarc{AB}$ of a $\odot$. **To Construct:** A line bisecting $\overarc{AB}$.

Steps: (Study the indicated construction of the desired line, $\overleftrightarrow{XY}$. Then write a description of the construction.)

Justification: (Write a justification based on the fact that congruent chords have congruent arcs.)

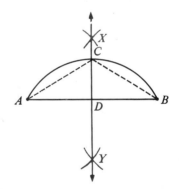

CONSTRUCTION 8 Given a point on a circle, construct the tangent to the circle at the given point.

Given: Pt. *P* on $\odot O$. **To Construct:** A tangent to $\odot O$ at *P*.

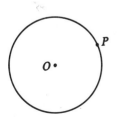

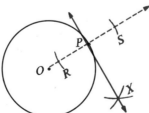

Steps: (Study the indicated construction of the desired tangent, $\overleftrightarrow{PX}$.
Justification: Then complete these two parts.)

CONSTRUCTION 9   Given a point outside a circle, construct the tangents to the circle from the point.

(*Note*: This is the construction for which an incorrect solution was described on page 408.)

Given: ⊙*O* and Pt. *A*.

To Construct: The tangents to ⊙*O* from *A*.

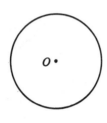

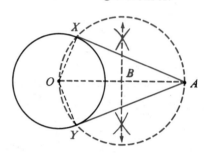

Steps: (Study the indicated construction of tangents $\overline{AX}$ and $\overline{AY}$. Then, write a description of the construction.)

Justification: (Note that ∠*OXA* and ∠*OYA* are inscribed in semicircles. Write a justification.)

CONSTRUCTION 10   Given a triangle, circumscribe a circle about the triangle.

Given: △*ABC*.

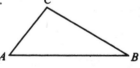

To Construct: A circle passing through *A*, *B*, and *C*.

Steps: Construct the ⊥ bisectors of any two sides of △*ABC*, ($\overline{AB}$ and $\overline{BC}$ in figure shown). The intersection of these nonparallel ⊥ bisectors is a point, *O*. With *O* as center and *OA* as radius construct a circle. **Circle O is the desired circle.**

Justification: (Write a justification explaining why circle *O*, with radius *OA*, must pass through *B* and *C*. See Exercise 20, p. 213.)

CONSTRUCTION 11   Given a triangle, inscribe a circle in the triangle.

Given: △*ABC*.

To Construct: A circle tangent to $\overline{AB}$, $\overline{AC}$ and $\overline{BC}$.

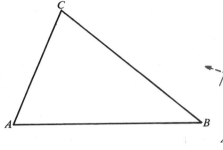

Steps: Construct the bisectors of any two angles of △*ABC*, (∠*A* and ∠*B* in figure shown). The bisectors intersect at a point *O*. From *O* construct $\overline{OP} \perp \overline{AB}$. With *O* as center and *OP* as radius construct a circle. **Circle O is the desired circle.**

Justification: (Write a justification explaining why circle *O*, with radius *OP*, must be tangent to $\overline{AC}$, $\overline{BC}$, and $\overline{AB}$. See Exercise 19, p. 213.)

ORAL EXERCISES

1. Given a circle, but not the location of its center. Describe a construction by which the center of the circle can be located.

2. Given an arc of a circle. Describe a construction by which the center of the circle can be located.

3. Does the method described for inscribing a circle in a triangle work when the triangle is obtuse?

4. Can you construct more than one circle that will pass through two given points? through three given points not on a line?

5. Can you construct a right angle by selecting any point on a semicircle and drawing rays from that point through the endpoints of the diameter?

6. Describe a method for constructing two parallel tangents to a circle.

In the following exercises show only your constructions. Where a circle is pictured, you may use a larger circle than the one shown. However, place the given points in the same relative positions.

A

1. Construct a tangent to ⊙O at D.
2. Construct a tangent to ⊙O from B.
3. Locate the midpoint of $\overset{\frown}{AD}$.
4. Construct a diameter parallel to $\overline{AD}$.
5. Construct an inscribed right angle with vertex at A.
6. Through C construct a chord perpendicular to $\overline{OC}$.

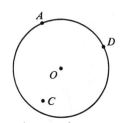

Exs. 1–6

7. Construct a right triangle. Inscribe a circle in the right triangle.
8. Draw an obtuse triangle. Inscribe a circle in the triangle.
9. Construct a right triangle and then circumscribe a circle about it.
10. Draw any obtuse triangle and then circumscribe a circle about it.

B

11. Construct a tangent to ⊙O which will be parallel to $\overline{AB}$.
12. Construct a tangent to ⊙O at B.
13. Through C construct a chord parallel to $\overline{AB}$.
14. Construct an inscribed isosceles triangle having $\overline{AB}$ as its base.
15. Construct a chord which will have C as its midpoint.
16. Construct a tangent parallel to $\overline{XY}$.

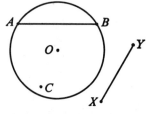

Exs. 11–16

17. Construct a square. Then circumscribe a circle about it.
18. Construct a rectangle. Then circumscribe a circle about it.
19. Given a line that does not intersect a circle, construct a tangent to the circle that is perpendicular to the given line.
20. Given a line outside a circle, construct a tangent to the circle that makes a 45° angle with the line.

C

21. Given its base and the radius of the inscribed circle, construct an isosceles triangle.
22. Construct a square ABCD. Then circumscribe a semicircle about ABCD as in the figure shown.

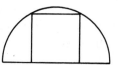

23. Given a circle, construct two tangents that meet at a 60° angle.

24. Choose a point in the interior of a given acute angle, but not on the bisector. Construct a line passing through that point that cuts off congruent segments on the sides of the angle.

25. Given two noncongruent circles, each lying in the exterior of the other, construct a common external tangent to the circles.

26. Given two noncongruent circles, each lying in the exterior of the other, construct a common internal tangent to the circles.

11–4   Constructing Special Segments

By means of constructions based upon properties of similar triangles, it is possible to construct certain special segments.

CONSTRUCTION 12   Given a segment, divide the segment into any given number of congruent segments. (3 shown.)

Given: $\overline{AB}$.

To Construct: Three segments of length $\frac{1}{3}AB$.

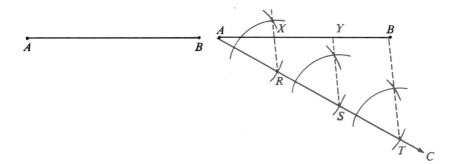

Steps: Draw any ray $\overrightarrow{AC}$ that is not on $\overleftrightarrow{AB}$. On $\overrightarrow{AC}$ mark off 3 congruent segments, $\overline{AR}, \overline{RS},$ and $\overline{ST}$. Draw $\overline{TB}$. Then construct lines parallel to $\overline{TB}$ through R and S, intersecting $\overline{AB}$ at X and Y. $\overline{AX}, \overline{XY}, \overline{YB}$ **are the three desired segments.**

Justification: Parallel lines divide two transversals proportionally. Since $\overline{AR} \cong \overline{RS} \cong \overline{ST}$ by construction, $\overline{AX} \cong \overline{XY} \cong \overline{YB}$.

CONSTRUCTION 13   Given three segments whose lengths are the first three terms of a proportion, construct a segment whose length is the fourth term of the proportion.

Given: *a, b, c.*

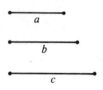

To Construct: A segment of length x such that $\dfrac{a}{b} = \dfrac{c}{x}$.

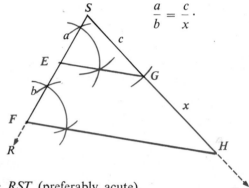

Steps: Draw an angle *RST* (preferably acute).
On $\overrightarrow{SR}$ mark off $SE = a$ and $EF = b$.
On $\overrightarrow{ST}$ mark off $SG = c$. Draw $\overline{EG}$.
At F construct $\overline{FH} \parallel \overline{EG}$ intersecting $\overrightarrow{ST}$ at H. $\overline{GH}$ **is the desired segment of length** *x.*

Justification: (The justification is left for you to provide.)

Note: When given three segments having lengths a, b, and c respectively, you can use Construction 13 to construct a segment of length x such that

$$x = \frac{ab}{c} \qquad x = \frac{b^2}{a} \qquad x = \frac{2ac}{b} \qquad \frac{x}{a} = \frac{b}{c}$$

You simply transform each equation into an equivalent proportion in which x is the fourth term and then carry out Construction 13.

$$\frac{c}{a} = \frac{b}{x} \qquad \frac{a}{b} = \frac{b}{x} \qquad \frac{b}{c} = \frac{2a}{x} \qquad \frac{c}{a} = \frac{b}{x}$$

CONSTRUCTION 14   Given two segments, construct a segment whose length is the geometric mean between the lengths of the given segments.

Given: *a and b.*

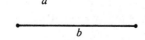

To Construct: A segment of length

x such that $\dfrac{a}{x} = \dfrac{x}{b}$,

or $x = \sqrt{ab}$.

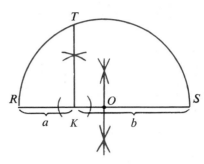

Steps: (Study the indicated construction of the desired segment $\overline{TK}$, and write a description of the steps taken.)

Justification: (Explain why $\overline{TK}$ has the desired length x.)

ORAL EXERCISES

1. Can a segment be divided into five congruent segments by a construction?

2. Given segments of lengths r, s, and t, into what proportion would you transform $x = \dfrac{rt}{s}$ if you were trying to construct a segment of length x?

3. Given a scale marked in inches, tell how to construct a segment that is $\sqrt{6}$ in. long.

4. If you constructed a right triangle with legs 1 in. and 2 in. long, what would be the length of its hypotenuse?

5. What would be the radius of the semicircle you would use in constructing a segment whose length was the geometric mean between two segments of lengths c and d?

6. Given two segments of lengths a and b. If you wish to construct a segment of length x such that $x = \sqrt{2ab}$, tell two different diameters you can use for the semicircle needed in carrying out the construction.

7. Describe a method of dividing a given segment into two segments whose lengths have the ratio 2 to 3.

WRITTEN EXERCISES

Begin each exercise (Exs. 1–4) by drawing a segment $\overline{AB}$.

 1. Divide $\overline{AB}$ into three congruent segments.

2. Divide $\overline{AB}$ into five congruent segments.

3. Divide $\overline{AB}$ into two segments whose lengths have the ratio $2:3$.

4. Divide $\overline{AB}$ into two segments whose lengths have the ratio $1:3$.

On your paper draw segments whose lengths approximate those of the segments shown. Then construct a segment of length x such that

5. $\dfrac{a}{b} = \dfrac{c}{x}$

6. $x = \dfrac{ac}{b}$

7. $x = \sqrt{ab}$

8. $x = 2\sqrt{ac}$

9. $x = \dfrac{b^2}{a}$

10. $x = \frac{1}{3}(a + b + c)$

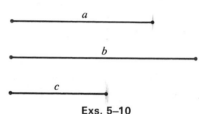

Exs. 5–10

[B] 11. Draw two segments with lengths s and t. Construct a segment of length $\sqrt{3st}$.

12. Draw a segment with length k. Construct a segment of length $k\sqrt{2}$.

13. Draw a segment with length a. Construct a segment of length $\frac{2}{3}a$.

14. In a given triangle ABC construct a segment that divides sides $\overline{BA}$ and $\overline{BC}$ into segments whose lengths have the ratio $1:3$. (Show two solutions.)

On your paper draw, and label, three segments with lengths approximating those of the segments shown.

15. Construct an equilateral triangle with perimeter t.

16. Divide a segment of length t into two segments whose lengths have the ratio $r:s$.

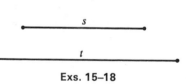

Exs. 15–18

17. Construct an isosceles trapezoid whose bases have lengths t and s and whose altitude has length r.

18. Construct a segment whose length is $\sqrt{t^2 - s^2}$.

[C] 19. Given a segment whose length is the sum of the lengths of the sides of a desired triangle, and the fact that the lengths of its sides have the ratio $2:3:4$, construct the triangle.

20. Through any given point X in the interior of a given angle, construct a segment terminated by the sides of the angle such that X divides the constructed segment into two segments whose lengths have the ratio $1:2$. (Two solutions.)

21. Given a line and two points located on the same side of the line but not at the same distance from the line. Construct through these points two lines which intersect on the given line and form congruent angles with it.

22. Given circle O with chord $\overline{AB}$. On $\overparen{AB}$ locate P such that $\dfrac{PA}{PB} = \dfrac{2}{3}$.

■ Locus

11–5 The Meaning of Locus

In solving construction problems you located a particular point or set of points that satisfied some condition. In this section you will describe but not necessarily construct geometric figures formed by points that satisfy one or more conditions.

Consider this problem.

> *Indicate by a drawing, and then describe, the location of all points which lie in the plane of two parallel lines l and m and are equidistant from l and m.*

It is not difficult to determine the location of two or three points which meet the given conditions.

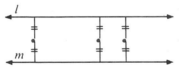

If you mentally consider all points that meet the conditions, you conclude that all the points lie on a line, *t*.

An accurate description of the location of these points must specify the geometric figure they form and its location with respect to *l* and *m*. One satisfactory description is: A line parallel to *l* and *m*, lying in their plane and located midway between them.

If the initial condition that the points lie in the plane of *l* and *m* were removed, both your drawing and description would change.

Description: The plane *T* parallel to *l* and *m*, located midway between them, and perpendicular to the plane containing them.

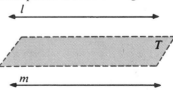

A **locus** is the set of all those points that satisfy a given condition. Thus, in our first illustration, the line *t* is said to be the *locus* of points equidistant from *l* and *m* and in the plane of *l* and *m*. In our second illustration, the locus is plane *T*. The plural of locus is *loci* (**lo**-sigh). A locus is a geometric figure, a set of points. It contains all points which satisfy some condition and no points which do not satisfy the condition.

Each locus discussed above could be described using set notation where *P* represents a point.

$t = \{P\colon P$ is equidistant from l and $m\} \cap \{P\colon P \in$ plane of l and $m\}$
$T = \{P\colon P$ is equidistant from l and $m\}$

In solving locus problems you need not construct the locus unless specifically instructed to do so. However, in more difficult problems you may wish to use constructions to locate a few sample points which satisfy all conditions. It is possible, of course, for the set of desired points to be the empty set.

Unless the statement of a problem restricts a locus to two dimensions, you should always think in terms of three dimensions.

The solution to a locus problem consists of two parts:

1. A diagram in which the figure representing the locus is clearly indicated.
2. An accurate word description in which all specific details of the locus are mentioned.

EXAMPLE 1. What is the locus of points in the plane of an angle that are equidistant from the sides of the angle and lie in the interior of the angle?

Solution: The locus is the ray that bisects the angle (excluding its endpoint).

EXAMPLE 2. What is the locus of points that are equidistant from two given points?

Solution: The locus is the plane that bisects the segment joining the two given points and is perpendicular to that segment.

EXAMPLE 3. What is the locus of points at a given
distance k from a fixed point O?

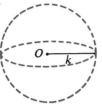

Solution: The locus is a sphere with center O and
radius k.

ORAL
EXERCISES

1. Describe the locus of points in your classroom and one foot from the ceiling.
2. What is the locus of points in a plane and 6 in. from a given line l in that plane?
3. What is the locus of points equidistant from the four vertices of a square? In the plane of the square and equidistant from the four vertices?
4. Describe the locus of points that are equidistant from two parallel planes.
5. What is the name of the surface every point of which is at a given distance from a fixed line?
6. If you know that a point is not contained in a locus, can you conclude that it does not satisfy the conditions specified for that locus?

WRITTEN
EXERCISES

In each exercise illustrate the locus by a diagram and describe the locus in words.

1. A given circle has center O and a radius of 2 in. What is the locus of the midpoints of all radii of the circle?
2. What is the locus of points in a plane and 4 in. from a given line j in the plane?
3. What is the locus of the centers of all circles that are tangent to each of two parallel lines?
4. Find the locus of the centers of all circles that are tangent to both sides of a given angle.
5. What is the locus of the center of a sphere of radius 4 in. that rolls around on top of a rectangular table whose surface is 24 in. by 36 in.?

6. What is the locus of points that are 3 in. from a given line *l*?

7. Given two concentric circles with radii of 3 in. and 5 in. What is the locus of points in the plane of the two circles and equidistant from them?

8. Given a segment $\overline{AB}$ and a point *P* outside $\overleftrightarrow{AB}$. What is the locus of the midpoints of all segments joining point *P* to points of $\overline{AB}$?

9. Construct two perpendicular lines, *l* and *m*. Construct and describe the locus of points that are equidistant from *l* and *m* and are in the plane of *l* and *m*.

10. Draw two intersecting lines, *a* and *b*. Construct and describe the locus of points that are in the plane of lines *a* and *b* and are equidistant from *a* and *b*.

11. Plane *M* contains a segment $\overline{XY}$. What is the locus of points that are in *M* and are the vertices of isosceles triangles having $\overline{XY}$ as base?

12. What would the locus be in Exercise 11 if the condition that the vertices lie in plane *M* were removed?

13. Plane *X* contains a segment $\overline{AB}$. What is the locus of points each of which is the intersection of the two diagonals of a rectangle that lies in *X* and has $\overline{AB}$ as a base?

14. What would the locus be in Exercise 13 if the rectangles were not restricted to those lying in plane *X*?

15. Given two points *R* and *S* lying in plane *T*. What is the locus of the centers of all circles that lie in plane *T* and pass through *R* and *S*?

16. What would be the locus in Exercise 15 if the circles were not restricted to those lying in plane *T*?

17. In a given $\triangle ABC$, segments with endpoints on $\overline{AC}$ and $\overline{BC}$ are drawn parallel to $\overline{AB}$. What is the locus of the midpoints of all such segments?

18. Given a segment $\overline{RS}$. What is the locus of the vertices of the right angles of all right triangles that lie in a plane and have $\overline{RS}$ as hypotenuse? (*Hint:* The locus is, except for two missing points, a familiar figure.)

19. Given three noncollinear points *A*, *B*, and *C*. What is the locus of points that are equidistant from the points?

20. Discuss Exercise 19 when the given points are collinear.

21. Given circle *P* with radius *r*. A second circle, with radius *s* ($s < r$) moves so that it is always tangent to $\odot P$. Describe the locus of the center of the second circle.

22. Find the locus of the middle point of an eight-foot ladder as the ladder is pulled away from a house, one end sliding down the house and the other end sliding along the ground. (Assume the ground to be level.)

23. Construct and describe the locus of the midpoints of all chords that can be drawn through a fixed point P on a circle with center O and radius r.

24. Construct a square with a 4 in. side. A three-inch segment moves so that its endpoints are always on the sides of the square. Construct the locus of the midpoint of the moving three-inch segment.

25. Given a segment $\overline{XY}$. Find the locus of the points of intersection of the diagonals of all possible rhombuses in space which have $\overline{XY}$ as a side.

26. Given segment $\overline{AB}$ and $\angle X$. Construct, in a plane containing $\overline{AB}$, the locus of vertex C of $\triangle ACB$ if

$$\angle ACB \cong \angle X.$$

11-6   Intersection of Loci

Sometimes more than one condition is specified for a set of points. In such cases the locus contains those points and only those points that are common to the loci for the separate conditions. The points of intersection, if any, of the loci, are the desired points. All possible relative positions of the separate loci must be considered, as the following examples illustrate.

EXAMPLE 1. In a plane find the locus of points which are equidistant from two given points A and B and at a given distance d from a given point P.

Solution: The first locus is the perpendicular bisector of $\overline{AB}$. The second locus is a circle with center P and radius d. Possible intersections of these loci are the following.

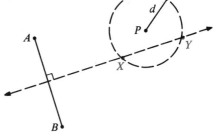

Possibility 1. The locus is the set consisting of points X and Y in which the circle and perpendicular bisector intersect.

Possibility 2. The locus is the set consisting of the point X at which the circle is tangent to the perpendicular bisector.

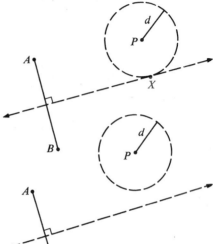

Possibility 3. The locus is the empty set.

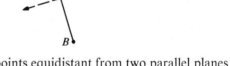

EXAMPLE 2. Find the locus of points equidistant from two parallel planes A and B and at distance r from a given point P.

Solution: The first locus is plane X, parallel to A and B and midway between them. The second locus is a sphere with center P and radius r. Possible intersections of these loci are the following.

Possibility 1. The locus is the set containing all points of circle Q.

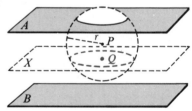

Possibility 2. The locus is the set containing point T, a point of tangency.

Possibility 3. The locus is the empty set.

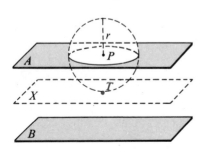

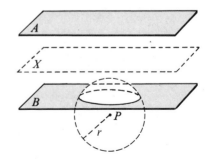

In Exercises 1–6 suppose that you have found the loci to be the figures indicated. Describe the different possible sets of points the two loci could have in common.

1. Two lines

2. A line and a plane

3. Two circles

4. A plane and a sphere

5. Two parallel lines and a sphere

6. Two spheres

1. Given point P in the interior of $\angle ABC$. Find the locus of points that are in the interior of $\angle ABC$, are equidistant from the sides of $\angle ABC$, and are a given distance r from point P.

2. Given two points A and B in the plane of two parallel lines l and m. Find the locus of points that are in the plane, are equidistant from A and B, and are equidistant from l and m.

3. Given two points R and S in the plane of $\angle ABC$. Find the locus of points that are in the interior of $\angle ABC$, are equidistant from the sides of $\angle ABC$, and are equidistant from R and S.

4. Given two parallel lines l and m and a third line j all in a plane. Find the locus of points that are in the plane, are equidistant from l and m, and are a given distance d from j.

5. If one locus is a sphere and a second locus is a pair of parallel planes, illustrate a placement such that the set of points common to the two loci is the union of a circle and a point not on the circle.

6. What is the locus of points that are equidistant from two given points and are also equidistant from two parallel planes?

7. Given point X is 3 in. from plane M. What is the locus of points that are in M and are 5 in. from X?

8. A is a given point in a plane M. What is the locus of points 5 in. from point A and 3 in. from plane M.

9. Find the locus of all points that are 13 in. from each of the vertices of a given right triangle whose sides are 6 in., 8 in., and 10 in. long.

10. Given two intersecting lines l and m and point O, all in a plane. Find the locus of points that are in the plane, are equidistant from l and m, and are a given distance d from point O.

11–7   Constructions and Loci

The solutions to many construction problems depend on locating points that satisfy two conditions. Such problems are best approached by constructing separate loci for the individual conditions. Then you can use the intersection points, for they meet both conditions.

Suppose you are given two segments, $\overline{RS}$ and $\overline{TQ}$, and an angle, $\angle 1$. You are to construct a triangle XYZ with: $\overline{XY} \cong \overline{RS}$; $\angle X \cong \angle 1$; the altitude (upon $\overline{XY}$) congruent to $\overline{TQ}$.

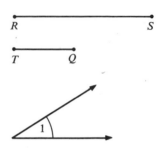

After $\overline{XY}$ and $\angle YXW$ are constructed, the solution requires the locating of vertex Z. Point Z must meet two conditions: it must lie on the side of an angle congruent to $\angle 1$ and it must be at a distance TQ from $\overleftrightarrow{XY}$.

1. The locus of points meeting the condition that $\angle X$ be congruent to $\angle 1$ is $\overrightarrow{XW}$ and $\overrightarrow{XV}$.

2. The locus of points meeting the condition that the altitude be congruent to $\overline{TQ}$ is 2 lines j and k parallel to $\overleftrightarrow{XY}$ and at distance TQ from $\overleftrightarrow{XY}$.

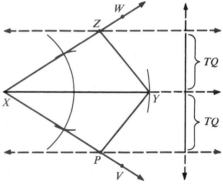

The intersection of the two loci is point Z and point P. Therefore, both triangle XYZ and triangle XYP meet all the given conditions.

EXAMPLE. Given segments $\overline{MN}$ and $\overline{PQ}$, construct a right triangle ABC whose hy. $\overline{AB} \cong \overline{MN}$ and whose altitude (upon $\overline{AB}$) $\cong \overline{PQ}$.

Solution: (The solution consists of a figure showing the given parts, the construction of loci, and a labeled solid-line figure that meets all the given conditions. For convenience, the length of $\overline{MN}$ is labeled c and the length of $\overline{PQ}$ is labeled h.)

Given:

$$M \overset{c}{\rule{3cm}{0.4pt}} N$$

$$P \overset{h}{\rule{1.5cm}{0.4pt}} Q \qquad \left(h < \tfrac{1}{2}c \right)$$

Answer. $\triangle ABC$

Any one of four triangles could be named as a triangle that meets the given conditions. Since the problem called for constructing *a triangle*, just one triangle is indicated by solid lines. Do you see that no triangle would be possible if you started with lengths such that h was greater than $\frac{1}{2}c$?

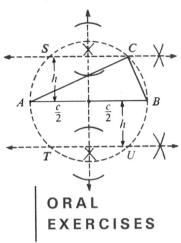

ORAL EXERCISES

1. Given an angle and two segments, can you construct a triangle with two sides congruent to the given segments and with their included angle congruent to the given angle?

2. Given any three segments, can you construct a triangle with sides congruent to those segments?

3. Given a segment $\overline{RS}$, how many right triangles can you construct that have $\overline{RS}$ as hypotenuse?

4. Can you construct two squares with sides of unequal lengths but diagonals of equal lengths?

5. Given two segments, can you construct an isosceles triangle with a leg congruent to one segment and the altitude upon the base congruent to the other segment?

6. Given a segment, can you construct an equilateral triangle with an altitude congruent to that segment?

WRITTEN EXERCISES

On your paper draw and label three segments and an angle approximately congruent to the segments and angle shown. Use your given segments and angle in each of your constructions.

A

1. Construct an isosceles triangle with a base angle congruent to $\angle 1$ and the altitude upon the base congruent to $\overline{AB}$.

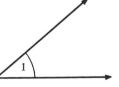

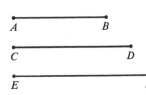

2. Construct a right triangle with an acute angle congruent to $\angle 1$ and the altitude upon the hypotenuse congruent to $\overline{AB}$.

3. Construct a triangle with two sides congruent to $\overline{CD}$ and $\overline{EF}$ and with the altitude upon $\overline{EF}$ congruent to $\overline{AB}$. Are two triangles possible? Could $\overline{AB}$ be of such length that two triangles would not be possible?

4. Construct a right triangle with a leg congruent to $\overline{CD}$ and with the altitude upon the hypotenuse congruent to $\overline{AB}$.

5. Construct an isosceles triangle such that the radius of the circumscribed circle is congruent to $\overline{AB}$ and the base is congruent to $\overline{CD}$. (2 Solutions)

6. Construct a parallelogram with an angle congruent to $\angle 1$, a side congruent to $\overline{EF}$, and the altitude upon that side congruent to $\overline{AB}$.

B 7. Construct a triangle with two sides congruent to $\overline{CD}$ and $\overline{EF}$ and the altitude upon the third side congruent to $\overline{AB}$. (2 Solutions)

8. Construct an isosceles right triangle such that the radius of the circumscribed circle is congruent to $\overline{AB}$.

9. Construct an equilateral triangle such that the radius of the inscribed circle is congruent to $\overline{AB}$.

10. Draw a line l. Choose a point P on l and a point R not on l. Construct a circle that passes through points P and R and is tangent to l.

11. Construct a triangle such that one side is congruent to $\overline{EF}$, the altitude upon that side is congruent to $\overline{AB}$, and the median to that side is congruent to $\overline{CD}$.

12. Draw three noncollinear points X, Y, Z. Construct a triangle such that points X, Y, and Z are the midpoints of the three sides of the triangle.

C 13. Construct a right triangle such that the bisector of the right angle divides the hypotenuse into segments congruent to $\overline{AB}$ and $\overline{CD}$.

14. Construct a triangle with one side congruent to $\overline{AB}$ and with medians to the other two sides congruent to $\overline{AB}$ and $\overline{CD}$.

15. Construct two parallel lines. Draw a point P between the lines. Construct a circle that passes through P and is tangent to both lines.

CHAPTER SUMMARY

Inventory of Structure and Method

1. A compass and a straightedge are the only instruments that may be used in making constructions.

2. Basic Constructions
   An angle congruent to a given angle
   The bisector of a given angle

A line perpendicular to a given line at a given point on the line

A line perpendicular to a given line from a given external point

The perpendicular bisector of a given segment

A line parallel to a given line through a given point not on the line

A line that bisects a given arc of a circle

A tangent at a given point on a circle

A tangent to a circle from a given external point

Circumscribing a circle about a given triangle

Inscribing a circle in a given triangle

Dividing a segment into any number of congruent segments

A segment whose length is the fourth term of a proportion in which the first three terms are the lengths of three given segments

A segment whose length is the geometric mean between the lengths of two given segments

3. A locus is a set of all the points, and only those points, that satisfy a given condition. A solution to a locus exercise consists of
   (a) a figure in which the locus is clearly indicated
   (b) an accurate word description of the locus

4. The locus of points that satisfy two or more given conditions is the intersection of the sets of points that are the loci for the conditions. All possible placements of the locus for each given condition must be considered.

Vocabulary and Spelling

a construction (*p. 407*)

a drawing (*p. 407*)

straightedge (*p. 408*)

complete solution of a construction problem (*p. 410*)

a locus (*p. 426*)

CHAPTER TEST

11–1   Classify each statement as true or as false.

1. In making a construction a protractor may be used to measure an angle.

2. Any angle can be bisected using only a compass and a straightedge.

3. Two circles intersect in two points if the distance between their centers is greater than the sum of their radii.

4. Any two nonconcentric coplanar circles intersect in two points.

11–2   Exercises 5–8 refer to the given figure.

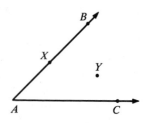

5. To construct a line perpendicular to $\overline{AB}$ at X, the point of the compass would first be placed at point __?__.

6. To construct a perpendicular to $\overline{AC}$ from Y, first construct an arc with center at point __?__ that will inter· sect __?__ in two points.

7. To construct a line parallel to $\overline{AC}$ through Y, first draw a line through __?__ that intersects __?__.

8. To construct the perpendicular bisector of $\overline{AB}$, construct intersecting arcs with congruent radii and with centers at points __?__ and __?__.

11–3   The figure shown illustrates the construction of tangents from P to $\odot O$.

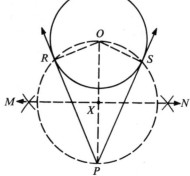

9. What construction must be made to determine point X?

10. Why does $\angle OSP$ have a measure of 90?

11. Name the two segments that are tangent to $\odot O$.

12. If point P had been located closer to point O, which of the following angles would have increased in measure?

    a. $\angle ORP$ **b.** $\angle ROS$ **c.** $\angle RPS$

11–4   In the following, a, b, and c represent the lengths of three segments.

13. Can you construct a triangle with sides of length a, b, and c if $a + b < c$? if $a + b = c$? if $a^2 + b^2 = c^2$?

14. If you wished to construct a segment of length x such that $x = \dfrac{ab}{c}$, write a proportion upon which you could base your construction.

15. Can you construct a segment of length ab? of length $\sqrt{ab}$?

16. What would be a convenient length to use for the diameter of the circle you would use in constructing the geometric mean of a and b?

11–5   Describe, and draw a figure illustrating, the locus of points

17. In space, at a given distance k from a given point P.

18. In a plane, equidistant from the sides of an angle *ABC* and in the interior of the angle.

19. In a plane, at a distance *d* from a given line *l*.

20. Equidistant from two given parallel planes *M* and *N*.

11–6 Given: The locus of points satisfying one set of conditions is a sphere and the locus of points satisfying a second set of conditions is a pair of parallel planes. Could the set of points satisfying both sets of conditions be

21. two circles?   **23.** two lines?

22. two points?   **24.** a point and a circle?

CHAPTER REVIEW

11–1 **What Construction Means: Permissible**   *Pages 407–413*
Instruments and Basic Angle Constructions

1. In *constructing* a figure a __?__ and a __?__ are the only instruments that may be used.

2. If a line contains a point in the interior of a circle then it intersects the circle in __?__.

3. The first step in constructing the bisector of an angle is to construct an arc whose __?__ is located at the __?__ of the angle.

4. Two coplanar circles with radii of 2 in. and 5 in. will intersect in two points if the distance between their centers is < __?__ in. but > __?__ in.

11–2 **Constructing Parallel Lines and**   *Pages 413–417*
Perpendicular Lines

5. The midpoint of a segment can be located by constructing the __?__ of the segment.

6. To construct a perpendicular to a line from an external point your first step is to construct an arc whose radius is greater than the __?__ from the point to the __?__.

7. If you bisect each of two adjacent supplementary angles, the bisecting rays will be __?__ to each other.

8. If in the figure shown, $\angle 2$ was constructed so that $\angle 2 \cong \angle 1$, why must $\overleftrightarrow{XY}$ be parallel to $\overleftrightarrow{AB}$?

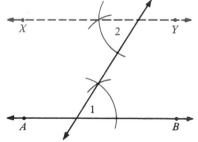

11–3 **Constructions Involving Circles** *Pages 417–421*

9. To bisect an arc, you construct the __?__ of its __?__.

10. To construct a tangent at a point of a circle, you construct a line that is __?__ to the __?__ drawn to the point.

11. To inscribe a circle in a given triangle you first must locate its center by constructing the __?__ of two __?__ of the triangle.

12. To circumscribe a circle about a given triangle you first must locate its center by constructing the __?__ of two __?__ of the triangle.

11–4 **Constructing Special Segments** *Pages 421–425*

13. To divide $\overline{AB}$ into n congruent segments, you first draw a ray whose endpoint is __?__ or __?__ and then mark off n congruent non-overlapping segments on the ray.

14. The construction of a segment whose length is a fourth proportional to the lengths of three given segments is based on the theorem that a line __?__ to one side of a __?__ and intersecting the other two __?__ divides them __?__.

15. Given segments of lengths a, b, and c. If you construct a segment of length x such that $\dfrac{a}{b} = \dfrac{c}{x}$, then $x =$ __?__.

16. Given segments of length a and b. Describe a triangle construction by which you could construct a segment of length $\sqrt{a^2 + b^2}$.

11–5 **The Meaning of Locus** *Pages 425–429*

17. A locus is the __?__ of all __?__, and only those __?__, which satisfy a given set of __?__.

18. A sphere with center O and radius k is the locus of all points at a distance __?__ from O.

19. The locus of the midpoints of all radii of a circle of 4 in. radius is a circle with radius __?__.

20. The locus of the centers of all circles that are tangent to both sides of an angle is the __?__ of the angle excluding the __?__ of the angle.

11–6 **Intersection of Loci** *Pages 429–432*

21. In a plane the locus of points equidistant from the sides of an angle *and* equidistant from two given points can be a __?__, a __?__, or the __?__ set.

22. In space the locus of points equidistant from two parallel planes *and* at a distance d from a given point can be __?__, a __?__, or the __?__ set.

▶ The Three Famous Construction Problems

For 2000 years after Plato (*c.* 330 B.C.) and his followers ruled that only a compass and an unmarked straightedge could be used in geometric constructions, mathematicians and non-mathematicians sought to solve what are now commonly called the *Three Famous Construction Problems.*

1. *The Trisection of An Angle:* Given any angle construct two rays which will divide the angle into three angles of equal measure.
2. *The Duplication of a Cube:* Determine by construction the exact length of the side of a cube whose volume is twice that of a given cube.
3. *The Squaring of a Circle:* Determine by construction the exact length of the side of a square whose area equals that of a given circle.

In the past 200 years it has been proved by algebraic means beyond the scope of this course that no one of these constructions is possible using only straightedge and compass. Despite this fact, one still reads occasionally that someone seems to have solved one or more of these problems. Some of these solutions are based on false assumptions. Others, while otherwise correct, violate the rule that a straightedge may only be used for drawing straight lines through a given point, or the unique straight line through two known points, but may not be used for anything else.

Archimedes (287–212 B.C.), at right, developed a method for trisecting an angle which violated Plato's rules only in that it involved placing two marks on a straightedge. Pascal (1623–62) invented an instrument for trisecting angles based upon the method used by Archimedes. Earlier mathematicians invented special curves which could be used for the same purpose. However, keep in mind that these three famous problems *cannot be solved* by use of straightedge and compass alone.

• EXTRA FOR EXPERTS

As illustrated in the diagrams below, four different types of intersections can be obtained when a conical surface of two nappes (branches) is intersected by a plane not passing through the vertex. These four special curves are called **conic sections** or simply **conics.** Each can be described as the locus of a point in a plane. You are already familiar with one of these conic sections, namely, the circle. You will study the special properties of the remaining three conic sections in later Analytic Geometry courses. However, with your present knowledge of loci and constructions, you should be able to sketch these special curves.

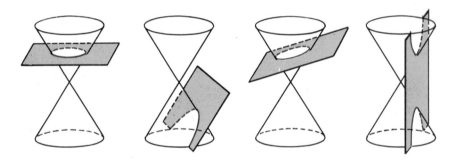

1. **Parabola:** The locus, in a plane, of a point that is equidistant from a fixed point P and a fixed line l.

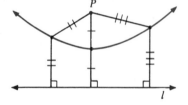

2. **Ellipse:** The locus, in a plane, of a point the sum of whose distances from two fixed points P_1 and P_2 is a given constant c.

$$d_1 + d_2 = c.$$

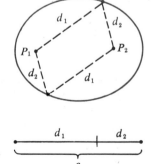

3. **Hyperbola:** The locus, in a plane, of a point the difference of whose distances from two fixed points P_1 and P_2 is a given constant c.

$$|d_1 - d_2| = c.$$

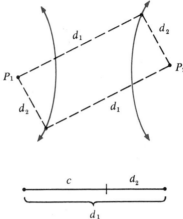

EXERCISES

1. Illustrate, by drawing, a position for a plane whose intersection with a cone of two nappes is **(a)** a point; **(b)** a line; **(c)** two lines.

2. A fixed point A is located 2 in. from a fixed line l. By means of constructed arcs and perpendicular segments, locate at least 8 points which are equidistant from both A and l. Sketch the parabola on which these points lie.

3. Pictured is a point P, the sum of whose distances a and b from F_1 and F_2 is equal to c, the length of a given segment. Make a similar figure and locate by construction at least 6 other points, for each of which the sum of its distances from F_1 and F_2 is also c. Sketch and name the conic on which these points lie.

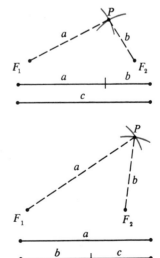

4. Pictured is a point P, the difference of whose distances a and b from F_1 and F_2 is equal to c, the length of a given segment. Make a similar figure and locate by construction at least 8 other points, for each of which the difference of its distances from F_1 and F_2 is also c. Choose points such that sometimes $PF_1 > PF_2$ while at other times $PF_2 > PF_1$. Sketch and name the conic on which these points lie.

12

Coordinate Geometry — Methods

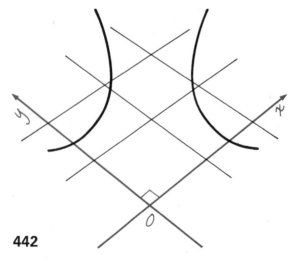

Maurits Cornelis Escher has tilted and distorted a grid pattern of a coordinate plane in his woodcut entitled "Day and Night."

You can specify a position on the earth by giving just two numbers. For example, 40N, 83W locates a particular spot within the city limits of Columbus, Ohio, and 38N, 108W marks Saw Pit, Colorado. The numbers locate the point with respect to the equator and the prime meridian.

You can describe a star's position in the sky by a similar pair of numbers. A third number is needed to tell how far the star is from the earth.

Scientists and mathematicians use the idea of associating points with numbers. Mathematicians make this association the basis of **coordinate geometry**.

■ Graphing Ordered Pairs

12–1   Plotting Points in Two Dimensions

In Chapter 1 you represented numbers by points on a line. In this section you will represent *ordered pairs* of numbers by points in a plane. A pair of numbers is an **ordered pair** when the order in which they are named has significance. Thus $(4, -7)$ and $(-7, 4)$ are different ordered pairs. Even when the two numbers are equal, as in $(5, 5)$, it is convenient to use the term *ordered pair*.

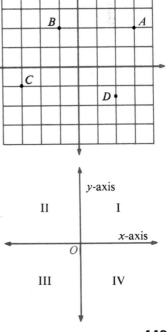

In the diagram at the right, point A represents the ordered pair $(3, 2)$. Notice that the first number of the ordered pair is 3 and that A is 3 units to the right of the heavily-drawn vertical line. The second number is 2, and A is 2 units above the heavily-drawn horizontal line. Do you see that points B, C, and D are the graphs of the ordered pairs $(-1, 2)$, $(-3, -1)$, and $(2, -1\frac{1}{2})$?

To plot points in a plane you use two number lines. The first one, usually horizontal, is called the *x*-**axis**. A second number line, perpendicular to the first one at the zero point, is called the *y*-**axis**. The point of intersection O is called the **origin**. The two lines, called **coordinate axes** (**ax**-eez), separate the plane into four regions called **quadrants**, which are numbered as shown.

443

The **x-coordinate** of a point is the number that corresponds to the projection of the point on the x-axis. The **y-coordinate** of a point is the number that corresponds to the projection on the y-axis. When a point is described by an ordered pair of numbers, the order is always first x, then y.

For every point in the plane there is a unique ordered pair of real numbers, and vice versa. This one-to-one correspondence between the set of points in the plane and the set of ordered pairs of real numbers is called a **coordinate system.**

The point corresponding to the ordered pair (*j*, *k*) is often called *point (j, k)*. Point *P*, in the diagram, is point (1, −1). Besides giving you coordinates of points *P*, *Q*, and *R*, the diagram shown gives you these bits of information:

$PQ = 2 \quad QR = 3 \quad \angle PQR$ is a rt. $\angle$.

**ORAL
EXERCISES**

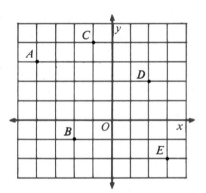

1. What is the name of the heavily-drawn horizontal line? the heavily-drawn vertical line?

2. What is the name of the intersection of the two heavily-drawn lines?

3. Which labeled point lies farthest to the left? Which labeled point is farthest from the horizontal axis?

4. State the x-coordinate of each labeled point; the y-coordinate.

5. State, as an ordered pair, the coordinates of each labeled point.

6. State the quadrant in which each labeled point lies.

7. State the quadrant in which each of the following points lies.

$$(-5, 1) \qquad (3, -\tfrac{2}{5}) \qquad (100, -1) \qquad (-3, -\pi)$$

8. If j is a positive number, and k is a negative number, state the quadrant containing the point:

$$(j, k), \qquad (-j, k), \qquad (j, -k), \qquad (-j, -k).$$

WRITTEN EXERCISES

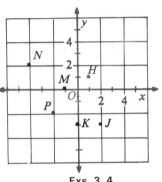

1. Graph the following points, using one set of axes: $A(1, 1)$; $B(-3, 0)$; $C(-4, -1)$; $D(3, -2)$.

2. Graph the following points, using one set of axes: $E(2, 0)$; $F(2, -3)$; $G(-2, 3)$; $H(0, -4)$.

3. Name the x-coordinate of each labeled point; the y-coordinate.

4. Write the ordered pair for each labeled point.

Exs. 3, 4

Find the distance between the points named. Use squared paper if necessary.

5. $(3, 2)$ and $(7, 2)$

6. $(1, -3)$ and $(1, 4)$

7. $(0, -1)$ and $(-3, -1)$

8. $(-2, 3)$ and $(-2, -2)$

Draw a graph and then write your answer.

9. Three of the vertices of a square are pts. $(2, 3)$, $(2, 6)$, and $(5, 3)$. State the coordinates of the fourth vertex.

10. Three of the vertices of a rectangle are pts. $(-1, -1)$, $(6, -1)$, and $(-1, 2)$. State the coordinates of the fourth vertex.

11. The longer base of an isosceles trapezoid joins pts. $(-3, -2)$ and $(7, -2)$. One endpoint of the shorter base is $(-1, 4)$. State the coordinates of the other endpoint.

12. Two vertices of a square are pts. $(3, -2)$ and $(3, 6)$. State the coordinates of two possible pairs of points for the other two vertices.

Three coordinate axes are needed for locating points in three dimensions. Think of the y-axis and the z-axis as lying in the plane of the paper and of the x-axis as being perpendicular to the plane of the paper, with the positive direction towards you.

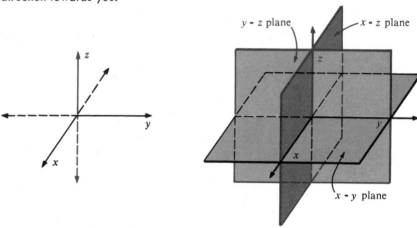

The x-coordinate of a point is the coordinate of its projection on the x-axis, and so on. Each point is located by an ordered triple of numbers. The point (3, 1, −2) lies 3 units on this side of the y-z plane, one unit to the right of the x-z plane, and 2 units below the x-y plane.

C **13.** On which axis does each of the following points lie?

　　a. (5, 0, 0)　　**b.** (0, 0, −2)　　**c.** (0, 3, 0)

14. On which plane does each of the following points lie?

　　a. (0, 4, 6)　　**b.** (−2, −1, 0)　　**c.** (3, 0, −5)

15. Five of the eight vertices of a cube are pts. (−1, 3, −2), (4, 3, −2), (4, −2, −2), (−1, −2, −2), and (4, 3, 3). State the coordinates of the other three vertices.

16. Five of the vertices of a rectangular solid are pts. (−1, −1, −5), (−1, −1, 2), (−1, 3, 2), (−1, 3, −5), and (1, −1, −5). State the coordinates of the other three vertices.

12–2 Symmetry

You admire the beauty of some objects partly because of their symmetry. The left side and right side in a jet plane are balanced just as they are in a butterfly. A well-formed tree has symmetry with respect to its trunk. An artistic design may have symmetry with respect to a central point. Although people speak of physical objects as being symmetrical when they appear to be well-balanced, mathematicians give the idea precise meaning in three different cases, as described below.

A figure has **symmetry with respect to a point** P if for every point Q in the figure there is a corresponding point Q' in the figure such that P is the midpoint of $\overline{QQ'}$ Point Q' is said to be *symmetric* to point Q.

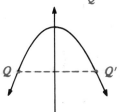

A figure has **symmetry with respect to a line** l if for every point Q of the figure there is a corresponding point Q' in the figure such that l is the perpendicular bisector of $\overline{QQ'}$.

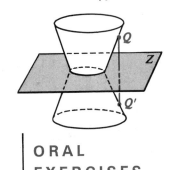

A figure has **symmetry with respect to a plane** Z if for every point Q of the figure there is another point Q' in the figure such that Z is the perpendicular bisector of $\overline{QQ'}$.

ORAL EXERCISES

1. Which of the following have symmetry with respect to a point? with respect to at least one line?

Scalene Triangle

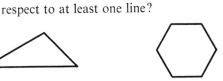

Regular Hexagon

Circle

Parallelogram

Rhombus

Church Window

2. Which figures shown in red appear to have symmetry with respect to the plane shown?

a.

b.

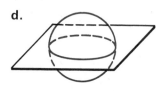

c.

d.

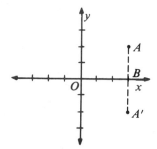

3. Name all possible lines of symmetry in the following.

a.

D   T   C

Q   *S*

A   R   B

b.

H   Z   G

W   *V*

E   X   P

c.

N   T   M

Q   *S*

K   R   L

4. Does a sphere have symmetry with respect to (a) a plane through the center; (b) the point at the center; (c) a point on the sphere; (d) a line through the center?

WRITTEN EXERCISES

EXAMPLE. Points *A* and *A'* have symmetry with respect to the *x*-axis. *A* is pt. (3, 2). State the coordinates of *A'*.

Solution: Draw $\overrightarrow{AB} \perp$ to the *x*-axis.
Take *A'*, on $\overrightarrow{AB}$, so that
A'B = AB.
Pt. (3, −2), **Answer.**

A

1. Points *A* and *A'* have symmetry with respect to the *x*-axis. State the coordinates of *A'* when *A* is pt. (−2, 1); (−3, −3); (4, 2); (3, −1).

2. Same as Exercise 1, but symmetry with respect to the *y*-axis.

3. Points C and C' have symmetry with respect to the line that is parallel to, and 2 units above, the x-axis. State the coordinates of C' when C is pt. $(4, 3)$; $(4, 1)$; $(-3, 5)$; $(-3, -2)$.

4. Same as Exercise 3, but symmetry with respect to the line that is parallel to, and 2 units to the left of, the y-axis.

5. Points E and E' have symmetry with respect to the origin. State the coordinates of E when E' is pt. $(5, 0)$; $(0, 2)$; $(-3, 0)$; $(2, 0)$.

6. Points F and F' have symmetry with respect to the origin. State the coordinates of F when F' is pt. $(4, 1)$; $(-3, 2)$; $(-1, 5)$; $(-2, -2)$.

7. Points G and G' have symmetry with respect to the point $(0, 3)$. State the coordinates of G' when G is pt. $(0, 5)$; $(4, 3)$; $(-1, 6)$; $(-2, -2)$.

8. Points H and H' have symmetry with respect to the point $(-2, 1)$. State the coordinates of H' when H is pt. $(-2, -3)$; $(3, 1)$; $(4, 2)$; $(-5, 2)$.

9. Points K and K' have symmetry with respect to a point R. State the coordinates of R (a) when K is pt. $(2, 5)$ and K' is pt. $(4, 5)$; (b) when K is pt. $(2, 5)$ and K' is pt. $(-4, 5)$.

10. Points J and J' have symmetry with respect to a point S. State the coordinates of S (a) when J is pt. $(-3, 2)$ and J' is pt. $(-7, -4)$; (b) when J is pt. $(5, -6)$ and J' is pt. $(1, -2)$.

In Exercises 11–14, consider the line that lies in the first and third quadrants and bisects one pair of the vertical angles formed by the coordinate axes. Figure S, described in the exercises, has symmetry with respect to that line. Draw the line and plot points carefully.

B

11. S contains pt. $(4, 0)$. State the coordinates of another point that must lie in S.

12. S contains pt. $(-2, 1)$. State the coordinates of another point that must lie in S.

13. One subset of S is $\{(5, 0), (0, 3), (-4, 0)\}$. State a different three-member set that must be a subset of S.

14. One subset of S is $\{(-3, -3), (-1, 2), (4, -6)\}$. State a different three-member set that must be a subset of S.

C

15. Find the coordinates of K in three dimensions, given that point K and the point $(2, 1, 4)$ have symmetry with respect to the (a) x-y plane; (b) y-z plane; (c) x-z plane; (d) x-axis; (e) y-axis; (f) z-axis; (g) the origin; (h) the point $(3, 2, 0)$.

16. Same as Exercise 15, but use point $(-2, 1, -6)$ in place of point $(2, 1, 4)$.

12–3   Graphs Meeting Given Conditions

A **graph** in a plane is a set of points, a geometric figure. In Chapter 11 you called a set of points a *locus* when the points met certain geometric conditions. You often use the term *graph* for a set of points whose coordinates meet certain algebraic conditions. The graph is represented by a drawing in a coordinate plane.

In Example 1 below, you see that each point in the graph has a y-coordinate that meets the condition $y \leq -1$. For x there is no condition given, but one is always understood: that x be a real number. You can describe the set algebraically in the following way: $\{(x, y): y \leq -1\}$. You read this: "The set of all ordered pairs of numbers (x, y) such that $y \leq -1$."

EXAMPLE 1.

$\{(x, y): y \leq -1\}$

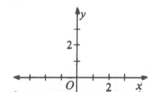

EXAMPLE 2.

$\{(x, y): -3 < x \leq 1\}$

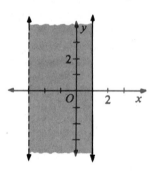

Shading means that points in the shaded region are included. Dashed lines mean that points of the lines are not included. Solid lines mean that points of the lines are included.

EXAMPLE 3.

$\{(x, y): x = 3\} \cap \{(x, y): y \geq -1\}$

EXAMPLE 4.

$\{(x, y): x = 3\} \cup \{(x, y): y \geq -1\}$

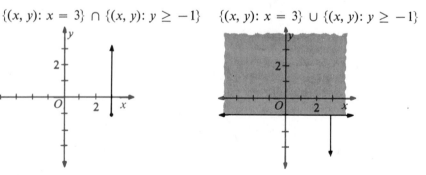

State conditions which the following graphs meet.

EXAMPLE 1. 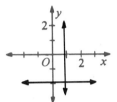 EXAMPLE 2.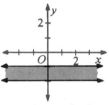

Solution:

The union of the set of ordered pairs such that $x = 1$ and the set of ordered pairs such that $y = -2$.

or

The set of ordered pairs such that $x = 1$ or $y = -2$.

Solution:

The set of ordered pairs such that $-2 \leq y \leq -1$.

or

The set of ordered pairs such that y lies between -2 and -1, inclusive.

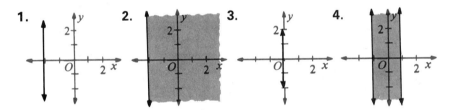

1. **2.** **3.** **4.**

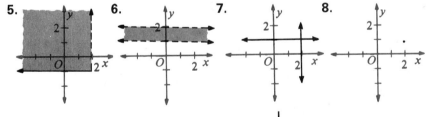

5. **6.** **7.** **8.**

Draw the graphs, in the coordinate plane, of the conditions stated.

A

1. $x = 2$	**5.** $|x| = 2$	**9.** $2 > x \geq 0$
2. $y = -3$	**6.** $|y| < 1$	**10.** $|y| > 1$
3. $x > -1$	**7.** $-1 < y \leq 2$	**11.** $x + 3 = 0$
4. $y \leq 2$	**8.** $2 \leq x < 3$	**12.** $y + 2 = 4$

B

13. $\{(x, y): x = 2\} \cup \{(x, y): y = -3\}$
14. $\{(x, y): x \leq 0\} \cup \{(x, y): y > -1\}$
15. $\{(x, y): x > 1\} \cup \{(x, y): y \geq 2\}$
16. $\{(x, y): x = 1\} \cup \{(x, y): x < 0\}$
17. $\{(x, y): x = 2\} \cap \{(x, y): y = -3\}$
18. $\{(x, y): x < 2\} \cap \{(x, y): y = -3\}$
19. $\{(x, y): x = 2\} \cap \{(x, y): y > -3\}$
20. $\{(x, y): x \geq 1\} \cap \{(x, y): y \leq 1\}$

C

21. $\{(x, y): x^2 - x - 6 > 0\}$ 23. $\{(x, y): y^2 - 3y < 0\}$
22. $\{(x, y): x^2 - x - 6 \leq 0\}$ 24. $\{(x, y): y^2 \geq 2y\}$
25. $\{(x, y): y = 2\} \cap \{(x, y): x^2 + 2x > 0\}$
26. $\{(x, y): x^2 < 4\} \cup \{(x, y): y > 1\}$

■ Finding and Using Distances

12–4   The Distance Formula

Suppose that you wish to find the distance between the points $(2, -1)$ and $(5, 4)$. You cannot find the distance by inspection, but you can complete a right triangle and use the Pythagorean Theorem.

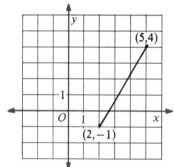 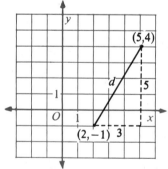

Draw the horizontal and vertical segments shown. Their lengths are 3 and 5. Then $d^2 = 3^2 + 5^2$, $d^2 = 9 + 25$, and $d = \sqrt{34}$.

Often you can compute distances without using pencil and paper. Consider the segment joining points $(-2, 6)$ and $(4, 5)$. Picture a right triangle mentally. The length of the horizontal side is $|4 - (-2)|$, or 6. The length of the vertical side is $|5 - 6|$, or 1. Then $d^2 = 6^2 + 1^2$, and $d = \sqrt{37}$.

To derive a general formula for the distance between $P_1(x_1, y_1)$ and $P_2(x_2, y_2)$, you complete a right triangle as shown.

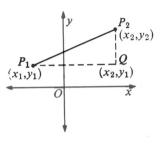

$$P_1Q = |x_2 - x_1|; \quad P_2Q = |y_2 - y_1|$$
$$d^2 = (P_1Q)^2 + (P_2Q)^2$$
$$d^2 = |x_2 - x_1|^2 + |y_2 - y_1|^2$$
$$d^2 = (x_2 - x_1)^2 + (y_2 - y_1)^2.$$

THEOREM 12–1   The distance d between two points (x_1, y_1) and (x_2, y_2) is:

$$d = \sqrt{(x_2 - x_1)^2 + (y_2 - y_1)^2}.$$

EXAMPLE. Find the distance between pts. $(0, 5)$ and $(-3, 1)$.

Solution A: Let P_1 be pt. $(0, 5)$. Then $x_1 = 0$ and $y_1 = 5$.
Let P_2 be pt. $(-3, 1)$. Then $x_2 = -3$ and $y_2 = 1$.

$$d = \sqrt{(x_2 - x_1)^2 + (y_2 - y_1)^2}$$
$$d = \sqrt{(-3 - 0)^2 + (1 - 5)^2}$$
$$d = \sqrt{9 + 16} \qquad d = \sqrt{25} \qquad d = 5. \quad \textbf{Answer.}$$

Solution B: Visualize horizontal and vertical sides to complete a triangle.
The length of the horizontal side is 3.
The length of the vertical side is 4.
Think: $d^2 = 3^2 + 4^2 = 9 + 16 = 25$
$$d = 5. \quad \textbf{Answer.}$$

ORAL
EXERCISES

1. Given: P_1 is pt. $(7, -2)$. $x_1 = \underline{\quad?\quad}$; $y_1 = \underline{\quad?\quad}$.
2. Given: P_2 is pt. $(0, 3)$. $x_2 = \underline{\quad?\quad}$; $y_2 = \underline{\quad?\quad}$.
3. Given: P_1 is pt. $(7, -2)$, and P_2 is pt. $(0, 3)$.
   State the value of $|x_2 - x_1|$, $|y_2 - y_1|$, $(x_2 - x_1)^2$, $(y_2 - y_1)^2$.
4. Given: P_1 is pt. $(-1, 2)$, and P_2 is pt. $(2, 5)$.
   State the value of $|x_2 - x_1|$, $|y_2 - y_1|$, $(x_2 - x_1)^2$, $(y_2 - y_1)^2$.
5. What is the distance between pts. $(0, 0)$ and $(3, 4)$?
   between pts. $(0, 0)$ and $(-3, 4)$?
6. What is the distance between pts. $(2, -1)$ and $(8, -1)$?
   between pts. $(2, -1)$ and $(2, 4)$?

| WRITTEN |
| EXERCISES |

Find the distance between the specified points.

[A]
1. $(0, 2)$ and $(4, 5)$
2. $(0, -2)$ and $(4, 5)$
3. $(0, 2)$ and $(4, -5)$
4. $(0, -2)$ and $(-4, -5)$
5. $(3, -1)$ and $(7, -4)$

6. $(-1, -6)$ and $(2, 5)$
7. $(0, 0)$ and (j, k)
8. $(2, 3)$ and (j, k)
9. (m, n) and $(-1, 4)$
10. (e, f) and (g, h)

In Exercises 11–15, show by comparing the lengths of segments that the statements are true.

EXAMPLE. The triangle whose vertices are pts. $(3, 4)$, $(2, 2)$, and $(5, 5)$ is isosceles.

Solution:

Between pts. $(3, 4)$ and $(2, 2)$, $d_1 = \sqrt{(2 - 3)^2 + (2 - 4)^2}$, or $\sqrt{5}$
Between pts. $(3, 4)$ and $(5, 5)$, $d_2 = \sqrt{(5 - 3)^2 + (5 - 4)^2}$, or $\sqrt{5}$
Since $d_1 = d_2$, the triangle is isosceles.

[B]
11. The triangle whose vertices are pts. $(0, 0)$, $(3, 4)$, and $(-1, 1)$ is isosceles.
12. The triangle whose vertices are pts. $(-2, 1)$, $(5, 5)$, and $(-1, -7)$ is isosceles.
13. The triangle whose vertices are pts. $(5, -2)$, $(3, -4)$, and $(6, -5)$ is not equilateral.
14. The quadrilateral whose vertices are pts. $(2, 1)$, $(2, 6)$, $(5, 10)$, and $(5, 15)$ has two pairs of congruent opposite sides.
15. The parallelogram whose vertices are pts. $(-1, -3)$, $(2, 1)$, $(1, 5)$, and $(-2, 1)$ is not a rhombus.
16. Use the converse of the Pythagorean Theorem to show that the triangle whose vertices are pts. $(0, 1)$, $(2, 0)$, $(3, 7)$ is a right triangle. Which of the points is the vertex of the right angle?
17. Three of the vertices of a rectangle are pts. $(-1, -1)$, $(4, -1)$, and $(-1, 2)$. Show that the diagonals are congruent.
18. The vertices of a parallelogram are pts. $(1, -2)$, $(5, -2)$, $(6, 1)$, and $(2, 1)$. Show that the diagonals are not congruent.

Find the distance between

[C]
19. The origin and pt. $(3, 4, 12)$.
20. Pts. $(0, 0, 0)$ and $(4, 2, 1)$.

21. Pts. $(3, -1, -2)$ and (j, k, m).
22. Pts. (x_1, y_1, z_1) and (x_2, y_2, z_2).

12–5   The Circle

The distance formula makes it possible to develop a general equation for a circle. First consider a circle of radius r with center at the origin. For any point $P(x, y)$ on the circle

$$PO = \sqrt{(x - 0)^2 + (y - 0)^2} = r \quad \text{or} \quad x^2 + y^2 = r^2$$

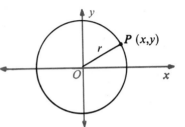

Any point on the circle has coordinates that satisfy the equation, and any point whose coordinates satisfy the equation must be r units from the origin and therefore on the circle.

An equation for a circle whose center is not at the origin is only slightly more difficult to develop. Consider a circle with center $Q(a, b)$ and radius r. For any point $P(x, y)$ on the circle,

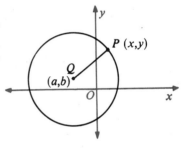

$$PQ = \sqrt{(x - a)^2 + (y - b)^2} = r$$
$$\text{or} \quad (x - a)^2 + (y - b)^2 = r^2$$

THEOREM 12–2   The circle with center (a, b) and radius r has the equation $(x - a)^2 + (y - b)^2 = r^2$.

You have just seen that the coordinates of any point on a given circle must satisfy a particular equation. Now begin with the equation $(x - a)^2 + (y - b)^2 = r^2$, $r > 0$, and see if all ordered pairs that satisfy this equation represent points on one circle. Write the equation in the form $\sqrt{(x - a)^2 + (y - b)^2} = r$. Notice that the left member represents the distance between a point (x, y) and the point (a, b). If ordered pair (x, y) satisfies the equation, then the distance between point (x, y) and point (a, b) is r.

THEOREM 12–3   All points whose coordinates satisfy the equation $(x - a)^2 + (y - b)^2 = r^2, r > 0$, lie on the circle with center (a, b) and radius r.

To describe the interior or exterior of a circle algebraically, you merely replace the symbol for equality by a symbol for inequality. Thus $(x - a)^2 + (y - b)^2 < r^2$ describes the interior of a circle, $(x - a)^2 + (y - b)^2 \leq r^2$ describes the union of a circle and its interior, $(x - a)^2 + (y - b)^2 > r^2$ describes the exterior of a circle, and $(x - a)^2 + (y - b)^2 \geq r^2$ describes the union of a circle and its exterior. To describe the intersection of the exteriors of two circles, you write two inequalities. You write one equation and one inequality to describe the intersection of one circle and the interior of another circle.

ORAL EXERCISES

1. What are the coordinates of the center of each circle?

   a. $(x - 3)^2 + (y - 2)^2 = 6^2$　　　**e.** $(x + 2)^2 + (y - 4)^2 = 25$

   b. $(x - 3)^2 + (y + 2)^2 = 6^2$　　　**f.** $(x + 3)^2 + (y + 1)^2 = 49$

   c. $(x - 3)^2 + (y - 0)^2 = 11^2$　　　**g.** $x^2 + y^2 = 100$

   d. $(x - 3)^2 + y^2 = 3^2$　　　　　　**h.** $x^2 + (y + 4)^2 = 71$

2. What is the radius of each circle named in Exercise 1?

3. State the equation of the circle with the center $(0, 0)$ and

   a. radius 6　　　　**b.** radius 20　　　　**c.** radius 1　　　　**d.** radius $\frac{2}{3}$

4. State the equation of the circle with radius 5 and

   a. center $(0, 0)$　**b.** center $(3, 1)$　**c.** center $(-3, 1)$　**d.** center $(0, -4)$

WRITTEN EXERCISES

Find the radius and the center of each circle.

A

1. $x^2 + y^2 = 4^2$　　　　　　　　　　3. $(x + 5)^2 + y^2 = 100$

2. $x^2 + (y - 3)^2 = 16$　　　　　　　4. $(x - 2)^2 + (y - 3)^2 = 17$

In Exercises 5–8 write the equation of the circle described.

5. The center is pt. $(3, 4)$ and the radius is 2.

6. The center is pt. $(1, 0)$ and the radius is 7.

7. The center is pt. $(-1, 0)$ and the radius is 11.

8. The center is pt. $(-3, -5)$ and the radius is 19.

The center of a circle is pt. (3, 7) and the radius is 2. Write the inequality that describes the set of points named.

9. The interior of the circle.

10. The union of the circle and its interior.

11. The exterior of the circle.

12. The union of the circle and its exterior.

In Exs. 13–18 find the equation of the circle described.

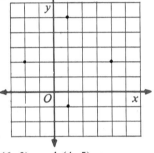

EXAMPLE. The circle contains the points $(-2, 2)$, $(1, -1)$, $(4, 2)$, and $(1, 5)$.

Solution: Plot the points. You see that the center is pt. $(1, 2)$ and that the radius is 3.

$(x - 1)^2 + (y - 2)^2 = 9$, **Answer.**

B **13.** The circle contains the points $(2, 3)$, $(4, 1)$, $(6, 3)$, and $(4, 5)$.

14. The circle contains the points $(3, 3)$, $(-3, 3)$, $(-3, -3)$, and $(3, -3)$.

15. The circle has center $(3, 4)$ and contains the origin.

16. The circle has center $(3, 4)$ and contains pt. $(5, -1)$.

17. The circle has center $(3, -2)$ and is tangent to the x-axis.

18. The circle has center $(5, 5)$ and is tangent to both axes.

In Exercises 19–22 find the center and the radius of the circle whose equation is given.

EXAMPLE. $x^2 - 4x + y^2 + 8y - 5 = 0$

Solution:
$$\begin{aligned} x^2 - 4x \qquad + y^2 + 8y \qquad &= 5 \\ x^2 - 4x + 4 + y^2 + 8y + 16 &= 5 + 4 + 16 \\ (x - 2)^2 \qquad + \quad (y + 4)^2 \quad &= 25 \end{aligned}$$

The center is pt. $(2, -4)$. The radius is 5. **Answer.**

C **19.** $x^2 + 6x + y^2 + 8y = 0$ **21.** $x^2 + 2x + y^2 = 35$

20. $x^2 - 6x + y^2 - 8y = 0$ **22.** $x^2 + y^2 - 10y = 75$

Circle A has the equation: $(x - 2)^2 + (y + 1)^2 = 25$.
Circle B has the equation: $(x - 4)^2 + y^2 = 36$.

23. Write the equations or inequalities that describe the intersection of the exterior of circle *A* and the interior of circle *B*.

24. Write the equations or inequalities that describe the intersection of circle *A* and the exterior of circle *B*.

25. Draw the four circles obtained by using the four possible combinations of signs in $(x \pm 1)^2 + (y \pm 1)^2 = 1$. Write the equation of the circle tangent to the four circles and having the four circles (except for the points of tangency) in its interior.

26. Repeat Exercise 25, but write the equation of the circle that has the four circles (except for the points of tangency) in its exterior.

27. Find the equation of the sphere whose center is the origin and whose radius is 5. (*Hint:* The distance from a point (x, y, z) of the sphere to the origin is 5.)

28. Find the equation of the sphere whose center is pt. $(1, -2, 4)$ and whose radius is 7.

29. Find the equation of the sphere whose center is pt. $(3, 2, 4)$ and which is tangent to the *y-z* plane.

30. A sphere is tangent to the *x-y* plane, the *x-z* plane, and the *y-z* plane. The radius of the sphere is 5. State the coordinates of the possible centers.

12–6   The Midpoint Formula

By making a careful drawing on a grid you can verify the statement:

The segment joining points $(1, 2)$ and $(9, 4)$ has midpoint $(5, 3)$.

Note the *x*-coordinates. The average of 1 and 9 is 5.
Note the *y*-coordinates. The average of 2 and 4 is 3.

If the averaging technique were to work for points $(-4, 5)$ and $(0, -1)$, the segment joining these points would have as midpoint a point with *x*-coordinate -2 (note that the average of -4 and 0 is -2), and *y*-coordinate 2. You can verify this result by making a drawing on a grid.

You might now suspect that the segment joining points (x_1, y_1) and (x_2, y_2) has midpoint $\left(\dfrac{x_1 + x_2}{2}, \dfrac{y_1 + y_2}{2}\right)$. To see that the formula is correct, consider first a horizontal number line. Take a segment whose endpoints have coordinates x_1 and x_2. Remember that neither x_1 nor x_2 is necessarily positive.

Case 1: When $x_1 < x_2$

$$P_1P_2 = x_2 - x_1$$
$$P_1M = \tfrac{1}{2}(x_2 - x_1)$$

The coordinate of M is $x_1 + \tfrac{1}{2}(x_2 - x_1)$, or $\dfrac{x_1 + x_2}{2}$.

Case 2: When $x_1 > x_2$

$P_2P_1 = x_1 - x_2$

$P_2M = \frac{1}{2}(x_1 - x_2)$

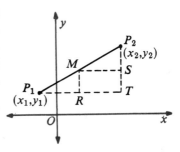

The coordinate of M is $x_2 + \frac{1}{2}(x_1 - x_2)$, or $\dfrac{x_1 + x_2}{2}$.

A vertical segment whose endpoints have coordinates y_1 and y_2 has, by similar reasoning, a midpoint with coordinate $\dfrac{y_1 + y_2}{2}$.

Now consider a segment with endpoints $P_1(x_1, y_1)$ and $P_2(x_2, y_2)$. To determine the coordinates of the midpoint M, draw the horizontal and vertical segments shown. Then T has the coordinates (x_2, y_1). Since $P_1M = \frac{1}{2}P_1P_2$ and $\overline{MR} \parallel \overline{P_2T}$, $P_1R = \frac{1}{2}P_1T$. R, the midpoint of $\overline{P_1T}$, has x-coordinate $\dfrac{x_1 + x_2}{2}$.

Therefore M has x-coordinate $\dfrac{x_1 + x_2}{2}$.

By similar reasoning, M has y-coordinate $\dfrac{y_1 + y_2}{2}$.

THEOREM 12–4 The midpoint of the segment joining the points (x_1, y_1) and (x_2, y_2) is the point $\left(\dfrac{x_1 + x_2}{2}, \dfrac{y_1 + y_2}{2}\right)$.

ORAL EXERCISES

Use the formula to find the midpoint of the segment joining the points named.

1. $(6, 0)$ and $(10, 0)$
2. $(-6, 0)$ and $(8, 0)$
3. $(-6, 0)$ and $(-2, 0)$
4. $(3, -1)$ and $(3, -5)$

5. $(2, 5)$ and $(6, -1)$
6. $(3, 3)$ and $(5, 7)$
7. $(2, 0)$ and (j, k)
8. (e, f) and (j, k)

WRITTEN EXERCISES

Use the formula to find the midpoint of the segment joining the points named.

A
1. $(3, 0)$ and $(-4, 7)$
2. $(3, -9)$ and $(0, 0)$
3. $(1.4, -2.3)$ and $(3.6, 1.1)$
4. $(-3.1, 5)$ and $(4.2, 7)$

5. $(-1, \frac{1}{2})$ and $(-4, 3\frac{1}{2})$
6. $(\frac{1}{3}, 2)$ and $(-1\frac{1}{3}, -2)$
7. (a, b) and $(c, 0)$
8. $(a + b, a - b)$ and (a, b)

In Exercises 9–12, state the coordinates of the second endpoint either by using the midpoint formula or by using a carefully-made graph.

B
9. One endpoint of a segment is pt. $(0, 0)$. The midpoint is pt. $(5, -3)$.
10. One endpoint of a segment is pt. $(-3, 2)$. The midpoint is pt. $(-1, 5)$.
11. One endpoint of a segment is pt. $(0, 2)$. The midpoint is pt. (j, k).
12. One endpoint of a segment is pt. (a, b). The midpoint is pt. (c, d).
13. The vertices of a rhombus are pts. $(-1, 1)$, $(1, -3)$, $(3, 1)$, and $(1, 5)$. Find the midpoints of the four sides. Draw a graph and connect the midpoints in order. What kind of quadrilateral is formed?
14. The vertices of a rectangle are pts. $(-2, 3)$, $(4, 3)$, $(4, 7)$, and $(-2, 7)$. Find the midpoints of the four sides. Draw a graph and connect the midpoints in order. What kind of quadrilateral is formed?
15. Check the midpoint formula for points $(3, -1)$ and $(5, 2)$ by showing that the distance between points $(4, \frac{1}{2})$ and $(3, -1)$ equals the distance between points $(4, \frac{1}{2})$ and $(5, 2)$.
16. Repeat Exercise 15, but use points (a, b) and (c, d).

State the midpoint of the segment joining

C
17. The origin and pt. $(4, 6, 2)$.
18. The origin and pt. $(-8, 0, 4)$.
19. Pts. $(3, 2, -4)$ and $(9, 0, 6)$.
20. Pts. $(1, 2, 3)$ and $(-6, -5, -4)$.
21. Pts. $(0, 2a, 2b)$ and $(0, 2c, 2d)$.
22. Pts. (x_1, y_1, z_1) and (x_2, y_2, z_2).
23. Point M is the midpoint of $\overline{RS}$. R is pt. $(0, 2, 2)$. M is pt. $(4, 2, 3)$. Find S.
24. Point K is the midpoint of $\overline{JN}$. N is pt. $(-6, -1, 5)$. K is pt. $(-5, 4, 3)$. Find J.

■ The Graphing of Lines

12–7   The Slope of a Line

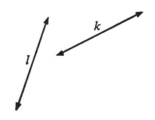

If asked to comment about the relative slopes of lines *l* and *k*, you would probably say that *l* is steeper than *k*, or that *l* has a greater slope than *k*. In mathematics we define *slope* in such a way that the general idea you already have is made precise.

The slope *m* of a segment whose endpoints are points (x_1, y_1) and (x_2, y_2), where $x_2 \neq x_1$, is

$$\frac{y_2 - y_1}{x_2 - x_1}.$$

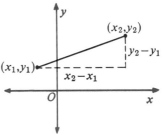

Slopes are numbers. Unlike distances, slopes can be positive, negative, or zero.

EXAMPLE.   State the slope of the segment joining pts. $(-2, 1)$ and $(3, 4)$.

Solution A: Let $(-2, 1)$ be (x_1, y_1) and $(3, 4)$ be (x_2, y_2).

$$m = \frac{y_2 - y_1}{x_2 - x_1} = \frac{4 - 1}{3 - (-2)} = \frac{3}{5}. \quad \textbf{Answer.}$$

Solution B: Let $(3, 4)$ be (x_1, y_1) and $(-2, 1)$ be (x_2, y_2).

$$m = \frac{y_2 - y_1}{x_2 - x_1} = \frac{1 - 4}{-2 - 3} = \frac{-3}{-5} = \frac{3}{5}. \quad \textbf{Answer.}$$

The two solutions in the example illustrate the fact that the expressions $\dfrac{y_1 - y_2}{x_1 - x_2}$ and $\dfrac{y_2 - y_1}{x_2 - x_1}$ denote the same number. Either can be used in computing slope.

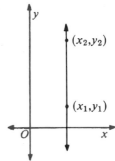

Notice that when x_1 and x_2 are equal, the denominator of the expression $\dfrac{y_2 - y_1}{x_2 - x_1}$ is 0 and the expression is meaningless. Segments that are parallel to the *y*-axis have no slope. For vertical segments slope is not defined.

When a segment is horizontal, no difficulty is encountered. $y_2 - y_1 = 0$, but $x_2 - x_1 \neq 0$. The slope of a horizontal segment is $\dfrac{0}{x_2 - x_1}$ or 0.

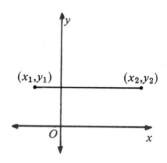

Suppose that two segments $\overline{P_1P_2}$ and $\overline{P_3P_4}$ lie on the same line, as shown. The slope of $\overline{P_1P_2}$ is $\dfrac{y_2 - y_1}{x_2 - x_1} = \dfrac{QP_2}{P_1Q}$.

The slope of $\overline{P_3P_4}$ is

$$\dfrac{y_4 - y_3}{x_4 - x_3} = \dfrac{RP_4}{P_3R}.$$

$\angle P_2P_1Q \cong \angle P_4P_3R$	since congruent corresponding angles are formed when parallel lines are cut by a transversal.
$\angle Q \cong \angle R$	since right angles are congruent.
$\triangle P_1QP_2 \sim \triangle P_3RP_4$	by the AA postulate.
$\dfrac{QP_2}{P_1Q} = \dfrac{RP_4}{P_3R}$	since lengths of corresponding sides of similar triangles are proportional.
$\dfrac{y_2 - y_1}{x_2 - x_1} = \dfrac{y_4 - y_3}{x_4 - x_3}$	by the substitution principle.

The foregoing argument shows that any two segments of a nonvertical line have the same slope. This makes it possible to talk about the slope of a nonvertical line. **The slope m of a line is** $\dfrac{y_2 - y_1}{x_2 - x_1}$, where pts. (x_1, y_1) and (x_2, y_2) are any two points of the line, and $x_2 \neq x_1$. Whenever $x_2 = x_1$, the line is vertical and has no slope.

Note that two distinct nonvertical lines through the same point (a, b) must have different slopes. For if one line contains point (c, d) the other line, being distinct, cannot contain point (c, d). On the other line, at the point whose x-coordinate is c, the y-coordinate must be some number t, which is different from d. Then the slopes $\dfrac{d - b}{c - a}$ and $\dfrac{t - b}{c - a}$ are unequal.

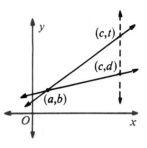

When you look at the graph of a line, you can tell whether the slope is positive or negative. Notice in the two figures at the left below, that when a line slants upward as you read from left to right: $y_2 - y_1 > 0$, $x_2 - x_1 > 0$, and the slope is a positive number. In the other two figures the line slants downward as you read from left to right. Then $y_2 - y_1 < 0$, $x_2 - x_1 > 0$, and the slope is a negative number.

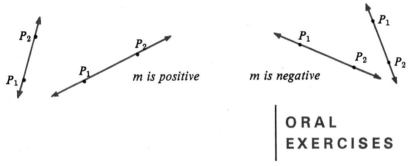

ORAL EXERCISES

1. For each line shown, tell whether the slope appears to be positive, negative, zero, or not defined.

2. The slope of a given line is positive. Is the slope of a parallel line positive, negative, zero, or not defined?

3. For each pair of points state the value of $y_2 - y_1$.

   a. $P_1(0, 0); P_2(4, 3)$.   **d.** $P_1(-1, -1); P_2(-4, 2)$.

   b. $P_1(0, 0); P_2(-1, 2)$.   **e.** $P_1(2, 0); P_2(2, -3)$.

   c. $P_1(3, 1); P_2(5, 1)$.   **f.** $P_1(e, f); P_2(j, k)$.

4. For each pair of points listed in Exercise 3, state the value of $x_2 - x_1$.

Find the slope of the line containing the points named.

A
1. $(3, 2)$ and $(7, 8)$ **3.** $(2, -1)$ and $(0, 4)$ **5.** $(1, -4)$ and $(3, -1)$
2. $(0, 4)$ and $(5, 0)$ **4.** $(3, 8)$ and $(-2, 5)$ **6.** $(3, -2)$ and $(7, -2)$

7. $(0, 0)$ and (a, b) **8.** (e, f) and (j, k)

B
9. $(0, c)$ and $(c, 0)$ **11.** $(a, 2a)$ and $(b, a - b)$
10. (a, b) and $(a - b, b - a)$ **12.** $(c + d, c - d)$ and $(c - d, c + d)$

Use the slope formula to find the missing coordinate.

13. Pts. $(3, 2)$ and $(8, ?)$ lie on a line whose slope is $\frac{3}{5}$.
14. Pts. $(0, ?)$ and $(-4, 2)$ lie on a line whose slope is 5.
15. Pts. $(13, 2)$ and $(?, -5)$ lie on a line whose slope is $-\frac{7}{2}$.
16. Pts. (a, b) and $(c, ?)$ lie on a line whose slope is j.

17. Given points $P(-4, -1)$, $Q(-1, 1)$, $R(4, 1)$, and $S(7, 3)$.
   a. State the slope of $\overline{PQ}$ and the slope of $\overline{RS}$.
   b. Draw a graph to show that $\overline{PQ}$ and $\overline{RS}$ are not subsets of the same line.
18. Given points $G(-3, 1)$, $H(0,0)$, $J(2, -1)$, and $K(8, -3)$.
   a. State the slope of $\overline{GH}$, the slope of $\overline{JK}$, and the slope of $\overline{GK}$.
   b. Are points G, H, J, and K collinear?

12–8   Parallel and Perpendicular Lines

A careful look at a graph of two nonvertical parallel lines suggests that the lines have equal slopes. When the lines are both parallel to the *x*-axis, each has slope zero, and the slopes are equal. When two nonvertical parallel lines intersect the *x*-axis, you can prove their slopes equal in the following way.

Let the slope of line l_1 be m_1 and the slope of line l_2 be m_2. From points B and S, taken on l_1 and l_2 as shown, draw $\overline{BC}$ and $\overline{ST}$ perpendicular to the *x*-axis.

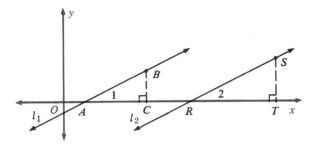

AC is the difference of the x-coordinates of A and B, and CB the difference of the y-coordinates.

$\dfrac{BC}{AC} = m_1$. Similarly, $\dfrac{ST}{RT} = m_2$.

$\triangle ACB \sim \triangle RTS$, since $\angle 1 \cong \angle 2$ and $\angle C \cong \angle T$.

$\dfrac{BC}{AC} = \dfrac{ST}{RT}$, since lengths of corresponding sides of $\sim \triangle$ are in proportion.

$m_1 = m_2$, by the substitution principle.

Conversely, when $m_1 = m_2$, you can show that $l_1 \parallel l_2$. This is true since a line through R and parallel to l_1 must have slope m_1, and it is not possible for two distinct lines through the same point to have equal slopes.

THEOREM 12–5   Two nonvertical lines are parallel if and only if they have equal slopes.

You will recall that the phrase *if and only if* permits one theorem to include both a statement and its converse. Theorem 12–5 could be replaced by two theorems:

If two nonvertical lines are parallel, they have equal slopes.
If two nonvertical lines have equal slopes, they are parallel.

The slopes of two perpendicular lines, neither one a vertical line, are also related in a particular way. To show that the product of the slopes is -1, let m_1 and m_2 be the slopes of perpendicular lines l_1 and l_2. Take points E, F, and G as shown in the figure on the next page.

$$m_1 = \frac{b-0}{a-c} = \frac{b}{a-c}. \qquad m_2 = \frac{b-0}{a-d} = \frac{b}{a-d}.$$

In rt. $\triangle EFG$, $(EF)^2 + (FG)^2 = (EG)^2$. Substitute for EF, FG, and EG expressions obtained by using the distance formula.

$$\left(\sqrt{(a-c)^2 + (b-0)^2}\right)^2 + \left(\sqrt{(a-d)^2 + (b-0)^2}\right)^2$$
$$= \left(\sqrt{(d-c)^2 + (0-0)^2}\right)^2$$

$$a^2 - 2ac + c^2 + b^2 + a^2 - 2ad + d^2 + b^2 = d^2 - 2cd + c^2$$

$$2a^2 - 2ac - 2ad + 2cd + 2b^2 = 0$$

$$a^2 - ac - ad + cd + b^2 = 0$$

$$a(a - c) - d(a - c) + b^2 = 0$$

$$(a - c)(a - d) + b \cdot b = 0$$

Divide by $(a - c)(a - d)$, which cannot have the value 0.

$$1 + \frac{b}{a-c} \cdot \frac{b}{a-d} = 0.$$

Then $1 + m_1 \cdot m_2 = 0$,   and $m_1 \cdot m_2 = -1$.
Conversely, when $m_1 \cdot m_2 = -1$ is given, you can reverse the order of the algebraic steps and deduce that $\triangle EFG$ is a rt. $\triangle$, by the converse of the Pythagorean Theorem.

THEOREM 12–6   Two nonvertical lines are perpendicular if and only if the slope of one line is the negative reciprocal of the slope of the other line.

$$m_1 = -\frac{1}{m_2}, \qquad \text{or} \qquad m_1 \cdot m_2 = -1$$

ORAL EXERCISES

1. Line l has slope $\frac{2}{3}$. Any line parallel to l has slope __?__. Any line perpendicular to l has slope __?__.

2. The slope of line k is $-\frac{5}{2}$. The slope of any line parallel to k is __?__. The slope of any line perpendicular to k is __?__.

3. Line g has slope $\frac{1}{2}$. Line h has slope .5. Lines g and h must be __?__ because their slopes are __?__ .

4. Line j has slope $\frac{2}{3}$. Line k has slope $-\frac{3}{2}$. Lines j and k must be __?__ because their slopes are __?__ .

5. Line c has slope 3. Line d has slope -2. Lines c and d cannot be parallel because their slopes are not __?__ .

6. Line c has slope 3. Line d has slope -2. Lines c and d cannot be perpendicular because their slopes are not __?__ .

7. Lines e and f are parallel. The slope of e is $\frac{10}{4}$. The slope of f is $\dfrac{5}{k}$. k must equal __?__ .

8. Lines g and h are perpendicular. The slope of g is $-\frac{2}{5}$. The slope of h is $\dfrac{5}{k}$. Then k must equal __?__ .

WRITTEN EXERCISES

Given points A, B, C, and D. Tell which sides, if any, of quadrilateral ABCD are parallel. Also tell which sides, if any, are perpendicular.

EXAMPLE. $A(-1, 0)$; $\quad B(1, 1)$; $\quad C(0, 3)$; $\quad D(-3, 4)$.

Solution: m of $\overline{AB} = \dfrac{1 - 0}{1 - (-1)} = \dfrac{1}{2}$. $\quad m$ of $\overline{BC} = \dfrac{3 - 1}{0 - 1} = -2.$

m of $\overline{CD} = \dfrac{4 - 3}{-3 - 0} = -\dfrac{1}{3}$. $\quad m$ of $\overline{DA} = \dfrac{0 - 4}{-1 - (-3)} = -2.$

$\overline{DA} \parallel \overline{BC}$, since each segment has slope -2.
$\overline{AB} \perp \overline{BC}$, since $\frac{1}{2} \cdot (-2) = -1$.   **Answer.**
$\overline{AB} \perp \overline{DA}$, since $\frac{1}{2} \cdot (-2) = -1$.

A

1. $A(0, 0)$; $B(6, 3)$; $C(5, 5)$; $D(-1, 2)$.

2. $A(1, -3)$; $B(4, -1)$; $C(2, 2)$; $D(-4, -2)$.

3. $A(-1, -5)$; $B(8, 2)$; $C(5, 5)$; $D(-4, -2)$.

4. $A(-1, 1)$; $B(1, -2)$; $C(4, 0)$; $D(3, 3)$.

State the slope of each side and each altitude of triangle EFG.

5. $E(2, 1)$; $F(3, 5)$; $G(7, 2)$.   **6.** $E(-3, 0)$; $F(-5, -4)$; $G(-7, 0)$.

Is quadrilateral ABCD a special kind of quadrilateral? Are the diagonals perpendicular to each other?

B

7. $A(0, 0)$; $B(6, 8)$; $C(2, 2)$; $D(-1, -2)$.

8. $A(-6, 4)$; $B(-6, 2)$; $C(0,0)$; $D(-4, 5)$.

State the value of j such that $\angle ABC$ is a right angle.

C   **9.** $A(j, 7)$; $B(-3, j)$; $C(-1, 0)$.

10. $A(2, j)$; $B(j, -1)$; $C(-1, -5)$.

12–9 Writing Equations of Lines

Some graphs meet conditions that are expressed algebraically in the form of equations in two variables. Take, for example, the set of points whose coordinates satisfy the condition $2x + 3y = 12$. One way to find points belonging to this set is shown:

When y has the value 0,

$$2x + 3y = 12$$
$$2x + 3(0) = 12$$
$$x = 6$$

The point $(6, 0)$ satisfies the condition, since $2(6) + 3(0) = 12$.

When y has the value 2,

$$2x + 3y = 12$$
$$2x + 3(2) = 12$$
$$x = 3$$

The point $(3, 2)$ satisfies the condition, since $2(3) + 3(2) = 12$.

You can assign values to x also. Do you see that when the value of x is -1 the corresponding value of y is $4\frac{2}{3}$? Then check to see that the point $(-1, \frac{14}{3})$ satisfies the condition: $2x + 3y = 12$.

A short table of values and the graphs of the eight points listed in the table are shown.

x	y
9	-2
7	$-\frac{2}{3}$
6	0
$4\frac{1}{2}$	1
3	2
0	4
-1	$4\frac{2}{3}$
-3	6

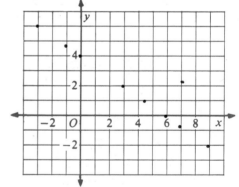

Some points whose coordinates satisfy $2x + 3y = 12$.

The eight points are collinear, as a theorem says they must be.

THEOREM 12–7   The graph of any equation that can be written in the form $ax + by = c$, a and b not both 0, is a line.

For a proof of the theorem see Extra for Experts, pages 480–481.

Given any particular line, you can write an equation in the form $ax + by = c$ for that line. There are times, however, when equations written in other forms have advantages. Notice, in the example that follows, how the given numbers appear in the answer.

EXAMPLE. State the equation of the line passing through the point $(1, 2)$ and having slope $-\frac{3}{2}$.

Solution: Take pt. $(1, 2)$ as P_1.

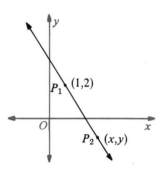

Take pt. (x, y), any other point of the line, as P_2.

The slope of $\overline{P_1P_2}$ is expressed by

$$\frac{y - 2}{x - 1}.$$

Since the slope of $\overleftrightarrow{P_1P_2}$ must be $-\frac{3}{2}$,

$$\frac{y - 2}{x - 1} = -\frac{3}{2},$$

$$y - 2 = -\tfrac{3}{2}(x - 1). \quad \textbf{Answer.}$$

In the example, the equation $\dfrac{y - 2}{x - 1} = -\dfrac{3}{2}$ has an interesting weakness in describing the line. The equation is meaningless when x has the value 1 and hence does not account for the given point $(1, 2)$. The equation $\dfrac{y - 2}{x - 1} = -\dfrac{3}{2}$ is not the equation of a line; it is the equation of a line with a single point $(1, 2)$ omitted.

The equation $y - 2 = -\frac{3}{2}(x - 1)$, on the other hand, provides for the point $(1, 2)$ as well as for all other points on the line. The equation is said to be in *point-slope* form. From an equation in point-slope form you can get two facts by inspection.

The line $y - 2 = -\frac{3}{2}(x - 1)$ has slope $-\frac{3}{2}$, and contains point $(1, 2)$.

THEOREM 12–8 The equation of the line passing through the point (x_1, y_1) and having slope m is $y - y_1 = m(x - x_1)$.

The proof of Theorem 12–8 is left for you. Follow the Example shown above using (x_1, y_1) in place of $(1, 2)$ and m in place of $-\frac{3}{2}$.

COROLLARY The equation of the line containing points (x_1, y_1) and (x_2, y_2) is $y - y_1 = m(x - x_1)$, where $m = \dfrac{y_2 - y_1}{x_2 - x_1}$ and $x_2 \neq x_1$.

EXAMPLE. Find the equation of the line containing pts. $(-3, 1)$ and $(2, 4)$.

Solution: The slope of the line is $\dfrac{4 - 1}{2 - (-3)} = \dfrac{3}{5}$.

The equation of the line through pt. $(-3, 1)$ with slope $\frac{3}{5}$ is:
$y - 1 = \frac{3}{5}(x + 3)$.   **Answer.**

ORAL
EXERCISES

State the slope and one point of each line.

1. $y - 3 = \frac{2}{3}(x - 7)$

2. $y + 2 = \frac{5}{2}(x - 3)$

3. $y + 0 = 4(x + 2)$

4. $y = -\frac{2}{9}(x + 6)$

5. $y - 3 = \frac{2}{5}(x - 0)$

6. $y = x$

7. The equations $\dfrac{y - 3}{x - 2} = \dfrac{3}{4}$ and $y - 3 = \frac{3}{4}(x - 2)$ differ in this respect: the first equation does not account for the point $(?, ?)$.

WRITTEN
EXERCISES

Make a table of at least three ordered pairs of numbers for each equation. Plot the points and draw the graph of the equation.

A   **1.** $x + y = 6$

2. $x - y = 6$

3. $2x - 3y = 12$

4. $2x - 3y = -12$

5. $2x + 3y = 12$

6. $2x + 3y = -12$

7. $5x - 4y = 20$

8. $x + y = 0$

State the equation of the line passing through P and having slope m. .

9. $m = \frac{5}{2}$; $P(3, 4)$.

10. $m = \frac{2}{3}$; $P(4, -1)$.

11. $m = 1$; $P(1, 3)$.

12. $m = -4$; $P(-2, -3)$.

13. $m = -\frac{3}{5}$; $P(2, 0)$.

14. $m = -4$; $P(0, 0)$.

15. $m = 0$; $P(5, 2)$.

16. $m = 0$; $P(0, 0)$.

State the equation of the line containing the points

17. $(1, 2)$ and $(6, 5)$.

18. $(2, -3)$ and $(4, 6)$.

19. $(0, 2)$ and $(-3, 4)$.

20. $(-4, 0)$ and $(2, -1)$.

21. $(0, 6)$ and $(5, 0)$.

22. $(0, 0)$ and $(-3, 2)$.

In Exercises 23–28 state the equation of the line.

B 23. Through pt. $(2, -1)$ and parallel to a line that has slope $\frac{3}{4}$.

24. Through pt. $(-3, -4)$ and perpendicular to a line that has slope $\frac{2}{5}$.

25. With slope $\frac{9}{7}$ and containing the midpoint of the segment joining pts. $(2, -3)$ and $(-6, 5)$.

26. Through the midpoint of, and perpendicular to, the segment joining pts. $(1, 0)$ and $(5, -2)$.

27. Containing the midpoints of the legs of right triangle *RST*, where *R* is pt. $(-5, 5)$, *S* is pt. $(1, 1)$, and *T* is pt. $(3, 4)$.

28. Containing the longer diagonal of a quadrilateral whose vertices are pts. $(2, 2)$, $(-2, -2)$, $(1, -1)$, and $(6, 4)$.

29. Show that the equations $y - 1 = \frac{3}{5}(x + 3)$ and $y - 4 = \frac{3}{5}(x - 2)$ are equivalent.

30. An equation of the line containing pts. $(-2, 3)$ and $(4, -1)$ can be written in the form $y - 3 = -\frac{2}{3}(x + 2)$ or in the form $y + 1 = -\frac{2}{3}(x - 4)$, depending upon which point you take as pt. (x_1, y_1). Show that the two equations are equivalent.

C 31. Show that the equations are equivalent.

$$y - y_1 = \frac{y_2 - y_1}{x_2 - x_1}(x - x_1) \qquad y - y_2 = \frac{y_1 - y_2}{x_1 - x_2}(x - x_2)$$

32. State the equation of a line through pt. (p, q) and parallel to a line containing pts. (a, b) and (c, d). $(a \neq c)$.

33. In some cases the line described in Ex. 32 does not exist. Write an equation expressing a relationship between a, b, c, d, p, and q for such cases.

34. State the equation of the line that is the perpendicular bisector of the segment joining pts. $(2e, 2f)$ and $(2g, 2k)$. $(e \neq g, f \neq k)$.

12–10   Additional Properties of Lines

In many cases you can graph a line quickly by locating the two points at which it intersects the axes. This method is recommended when the points are not both so close to the origin as to make sketching difficult.

EXAMPLE 1. Graph $2x + 3y = 12$.

Solution: When y is 0, x is 6; when x is 0, y is 4. Plot the two points and draw the line.

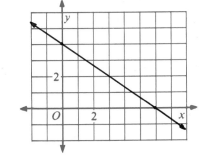

When the equation of a line is given in point-slope form, you can quickly plot two points and draw the graph of the line.

EXAMPLE 2. Graph $y - 3 = -\frac{2}{3}(x + 1)$.

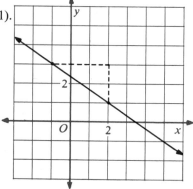

Solution: One point is pt. $(-1, 3)$.
The line slants downward from left to right, with slope $-\frac{2}{3}$.
Plot the point $(-1, 3)$.
From pt. $(-1, 3)$ count 3 to the right and 2 down. Plot the new point. Draw the line.

Suppose you are given the equations of two lines and are asked to find the coordinates of the point at which they intersect. One method is to graph each line and estimate the coordinates of the point of intersection. However, it is usually better to solve the pair of equations algebraically.

EXAMPLE 3. Find, by an algebraic method, the point of intersection of line $3x - y = 7$ and line $x + 2y = 7$.

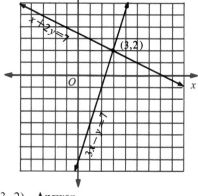

Solution: By the addition and subtraction method.

$$6x - 2y = 14$$
$$\underline{x + 2y = 7}$$
$$7x = 21$$
$$x = 3$$

Substitute 3 for x in either of the original equations:

$$3 + 2y = 7, \; y = 2.$$

The point of intersection is pt. $(3, 2)$. **Answer.**

(The graph verifies the solution.)

EXAMPLE 4. Find, by an algebraic method, the point of intersection of line $y + 1 = \frac{3}{2}(x + 1)$ and line $y - 1 = -1(x - 2)$.

Solution: By the substitution method.
Solve the second equation for y in terms of x.

$$y = -1(x - 2) + 1; \quad y = -x + 2 + 1; \quad y = -x + 3$$

Substitute $(-x + 3)$ for y in the first equation.

$$(-x + 3) + 1 = \tfrac{3}{2}(x + 1)$$
$$-x + 4 = \tfrac{3}{2}(x + 1)$$
$$-2x + 8 = 3x + 3$$
$$-5x = -5$$
$$x = 1$$

Now substitute 1 for x in $y = -x + 3$. $y = 2$. The point of intersection is pt. (1, 2). **Answer.**

ORAL EXERCISES

State two points on the line.

EXAMPLE. $2x + y = 8$

Solution: When x is 0, y is 8. One point is pt. (0, 8).
When y is 0, x is 4. A second point is pt. (4, 0).

1. $4x + 5y = 20$ **5.** $3x + y = -6$

2. $3x - y = 6$ **6.** $2x - 3y = -24$

3. $8x + 2y = 4$ **7.** $y = 2x$

4. $-x + y = 5$ **8.** $x = 5$

WRITTEN EXERCISES

Draw the graph of the equation.

A

1. $3x + y = 3$ **7.** $x = 3$

2. $x - 2y = 4$ **8.** $y = -1$

3. $2x + y = -4$ **9.** $y - 1 = 2(x - 2)$

4. $4x + 5y = 10$ **10.** $y + 1 = \tfrac{1}{2}(x + 1)$

5. $y = x$ **11.** $y = 3(x - 1)$

6. $y = \tfrac{1}{2}x$ **12.** $y - 3 = \tfrac{1}{2}x$

Use an algebraic method to find the point of intersection of the given lines.

13. $x + y = 5$, $3x - y = 1$.   **15.** $x - 2y = 1$, $3x - y = -2$.

14. $2x - y = 5$, $x + 2y = 5$.   **16.** $3x + 2y = 12$, $5x - 3y = 20$.

17. $y - 2 = 1(x - 2)$, $y + 1 = -1(x - 8)$.

18. $y - 3 = \frac{1}{2}(x - 1)$, $y + 1 = -\frac{3}{2}(x - 1)$.

19. $y - 3 = \frac{4}{5}(x - 5)$, $y = -1$.   **20.** $y + 3 = -\frac{2}{3}(x - 5)$, $x = 2$.

$\boxed{\text{B}}$ **21.** $2x - y = 5$, $x = a$.   **23.** $ax + by = c$, $x = d$.

22. $ax + 2y = 4$, $y = 2$.   **24.** $ax + by = c$, $y = 3x$.

$\boxed{\text{C}}$ **25.** $ax + by = c$, $dx + ey = f$.

26. $y - g = h(x - j)$, $y - k = l(x - n)$.

27. State the coordinates of the point in which the line determined by pts. $(0, a)$ and (b, c) intersects the line determined by pts. $(d, 0)$ and (e, f).

28. State the coordinates of the point in which the line determined by pts. (a, b) and (c, d) intersects the line determined by pts. (e, f) and (g, h).

To describe a line algebraically you use an equation of the form $ax + by = c$. To describe a half-plane you use an inequality of the form $ax + by < c$ or $ax + by > c$.

Graph the sets of points specified in Exercises 29–36.

EXAMPLE. $\{(x, y): 2x + 3y < 6\}$

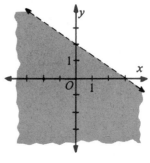

Solution: First graph $2x + 3y = 6$ as a dashed line.   Take some convenient point, $(4, 1)$, for instance, on one side of the line.   When $x = 4$ and $y = 1$, $2x + 3y = 2(4) + 3(1) = 11$.   The original inequality $2x + 3y < 6$ is not satisfied, and $(4, 1)$ is not a point belonging to the desired set. Try any particular point below the dashed line and the inequality is satisfied. Shade the region to the lower left of the dashed line to show your answer.

29. $\{(x, y): 3x - y \geq 3\}$ **30.** $\{(x, y): y > \frac{1}{2}x - 3\}$

31. $\{(x, y): x + 2y < 4\} \cap \{(x, y): 2x - y \geq 4\}$

32. $\{(x, y): |x| < 2\} \cap \{(x, y): x + 3y < 6\}$

33. $\{(x, y): |x| = |y|\}$ **35.** $\{(x, y): |x| + |y| \leq 4\}$

34. $\{(x, y): |x| + |y| = 4\}$ **36.** $\{(x, y): y > |x - 2| + 2\}$

37. Given points $A(1, 2)$, $B(-1, 1)$, and $C(3, 0)$. Use algebraic symbols to state three sets whose intersection is the interior of $\triangle ABC$.

38. Given points $R(-3, -2)$, $S(0, 0)$, and $T(2, -3)$. Use algebraic symbols to state three sets whose intersection is the union of $\triangle RST$ and its interior.

CHAPTER SUMMARY

Inventory of Structure and Methods

1. There is a one-to-one correspondence between the set of points in a plane and the set of ordered pairs of real numbers. A graph is a set of points described algebraically and pictured on a coordinate plane.

2. The distance between points (x_1, y_1) and (x_2, y_2) is

$$d = \sqrt{(x_2 - x_1)^2 + (y_2 - y_1)^2}.$$

The midpoint of the segment joining points (x_1, y_1) and (x_2, y_2) is point

$$\left(\frac{x_1 + x_2}{2} , \frac{y_1 + y_2}{2} \right).$$

The circle with center (a, b) and radius r has the equation

$$(x - a)^2 + (y - b)^2 = r^2.$$

3. The slope of the segment joining (and of the line through) pts. (x_1, y_1) and (x_2, y_2) is $m = \dfrac{y_2 - y_1}{x_2 - x_1}.$ $(x_2 \neq x_1)$.

When $x_2 = x_1$, the line is vertical and its slope is not defined.
When $m > 0$, the line slopes up to the right.
When $m < 0$, the line slopes down to the right.
When $m = 0$, the line is horizontal.
Parallel lines: $m_1 = m_2$.
Perpendicular lines: $m_1 \cdot m_2 = -1$.

4. The graph of all points (x, y) meeting the condition $ax + by = c$, (a and b not both 0), is a line.
The equation of the line through pt. (x_1, y_1) and having slope m is

$$y - y_1 = m(x - x_1).$$

To state the equation of the line through pts. (x_1, y_1) and (x_2, y_2), use the same formula and compute m by using $m = \dfrac{y_2 - y_1}{x_2 - x_1}.$ $(x_2 \neq x_1)$.

5. To sketch a line, given its equation, you find points by substituting convenient numbers for either x or y in the equation and solving for the other variable. When an equation is given in point-slope form, you can identify one point at sight and then move to another point by using the slope. An algebraic solution is generally the best way to find the intersection of two lines, given their equations.

Vocabulary and Spelling

ordered pair (*p. 443*)
coordinate axes (*p. 443*)
  x-axis (*p. 443*)
  y-axis (*p. 443*)
origin (*p. 443*)
quadrant (*p. 443*)
x-coordinate (*p. 444*)
y-coordinate (*p. 444*)
coordinate system (*p. 444*)
symmetry
  with respect to a point (*p. 447*)
  with respect to a line (*p. 447*)

with respect to a plane (*p. 447*)
graph in a plane (*p. 450*)
distance formula (*p. 453*)
equation of a circle (*p. 455*)
midpoint formula (*p. 459*)
slope *m* (*p. 461*)
  of a segment (*p. 461*)
  of a line (*p. 462*)
if and only if (*p. 465*)
equation of a line (*p. 468*)
  point-slope form (*p. 469*)

CHAPTER TEST

12–1   **1.** What is the *x*-coordinate of pt. $(-3, 6)$? the *y*-coordinate?

      2. In which quadrant does each of the following points lie?

        a. $(-1, 2)$ **b.** $(3, -5)$ **c.** $(4, 4)$ **d.** $(-1, -2)$

      3. On which axis does the point $(0, 5)$ lie?

      4. What special name does the point $(0, 0)$ have?

12–2   Q is pt. $(4, 2)$. Find Q' if it is given that Q and Q' have symmetry with respect to

      5. The point $(0, 0)$.   **7.** The *x*-axis.

      6. The point $(5, 6)$.   **8.** The line $x = -1$.

12–3   In the coordinate plane draw graphs meeting the conditions.

      9. $x = 3$ **10.** $y > 1$ **11.** $-1 \leq x \leq 2$ **12.** $|y| < 2$

12–4   State the distance between the points named.

      13. $(0, 0)$ and $(5, 12)$ **15.** $(-1, 2)$ and $(2, 6)$

      14. $(0, 0)$ and $(-3, -4)$ **16.** $(4, -6)$ and $(-1, 0)$

12–5   Write the equation of the circle

      17. With center $(0, 0)$ and radius 2.

      18. With center $(3, 2)$ and radius 6.

      19. With center $(-3, 0)$ and radius $\sqrt{7}$.

      20. Containing pts. $(-1, -1)$, $(3, -1)$, and $(3, 3)$.

12–6 Find the midpoint of the segment joining the points

21. (4, 4) and (6, 12). **22.** (-3, 0) and (4, -6).

One endpoint of a segment is the point (3, 5). Find the other endpoint, given that the midpoint is the point

23. (-1, 5). **24.** (4, -2).

12–7 Does the line described have a slope?

25. A horizontal line. **26.** A vertical line.

State the slope of the line through the points described.

27. (2, 2) and (5, 8). **28.** (-4, 1) and (5, -2).

12–8 Given a line l. State the slope of a line (a) parallel to l, and (b) perpendicular to l when

29. The slope of l is 3. **30.** The slope of l is $-\frac{7}{5}$.

Given the segments $\overline{AB}$, $\overline{BC}$, $\overline{CD}$, $\overline{DE}$, and $\overline{EA}$. A is pt. (1, -2), B is pt. (4, 1), C is pt. (1, 3), D is pt. (0, 2), and E is pt. (-1, 0). Name

31. Two parallel segments. **32.** Two perpendicular segments.

12–9 Write the equation of the line

33. Through pt. (2, -3) with slope $\frac{4}{5}$.

34. Containing pts. (2, 0) and (5, -2).

12–10 **35.** Use coordinate axes and draw the lines $2x - y = 6$ and $x + 2y = 8$. The point of intersection is pt. (?, ?).

36. Find algebraically the intersection of the lines $x - 2y = -3$ and $3x + y = 5$.

CHAPTER REVIEW

12–1 **Plotting Points in Two Dimensions** *Pages 443–446*

1. The x-coordinate of a point tells the distance from that point to the __?__ axis.

2. The origin is the point (?, ?).

3. The y-coordinate of any point on the x-axis is __?__.

4. In which quadrant does each of the points described lie?

a. (2, 3) **b.** (-4, -4) **c.** (-1, 2) **d.** (3, 5)

12–2 **Symmetry** *Pages 446–449*

5. A figure has symmetry with respect to a point P if for every point Q in the figure there is a point Q' in the figure such that P is the __?__ of __?__.

6. A figure has symmetry with respect to a plane Z if for every point Q in the figure there is a point Q' in the figure such that Z is the __?__ of __?__.

Choose from a scalene triangle, a nonequilateral isosceles triangle, an equilateral triangle, and a nonequilateral rectangle, that figure which has symmetry with respect to

7. no line   9. exactly 2 lines

8. 3 lines   10. exactly 1 line

11. Points A and B have symmetry with respect to pt. $(2, -1)$. A is pt. $(-2, -3)$. Find B.

12. Points C and D have symmetry with respect to the line $y = -2$. C is pt. $(4, 4)$. Find D.

12–3 **Graphs Meeting Given Conditions** *Pages 450–452*

In the coordinate plane, draw graphs meeting the conditions named.

13. $y = 2$ 14. $x < 1$ 15. $-2 \le y < 1$ 16. $|x| = 1$

17. $\{(x, y): x \ge 1\} \cup \{(x, y): y \ge 0\}$

18. $\{(x, y): 0 \le x \le 2\} \cap \{(x, y): y \le -1\}$

12–4 **The Distance Formula** *Pages 452–454*

19. The distance between the points (x_1, y_1) and (x_2, y_2) is given by the formula $d =$ __?__.

20. The distance between the points (a, b) and (c, d) is __?__.

Find the distance between the points named.

21. $(0, 0)$ and $(3, 4)$ 23. $(2, 1)$ and $(4, -4)$

22. $(0, 0)$ and $(-3, -4)$ 24. $(2, 1)$ and $(-4, 4)$

12–5 **The Circle** *Pages 455–458*

25. $(x - a)^2 + (y - b)^2 = r^2$ is the equation of a circle whose center is pt. $(?, ?)$ and whose radius is __?__.

26. The center of the circle $x^2 + y^2 = 25$ is __?__.

Write the equation of the circle

27. With center $(0, 3)$ and radius 1.

28. With center $(-2, -7)$ and radius 3.

12–6   **The Midpoint Formula**   *Pages 458–460*

29. The midpoint of the segment joining pts. (x_1, y_1) and (x_2, y_2) is pt. (_?_ , _?_).

30. The midpoint of the segment joining pts. $(0, 0)$ and $(-8, 10)$ is pt. (_?_ , _?_).

31. The midpoint of the segment joining pts. (a, b) and (c, d) is pt. (_?_ , _?_).

32. Pt. $(2, -3)$ is the midpoint of $\overline{RS}$. R is pt. $(-1, 1)$. S is pt. (_?_ , _?_).

12–7   **The Slope of a Line**   *Pages 461–464*

33. When the slope of a line is 0, the line must be parallel to the _?_ axis.

34. The slope formula is meaningless for any line which is parallel to the _?_ axis.

35. The slopes of any two segments of a nonvertical line are _?_ .

36. Find the slope of the segment joining pts. $(-2, 0)$ and $(6, -1)$.

Write the slope of the line containing the points named.

37. $(2, 3)$ and $(4, 4)$ 38. $(2, 3)$ and $(4, -2)$

12–8   **Parallel and Perpendicular Lines**   *Pages 464–468*

39. When the slopes of two lines are equal, the lines are _?_ .

40. When the slope of one line is the negative reciprocal of the slope of another line, the lines are _?_ .

A is pt. $(-1, 1)$.   B is pt. $(1, 4)$.   C is pt. $(3, 4)$.   Write the slope of any line

41. Parallel to $\overleftrightarrow{AB}$.   43. Parallel to $\overleftrightarrow{BC}$.

42. Perpendicular to $\overleftrightarrow{AB}$.   44. Perpendicular to $\overleftrightarrow{CA}$.

12–9   **Writing Equations of Lines**   *Pages 468–471*

45. The equation of the line containing point (x_1, y_1) and having slope m is _?_ .

46. To apply the formula of Exercise 45, given two points (x_1, y_1) and (x_2, y_2), you first find m by using the formula $m =$ _?_ .

47. The equation of the line containing the point $(-2, 4)$ and having slope $-\frac{5}{3}$ is _?_ .

48. The equation of the line containing pts. $(-3, 0)$ and $(1, 4)$ is _?_ .

12–10   Additional Properties of Lines   *Pages 471–474*

49. To graph $3x - y = 6$ quickly, you can let $x = 0$ and find the point $(0, ?)$.

50. In $3x - y = 6$, you can let $y = 0$ and find the point $(?, 0)$.

By algebraic means, find the intersection of the lines.

51. $x + 3y = 8$ and $3x - 2y = 2$

52. $y - 2 = \frac{3}{4}(x - 5)$ and $y = -2x + 1$

● EXTRA FOR EXPERTS

The Theorem: *The graph of any equation which can be written in the form* $ax + by = c$, a *and* b *not both 0, is a line.*

Every ordered pair of numbers that satisfies the equation $ax + by = c$ is represented by a point. Consider the set T of all such points. To prove the theorem we shall show: (1) that every point of the set T is contained in a particular line, and (2) that every point in that line is contained in set T.

Sketch of Proof: Let T be the graph of $\{(x, y): ax + by = c\}$.

If a is 0, T is a horizontal line; if b is 0, T is a vertical line. For these cases no further proof is necessary.

If $a \neq 0$, $b \neq 0$, $c = 0$, pts. $(0, 0)$ and $(-b, a)$ are members of T. (Why?) These points determine a line with slope $\dfrac{a - 0}{-b - 0} = -\dfrac{a}{b}$.

If $a \neq 0$, $b \neq 0$, $c \neq 0$, pts. $\left(0, \dfrac{c}{b}\right)$ and $\left(\dfrac{c}{a}, 0\right)$ are members of T. (Why?) These points determine a line l with slope $\left(0 - \dfrac{c}{b}\right) \div \left(\dfrac{c}{a} - 0\right) = -\dfrac{a}{b}$.

In each case two points of T determine a line l with slope $-\dfrac{a}{b}$.

We shall show that T and l are the same figure by showing (1) Every point on T also lies on l, and (2) every point on l also lies on T. First suppose that pt. (p, q) is on T and consider this question: Must pt. (p, q) also lie on l? Since pt. (p, q) is on T, $ap + bq = c$. (Why?) If $p = \dfrac{c}{a}$, then $q = 0$

and so (p, q) is on l. If (p, q) is not $\left(\dfrac{c}{a}, 0\right)$, pts. (p, q) and $\left(\dfrac{c}{a}, 0\right)$ determine a line l'.

Line l' has slope

$$\frac{q - 0}{p - \dfrac{c}{a}} = \frac{aq}{ap - c}$$

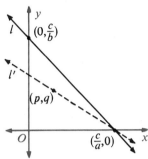

$$= \frac{aq}{ap - (ap + bq)} = -\frac{a}{b}.$$

Lines l and l' both contain pt. $\left(\dfrac{c}{a}, 0\right)$, and both

have slope $-\dfrac{a}{b}$. Therefore l and l' are the same

line, and (p, q) lies on l. We now know:

1. Every point on T also lies on line l.

Now suppose that a pt. (r, s) lies on l and consider this question: Must pt. (r, s) also lie on T?

If $r = \dfrac{c}{a}$, $s = 0$ and (r, s) is on T. If (r, s) is

not $\left(\dfrac{c}{a}, 0\right)$, the slope of l, known to be $-\dfrac{a}{b}$,

also equals $\dfrac{s - 0}{r - \dfrac{c}{a}}$. Hence $\dfrac{s - 0}{r - \dfrac{c}{a}} = -\dfrac{a}{b}$.

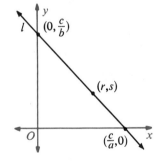

Then $bs = -ar + c$, and $ar + bs = c$.

Since the coordinates of pt. (r, s) satisfy the equation $ax + by = c$, pt. (r, s) must lie on T. We now know:

2. Every point on l also lies on T.

Each of the sets T and l contains all points of the other. T and l are identical sets. Since l is known to be a line, T, defined to be the graph of $ax + by = c$, must be a line.

EXERCISES

1–3. Answer the three questions *Why?* inserted in the proof.

4. Explain why the expression $\dfrac{aq}{ap - c}$ can be replaced by the expression

$\dfrac{aq}{ap - (ap + bq)}$. (This replacement is shown four lines above statement 1 in the proof.)

13

Coordinate
Geometry — Proofs

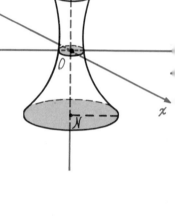

*This hyperbolic-shaped
natural-draft cooling
tower is part of an
electrical power plant in
Kentucky.*

In Chapter 12 you associated ordered pairs of numbers with points in a plane, and equations and inequalities with sets of points. In this chapter you will use the distance and midpoint formulas, together with equations of lines and circles, to prove theorems — some of them already familiar to you — about figures in a plane.

■ Proofs of Properties of Lines and Segments

13–1 Placing Coordinate Axes

In working exercises in the last chapter you saw that the location of a line, triangle, or circle with respect to a pair of coordinate axes is an important factor in determining the complexity of the algebraic work involved. Hence, it will be profitable to take a closer look at the question of how to place axes most advantageously for the study of various plane figures.

Suppose that you intend to use coordinate geometry to study the properties of a circle. You start with a circle, and there are no co-ordinate axes until you introduce them. You naturally want to select the placement of axes that will make relationships in the figure easiest to recognize, and at the same time make any necessary algebraic work as simple as possible. Three ways of drawing axes to study a circle of radius r are illustrated.

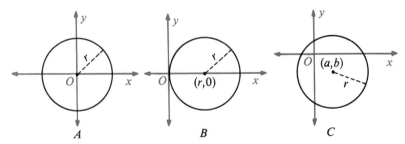

In Figure A the circle has symmetry with respect to both the x-axis and the y-axis. Furthermore, the equation of the circle has the simplest possible form: $x^2 + y^2 = r^2$.

In Figure B the circle has symmetry with respect to the x-axis. The equation of the circle with this axis placement is more complex:

$$(x - r)^2 + y^2 = r^2.$$

483

In Figure *C* the circle is not symmetrical with respect to either axis. This axis placement makes the equation of the circle even more complex:

$$(x - a)^2 + (y - b)^2 = r^2.$$

The placement shown in Figure *A* is usually the most advantageous and the one shown in Figure *C* the least advantageous.

Next consider an isosceles triangle.

It is reasonable to choose the *x*-axis so that it contains the base of the triangle as in Figures *E* and *F*. These same figures show two convenient placements for the *y*-axis.

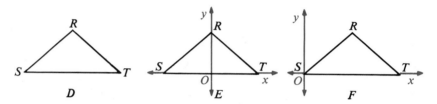

Suppose you use the placement illustrated in Figure *E* to treat isosceles $\triangle RST$ in which $RS = RT$. Since *T* and *R* lie on the *x*-axis and *y*-axis respectively, they can be assigned general coordinates such as $(k, 0)$ and $(0, j)$. Since $\triangle RST$ is isosceles and $\overline{RO} \perp \overline{ST}$, you know that $OS = OT$ and that *S* has coordinates $(-k, 0)$. To verify that the *x*-coordinate of *S* is $-k$ you can use the definition of an isosceles triangle in the following manner: Let *S* have coordinates $(q, 0)$. Since $RS = RT$,

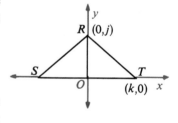

$$\sqrt{j^2 + q^2} = \sqrt{j^2 + k^2}.$$

Therefore $j^2 + q^2 = j^2 + k^2$, or $q^2 - k^2 = 0$. Then $q = k$ or $q = -k$. Since *S* and *T* are different points, $q \neq k$. It follows that $q = -k$.

In the axis placement shown in Figure *F*, you can assign coordinates to *R*, and determine those for *T* in several ways. You can reason that if *R* has *x*-coordinate *g*, then the midpoint of $\overline{ST}$ must have that same *x*-coordinate and hence *T* has coordinates $(2g, 0)$. You can reach the same conclusion more formally: Let *T* be point $(n, 0)$, *R* be point (g, j), and write the equation which expresses the fact that $RS = RT$.

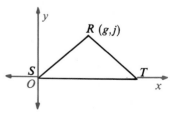

$$\sqrt{(n - g)^2 + j^2} = \sqrt{g^2 + j^2} \text{ or } n^2 - 2ng + g^2 + j^2 = g^2 + j^2.$$

$n^2 = 2ng.$ Since $n \neq 0$, $n = 2g$.

When developing coordinate geometry proofs, people often use the more obvious properties of a figure in assigning coordinates to points. When you do this, you must, if your coordinates are questioned, be able to show algebraically that they are correct.

ORAL
EXERCISES

In each exercise state which placement of the axes shown seems to be the most advantageous for the geometric figure named.

1. A rectangle

a. 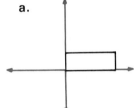 b. 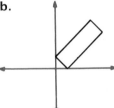 c.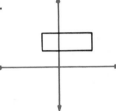

2. An equilateral triangle

a. 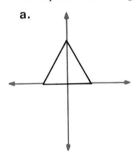 b. 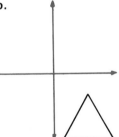 c.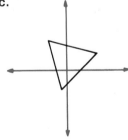

3. An isosceles triangle

a. 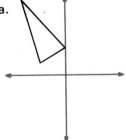 b. 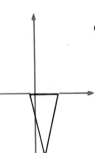 c.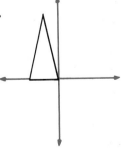

4. A trapezoid

a.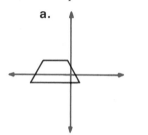

b.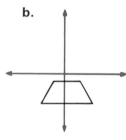

c.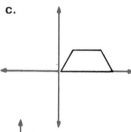

Axes are placed on square *ABCD* as shown.

5. *A* is pt. (?, ?). If *B* is taken as pt. (k, 0), then *D* is pt. (0, ?) and *C* is pt. (?, ?).

6. If *D* is taken as pt. (0, $2n$), then *B* is pt. (?, 0) and *C* is pt. (?, ?).

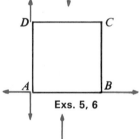

Exs. 5, 6

Axes are placed on rectangle *RSTQ* so that the x-axis contains $\overline{RS}$ and the y-axis bisects $\overline{RS}$.

7. If *T* has coordinates (a, b), then *S* is pt. (?, ?), *Q* is pt. (?, ?), and *R* is pt. (?, ?).

8. If *Q* has coordinates ($-6k$, j), then *T* is pt. (?, ?), *R* is pt. (?, ?), and *S* is pt. (?, ?).

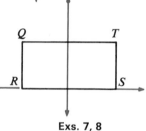

Exs. 7, 8

WRITTEN EXERCISES

Draw a graph using the information given. Then answer the questions.

EXAMPLE. The x-axis contains the base of an equilateral triangle *ABC*, with the origin at *B*. Vertex *C* has coordinates ($2f$, 0) and the y-coordinate of *A* is g, with $g > 0$.

    a. Find the x-coordinate of *A*.

    b. What relation exists between f and g?

Solution: **a.** The x-coordinate of *A* is f, since
$$\tfrac{1}{2}BC = \tfrac{1}{2} \cdot 2f = f.$$

    b. Since $AB = BC$,
$$\sqrt{f^2 + g^2} = 2f,$$
$$f^2 + g^2 = 4f^2,$$
and $g = f\sqrt{3}$.

1. Coordinate axes contain two sides of a rectangle. If pts. $(0, a)$, $(0, 0)$, and $(b, 0)$ are three vertices, give the coordinates of the fourth vertex.

2. The x-axis contains the base of a square with the origin at the midpoint of the base. If the lower right vertex has coordinates $(k, 0)$, what are the coordinates of the remaining three vertices?

3. The lower base of a trapezoid is contained in the x-axis and has endpoints $(0, 0)$ and $(a, 0)$. One endpoint of the upper base is pt. (c, d). What is the y-coordinate of the fourth vertex?

4. The lower base of a trapezoid is contained in the x-axis with the origin located at the midpoint of the base. If one endpoint of the base is pt. $(e, 0)$, what is the other endpoint? If one endpoint of the upper base is pt. (f, g), is the other endpoint necessarily pt. $(-f, g)$?

5. The x-axis is located parallel to the base of an isosceles triangle, with the y-axis passing through an endpoint of the base. If the endpoints of the base are pts. $(0, j)$ and $(4n, j)$, what is the x-coordinate of the vertex of the isosceles triangle?

6. The base of an isosceles triangle is a vertical segment parallel to the y-axis, and the x-axis does not intersect the triangle. If the lower endpoint of the base is labeled $(10c, 4d)$, what is the x-coordinate of the upper endpoint of the base? If the y-coordinate of the upper endpoint is $6d$, what is the y-coordinate of the vertex of the isosceles triangle?

7. The line containing the base of a parallelogram is taken as the x-axis, and the origin is located at the left endpoint of that base. Three consecutive vertices are pts. (b, c), $(0, 0)$, and $(a, 0)$, where $b > 0$.
   a. What is the y-coordinate of the fourth vertex?
   b. How many units to the right of the y-axis is the point (b, c)?
   c. How many units to the right of a vertical line through pt. $(a, 0)$ must the fourth vertex lie?
   d. What, in terms of a and b, is the x-coordinate of the fourth vertex?

8. The lower base of an isosceles trapezoid is located on the x-axis with the left endpoint at the origin. Three consecutive vertices are pts. (b, c), $(0, 0)$, and $(a, 0)$, where $b > 0$.
   a. What is the y-coordinate of the fourth vertex?
   b. How many units to the right of the y-axis is vertex (b, c)?
   c. How many units to the left of a vertical line through pt. $(a, 0)$ must the fourth vertex lie?
   d. What, in terms of a and b, is the x-coordinate of the fourth vertex?

C

9. Using no geometric properties of a parallelogram other than those given by the definition, prove the following:

A parallelogram with consecutive vertices (f, g), $(0, 0)$, and $(e, 0)$ has pt. $(e + f, g)$ as its fourth vertex.

10. Prove that an isosceles trapezoid with consecutive vertices (f, g), $(0, 0)$, and $(e, 0)$, and with the segment joining $(0, 0)$ and $(e, 0)$ as its lower base, has pt. $(e - f, g)$ as its fourth vertex.

13–2 Parallel and Perpendicular Lines

In Chapter 12, two theorems about slopes of lines were established:

Two nonvertical lines are parallel if and only if they have equal slopes.
Two nonvertical lines are perpendicular if and only if the slope of one line is the negative reciprocal of the slope of the other.

These theorems can be used to prove that lines are parallel or perpendicular in a coordinate system. Furthermore, they can be used to prove theorems introduced earlier in the book, before coordinate methods were available.

ORAL EXERCISES

1. Given line l with slope $\frac{2}{5}$, line j with slope 0.4, and line k with slope $-\frac{5}{2}$. What can you conclude (a) about lines l and j? (b) about lines l and k? (c) about lines j and k?

2. Is it possible for two lines with negative slopes to be perpendicular to each other? parallel to each other?

3. What is the slope of a line containing pts. $(-2, 0)$ and $(3, 6)$?

4. Line l contains point $(2, 4)$ and has slope $\frac{3}{1}$. Point P lies on l and has x-coordinate 3. What is the y-coordinate of P?

WRITTEN EXERCISES

Consider the figure that consists of all lines containing pairs of the points named. Prove that the figure contains two parallel lines.

EXAMPLE. $A(2, -1)$, $B(3, 4)$, $C(3, 0)$, and $D(4, 5)$.

Proof: The slope of $\overleftrightarrow{AB}$ is $\dfrac{4 - (-1)}{3 - 2} = \dfrac{5}{1}$.

The slope of $\overleftrightarrow{CD}$ is $\dfrac{5-0}{4-3} = \dfrac{5}{1}$.

$\overleftrightarrow{AB}$ and $\overleftrightarrow{CD}$ are not the same line, for the slope of $\overleftrightarrow{AD}$ is

$\dfrac{5-(-1)}{4-2}$, or $\dfrac{6}{2}$, or $\dfrac{3}{1}$. Observe that $\dfrac{3}{1} \neq \dfrac{5}{1}$.

$\overleftrightarrow{AB} \parallel \overleftrightarrow{CD}$, because the lines have equal slopes.

1. $E(-1, 3)$, $F(2, 1)$, $G(0, 0)$, and $H(4, -5)$.
2. $A(5, 5)$, $B(0, 0)$, $C(-3, 1)$, and $D(6, 3)$.
3. $A(0, 0)$, $B(0, h)$, $C(h, h)$, and $D(k, 0)$.
4. $A(5, 6)$, $B(-1, 1)$, $C(4, 0)$, $D(1, 2)$, $E(0, -2)$.

Consider the figure that consists of all lines containing pairs of the points named. Prove that the figure contains two perpendicular lines.

5. $A(0, 0)$, $B(6, 2)$, and $C(1, -3)$.
6. $A(2, 1)$, $B(-3, -4)$, and $C(5, -2)$.
7. $E(-4, 5)$, $F(-5, 5)$, $G(0, 6)$, and $H(-2, 3)$.
8. $E(0, 5)$, $F(-2, -2)$, $G(9, -5)$, $H(1, 6)$, and $K(12, -6)$.

EXAMPLE. Prove: In a plane, two lines perpendicular to the same line are parallel to each other.

Proof: 1. Let r and s be the given lines both perpendicular to line t.
2. Choose axes so that neither of them is parallel to r, s, or t.
3. Let m be the slope of t. $(m \neq 0)$.
4. Then r and s must each have slope $-\dfrac{1}{m}$, since the slope of any line perpendicular to t must be the negative reciprocal of the slope of t.
5. Therefore $r \parallel s$, since lines having equal slopes are $\parallel$.

9. Prove: In a plane, two lines parallel to the same line are parallel to each other.
10. Prove: A line lying in the plane of two parallel lines and perpendicular to one of them is perpendicular to the other.

EXAMPLE. Given: Line $r \parallel$ line s; r contains pt. (a, b); s contains pts. $(0, 0)$ and (c, d); pt. P lies on r and has x-coordinate e.

Prove: Pt. P has y-coordinate

$$b + \frac{d}{c}(e - a).$$

Proof: Let v denote the y-coordinate of P. Since $r \parallel s$, the lines have equal slopes: $\dfrac{v - b}{e - a} = \dfrac{d - 0}{c - 0}$. Hence, $v = b + \dfrac{d}{c}(e - a)$.

11. Given: Line $q \parallel$ line s; q contains pt. $(a, 0)$; s contains pts. $(0, 0)$ and (c, d); pt. P lies on q and has x-coordinate j.

Prove: Pt. P has y-coordinate $\dfrac{d}{c}(j - a)$.

12. Given: Line r containing point (a, b) is perpendicular to a line with slope $\dfrac{e}{f}$; pt. P lies on r and has y-coordinate g.

Prove: Pt. P has x-coordinate $\dfrac{af + be - eg}{f}$.

C   **13.** Prove: The vertices of all right angles with one side through pt. $(a, 0)$ and the other side through pt. $(-a, 0)$ lie on a circle.

14. Given: Q and R are the points in which the circle $x^2 + y^2 = a^2$ $(a > 0)$ intersects the x-axis; P is any other point on the circle. Prove: $\overline{PQ} \perp \overline{PR}$.

13–3   Distances

Midpoint problems and distance problems are closely related. Often there are two or more methods of approaching problems dealing with midpoints. Suppose, for example, that four points A, B, Q, and T are arranged as shown, with coordinates known, and you wish to prove that $\overline{AB}$ and $\overline{TQ}$ bisect each other.

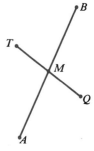

Method I: **1.** Write the equations of $\overleftrightarrow{AB}$ and $\overleftrightarrow{TQ}$.

2. Determine the coordinates of M by solving the pair of equations found in (1).

3. Use the distance formula to compute AM, MB, QM, and MT. Show that $AM = MB$ and $QM = MT$.

Method II: **1.** Find the coordinates of the midpoint of $\overline{AB}$.

2. Find the coordinates of the midpoint of $\overline{TQ}$.

3. Establish the fact that the two midpoints are the same, thereby showing that $\overline{AB}$ and $\overline{TQ}$ bisect each other.

Other points of division of a segment are also closely related to the idea of distance. Consider, for example, the **points of trisection** of $\overline{RS}$, whose endpoints are pts. (a, b) and (c, d) as shown. Points M and N are said to **trisect** $\overline{RS}$ in the figure if $RM = MN = NS$.

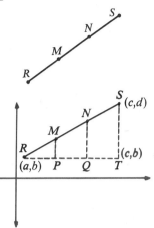

Draw the horizontal and vertical segments shown. Since $RM = \frac{1}{3}RS$, $RP = \frac{1}{3}RT = \frac{1}{3}(c - a)$. The x-coordinate of P is $a + \frac{1}{3}(c - a)$, or $\dfrac{2a + c}{3}$.

The x-coordinate of Q is $a + \frac{2}{3}(c - a)$, or $\dfrac{a + 2c}{3}$. Hence the x-coordinates of M and N are $\dfrac{2a + c}{3}$ and $\dfrac{a + 2c}{3}$ respectively. You should be able to use a similar method to show that the y-coordinates of M and N are $\dfrac{2b + d}{3}$ and $\dfrac{b + 2d}{3}$, respectively.

You can prove many distance relationships by applying the distance formula directly.

EXAMPLE. Prove that any point which is equidistant from the ends of a segment lies on the perpendicular bisector of the segment.

Proof: 1. Choose a coordinate system so that the x-axis contains the given segment $\overline{RS}$ and the y-axis is the perpendicular bisector of $\overline{RS}$.

2. Let S have coordinates $(a, 0)$. Then R must have coordinates $(-a, 0)$.

3. Let P, with coordinates (c, d), be any point equidistant from R and S.

4. Since $PR = PS$, $\sqrt{(c + a)^2 + d^2} = \sqrt{(c - a)^2 + d^2}$

$c^2 + 2ac + a^2 + d^2 = c^2 - 2ac + a^2 + d^2$, or $4ac = 0$.

5. But $a \neq 0$, since the midpoint of $\overline{RS}$ is pt. $(0, 0)$. Therefore $c = 0$, and point P must lie on the y-axis, the perpendicular bisector of $\overline{RS}$.

ORAL
EXERCISES

Points *B* and *C* are points of trisection of $\overline{AD}$.
Vertical and horizontal segments are drawn
as shown.

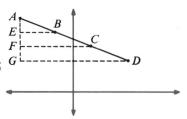

1. What three segments contained in $\overline{AD}$
must have equal lengths?
What fractional part of *AD* is *AB*?

2. What fractional part of *AG* is *AE*?
AF?

Exs. 1, 2

Circle O trisects $\overline{HK}$. *H* is pt. (0, 3).

3. The *x*-coordinate of *I* is 2. What is the
x-coordinate of *J*? of *K*?

4. The *y*-coordinate of *K* is 6. What is the
y-coordinate of *I*? of *J*?

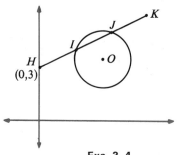

Exs. 3, 4

In the adjoining figure a coordinate system
has been chosen so that the x-axis is parallel
to $\overline{RS}$. It is given that $\overline{PQ}$ is the perpendicular
bisector of $\overline{RS}$.

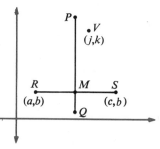

5. What is the *y*-coordinate of point *M*?
the *x*-coordinate of *M*?

6. What is the equation of $\overleftrightarrow{PQ}$? What
can you say about $\overleftrightarrow{PQ}$ with respect to
the *y*-axis?

Exs. 5–8

7. It is given that $VR = VS$. Complete this statement:

$$\sqrt{(j - a)^2 + (k - b)^2} = \sqrt{(? - ?)^2 + (? - ?)^2}.$$

8. To prove that *V* lies on $\overleftrightarrow{PQ}$, you need only show that $j = \underline{\ ?\ }$.

9. Explain how it is possible for two segments to have the same midpoint
without being bisectors of each other.

WRITTEN EXERCISES

In Exercises 1 and 2, points R, S, T, and Q are given. Prove that $\overline{RS}$ and $\overline{TQ}$ bisect each other.

A   **1.** $R(-1, -1)$, $S(4, 4)$, $T(5, 1)$, and $Q(-2, 2)$.

       2. $R(0, 0)$, $S(2a, 2b)$, $T(2c, 2b - 2d)$, and $Q(2a - 2c, 2d)$.

In Exercises 3–6, introduce a coordinate system and prove the conclusion stated. Be sure to make a figure illustrating the placement of axes. In your proof describe the location of axes.

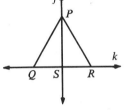

3. Given that line $j \perp$ line k, point P is on j, and $PQ = PR$ in the figure shown. Prove that $QS = RS$.

4. In the figure shown it is given that line $j \perp$ line k, P is a point on j, and k contains points Q and R, with $QS = RS$. Prove that $PQ = PR$.

                                                     Exs. 3, 4

B   **5.** Prove: If line g is perpendicular to line h at point M, and unequal segments are drawn to h from any point on g, then these segments intersect h at points which are unequally distant from M.

       6. State and prove the converse of the statement made in Ex. 5.

Axes are placed, with respect to $\overline{RS}$, in the manner shown.

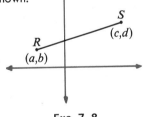

7. Show that the y-coordinates of the points of trisection of $\overline{RS}$ are $\dfrac{2b + d}{3}$ and $\dfrac{b + 2d}{3}$.

8. Observe that a is a negative number in this exercise. Show that the x-coordinates of the trisection points are $\dfrac{2a + c}{3}$ and $\dfrac{a + 2c}{3}$.

                                                 Exs. 7, 8

C   **9.** Prove that every point located so that the sum of the squares of its distances from the points $(a, 0)$ and $(-a, 0)$ is a given number k, lies on a circle of radius $\sqrt{\dfrac{k}{2} - a^2}$.

   10. Develop a formula for the coordinates of a point that divides the segment joining pts. (g, h) and (j, k) into parts having the ratio $r:s$.

▪ Proofs of Properties of Polygons

13-4   Triangles

You can use the distance formula and the properties of parallel and perpendicular lines to prove facts about triangles and other polygons. Choose your coordinate systems in such a way that your algebraic work will be simple and direct.

EXAMPLE. Prove that the segment joining the midpoints of two sides of a triangle is parallel to the third side.

Proof: Given $\triangle ABC$ with R and S the midpoints of $\overline{AC}$ and $\overline{BC}$ respectively. Let the line containing $\overline{AB}$ be the x-axis, let the perpendicular from C to $\overline{AB}$ be the y-axis, and let the coordinates of points A, B, and C be as shown in the figure.

By the midpoint formula, R is the point (m, q) and S is the point (p, q).

The slope of $\overline{RS}$ is $\dfrac{q - q}{p - m} = 0$.

The slope of $\overline{AB}$ is 0.
Therefore $\overline{RS} \parallel \overline{AB}$.

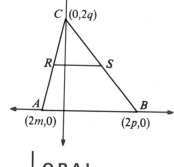

ORAL
EXERCISES

In the figure shown, points R, S, and T are the midpoints of $\overline{AC}$, $\overline{BC}$, and $\overline{AB}$ respectively.

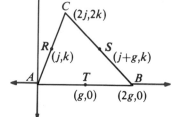

1. What is the difference of the y-coordinates of R and S?

2. What is the slope of $\overline{RS}$?

3. What is the slope of $\overline{AB}$?

4. Since $\overline{RS}$ and $\overline{AB}$ have __?__ slopes, $\overline{RS}$ __?__ $\overline{AB}$.

5. What is the difference of the y-coordinates of S and T? the difference of the x-coordinates?

6. What is the slope of $\overline{TS}$? of $\overline{AC}$?

7. What is the length of $\overline{RS}$? of $\overline{AB}$?

8. What is the length of $\overline{TS}$?

9. $AC = \sqrt{4j^2 + 4k^2}$, or $\sqrt{4(j^2 + k^2)}$. In simplified radical form, $AC = ?\sqrt{\ ?}$

10. How does AC compare with TS?

| WRITTEN
| EXERCISES

Begin each proof by telling how you place the coordinate axes.

A   **1.** Prove: The length of the segment joining the midpoints of two sides of a triangle is equal to half the length of the third side.

2. Prove: The midpoint of the hypotenuse of a right triangle is equidistant from the three vertices.

B   **3.** Prove: In an isosceles triangle, two medians are congruent.

4. Prove: In an equilateral triangle, the three medians are congruent.

5. Prove: The union of the three segments joining, in pairs, the midpoints of the sides of an isosceles triangle is an isosceles triangle.

6. Prove: The union of the three segments joining, in pairs, the midpoints of the sides of an equilateral triangle is an equilateral triangle.

C   **7.** Prove: The medians of a triangle meet in a point, and this point separates each median into segments whose lengths have the ratio 1:2.

8. Prove: The lines containing the altitudes of a triangle meet in a point.

13–5   Parallelograms

When you introduce a coordinate system in an exercise for a parallelogram, you will be able to work most efficiently with coordinate axes located as shown in the adjacent figure. Following is a proof that the fourth vertex T of parallelogram $QRST$ has the coordinates $(a + b, c)$. You may use this fact in your work without proving it each time.

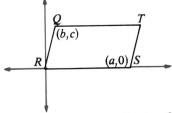

1. $\overline{QT}$ and $\overline{RS}$ are $\parallel$ and have slope 0. Therefore the y-coordinate of T is equal to that of Q. The y-coordinate of T is c.

2. Let w be the x-coordinate of T. The slope of $\overline{ST} = \dfrac{c - 0}{w - a}$.

3. The slope of $\overline{RQ}$ is $\dfrac{c}{b}$.

4. Since $\overline{RQ} \parallel \overline{ST}$, the slopes of the segments are equal. $\dfrac{c}{b} = \dfrac{c - 0}{w - a}$.

5. Therefore, $cw - ac = bc$ and, since $c \neq 0$, $w = a + b$.

ORAL
EXERCISES

Vertices J, K, and L of parallelogram JKLM have the coordinates shown.

1. What is the slope of $\overline{KJ}$? of $\overline{LM}$?
2. What are the coordinates of vertex M?
3. What are the coordinates of the midpoint of $\overline{KM}$? of $\overline{JL}$?
4. Since the midpoint of $\overline{KM}$ is the same as the midpoint of $\overline{JL}$, $\overline{JL}$ and $\overline{KM}$ __?__ each other.

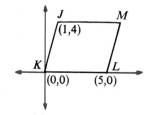

Vertices U, V, and W of parallelogram UVWZ have the coordinates shown.

5. Which, if any, of these numbers are negative? $e,\ f,\ g,\ e + f.$
6. What are the coordinates of vertex Z?

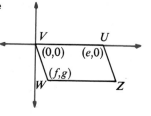

Vertices Q, R, and S of parallelogram QRST have the coordinates shown.

7. What is the y-coordinate of vertex T?
8. Is the x-coordinate of T greater than, equal to, or less than j for the figure shown?
9. For the figure shown, which of the following is true?
$$k + j = j \quad k + j > j \quad k + j < j$$

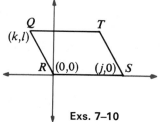

Exs. 7–10

10. According to the idea developed on page 495, the x-coordinate of T should be $k + j$. Does this seem reasonable?

WRITTEN
EXERCISES

Begin each proof by telling how you place the coordinate axes.

A   **1.** Prove: The opposite sides of a parallelogram are congruent.

    2. Prove: The diagonals of a parallelogram bisect each other. (*Hint:* Show that the midpoints of the diagonals are the same point.)

    3. Prove: The diagonals of a rectangle are congruent.

    4. Prove: If the diagonals of a quadrilateral bisect each other, the quadrilateral is a parallelogram.

B   **5.** Prove: The diagonals of a rhombus are perpendicular. (*Hint:* $RS = QR$. Express the x-coordinate of S in terms of b and c. Then use your knowledge of parallelograms to express the x-coordinate of T.)

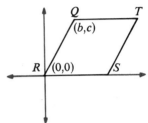

    6. Prove: If the diagonals of a parallelogram are perpendicular, the parallelogram is a rhombus.

C   **7.** Prove: If two sides of a quadrilateral are congruent and parallel, the quadrilateral is a parallelogram.

    8. In the parallelogram shown, U and V are the midpoints of $\overline{QT}$ and $\overline{RS}$ respectively. Prove that $\overline{QV}$ and $\overline{US}$ are parallel segments and that they trisect $\overline{RT}$.

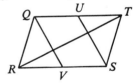

13–6   Trapezoids and General Quadrilaterals

Given a quadrilateral, you can choose your coordinate axes in such a way that the x-axis contains one side of the quadrilateral and the origin is an endpoint of that side.

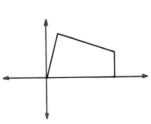
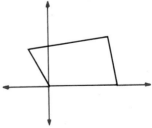

When a given quadrilateral is a trapezoid, you will want the x-axis to contain one base of the trapezoid, as shown in the figure. Sometimes you may wish to take the midpoint of $\overline{RS}$ as the origin. Usually, however, you will take R as the origin. When points Q, R, and S have the coordinates shown, the y-coordinate of point T must be c. For a general trapezoid, the x-coordinate of T cannot be expressed in terms of a and b.

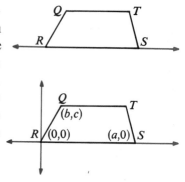

EXAMPLE. Prove: The diagonals of an isosceles trapezoid are congruent.

Proof: 1. Let $\overline{QR}$ and $\overline{TS}$ be congruent legs in trapezoid $QRST$.

2. Choose coordinate axes and label coordinates as shown.

3. Use the fact that $TS = QR$ and solve for u in terms of a and b.
$$\sqrt{(u-a)^2 + c^2} = \sqrt{b^2 + c^2}$$
$$(u-a)^2 + c^2 = b^2 + c^2$$
$$(u-a)^2 - b^2 = 0$$
$$[(u-a) + b][(u-a) - b] = 0$$
Then $u = a - b$, or $u = a + b$.
But $u \neq a + b$, since the figure is not a parallelogram.
Therefore $u = a - b$.

4. $RT = \sqrt{u^2 + c^2}$ $QS = \sqrt{(a-b)^2 + (0-c)^2}$
   $RT = \sqrt{(a-b)^2 + c^2}$ $QS = \sqrt{(a-b)^2 + c^2}$

5. Therefore the diagonals of the trapezoid are congruent.

ORAL EXERCISES

In the trapezoid shown, $\overline{QT} \parallel \overline{RS}$, and vertices have the coordinates shown.

1. What are the coordinates of the midpoint of $\overline{RS}$? of $\overline{QT}$?

2. Do the midpoints of $\overline{QT}$ and $\overline{RS}$ lie on a line parallel to the y-axis?

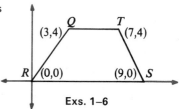

Exs. 1–6

3. What are the coordinates of the midpoint of $\overline{RQ}$? of $\overline{ST}$?

4. Is the midpoint of $\overline{RQ}$ the same distance from the x-axis as is the midpoint of $\overline{ST}$?

5. What are the coordinates of the midpoint of $\overline{RT}$? of $\overline{QS}$?

6. Are the midpoints of $\overline{RT}$ and $\overline{QS}$ the same point? Do the diagonals of trapezoid $QRST$ bisect each other?

Coordinate axes have been placed on an isosceles trapezoid and coordinates assigned to the vertices as shown.

7. Which of the following numbers are positive for the figure shown?

$a, \quad -a, \quad b, \quad c, \quad d$

8. Suppose that $d = 5$. Then it seems likely that $b = \underline{\quad?\quad}$.

9. Suppose that $b = -11$. Then it seems likely that $d = \underline{\quad?\quad}$.

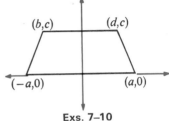

Exs. 7–10

10. For the isosceles trapezoid shown, it can be proved that $b = -d$. Complete this first step of a proof:

$$\sqrt{(b - (-a))^2 + (? - ?)^2} = \sqrt{(d - ?)^2 + (c - 0)^2}$$

WRITTEN EXERCISES

A

1. Prove: The segments joining the midpoints of the opposite sides of a quadrilateral bisect each other.

2. Prove: The segment joining the midpoints of the diagonals of a trapezoid is parallel to the bases.

B

3. Prove: The length of the segment joining the midpoints of the diagonals of a trapezoid is equal to half the difference of the lengths of the bases.

4. Prove: If a line parallel to the bases of a trapezoid bisects one leg, it bisects the other leg also.

C

5. Prove: The union of the segments joining, in order, the midpoints of the sides of an isosceles trapezoid is a rhombus.

6. Given: The union of the segments joining, in order, the midpoints of the sides of a particular trapezoid is a square; three consecutive vertices of the trapezoid are pts. $(2b, 2c)$, $(0, 0)$, and $(2a, 0)$. Prove: The length of the altitude of the trapezoid is $2a - 2b$.

CHAPTER SUMMARY

Inventory of Structure and Methods

1. When you are given a figure in which numerical coordinates have been assigned to certain points, the position of the coordinate axes is determined. When you are given a figure, but no numerical coordinates of points, you can select your own placement of coordinate axes.

2. By introducing axes and assigning coordinates to points, you can use algebra to prove conclusions about geometric figures. The most advantageous placement of axes depends upon the given figure and the conclusion to be proved. The following facts concerning the coordinates of the vertices of certain special polygons are useful.

   a. If the x-axis contains the base of an isosceles triangle, and one endpoint of the base is pt. $(0, 0)$, and the vertex is called pt. (a, b), then the third vertex is pt. $(2a, 0)$.

   b. If three consecutive vertices of a parallelogram are pts. (b, c), $(0, 0)$, and $(a, 0)$, then the fourth vertex is pt. $(a + b, c)$.

   c. If the x-axis contains the longer base of an isosceles trapezoid and three consecutive vertices are pts. (b, c), $(0, 0)$, and $(a, 0)$, then the fourth vertex is pt. $(a - b, c)$.

3. Many plane geometry theorems can be proved by coordinate geometry. In developing proofs you often apply the distance formula, the midpoint formula, and the slope properties of parallel and perpendicular lines.

Vocabulary and Spelling

points of trisection (*p. 491*)   trisect (*p. 491*)

CHAPTER TEST

13–1 Coordinate axes have been placed on triangle *DEF* as shown. *DE = DF.*

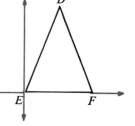

1. Prove: If *D* is the point $(2, 5)$, then the x-coordinate of *F* is 4.

2. Prove: If *F* is the point $(2n, 0)$, then the x-coordinate of *D* is n.

13–2 A figure consists of segments $\overline{AB}$, $\overline{BC}$, $\overline{CD}$, $\overline{DE}$, and $\overline{EA}$. Given points are: $A(5, 2)$, $B(3, 2)$, $C(0, 0)$, $D(2, -3)$, and $E(6, -3)$.

3. Prove that the figure contains two parallel segments.

4. Prove that the figure contains two perpendicular segments.

13–3 The vertices of triangle *DEF* are given: $D(3, 2)$, $E(-1, -1)$, and $F(4, -1)$.

    5. Prove that $DE = FE$.

    6. Prove that $DE > DF$.

    7. The coordinates of the midpoint of $\overline{DF}$ are ___?___.

    8. The coordinates of *G*, given that points *G* and *H* trisect $\overline{ED}$, with $EG = GH = HD$, are ___?___.

13–4 **9.** Prove: A line bisecting one side of a triangle and parallel to a second side bisects the third side. (Use the given figure and the indicated placement of axes.)

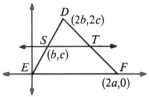

13–5 **10.** Prove: If the lengths of the diagonals of a parallelogram are equal, the parallelogram is a rectangle. (*Hint:* Label the coordinates of *T*. Substitute in the equation $RT = QS$ and prove that *b* must be 0.)

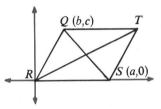

13–6 **11.** Prove: The median of a trapezoid is parallel to the bases of the trapezoid.

    12. Prove: The union of the segments joining, in order, the midpoints of the sides of any quadrilateral is a parallelogram.

[C] **13.** Prove: The perpendicular bisectors of the sides of any triangle meet in a point. (*Hint:* Explain how to place coordinate axes in the manner suggested by this figure. Find the equations of the perpendicular bisectors of $\overline{RQ}$ and $\overline{QS}$.)

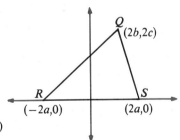

CHAPTER REVIEW

13–1 **Placing Coordinate Axes**   *Pages 483–488*

    1. Draw a sketch showing a nonadvantageous placement of coordinate axes with respect to a parallelogram.

    2. Draw two sketches showing two different advantageous placements of coordinate axes with respect to an isosceles trapezoid.

In isosceles triangle JKM, JK = JM. Coordinate axes have been drawn so that the x-axis is parallel to $\overline{KM}$ and the y-axis contains point K.

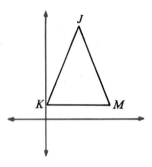

3. Prove: If K has coordinates $(0, t)$, then the y-coordinate of M is t.

4. Prove: If K is pt. $(0, 2)$ and M is pt. $(8, 2)$, then the x-coordinate of J is 4.

13–2 Parallel and Perpendicular Lines
Pages 488–490

5. The slope of line l is $\frac{2}{3}$. State the slope of any segment contained in l; any line parallel to l; any line perpendicular to l.

6. The slope of line j is $\frac{2}{5}$ and that of line k is $\frac{4}{7}$. Tell how you know that j and k are neither parallel nor perpendicular.

A figure consists of lines containing pairs of the points named: $R(0, 0)$, $S(1, -2)$, $T(5, 0)$, and $Q(2, 1)$.

7. Prove that the figure contains two parallel lines.

8. Prove that the figure contains two perpendicular lines.

13–3 Distances
Pages 490–493

9. One way to prove that $\overline{GH}$ and $\overline{JK}$ bisect each other is to find their point M of intersection and then prove that $GM = \underline{}$ and that $\underline{} = \underline{}$.

10. A second way to prove that $\overline{GH}$ and $\overline{JK}$ bisect each other is to prove that the midpoint of $\overline{GH}$ and the midpoint of $\overline{JK}$ are the $\underline{}$ point.

Given quadrilateral $ABCD$: $A(2, 7)$, $B(0, 2)$, $C(0, 1)$, and $D(3, 1)$.

11. Prove that a particular side of quadrilateral $ABCD$ is three times as long as some other side.

12. Prove that one diagonal of quadrilateral $ABCD$ is twice as long as the other diagonal.

13–4 Triangles
Pages 494–495

The vertices of triangle ABC are $A(8, 7)$, $B(-6, -7)$, and $C(10, 1)$. Let D be the midpoint of $\overline{AB}$ and E the midpoint of $\overline{BC}$.

13. Point D is the point $(?, ?)$. Point E is the point $(?, ?)$.

14. Prove that $AC = 2 \cdot DE$.

15. Prove that $(AB)^2 > (BC)^2 + (AC)^2$.

16. Prove that $P(0, 1)$, is equidistant from the three vertices of the triangle.

13–5   Parallelograms   *Pages 495–497*

Quadrilateral EFGH is a parallelogram with three consecutive vertices E(2, 3), F(0, 0), and G(6, 0).

17. Vertex H is the point (?, ?).

18. Prove that the diagonals of $\square EFGH$ bisect each other.

19. Prove that the diagonals of $\square EFGH$ are not perpendicular to each other.

20. Prove that $GE < FH$.

13–6   Trapezoids and General Quadrilaterals   *Pages 497–499*

21. Three consecutive vertices of a trapezoid are points (1, 6), (0, 0), and (10,0). One base joins pts. (0, 0) and (10, 0). The y-coordinate of the fourth vertex of the trapezoid is __?__.

22. The x-axis contains one base of an isosceles trapezoid. Three consecutive vertices of the trapezoid are pts. (j, k), (0, 0), and (g, 0). Find the coordinates of the fourth vertex.

23. Prove: The length of the median of a trapezoid is equal to half the sum of the lengths of the bases.

24. Prove: If the lengths of the diagonals of a trapezoid are equal, the trapezoid is isosceles.

• EXTRA FOR EXPERTS

Vectors

By now you are accustomed to thinking of ordered pairs of real numbers as points in the coordinate plane. It may surprise you to learn that it is often convenient to assign other interpretations to ordered pairs of real numbers. One such interpretation is vectors.

A **vector** is defined to be an ordered pair of real numbers. Thus, (4, 3) is a vector that can be represented as a dot in the plane (Fig. 1). Such a representation can lead to confusion when vectors are added, since it is difficult to conceive of adding points. Hence it is convenient to use arrows rather than dots to picture vectors.

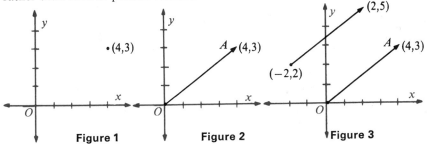

Figure 1   Figure 2   Figure 3

In Figure 2 the arrow from O to point A represents vector OA (designated by $\overrightarrow{OA}$). $\overrightarrow{OA}$ in this case represents the vector (4, 3) and is described as having **initial point** O and **terminal point** A.

In some cases it is desirable to represent a vector by an arrow whose initial point is some point other than the origin. Such a vector is equivalent to a vector whose initial point is at the origin, if the arrows representing these vectors are parallel, have equal lengths, and point in the same direction. Thus, in Figure 3, the vector with initial point $(-2, 2)$ and terminal point $(2, 5)$ is equivalent to vector $\overrightarrow{OA}$. You can think of moving the arrow representing vector $\overrightarrow{OA}$ to the position of the other arrow shown. Initial point O moves 2 units to the left and 2 units up. Terminal point A moves 2 units to the left and 2 units up. Similarly, every other point on the arrow representing $\overrightarrow{OA}$ moves 2 units to the left and 2 units up.

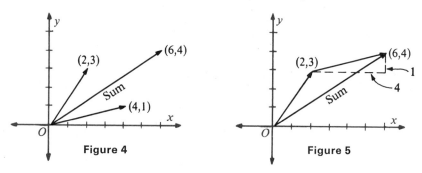

Figure 4   **Figure 5**

The **sum of two vectors** (r, s) and (t, q) is defined to be the vector $(r + t, s + q)$. For example, the sum of vectors (2, 3) and (4, 1) is vector (6, 4). In Figure 4 the vectors (2, 3), (4, 1), and (6, 4) are all pictured with their initial points at the origin.

Two vectors can be added geometrically. To find the sum of vectors (2, 3) and (4, 1) geometrically, you first represent vector (2, 3) by an arrow whose initial point is the origin. Then, taking point (2, 3) as your initial point (see Figure 5), you represent the vector (4, 1) by moving four units to the right and one unit up. The terminal point of this last vector is (6, 4), which is also the terminal point of the sum. The arrow from the origin to the terminal point (6, 4) represents the sum of the vectors (2, 3) and (4, 1).

For nonparallel vectors, another way to add them geometrically is by completing a parallelogram. To add vectors (2, 3) and (4, 1) by this method you represent both vectors by arrows with initial points at the origin, and then complete a parallelogram. The arrow from the origin to the opposite vertex of the parallelogram represents the sum, as shown in Figure 6.

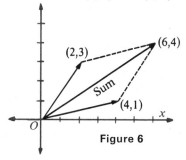

Figure 6

EXERCISES

1. Use coordinate axes and draw arrows to represent the following vectors.

   (3, 1)   (2, −2)   (5, 0)   (0, −4)   (−4, −2)

2. Represent (−2, 2) by an arrow with its initial point at the origin. Represent a vector equivalent to (−2, 2) by drawing an arrow whose initial point is the point (3, 0); whose initial point is the point (0, −4).

3. Use the definition of the sum of two vectors to find the following sums.

   a. (2, 3) + (4, 1)   **e.** (a, 0) + (0, b)
   b. (4, 1) + (2, 3)   **f.** (0, b) + (a, 0)
   c. (−1, 0) + (3, −4)   **g.** (r, s) + (t, q)
   d. (3, −4) + (−1, 0)   **h.** (t, q) + (r, s)

4. Use coordinate axes and a geometric drawing to represent the following sums.

   a. (2, 3) + (4, 1)   **c.** (2, 0) + (0, −4)
   b. (−1, 0) + (3, −4)   **d.** (1, 3) + (1, 3)

5. You see from Exercise 3 that vector addition is commutative. Show that vector addition is also associative.

6. The difference of vectors (g, h) and (j, k) is defined to be the sum (g, h) + (−j, −k). Show that vector subtraction is not commutative.

Applications of Vectors

Sometimes a vector is described informally as a quantity having both magnitude and direction. The *magnitude* of a vector (x, y) is the number $\sqrt{x^2 + y^2}$, the length of the arrow in its graphical representation. A meaningful illustration of a vector in this sense is one used in reporting wind velocity. A typical weather report might read: Wind velocity: N E, 10 m.p.h. With information provided in this form, you can draw a diagram using coordinate axes as shown. You are in reality translating the original information into the form of an ordered pair of real numbers $(-5\sqrt{2}, -5\sqrt{2})$. Can you see that the magnitude of the vector $(-5\sqrt{2}, -5\sqrt{2})$ is 10?

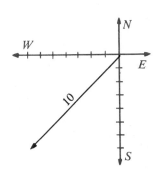

When a physicist works with vectors he uses the word **resultant** instead of the word sum. He can determine approximate resultants by drawing graphs, and more exact resultants by employing trigonometry. Experiments show that the single *resultant* has the same effect as the sum of the individual vectors.

EXAMPLE 1. A man walks three miles northeast and two miles directly
north. What is his final position with respect to his starting
point?

Solution: Draw a set of axes and select a
unit of a size sufficient for an
accurate representation of 2 miles
and 3 miles. Use a ruler to measure
distances and a protractor to measure angles. In the figure shown,
$\overrightarrow{OA}$ is the resultant. The final position is approximately 4.6 miles
from the starting point in the
direction 27° east of north.

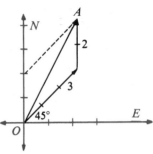

EXAMPLE 2. At the altitude at which an airplane is flying, there is a steady
wind of 120 m.p.h. coming from 30° west of north. Instru-
ments show the pilot that the airplane is moving at 400
m.p.h. and is heading due west in relation to the air. What
is the airplane's speed with respect to the ground?

Solution: The airplane is moving at
400 m.p.h. through a mass of
air, which is itself moving. We
get a resultant graphically. The
speed x of the plane with
respect to the ground is the
magnitude of the resultant,
approximately 350 or 360
m.p.h.

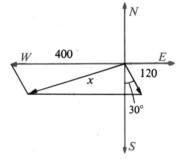

EXAMPLE 3. A force of 70 pounds acts on an object. An 80-pound force
acts on the same object, at a right angle to the 70-pound
force. What single force,
applied in what direction,
is sufficient to counteract
the two forces?

Solution: We first find the length of the
diagonal of the rectangle.

$$d^2 = 80^2 + 70^2$$
$$d \doteq 107$$

A force of 107 pounds applied in
a direction opposite to that of $\overrightarrow{OA}$
suffices.

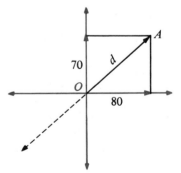

EXERCISES

Solve graphically.

1. A man goes 6 miles in a direction 30° east of north, and 6 miles in a direction 40° east of south. What is his final position with respect to his starting point?

2. A plane is headed 20° west of north at a speed of 500 m.p.h. A wind coming from 50° east of south has a speed of 200 m.p.h. What is the speed and direction of the airplane's flight with respect to the ground?

3. Two 20-pound forces act on an object at a 50° angle to each other. What is the magnitude of the resultant force?

4. Three forces act on an object. The first two forces, of 30 and 40 pounds, are directed at a 90° angle with respect to each other. The third force, of 60 pounds, is directed at an 80° angle to the 30-pound force and a 10° angle to the 40-pound force. Find the magnitude of the resultant force.

5. Make a sketch for this situation: Three forces act on an object, each in a direction perpendicular to the plane of the other two. The forces have magnitudes of 6, 8, and 5 pounds. Find, by computation, the magnitude of the resultant force.

6. Two forces act on an object. They are represented by arrows in the first quadrant. One force, of j pounds, is directed at an $e°$ angle with respect to the x-axis. The other force, one of k pounds, is directed at an $f°$ angle with respect to the x-axis. Prove that the resultant force is given by the vector $(j \cos e° + k \cos f°, j \sin e° + k \sin f°)$.

CUMULATIVE REVIEW: CHAPTERS 11–13

COMPLETION EXERCISES

Write the correct word, phrase, or number on your paper.

1. The two instruments permitted in geometric constructions by the ancient Greeks were the __?__ and the __?__.

2. To construct a line tangent to a circle O at a given point P on the circle, you begin by drawing __?__.

3. The set of points which are centers of spheres tangent to each of two given parallel planes is a __?__.

4. The slope of a line that slants upward from left to right is a __?__ number.

5. The set of points described by the inequality $x^2 + (y - 2)^2 < 49$ is the __?__ of a circle.

6. Slope is not defined for a __?__ line.

7. The graph of $y = 4$ is a line parallel to the __?__-axis.

8. Given points $A(3, -1)$ and $B(5, 3)$. The midpoint of $\overline{AB}$ is point __?__, and the slope of $\overline{AB}$ is __?__.

9. Line l is contained in plane P. The locus of points in P and 3 units from l is __?__.

10. The radius of a sphere is 5 units. The locus of points in the interior of the sphere and 11 units from the sphere is the __?__.

11. The distance between points $(0, -2)$ and $(0, 6)$ is __?__.

12. The line whose equation is $y - 3 = \frac{2}{5}(x + 1)$ passes through the point $(-1, ?)$ and has slope __?__.

13. The locus of the midpoints of the radii of a given sphere is __?__.

14. $\overline{RS}$ is given, with $RS = 5$. The locus of points on $\overline{RS}$ and 2 units from S is __?__.

B 15. In space, the locus of points n units from point R and n units from point S is the empty set when RS __?__ $2n$.

16. The equation of the line containing pts. $(0, 4)$ and $(3, 6)$ is __?__.

17. The locus of points in the fourth quadrant and in the interior of a circle with center $(-3, 4)$ is known to be a nonempty set. The radius of the circle must be greater than __?__.

18. Each one of a certain set of spheres has symmetry with respect to a given plane. The centers of all the spheres lie __?__.

19. Line l lies in plane P. The locus of points 3 units from l and 7 units from P is __?__.

20. A sphere with center P and radius j will intersect a sphere with center Q and radius k in a circle if $PQ <$ __?__, and $PQ >$ __?__ $(j > k)$.

TRUE-FALSE EXERCISES

A 1. If plane M contains $\overline{AB}$, there are exactly two points in M that are equidistant from points A and B.

2. To construct the bisector of an angle X you first draw an arc, or circle, with center X.

3. Where $A = \{(x, y): x^2 + y^2 < 9\}$ and $B = \{(x, y): x^2 + y^2 = 4\}$, the union of A and B is the empty set.

4. All points one inch from a given point P lie on a square whose edge is two units long.

5. In space, there is exactly one line perpendicular to a given line from a point outside the line.

6. The points $(2, 3)$ and $(2, -3)$ have symmetry with respect to the x-axis.

7. Slope is not defined for a horizontal line.

8. Where A is pt. $(j, -k)$ and B is pt. $(-j, k)$ the midpoint of $\overline{AB}$ is the origin.

9. It is possible to construct an angle with measure 45.

10. The point $(n, -3)$ lies in the fourth quadrant when n is a negative number.

11. A locus can be the empty set.

12. In space, the locus of points a given distance from a given line is a pair of lines.

13. The locus of points a given distance from a given plane is a single plane.

14. The segment joining pts. $(0, 0)$ and $(-4, -4)$ is parallel to the segment joining pts. $(3, 3)$ and $(5, 5)$.

15. The locus of points on $\overrightarrow{AB}$ and $\frac{1}{3}(AB)$ units from point B is a point.

16. The slope of a line perpendicular to a line with slope $-\frac{4}{7}$ is $\frac{7}{4}$.

17. It is possible to construct an angle with measure 15.

18. Given an arc of a circle it is possible, by construction, to find the center of the arc.

19. It is possible to construct a triangle whose sides have lengths 7, 8, and 15.

20. The locus of the midpoints of all 2-inch chords of a sphere of 6-inch radius is a sphere.

CONSTRUCTION EXERCISES

1. Draw an angle. Divide it into four angles of equal measure.

2. Draw a segment. Divide it into six segments of equal length.

In each exercise begin with a figure, drawn on your own paper, roughly like the figure shown.

3. Construct a line through P parallel to l.

4. Construct a line through P perpendicular to l.

5. Construct two segments, $\overline{PA}$ and $\overline{PB}$, such that points A and B lie on l and $PA = PB$.

6. Take any point T on l. On $\overrightarrow{PT}$ find a point X such that $PX = 3 \cdot PT$.

$\bullet P$

l

Exs. 3–6

On your paper draw two segments and an angle with measures approximating those shown. In Exercises 7–10 use the segments and angles you have drawn.

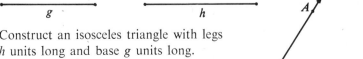

g

h

A

B C

7. Construct an isosceles triangle with legs h units long and base g units long.

8. Construct a parallelogram with sides g and h units long, and an angle with measure equal to that of $\angle B$.

9. Find, by construction, all points in the interior of $\angle ABC$ which are equidistant from $\overleftrightarrow{BA}$ and $\overleftrightarrow{BC}$ and at a distance g from point C.

10. Find, by construction, all points on $\overrightarrow{BC}$ which are at a distance g from $\overleftrightarrow{BA}$.

MISCELLANEOUS EXERCISES

$\overline{AB}$ is the base of isosceles triangle ABC.

[A] **1.** Point A is at the origin and vertex C is point (e, f). Write the ordered pair that represents point B if B is on the x-axis.

2. A is point $(-2, 0)$ and B is point $(6, 0)$. What is the x-coordinate of point C?

3. A is point $(0, 0)$ and B is point $(0, 7)$. What is the y-coordinate of point C?

4. In Exercise 3 can the x-coordinate of point C be a positive number? a negative number?

5. Point Q is the midpoint of $\overline{PR}$. P is point $(-3, 2)$ and Q is point $(1, -4)$. State the coordinates of point R.

6. The slope of $\overline{MN}$ is $\frac{7}{5}$. State the slope of the perpendicular bisector of $\overline{MN}$.

7. Three consecutive vertices of a square are points $(4, 0)$, $(0, 3)$, and $(-3, -1)$. State the coordinates of the fourth vertex.

8. In what kind of triangle is one point of the triangle the intersection point of the three altitudes?

9. Two parallel planes are j units apart. What is the length of the radius of a sphere tangent to both planes?

10. Points P and P' have symmetry with respect to the line $y = 3$. P is point $(-2, 5)$. What are the coordinates of P'?

Point A is the center of the circle whose equation is $x^2 + (y + 2)^2 = 25$.

[B] **11.** State the coordinates of point A and the radius of circle A.

12. Write the inequality that describes the interior of circle A.

13. Write the inequality that describes the union of circle A and its interior.

14. Line l has the equation $x = -5$. Describe the intersection of line l and circle A.

15. Circle B has the equation $(x - 7)^2 + (y - 1)^2 = 4$. Describe the intersection of circle B and circle A.

16. Write the equation that describes points one unit from circle A in the exterior of circle A.

17. For what integral values of x is there a triangle whose sides have lengths 3, 5, x?

18. $\overline{AB}$ is the fixed base of isosceles triangle APB. What is the locus of vertex P (a) in a plane? (b) in space?

19. Write the equation of the line which is the perpendicular bisector of the segment joining pts. (3, -1) and (5, 5).

20. Given $\overline{AB}$ in space. What is the locus of points P so located that $PA = \frac{1}{3}(AB)$ and $PB = \frac{1}{3}(AB)$?

GRAPHING EXERCISES

For each of the following exercises draw a pair of coordinate axes. Then draw a graph meeting the given condition.

A
1. $y = 2x$ **6.** $x = -3$ and $y > -2$

2. $y = -3$ **7.** $2x + y > 4$

3. $x - 2y = 4$ **8.** $(x - 3)^2 + (y - 2)^2 = 9$

4. $x \leq 2$ **9.** $x^2 + y^2 > 4$

5. $x^2 + y^2 = 9$ **10.** $y - 3 = \frac{1}{2}(x - 2)$

B
11. Represent $\{(x, y): x = 2\} \cup \{(x, y): y = -1\}$ graphically.

12. Represent $\{(x, y): x + y = 5\} \cap \{(x, y): x - y = 3\}$ graphically.

PROOF EXERCISES

In Exercises 1–6 use points $A(-3, -1)$; $B(1, 5)$; $C(-3, 6)$; $D(0, 0)$; $E(-1, -4)$; and $F(3, 2)$.

A
1. Prove: $\overleftrightarrow{AB} \parallel \overleftrightarrow{EF}$.   **4.** Prove: $\overleftrightarrow{CD}$ is not perpendicular to $\overleftrightarrow{AB}$.

2. Prove: $\overleftrightarrow{CD}$ bisects $\overline{AB}$.   **5.** Prove: $AE = BF$.

3. Prove: $m\angle CFE = 90$.   **6.** Prove: $AB > CD$.

In Exercises 7–10 use points $P(0, -4)$; $Q(8, -3)$; $R(4, 4)$; and $S(-4, 3)$.

B
7. Prove: Quadrilateral $PQRS$ is a parallelogram.

8. Prove: Parallelogram $PQRS$ is a rhombus.

9. Prove: Parallelogram $PQRS$ is not a rectangle.

C
10. Prove: A diagonal of quadrilateral $PQRS$ bisects the segment that joins the midpoints of two opposite sides.

11. Prove: The segment joining points $(a, 0)$ and (j, k) is trisected by points $\left(\dfrac{2a + j}{3}, \dfrac{k}{3}\right)$ and $\left(\dfrac{a + 2j}{3}, \dfrac{2k}{3}\right)$.

12. Prove: If A is point $(g, 0)$ and B is point $(0, 5)$ then the perpendicular bisector of $\overline{AB}$ intersects the line $x = 4$ in a point whose y-coordinate is $\dfrac{25 + 8g - g^2}{10}$.

14

Transformations

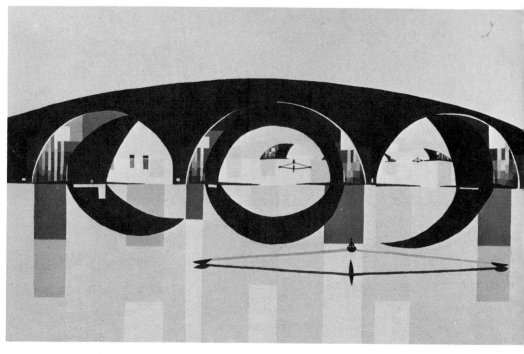

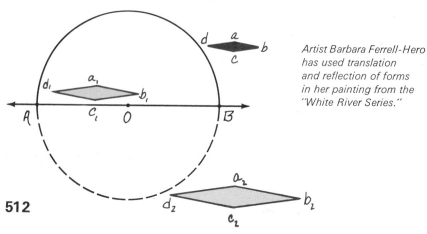

Artist Barbara Ferrell-Hero
has used translation
and reflection of forms
in her painting from the
"White River Series."

When you draw a triangle, you tend to think of the drawing as being the triangle. Since you can move the drawing, it seems that you can move the triangle. When you think critically, however, you realize that you must distinguish between a set of points, with "point" undefined, and a picture that represents the set. In carefully developed mathematics, there is no physical moving of sets of points.

Yet your intuition tells you that you can think of moving sets of points. For example, you can mentally move triangle *ABC* so that it fits upon (coincides with) triangle *RST*. Historically men have not only thought, on an informal level, about moving triangles; they have based proofs upon the idea of moving figures.

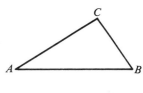

In this chapter you will see how words such as "stretching" and "contraction," words that suggest motion, are used in modern geometry. One figure can be

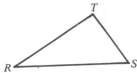

transformed into another figure in carefully defined ways that do not involve actual motion but do seem to show some effects of movement.

■ What Transformation Means

14–1 Mappings and Transformations

The figure below shows two concentric circles. The diagram suggests a way to associate, with each point of circle I, a unique point of circle II.

With point *P* pair point *P'*.
With point *Q* pair point *Q'*.

To describe all the ordered pairs of points let *X* represent any point of circle I and write $\{(X, X'): X'$ is the point in which $\overrightarrow{OX}$ intersects circle II$\}$.

The set of ordered pairs of points is a *function* or *mapping*.

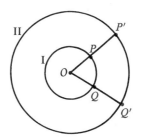

Figure 14–1

The *domain* is circle I.

The *range* is circle II.

Using *M* to represent the mapping, you say that *M* maps circle I into circle II. You also say that *M* maps, or carries, point *X* into

513

point X' and write: $M: X \rightarrow X'$. Since the mapping carries point P into point P', P' is called the **image** of P and P is called the **preimage** of P'.

In the example shown, one circle was mapped into a different circle. Sometimes a figure is mapped into itself. Figure 14–2 shows three ordered pairs that belong to a particular mapping of the number line into itself. Under the mapping, a point with coordinate x is mapped into a point with coordinate $3x$.

$$A \rightarrow A'$$
$$B \rightarrow B'$$
$$O \rightarrow O'$$

Figure 14–2

Because point O is mapped into itself, O is called a **fixed point**.

The mapping illustrates a *transformation of the line.* A **transformation of the number line into itself** is a mapping that carries each point of the number line into a unique point of the number line.

For a different kind of mapping see Fig. 14–3. The figure suggests a mapping under which each point of the plane is carried into a point lying two units to its right. Because each point of the plane has an image in the plane the mapping is called a *transformation of the plane.*

A **transformation of the coordinate plane into itself** is a mapping that carries each point P of the plane into a unique point P' of the plane.

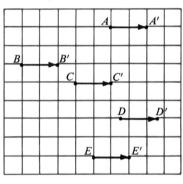

Figure 14–3

| ORAL
| EXERCISES

A partial table for a particular mapping of the set of nonnegative integers into the set of nonnegative even integers is shown.

Exs. 1–8

$0 \rightarrow 0$
$1 \rightarrow 2$
$2 \rightarrow 4$
$3 \rightarrow 6$
$4 \rightarrow 8$
$5 \rightarrow 10$
$6 \rightarrow 12$
$9 \rightarrow$
$\rightarrow 100$

1. State the image of 1; of 2; of 3.

2. State the preimage of 4; of 12.

3. The number 9 is mapped into the number __?__.

4. The number that is mapped into the number 100 is the number __?__.

5. The image of 6 is __?__, whereas the preimage of 6 is __?__.

6. The number that is equal to its image is __?__.

7. State the domain of the mapping.

8. State the range of the mapping.

A mapping of a segment $\overline{AB}$ into a segment $\overline{AC}$
is suggested by the figure.

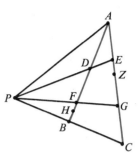

9. State the image of D; of B.

10. State the preimage of E; of G.

11. For how many points is it true that the image
of the point is the point itself?

12. Because the image of A is A, A is called a __?__.

13. State how to determine the image of H.

14. State how to determine the preimage of Z.

Exs. 9–14

15. The mapping used in Exercises 9–14 is not a transformation of the
plane. Explain why not.

16. Does the definition of *transformation of the coordinate plane* specify
that each point of the plane must be mapped into some point other than
itself?

WRITTEN EXERCISES

In Exercises 1–6, a transformation of the number line is suggested by the illustration. Point A is mapped into point A', point B into point B'.

a. Describe verbally a possible mapping that is suggested by the illustration.

b. Describe the mapping algebraically.

c. State the fixed points, if any.

EXAMPLE.

Solution:

a. Each point of the line is mapped into the point, on the other side of the
origin, that is at the same distance from the origin.

b. $M: x \rightarrow -x$

c. The point with coordinate 0 is a fixed point.

[A] **1.**

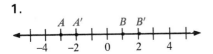

2.

3.

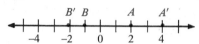

5.

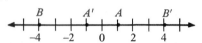

4.

6.

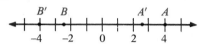

The rule for a transformation is given. In each exercise draw a number line. Select any two points A and B on the number line. Draw the images of A and B.

EXAMPLE $M:x \rightarrow 2x + 1$

Solution:

$$\begin{array}{cccccc} B' & B & & A & A' \\ \hline -5 & -4 & -2 & 0 & 2 & 4 & 5 \end{array}$$

7. $M:x \rightarrow x + 2$

8. $M:x \rightarrow 3x$

9. $M:x \rightarrow -2x$

10. $M:x \rightarrow 2 - x$

11. $M:x \rightarrow \frac{1}{2}x + 3$

12. $M:x \rightarrow 2x - \frac{3}{2}$

Under a certain transformation of the plane each point is mapped into some point according to the rule shown. State the coordinates of the image of
a. the point $A(0, 5)$ **b.** the point $B(4, -2)$.

EXAMPLE. $M:(x, y) \rightarrow (x, y + 1)$

Solution: **a.** When x is 0, x is 0.
  When y is 5, $y + 1$ is 6.
  The image of point A is point $(0, 6)$.   **Answer.**

b. When x is 4, x is 4.
  When y is -2, $y + 1$ is -1.
  The image of point B is point $(4, -1)$.   **Answer.**

13. $M:(x, y) \rightarrow (2x, y)$

14. $M:(x, y) \rightarrow (x - 1, y + 2)$

15. $M:(x, y) \rightarrow (-x, y)$

16. $M:(x, y) \rightarrow (x, -y)$

17. $M:(x, y) \rightarrow (2x, 2y)$

18. $M:(x, y) \rightarrow (-x, -y)$

19. $M:(x, y) \rightarrow (x + 1, y + 1)$

20. $M:(x, y) \rightarrow (3 - x, \frac{1}{2}y)$

In each exercise plot point C(−1, 1) and point D(3, 1) in the coordinate plane. Draw $\overline{CD}$. Select several points of $\overline{CD}$ and plot their images. Draw $\overline{C'D'}$.

EXAMPLE. $M:(x, y) \rightarrow (x - 1, y + 2)$

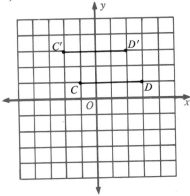

Solution:

(−1, 1) is mapped into (−2, 3).

(1, 1) is mapped into (0, 3).

(3, 1) is mapped into (2, 3).

(1.5, 1) is mapped into (.5, 3).

21. $M:(x, y) \rightarrow (x, y + 3)$

22. $M:(x, y) \rightarrow (x, y - 2)$

23. $M:(x, y) \rightarrow (x - 2, y + 2)$

24. $M:(x, y) \rightarrow (x + 3, y - 4)$

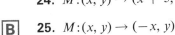

B

25. $M:(x, y) \rightarrow (-x, y)$

26. $M:(x, y) \rightarrow (x, -y)$

27. $M:(x, y) \rightarrow (2x, 2y)$

28. $M:(x, y) \rightarrow (-x, \frac{1}{2}y)$

C

29. $M:(x, y) \rightarrow (1 - x, y + 2)$

30. $M:(x, y) \rightarrow (-x, 3 - y)$

31. $M:(x, y) \rightarrow (2x - 1, y - 3)$

32. $M:(x, y) \rightarrow (x^2, 2y)$

14-2 Stretchings and Shrinkings; Expansions and Contractions

Often a transformation of the plane is specified by two equations. For instance, the mapping $M:(x, y) \rightarrow (2x, y)$ can be referred to as the *transformation specified by the equations*

$$x' = 2x$$
$$y' = y$$

or even more briefly as *the transformation $x' = 2x$, $y' = y$*. Each of the three notations describes a *stretching* of the plane.

For each positive number k, the equations

$$x' = kx$$
$$y' = y$$

determine a transformation called a **stretching of the plane** when $k > 1$, a **shrinking of the plane** when $0 < k < 1$.

EXAMPLE 1.

Plot the points $A(1, 1)$, $B(1, 3)$, $C(0, 5)$, $D(-2, -2)$. Plot their images under the transformation specified by the equations $x' = 3x$
$$y' = y.$$

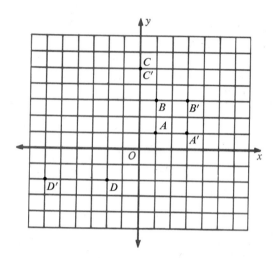

Solution:

$(1, 1) \rightarrow (3, 1)$
$(1, 3) \rightarrow (3, 3)$
$(0, 5) \rightarrow (0, 5)$
$(-2, -2) \rightarrow (-6, -2)$

In this example $k > 1$ and you can informally describe the stretching as being horizontal. Each of the points A', B', and D' lies three times as far from the y-axis as its preimage. However, point C is a fixed point. Do you see that every point on the y-axis is a fixed point under this mapping?

For each positive number k, the equations

$$x' = x$$
$$y' = ky$$

also determine a transformation of the plane that is a **stretching of the plane** when $k > 1$ and a **shrinking of the plane** when $0 < k < 1$. In this case the stretching or shrinking is vertical.

A different kind of mapping of the plane is the mapping

$$M:(x, y) \rightarrow (kx, ky).$$

For each positive number k the transformation specified by the equations

$$x' = kx$$
$$y' = ky$$

is called an **expansion of the plane** when $k > 1$ and a **contraction of the plane** when $0 < k < 1$. Do you see that the origin is, in general, the only fixed point? In the special case $k = 1$, however, the transformation maps each point of the plane into itself, and every point is a fixed point.

EXAMPLE 2.

Plot the points $R(-2, 3)$, $S(0, -2)$ and $T(3, -1)$. Draw the images of the points under the expansion

$$x' = 2x$$
$$y' = 2y.$$

Draw triangle RST and triangle $R'S'T'$, where R', S', and T' are images of R, S, and T, respectively.

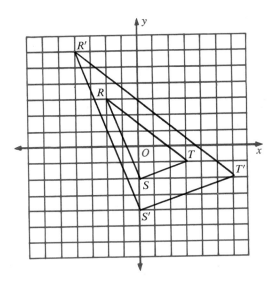

Solution:

$$(-2, 3) \to (-4, 6)$$
$$(0, -2) \to (0, -4)$$
$$(3, -1) \to (6, -2)$$

The example suggests that under an expansion of the plane any point P has as its image a point P' that lies on $\overrightarrow{OP}$ and is k times as far from the origin as P is. More precisely: P' lies on $\overrightarrow{OP}$; $OP' = k(OP)$. (See Exercises 29, 30.)

It can be proved that any line is mapped, under an expansion or contraction, into a line. (See Exercises 31, 32.) Example 2 suggests that a line is mapped into a line parallel to the original line, and an angle into an angle congruent to the original angle. (See Exercise 33.) Since any angle is mapped into an angle of equal measure, we say that angle measure is **invariant** under expansion or contraction. Do you see that segment length is not invariant?

ORAL EXERCISES

State two equations $x' = \underline{\ ?\ }$ x, $y' = \underline{\ ?\ }$ y that can be used to specify the transformation.

1. $M:(x, y) \to (5x, y)$

2. $M:(x, y) \to (7x, 7y)$

3. $M:(x, y) \to (\frac{1}{4}x, y)$

4. $M:(x, y) \to (\frac{2}{5}x, \frac{2}{5}y)$

State the image of the given point under the transformation $x' = x$
$$y' = \tfrac{1}{3}y.$$

5. $(5, 6)$ **6.** $(8, -12)$ **7.** $(0, 0)$ **8.** $(-5, 0)$

9. Is the transformation specified above a stretching or is it a shrinking?

10. The transformation above maps point $(j, 0)$ into point $(\underline{\ ?\ }, \underline{\ ?\ })$. Hence, for each real number j the point $(j, 0)$ is a $\underline{\ ?\ }$ point.

State the image of the given point under the transformation specified by the equations $x' = \tfrac{2}{3}x$
$$y' = \tfrac{2}{3}y.$$

11. $(6, 6)$ **12.** $(9, 0)$ **13.** $(-12, -3)$ **14.** (a, b)

15. Is the transformation an expansion or is it a contraction?

16. The point (c, d) and its image $(\tfrac{2}{3}c, \tfrac{2}{3}d)$ are different points unless c and d are both 0. Hence the only fixed point under the transformation is $\underline{\ ?\ }$.

Under the transformation with equations $x' = x$
$$y' = y,$$

17. The image of point $(3, -7)$ is point $(\underline{\ ?\ }, \underline{\ ?\ })$.

18. The preimage of point $(-2, -4)$ is point $(\underline{\ ?\ }, \underline{\ ?\ })$.

19. For all real numbers a, b, the image of point (a, b) is point $(\underline{\ ?\ }, \underline{\ ?\ })$.

20. Every point of the plane is a $\underline{\ ?\ }$.

WRITTEN EXERCISES

State the image of the point under each of the transformations.

a. $x' = \tfrac{1}{4}x$ **b.** $x' = x$ **c.** $x' = 4x$ **d.** $x' = \tfrac{1}{2}x$
$\quad y' = y$ $\quad y' = 3y$ $\quad y' = 4y$ $\quad y' = \tfrac{1}{2}y$

[A]

1. $(8, 0)$ **3.** $(-2, 2)$ **5.** $(-8, -8)$ **7.** $(0, k)$
2. $(-12, 3)$ **4.** $(0, 0)$ **6.** $(j, 0)$ **8.** (j, k)

Is the transformation specified by the equations shown a stretching, a shrinking, an expansion, or a contraction?

9. $x' = x$ **10.** $x' = \tfrac{7}{2}x$ **11.** $x' = .2x$ **12.** $x' = x$
$\quad y' = 3y$ $\quad y' = \tfrac{7}{2}y$ $\quad y' = .2y$ $\quad y' = \tfrac{1}{4}y$

State the equations for the stretching, shrinking, expansion, or contraction that maps the given point into the image shown.

13. $(5, 3) \rightarrow (5, 6)$ **14.** $(8, -8) \rightarrow (16, -16)$

15. $(8, -8) \rightarrow (4, -4)$

16. $(10, -2) \rightarrow (5, -2)$

17. $(-5, 8) \rightarrow (-10, 16)$

18. $(-5, 8) \rightarrow (-\frac{5}{2}, 4)$

19. $(-6, -9) \rightarrow (-4, -6)$

20. $(-8, -6) \rightarrow (-2, -\frac{3}{2})$

In Exercises 21–26 assume that every line maps into a line parallel to the original line under the expansion $x' = 2x$
$$y' = 2y.$$

Draw, in black, the polygon having the given vertices. Plot, in red, the image of each vertex and draw the image polygon.

B

21. $(3, 3), (3, -3), (-3, -3), (-3, 3)$

22. $(0, 0), (3, 0), (3, 3), (0, 3)$

23. $(-1, 1), (-3, 2), (-4, 0), (2, -1)$

24. $(0, 0), (4, 0), (0, -6)$

25. $(2, 2), (5, 0), (-1, -3)$

26. $(4, 0), (4, 2), (1, 3), (-2, -2), (1, -3)$

Thinking inductively and using your intuition, complete these statements that refer to an expansion specified by the equations $x' = kx$
$$y' = ky.$$

27. A segment d units long is mapped into ___?___.

28. Every polygon is mapped into ___?___.

In Exercises 29–33 use the transformation whose equations are $x' = kx$ and $y' = ky$ $(k > 0)$.

C

29. Prove: If the image of point P (c, d) is point P', then $OP' = k(OP)$.
   Hint: First state the coordinates of P' in terms of c, d, and k.

30. Prove: If the image of point $P(c, d)$ is point P', then point P' lies on $\overleftrightarrow{OP}$.
   Hint: Find the equation of $\overleftrightarrow{OP}$. Then show that the coordinates of point P' satisfy the equation.

31. Prove: A vertical line, $x = b$, maps into a line parallel to $x = b$.

32. Prove: A nonvertical line l maps into a line parallel to l.
   Hint: Let three points of line l be $P_1(x_1, y_1)$, $P_2(x_2, y_2)$, $P_3(x_3, y_3)$. State the slope of $\overline{P_1'P_2'}$ and of $\overline{P_1'P_3'}$.

33. Prove: Angle measure is invariant under expansion.
   Hint: Let any angle RST have the image angle $R'S'T'$. Draw $\overleftrightarrow{SS'}$ and treat it as a transversal. Use two pairs of corresponding angles.

34. If any two points P and Q have images P' and Q' under the stretching $x' = 3x$, $y' = y$, then $PQ \leq P'Q' \leq 3PQ$.

■ Rigid Transformations of the Plane

14–3   Translations

Suppose you lay a sheet of clear plastic over a drawing showing co-ordinate axes.   Three dots are marked on the plastic, as shown in Fig. 3–1a.   Slide the sheet (without rotating) two units to the right and one unit upwards (Fig. 3–1b).   Ignore the very slight bending and stretching of a sheet of plastic that is handled carefully.

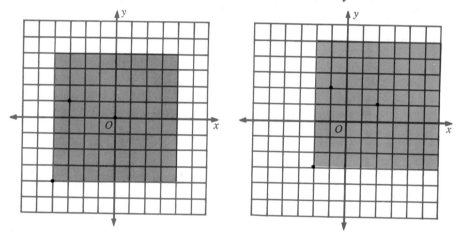

Figure 3–1a

Figure 3–1b

The point on the plastic that lay above the origin now lies at $(2, 1)$; the point that lay above $(-4, -4)$ now lies above $(-2, -3)$; the point that lay above $(-3, 1)$ now lies above $(-1, 2)$.   If a triangle had been drawn on the plastic before the motion, the motion would not affect the lengths of the sides or the measures of the angles of the triangle.   The physical situation described above will help you under-stand what is meant by a *rigid transformation.*

   A **rigid transformation of the plane** is a transformation such that distances between points and measures of angles are invariant under the transformation.

   There is more than one type of rigid transformation.   The type illus-trated in Fig. 3–1, and discussed more fully later in this section, is called a *translation.*

   A **translation of the plane** is a transformation specified, for any real numbers h and k, by the equations

$$x' = x + h$$
$$y' = y + k.$$

It can be proved (Exercises 43–46) that:

> **Under a translation:**
>
> Every line is mapped into a line parallel to the original line (or into itself).
>
> Every segment is mapped into a segment congruent to the original segment.
>
> Every angle is mapped into an angle congruent to the original angle.

You see, then, that a translation is a rigid transformation.

EXAMPLE. A translation maps point $(-1, 4)$ into point $(3, 2)$.

      a. Find the equations of the translation.

      b. Find the image of point $(7, 2)$ under the translation.

Solution:

a. Taking $(x, y) = (-1, 4)$ and $(x', y') = (3, 2)$ you have

$$x' = x + h \qquad\qquad y' = y + k$$
$$3 = -1 + h \qquad\qquad 2 = 4 + k$$
$$h = 4 \qquad\qquad\qquad k = -2.$$

The equations of the translation are: $x' = x + 4$
$$y' = y - 2. \quad \textbf{Answer.}$$

b. $x' = x + 4$ $y' = y - 2$
$$x' = 7 + 4 \text{ or } 11 \qquad\qquad y' = 2 - 2 \text{ or } 0$$

The image of point $(7, 2)$ is point $(11, 0)$.   **Answer.**

ORAL EXERCISES

The equations of a particular translation of the plane are: $x' = x - 1$
$$y' = y + 5.$$

State the image of the given point.

1. $(6, 6)$	**3.** $(4, -2)$	**5.** $(1, -5)$	**7.** $(8, 10)$
2. $(0, 0)$	**4.** $(-3, 1)$	**6.** $(0, -2)$	**8.** $(-5, -6)$

State values of h and k such that the translation

$$x' = x + h$$
$$y' = y + k$$

maps the first point into the second point.

EXAMPLE 1. $A \rightarrow A'$

Solution:

(By inspection of the graph)
$h = 4, k = -1.$ **Answer.**

9. $B \rightarrow B'$ **12.** $E \rightarrow E'$
10. $C \rightarrow C'$ **13.** $F \rightarrow F'$
11. $D \rightarrow D'$ **14.** $G \rightarrow G'$

EXAMPLE 2.

$(2, -3) \rightarrow (1, 4)$

Solution:

$1 = 2 + h.$
Therefore $h = -1.$
$4 = -3 + k.$
Therefore $k = 7.$ **Answer.**

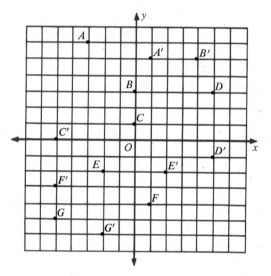

Exs. 9–14

15. $(0, 4) \rightarrow (3, 2)$ **17.** $(-3, 2) \rightarrow (2, 2)$ **19.** $(0, 0) \rightarrow (5, 3)$
16. $(5, 0) \rightarrow (1, 2)$ **18.** $(4, 7) \rightarrow (4, 3)$ **20.** $(5, 3) \rightarrow (0, 0)$

21. When not both h and k are zero can any point of the plane be a fixed point under the translation $x' = x + h, y' = y + k$?

22. Under the translation $x' = x + h, y' = y + k$, what points are fixed points when h and k are both zero?

WRITTEN EXERCISES

State the equations of the translation of the plane that maps the first point into the second point.

A

1. $(2, 3) \rightarrow (6, 3)$ **5.** $(-3, 4) \rightarrow (1, 2)$
2. $(4, 1) \rightarrow (5, -2)$ **6.** $(5, -2) \rightarrow (7, 0)$
3. $(3, 2) \rightarrow (0, -1)$ **7.** $(-3, 0) \rightarrow (-1, 5)$
4. $(4, 1) \rightarrow (0, 0)$ **8.** $(-4, -2) \rightarrow (1, -6)$

9–16. For the preceding exercises 1–8 state the image, under the translation, of point (0, 3).

In Exercises 17–20, plot, on a coordinate plane, the given point and its image under the translation

$$x' = x + 2$$
$$y' = y - 3.$$

17. $P(1, 7)$ **19.** $R(-4, 1)$

18. $Q(5, 0)$ **20.** $S(6, -3)$

In Exercises 21–24 use the translation $x' = x + 4$, $y' = y - 1$. Assume that a translation maps each segment into a segment parallel and congruent to the original segment.

21. a. Plot point $A(3, 1)$ and point $B(7, 1)$ on a coordinate plane. Draw $\overline{AB}$.

  b. Draw the image of $\overline{AB}$.

   Hint: Compute the coordinates of points A' and B'.

22. a. Plot points $C(-1, 0)$ and $D(-1, 4)$ and draw $\overline{CD}$.

  b. Draw the image of $\overline{CD}$.

23. a. Plot points $E(-2, -1)$, $F(1, -1)$, $G(1, 2)$ and $L(-2, 2)$. Draw quadrilateral *EFGL*.

  b. Draw the image of polygon *EFGL*.

24. a. Plot points $M(-4, 2)$, $N(-3, -1)$, and $P(5, 5)$. Draw triangle *MNP*.

  b. Draw the image of triangle *MNP*.

In Exercises 25–36 use the translation $x' = x - 3$, $y' = y + 2$ and the points $P(1, 0)$, $Q(3, 3)$, and $R(7, 9)$.

B **25.** State the slope of line $\overleftrightarrow{PQ}$. of line $\overleftrightarrow{PR}$. Are points P, Q, and R collinear?

26. State the coordinates of points P', Q', and R'.

27. State the slope of line $\overleftrightarrow{P'Q'}$. of line $\overleftrightarrow{P'R'}$. Are points P', Q', and R' collinear?

28. Are lines $\overleftrightarrow{PR}$ and $\overleftrightarrow{P'R'}$ parallel?

29. Compute the lengths of $\overline{PR}$ and $\overline{P'R'}$ and compare those lengths.

30. Plot, on a coordinate plane, points P, Q, R, P', Q', R'.

31–36. Repeat Exercises 25–30 using the same points P and Q and the same translation, but taking as the third given point $R(7, 7)$.

37–42. Use the translation $x' = x - 4$, $y' = y - 6$ and the points $P(1, 0)$, $Q(3, 3)$, and $R(7, 9)$. Repeat Exercises 25–30.

In Exercises 43–46 use the translation specified by the equations $x' = x + h$
$$y' = y + k.$$

C   **43.** Prove: Every vertical line is mapped into a vertical line under translation.

Hint: Let the line have the equation $x = c$. Take any three points $P(c, p)$, $Q(c, q)$, $R(c, r)$ on the line. Show that the image points P', Q', R' lie on a vertical line.

44. Prove: Every line maps into a line parallel to the original line (or into itself) under translation.

Hint: The case of the vertical line has already been proved. On any nonvertical line take any three points $P(a, b)$, $Q(c, d)$, $R(e, f)$.
Note that $\dfrac{d - b}{c - a} = \dfrac{f - b}{e - a}$. See Exercises 26, 27, 28.

45. Prove: Segment length is invariant under translation.

Hint: Let any given segment have endpoints $P(a, b)$ and $Q(c, d)$. State the coordinates of points P' and Q'. Compute PQ and $P'Q'$.

46. Prove: Angle measure is invariant under translation.

Hint: Given any angle PQR, prove: $\triangle PQR \cong \triangle P'Q'R'$.

14–4   Reflections

The idea of symmetry with respect to a line (page 447) is related to the type of transformation to be studied in this section.

Let the y-axis be a line of symmetry. Some pairs of points that have symmetry with respect to that line are:

$(3, 2)$ and $(-3, 2)$
$(-2, 1)$ and $(2, 1)$
$(-4, -4)$ and $(4, -4)$.

Figure 4–1 suggests the possibility of a transformation under which each point, in a symmetrical pair, is the image of the other. There are such transformations, and they are called reflections. The word "reflection" is suggested by mirrors. Think of a mirror perpendicular to the coordinate plane and containing the y-axis. Then think of a person at position $(3, 2)$. Do you see that he would view his reflection at the apparent position $(-3, 2)$?

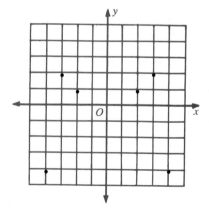

Figure 4–1

A **reflection of the plane in the y-axis** is the transformation specified by the equation $x' = -x$
$$y' = y.$$
A **reflection of the plane in the x-axis** is the transformation specified by the equations $x' = x$
$$y' = -y.$$

EXAMPLE 1. State the image, under reflection in the *x*-axis, of

        a. point (4, 3)   **b.** point $(-5, -2)$.

Solution: Use the equations $x' = x$, $y' = -y$.

        a. The image of point (4, 3) is point $(4, -3)$.

        b. The image of point $(-5, -2)$ is point $(-5, 2)$. **Answer.**

EXAMPLE 2. Under a particular reflection the image of point $(2, -4)$ is point $(-2, -4)$.

        a. State the equations of the transformation.

        b. The transformation is a reflection in which axis?

Solution: **a.** By inspection we have $x' = -x$, $y' = y$.

        b. From **(a)** and the definitions we see that the transformation is a reflection in the *y*-axis.

Notice, in Example 2, that a mental image of points $(2, -4)$ and $(-2, -4)$ would suggest the answers.

    In Figure 4–2 you see a line *l* and the reflections in the *x*-axis of several points that lie on *l*. The figure suggests that:

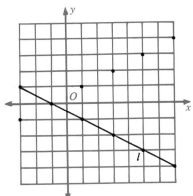

Figure 4–2

> ### Under a reflection:
>
> Every line is mapped into a line.
>
> Every segment is mapped into a segment congruent to the original segment.
>
> Every angle is mapped into an angle congruent to the original angle.

It can be proved that a reflection is a rigid transformation. (See Exercises 31, 32.)

**ORAL
EXERCISES**

In Exercises 1–12, the equations for a particular reflection of the plane are

$$x' = x$$
$$y' = -y.$$

1. Is the transformation a reflection in the x-axis or is it a reflection in the y-axis?
2. The image of point $(5, 2)$ is point $(\underline{}, \underline{})$.
3. Point $(5, 2)$ lies in Quadrant $\underline{}$.
4. The image of point $(5, 2)$ lies in Quadrant $\underline{}$.
5. If P is a point in Quadrant III, then point P' lies in Quadrant $\underline{}$.
6. The image of point $(7, 0)$ is point $(\underline{}, \underline{})$.
7. For any real number t the image of point $(t, 0)$ is point $(\underline{}, \underline{})$.
8. Since the image of any point on the x-axis is the point itself, every point on the x-axis is called a $\underline{}$.
9. Does the y-axis contain any fixed points?
10. Does Quadrant II contain any fixed points?
11. Suppose that under one application of the transformation the image of point P is point P'. Then under a second application of the transformation the image of point P' is point P''. Compare point P and point P''.
12. Describe the image of a horizontal line. Of a vertical line.

State the image of the point under a reflection of the plane
a. in the x-axis   **b.** in the y-axis.

13. $(3, 4)$	**15.** $(-1, 7)$	**17.** $(5, 0)$	**19.** $(a, 0)$
14. $(-2, -4)$	**16.** $(2, -8)$	**18.** $(0, -3)$	**20.** (c, d)

**WRITTEN
EXERCISES**

For each exercise, a transformation is specified by the equations $x' = -x$
$$y' = y.$$

$\boxed{A}$ 1. Describe the transformation verbally.
2. Point $(-3, 5)$ has what image?

3. Point $(2, -9)$ has what preimage?

4. Describe the set of all fixed points under the transformation.

State the equations of the reflection that maps the first point into the second point.

5. $(7, 4) \rightarrow (7, -4)$

7. $(0, 2) \rightarrow (0, 2)$

6. $(-3, 2) \rightarrow (3, 2)$

8. $(a, 4) \rightarrow (a, -4)$

In Exercises 9–16 use the transformation $x' = x$
$$y' = -y.$$
Assume that the image of every segment is a segment congruent to the original segment. Using a separate coordinate plane for each exercise draw $\overline{PQ}$ and its image.

9. $P(-1, 2); Q(5, 2)$

13. $P(3, 0); Q(7, 4)$

10. $P(0, -3); Q(5, -3)$

14. $P(3, 1); Q(7, 5)$

11. $P(3, 1); Q(3, 4)$

15. $P(3, -2); Q(7, -2)$

12. $P(-2, 0); Q(-2, 4)$

16. $P(-2, -1); Q(-2, 4)$

In Exercises 17–20 use the transformation $x' = -x$
$$y' = y.$$
Plot points A, B, C. Draw triangle ABC. On the same coordinate plane draw the image of triangle ABC.

17. $A(1, -1); B(1, 3); C(4, 4)$

19. $A(-3, 4); B(-2, 6); C(-5, 5)$

18. $A(0, 0); B(0, 6); C(-3, -5)$

20. $A(-3, -3); B(5, 0); C(2, 1)$

In Exercises 21–24 you are given points $P(1, 1)$, $Q(2, 3)$, and $R(4, 7)$. Use the reflection that has the equations: $x' = x$
$$y' = -y.$$

21. State the slope of $\overleftrightarrow{PQ}$. Of $\overleftrightarrow{PR}$. Are points P, Q, and R collinear?

22. State the coordinates of points P', Q', and R'.

23. State the slope of $\overleftrightarrow{P'Q'}$. Of $\overleftrightarrow{P'R'}$. Are points P', Q', and R' collinear?

24. Compute the lengths of $\overline{PR}$ and $\overline{P'R'}$. Compare the lengths.

25–28. Repeat Exercises 21–24 with just this one change in what is given: Point R is point $(4, 8)$.

In Exercises 29–32 a reflection in the y-axis is given.

29. Prove: Every vertical line maps into a vertical line under reflection.
    Hint: Let the line have the equation $x = c$. Take any three points $P(c, p)$, $Q(c, q)$ and $R(c, r)$ on the line. Show that the image points P', Q', and R' lie on a vertical line.

30. Prove: Every line maps into a line under reflection.

    Hint: The case of a vertical line has already been proved. Take any three points $P(a, b)$, $Q(c, d)$ and $R(e, f)$ on the line. Note that $\dfrac{d-b}{c-a} = \dfrac{f-b}{e-a}$. See Exercises 22, 23.

31. Prove: Segment length is invariant under reflection.

    Hint: For any segment let the endpoints be $P(a, b)$ and $Q(c, d)$. Compute the coordinates of points P' and Q'. Compute PQ and $P'Q'$.

32. Prove: Angle measure is invariant under reflection.

    Hint: Given any angle PQR, prove: $\triangle PQR \cong \triangle P'Q'R'$.

14–5   Products of Transformations

To get an idea of what is meant by the product of two transformations, look at the following example.

Two transformations f and g are specified by the equations:

$$f \quad \begin{aligned} x' &= x \\ y' &= -y \end{aligned} \qquad g \quad \begin{aligned} x' &= x + 5 \\ y' &= y + 2. \end{aligned}$$

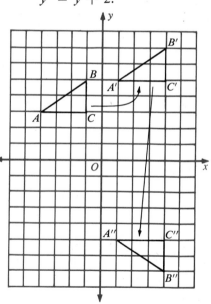

Triangle ABC has vertices $(-4, 3)$, $(-1, 5)$ and $(-1, 3)$. Apply transformation g and then apply transformation f. In Figure 5–1 you see:

1. $\triangle ABC$.

2. The image, $\triangle A'B'C'$, of $\triangle ABC$ under transformation g.

3. The image, $\triangle A''B''C''$, of $\triangle A'B'C'$ under transformation f.

Triangle $A''B''C''$ is the image of $\triangle ABC$ under the *product transformation fg.*

Figure 5–1

Of course *f* and *g* can name transformations different from the particular ones used above. Let *g* be any transformation that maps each point *P* into the unique point *P'*. Let *f* be a transformation that maps point *P'* into the unique point *P''*. Under the successive transformations, *g* followed by *f*, each point *P* is paired with a unique point *P''*. The mapping that maps *P* into *P''* is said to be the **product of transformations *f* and *g*.** It is denoted by *fg*. Notice the order of the symbols. *f* is applied to the image *previously* obtained by applying transformation *g*.

To see that *fg* and *gf* need not map a figure into the same image, we let *f* and *g* be, as at the beginning of this section, the transformations having the equations

$$f \quad \begin{array}{l} x' = x \\ y' = -y \end{array} \qquad g \quad \begin{array}{l} x' = x + 5 \\ y' = y + 2. \end{array}$$

In Figure 5–2 you see

1. △*ABC*.

2. The image, △*A'B'C'*, of △*ABC* under transformation *f*.

3. The image, △*A''B''C''*, of △*A'B'C'* under transformation *g*.

Triangle *A''B''C''* is the image of △*ABC* under the product transformation *gf*.

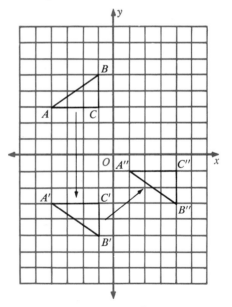

Figure 5–2

As Figures 5–1 and 5–2 suggest, both of the product transformations *fg* and *gf* are rigid transformations. Distance and angle measure are invariant in each case. However, *fg* and *gf* are not equivalent transformations, for they yield different images. Under *fg* point *A* has the image (1, −5). Under *gf* point *A* has the image (1, −1).

m and n are two transformations of the plane.

1. Does the product transformation *mn* mean
(a) that you apply transformation *m* and then transformation *n*, or
(b) that you apply transformation *n* and then transformation *m*?

2. Is *mn* necessarily the same mapping as *nm*?

3. Has it been shown that, for all *m* and *n*, *mn* must differ from *nm*?

4. Suppose *m* is a reflection in the *x*-axis. What is the image of a point *P*
under the product transformation *mm*?

Use transformations *f* and *g* that have the equations

$$f \quad \begin{cases} x' = x + 2 \\ y' = y \end{cases} \qquad\qquad g \quad \begin{cases} x' = x + 5 \\ y' = y. \end{cases}$$

5. State the image of point (4, 13) under transformation *g*.

6. State the image of point (9, 13) under transformation *f*.

7. State the image of point (4, 13) under the product transformation *fg*.

8. State the image of point (1, 6) under product transformation *fg*.

9. State the image of point (1, 6) under product transformation *gf*.

10. State the point that has as its image, under product transformation
fg, the point (4, 0).

In Exercises 1–8 use transformations *f* and *g* that have the equations

$$f \quad \begin{cases} x' = x - 4 \\ y' = y + 3 \end{cases} \qquad\qquad g \quad \begin{cases} x' = x - 5 \\ y' = y + 4. \end{cases}$$

Use points $A(1, 2)$; $B(1, -1)$; $C(5, 2)$.

A

1. Draw triangle *ABC* on a coordinate plane.

2. On the same coordinate plane draw the image, $\triangle A'B'C'$, of $\triangle ABC$
under transformation *g*.

3. On the same coordinate plane draw the image, $\triangle A''B''C''$, of $\triangle A'B'C'$ under transformation f.

4. Inspect your figure. Then state the equations of a single translation equivalent to the product transformation fg.

5. Draw triangle ABC on another coordinate plane.

6. On the same coordinate plane draw the image, $\triangle A'B'C'$, of $\triangle ABC$ under transformation f.

7. On the same coordinate plane draw the image, $\triangle A''B''C''$, of $\triangle A'B'C'$ under transformation g.

8. Inspect your figure. Then state the equations of a single translation equivalent to the product transformation gf.

In Exercises 9–16 use transformations f and g specified by the equations

$$f \qquad \begin{array}{l} x' = 2x \\[4pt] y' = 2y \end{array} \qquad\qquad g \qquad \begin{array}{l} x' = -x \\[4pt] y' = y. \end{array}$$

Use points $A(1, 0)$; $B(4, -1)$; $C(4, 3)$

9–11. Repeat Exercises 1–3, but use the points and transformations given above.

12. In this case is the product transformation fg a translation? a reflection? an expansion? a rigid transformation?

13–15. Repeat Exercises 5–7, but use the points and transformations given above.

16. Compare the image under product transformation gf with the image under product transformation fg.

In Exercises 17–24 use transformations f and g that have the equations

$$f \qquad \begin{array}{l} x' = x + 2 \\[4pt] y' = y - 1 \end{array} \qquad\qquad g \qquad \begin{array}{l} x' = 2x \\[4pt] y' = 2y. \end{array}$$

Use points $A(-2, 1)$; $B(-1, -1)$; $C(1, 0)$.

17–19. Repeat Exercises 1–3, but use the points and transformations given above.

20. In this case is the product transformation a translation? an expansion? a rigid transformation?

21–23. Repeat Exercises 5–7, but use the points and transformations given above.

24. Compare the image under product transformation gf with the image under product transformation fg.

In Exercises 25–27 use transformations f and g that have the equations

$$
\begin{array}{cc}
x' = 3x & x' = \tfrac{1}{2}x \\
f & g \\
y' = 3y & y' = \tfrac{1}{2}y.
\end{array}
$$

Use points $A(6, 8)$; $B(0, -8)$; $C(4, 5)$.

Find the image of triangle ABC under the product transformation named.

B **25.** fg **26.** gf **27.** ff

28. Make a conjecture about the nature of a product transformation when each of the individual transformations is an expansion or contraction of the plane.

C **29.** Prove: If f and g are translations, then the product transformation fg is a translation. Then prove that fg and gf yield the same image.

Hint: Let f and g have the equations

$$
\begin{array}{cc}
x' = x + h & x' = x + H \\
f & g \\
y' = y + k & y' = y + K.
\end{array}
$$

Let $P(a, b)$ be any point in the plane.

30. State and prove a theorem about expansions.

Hint: See Exercise 29.

31. State equations for two particular stretchings (f and g) of the plane such that the product transformation fg

a. Is a stretching of the plane.

b. Is an expansion of the plane.

c. Is of a type different from any transformation named in this chapter.

32. a. Find equations for three particular transformations (f, g, and m) of the plane such that the product transformation $f(gm)$ maps any point (a, b) into point $(-a, b)$.

b. Repeat **a**, but state three different transformations.

CHAPTER SUMMARY

Inventory of Structure and Methods

1. A transformation of the coordinate plane into itself carries each point $P(x, y)$ into a unique point $P'(x', y')$. Transformations are usually specified by two equations that relate the coordinates x' and y' of an image point to the coordinates x and y of its preimage.

2. Some transformations that affect distances are:

Horizontal stretching ($k > 1$) or shrinking ($0 < k < 1$): $x' = kx$
$$y' = y.$$

Vertical stretching ($k > 1$) or shrinking ($0 < k < 1$): $x' = x$
$$y' = ky.$$

Expansion ($k > 1$) or contraction ($0 < k < 1$): $x' = kx$
$$y' = ky.$$

3. Some rigid transformations, under which distances are invariant are:

Translation: $x' = x + h$
$$y' = y + k.$$
Reflection in the y-axis: $x' = -x$
$$y' = y.$$
Reflection in the x-axis: $x' = x$
$$y' = -y.$$

4. When a transformation g is followed by a transformation f, each point P of the plane is mapped into a unique point P'' of the plane under a product of transformations denoted by fg.

Vocabulary and Spelling

function (*p. 513*)
mapping (*p. 513*)
domain (*p. 513*)
range (*p. 513*)
image (*p. 514*)
preimage (*p. 514*)
fixed point (*p. 514*)
transformation of the
  number line (*p. 514*)
transformation of the
  coordinate plane (*p. 514*)

stretching (*p. 517*)
shrinking (*p. 517*)
expansion (*p. 518*)
contraction (*p. 518*)
invariant (*p. 519*)
rigid transformation
  of the plane (*p. 522*)
translation (*p. 522*)
reflection (*p. 526*)
product of transformations (*p. 531*)

CHAPTER TEST

14–1   The rule for a particular transformation of the number line into itself is $M: x \rightarrow 5 - \frac{1}{2}x$.

1. The image of 4 is __?__.

3. The image of a number t is __?__.

2. The preimage of 0 is __?__.

4. That number which is equal to its own image is __?__.

14–2   The rule for a particular transformation of the coordinate plane into itself is $M:(x, y) \rightarrow (3x, y)$.

  5. Two equations that specify the transformation are $x' = \underline{\ ?\ }$ and $y' = \underline{\ ?\ }$.

  6. The point $(-2, 4)$ is mapped into the point $(\underline{\ ?\ }, \underline{\ ?\ })$.

  7. The vertical line $x = 5$ is mapped into the line whose equation is $\underline{\ ?\ }$.

  8. The transformation is a (stretching/expansion) $\underline{\ ?\ }$.

14–3   A particular transformation of the plane into itself is specified by the equations $x' = x + 2$
$$y' = y - 3.$$

  9. The image of point $(4, -1)$ is point $(\underline{\ ?\ }, \underline{\ ?\ })$.

  10. The preimage of point $(-2, 0)$ is point $(\underline{\ ?\ }, \underline{\ ?\ })$.

  11. A segment 7 units long maps into a segment $\underline{\ ?\ }$ units long.

  12. Because any angle and its image have equal measures, angle measure is called $\underline{\ ?\ }$ under the transformation.

14–4   A reflection of the plane in the x-axis is specified by the equations

$$x' = x$$
$$y' = -y.$$

Classify the statements as true or false.

  13. Each point in Quadrant II maps into a point in Quadrant III.

  14. Every point on the y-axis is a fixed point.

  15. A horizontal line maps into a horizontal line.

  16. A line with slope $\frac{2}{3}$ maps into a line with slope $-\frac{5}{2}$.

14–5   Transformations f and g are specified by the equations

$$f \quad \begin{array}{l} x' = x + 1 \\ \\ y' = 2y \end{array} \qquad\qquad g \quad \begin{array}{l} x' = x - 3 \\ \\ y' = y - 1. \end{array}$$

  17. Which transformation, f or g, is a translation?

  18. Under the product transformation fg the image of point $(10, 4)$ is point $(\underline{\ ?\ }, 6)$.

  19. There is no fixed point under the product transformation fg because, for any real number j, every point with x-coordinate j maps into a point with x-coordinate $\underline{\ ?\ }$.

  20. Under the product transformation gf the preimage of point (r, s) is point $(\underline{\ ?\ }, \underline{\ ?\ })$.

CHAPTER REVIEW

14–1 Mappings and Transformations *Pages 513–517*

1. Under a transformation any point that is mapped into itself is called a __?__ point.

2. The mapping specified by the equation $x' = 5x$ can also be indicated by $M:x \rightarrow$ __?__.

3. Under the transformation of the plane given by $M:(x, y) \rightarrow (x - 3, 2y)$, the image of the origin is point (__?__, __?__).

4. Under the transformation of the plane given by $M:(x, y) \rightarrow (\frac{1}{2}x, 3 - y)$, the preimage of point (5, 6) is point (__?__, __?__).

14–2 Stretchings and Shrinkings; *Pages 517–521*
Expansions and Contractions

5. What kind of transformation, a stretching or a shrinking, is specified by the equations $x' = \frac{1}{3}x$
$$y' = y?$$

6. What kind of transformation, an expansion or a contraction, is specified by the equations $x' = 4x$
$$y' = 4y?$$

7. Under the transformation of Exercise 6, the image of point $(-3, 1)$ is point (__?__, __?__).

8. Under the transformation of Exercise 5, every point on the __?__-axis is a fixed point.

14–3 Translations *Pages 522–526*

9. Under a rigid transformation of the plane __?__ between points and __?__ of angles are invariant.

10. If under a certain translation the image of a line l is line l', then lines l and l' are __?__ lines.

11. If the image of $\angle C$ under a translation is $\angle C'$, then $\angle C$ and $\angle C'$ are __?__ angles.

12. Under a particular translation specified by the equations
$$x' = x + 10$$
$$y' = y + 2,$$
the image of point $(-7, 0)$ is point (__?__, __?__).

14–4 Reflections *Pages 526–530*

The equations of a particular reflection are $x' = -x$
$$y' = y.$$

13. The transformation is a reflection in the __?__ -axis.

14. For every fixed point the __?__ -coordinate is 0.

15. The point $(-7, -3)$ maps into the point (__?__, __?__).

16. The image of the segment with endpoints $(2, 1)$ and $(5, 3)$ is a segment with slope __?__.

14–5 Products of Transformations

Pages 530–534

Transformations f and g are specified by the equations

$$f \quad \begin{aligned} x' &= x - 2 \\ y' &= y \end{aligned} \qquad g \quad \begin{aligned} x' &= 2x \\ y' &= y + 5. \end{aligned}$$

17. Under transformation g the image of point $(3, 2)$ is point (__?__, __?__).

18. Under transformation f the image of point $(6, 7)$ is point (__?__, __?__).

19. By observing Exercises 17 and 18, you see that, under the product transformation fg, the image of point $(3, 2)$ is point (__?__, __?__).

20. Under the product transformation gg the image of point $(3, 2)$ is point (__?__, __?__).

• EXTRA FOR EXPERTS

Rotations of the Coordinate Plane

Suppose you lay a disk of clear plastic over a drawing showing coordinate axes. Three dots are marked on the plastic, as shown in Fig. 1a. Rotate the disk counterclockwise through an angle of forty-five degrees. (Fig. 1b).

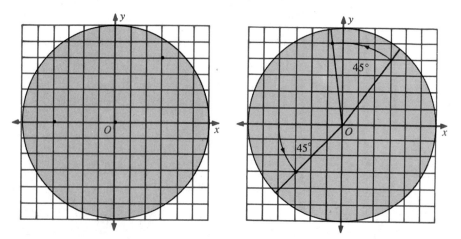

Figure 1a   Figure 1b

The point on the plastic that lay above the origin still lies above the origin; the point that lay above $(-4, 0)$ now lies above $(-2.8, -2.8)$, approximately; and the point that lay above $(3, 4)$ now lies above $(-.7, 4.9)$, approximately. Actually the image of point $(3, 4)$ has coordinates $x' = 3 \cos 45° - 4 \sin 45°$, $y' = 3 \sin 45° + 4 \cos 45°$.

As you might guess from the special case discussed above, the equations that specify a rotation of the coordinate plane about the origin, counterclockwise through $n°$, are

$$x' = x \cos n° - y \sin n°$$

$$y' = x \sin n° + y \cos n°.$$

Because of your limited knowledge of trigonometry we shall not dwell on these equations.

This whole section, in fact, will be informal. For instance, the meaning of directly congruent and oppositely congruent will be suggested by figures rather than established by definition.

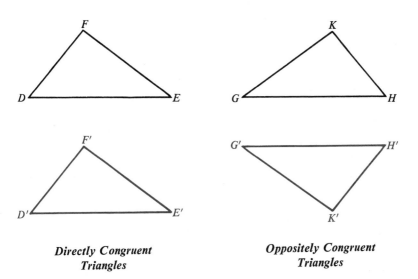

Directly Congruent Triangles   **Oppositely Congruent Triangles**

Three Rigid Transformations

Translations, rotations, and reflections can be discussed without reference to coordinate axes. The figures on the next page show the image of triangle ABC in an example of each type of rigid transformation.

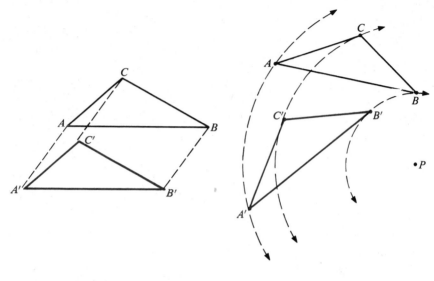

Translation   **Rotation About Point P**

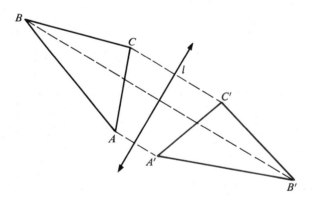

Reflection in Line l

The image of triangle *ABC* under any translation or rotation is a triangle directly congruent to triangle *ABC*, whereas the image of triangle *ABC* under a reflection is a triangle oppositely congruent to triangle *ABC*. Do you see that the image of triangle *ABC* under an even number of reflections is a triangle that is directly congruent to triangle *ABC*? And do you see that there is no product of translations and rotations that can yield the same image for a scalene triangle as one reflection yields?

EXERCISES

1. Use the equations found on page 539 to show that under a counter-clockwise rotation of forty-five degrees about the origin

    a. The image of point $(-4, 0)$ is point $(-2\sqrt{2}, -2\sqrt{2})$.

    b. The image of point $(3, 4)$ is point $(-.7, 4.9)$, approximately.

In Exercises 2 and 3 begin with a figure roughly like the one shown, but *much* larger.

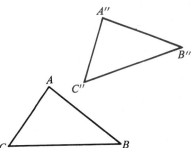

2. Make a sketch to illustrate how $\triangle ABC$ can be mapped into $\triangle A''B''C''$

    a. By the product, *rt*, of a rotation and a translation.

    b. By the product, *tr*, of a translation and a rotation.

3. Make a drawing, using a compass, to illustrate how $\triangle ABC$ can be mapped into $\triangle A''B''C''$ by one rotation.

    Hint: The center of rotation must be equidistant from points A and A''; it must also be equidistant from points B and B''.

4. Make a drawing to show the image of $\triangle XYZ$ under the product of two transformations: a reflection in line j followed by a reflection in line k. Notice that $j \parallel k$.

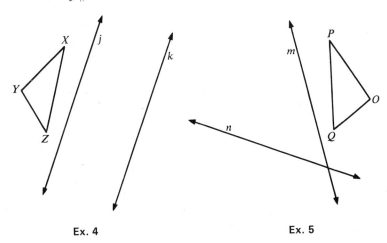

Ex. 4   Ex. 5

5. Make a drawing to show the image of $\triangle POQ$ under the product of two transformations: a reflection in line m followed by a reflection in line n.

15

Areas of Polygons and Circles

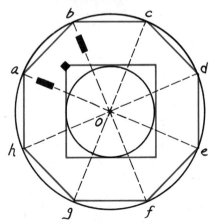

Two regular polygons, one inscribed in a circle and the other circumscribed about a circle, can be seen in this aerial view of the John Glenn Junior High School in San Angelo, Texas.

542

In previous mathematics courses you learned how to compute the areas of certain geometric figures by means of special rules or formulas. As a result, most of you have some familiarity with the meaning of the word "area" even though you might have difficulty defining it.

In this chapter the study of areas will be developed as a part of our deductive system. Basic terms will be defined, and essential postulates will be stated. Theorems will be proved about the areas of various polygons and the circle. Some of these theorems will establish area formulas with which you are already familiar. Others will serve as a basis for comparing areas of similar polygons.

■ Quadrilaterals and Triangles

15–1 What Area Means: Basic Definitions and Postulates

Recall that points lying in the interior of a triangle are *not* points of the triangle. The union of a triangle and its interior is called a **triangular region.**

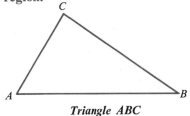

Triangle ABC

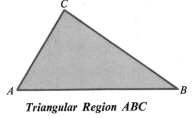

Triangular Region ABC

Triangular region *ABC* is said to be *bounded by* △*ABC*. Points on the sides of △*ABC* as well as those in its interior are points of the region. Two or more triangular regions are called *non-overlapping* if the intersection of any two of them is empty, or is a point, or is a segment. Each of the plane regions pictured below is the union of three non-overlapping triangular regions.

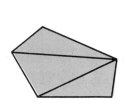 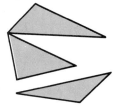 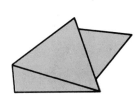

A **polygonal region** is the union of a finite number of non-overlapping coplanar triangular regions. A polygonal region can be cut into a finite number of coplanar triangular regions. Pictured below are four polygonal regions. Note that a triangular region is itself a polygonal region and that a polygonal region may have a so-called "hole" within itself.

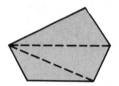 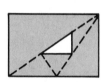

A region that can be cut up into non-overlapping triangular regions in one way can be so cut up in several ways.

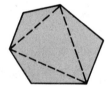 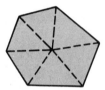

As in the case of triangular regions, two or more polygonal regions are said to be non-overlapping if the intersection of any two is empty, or is the union of a finite number of points or segments or both.

In our study of segments and angles we accepted postulates which enabled us to express the lengths of segments and the measures of angles by positive real numbers. We begin our investigation of polygonal regions with a postulate which likewise associates positive real numbers with polygonal regions.

P₁₈ Corresponding to each polygonal region there is a unique positive number called the **area** of that region.

It seems reasonable that two polygonal regions of the same size and shape should have the same area. This suggests the following two postulates.

P₁₉ If two triangles are congruent, then the regions they bound have the same area.

P₂₀ If a polygonal region is the union of *n* non-overlapping polygonal regions, then its area is the sum of the areas of those *n* regions.

To simplify the discussion of polygonal regions we shall adopt the following practices:

1. Diagrams of polygonal regions will be shaded only where possible confusion exists as to the region being represented.

2. Expressions such as 'the area of triangle *ABC*' and 'the area of rectangle *RSTU*' will be used as substitutes for 'the area of the triangular region *ABC*' and 'the area of the region bounded by rectangle *RSTU*'.

Postulate P₂₀ permits you to add areas in the same manner as you add lengths of segments or measures of angles.

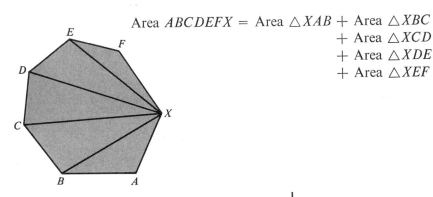

Area $ABCDEFX$ = Area $\triangle XAB$ + Area $\triangle XBC$
+ Area $\triangle XCD$
+ Area $\triangle XDE$
+ Area $\triangle XEF$

ORAL EXERCISES

1. Is the area of a polygon always a positive number?

2. Is a region bounded by a circle a polygonal region?

3. Can a rectangle and triangle have the same area?

4. Does a line have area?

5. A square with area *k* is contained exactly four times in a certain rectangle. What is the area of the rectangle?

6. Is a polygonal region a set of points?

WRITTEN EXERCISES

A 1. Does P_{19} permit you to conclude that if two triangles have the same area, then they are congruent?

2. Does it follow from P_{19} that if two triangles do not have the same area, then they are not congruent?

3. Does a chord of a circle have an area?

4. When a diagonal is drawn in a rectangle, what is true of the areas of the two triangles into which it divides the rectangle? Why?

5. Do the diagonals of a rhombus divide it into four triangles of equal area?

6. Does every polygonal region have an area?

7. Do our postulates assert that every plane figure that has an area must be a polygonal region?

8. On the basis of our postulates can a polygon have an area of
   a. $4\frac{1}{2}$? **b.** -6? **c.** $\sqrt{3}$? **d.** $-\sqrt{5}$?

9. Is it possible to draw a segment with endpoints on the sides of a rectangle that will divide it into two polygons neither of which is a rectangle or a triangle?

10. If two equilateral triangles have equal perimeters, must they also have equal areas?

11. If two isosceles right triangles have equal perimeters, must they also have equal areas?

12. If two polygons have the same area, must they have the same number of sides?

In Exercises 13 and 14 draw a figure like that shown. Then draw dashed segments to illustrate two different ways of dividing each figure into triangles.

13.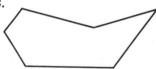

14.

C 15. Given: $\overline{CA} \perp \overline{AB}$; $\overline{DB} \perp \overline{AB}$;
$CX = XB$.

To Prove: Area $\triangle ABC =$
Area trap. $ABDE$.

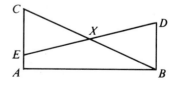

16. Given: $AC = BC$;
$\angle XAB \cong \angle YBA$.

To Prove: Area $\triangle XAC =$
Area $\triangle YBC$.

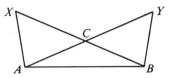

15–2 Areas of Rectangles and Parallelograms

As was true of our earlier distance postulate, our area postulate makes no mention of units. It simply states that an area is a positive number. However, in making applications to the physical world we have to think in terms of units.

The unit for measuring area can be selected at will. However, it is convenient to associate unit area with unit distance in this way: First select a unit of length. Then draw a square whose side is that unit. We shall agree to call the area of the square **1 square unit.**

a unit of length

1 square unit

Pictured is a rectangle *ABCD* of length 3 and width 2. The horizontal and vertical segments shown divide *ABCD* into six squares each of area 1. The area of *ABCD*, the sum of the areas of these six squares, is 6. This number is the same as the product of the length of the base $\overline{AB}$ by the length of $\overline{BC}$, an altitude to that base. Any side of a rectangle may be considered to be the base. Then, each side adjacent to it is an altitude to that base.

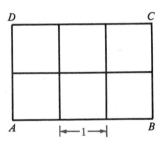

The preceding example suggests the following postulate.

P21 The area of a rectangle is the product of the length of a base and the length of an altitude to that base. ($A = bh$)

COROLLARY The area of a square is the square of the length of its side. ($A = s^2$)

When you apply area formulas in physical problems, you may use any unit of length. However, within any particular problem, all dimensions must be expressed in terms of just one unit. It is necessary to name, in the result of a practical problem, the particular square unit involved.

In describing a rectangle, the length of the base and the length of an altitude are often referred to as simply the *length* and the *width*.

EXAMPLE 1. Find the area of a rectangle whose length is 7 and whose width is 5.

Solution: $A = l \cdot w$; $A = 7 \cdot 5$; $A = 35$. **Answer.**

EXAMPLE 2. Find the area of a rectangle whose length is 2 ft. and whose width is 8 in.

Solution A: Let the linear unit be one inch. The length is $2 \times 12 = 24$ (in.)

$A = bh$; $A = 24 \cdot 8$; $A = 192$ sq. in. **Answer.**

Solution B: Let the linear unit be one foot. The width is $\frac{8}{12} = \frac{2}{3}$ ft.

$A = bh$; $A = 2 \cdot \frac{2}{3}$; $A = \frac{4}{3}$ sq. ft. **Answer.**

By the combined use of our postulates about the areas of congruent triangles and the area of a rectangle, it is possible to prove a theorem about the area of a parallelogram.

Any side of a parallelogram may be termed its **base**. The **altitude** corresponding to a base is a segment perpendicular to the line containing the base from any point on the opposite side of the parallelogram.

In parallelogram *ABCD*, shown at the left below, any one of the dotted parallel and congruent segments is an altitude to the base *b*.

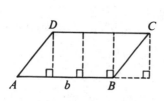   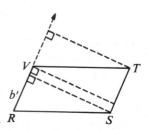

In parallelogram *RSTV*, in the diagram at the right above, any one of the dotted parallel and congruent segments is an altitude to the base *b'*.

THEOREM 15–1 The area of a parallelogram is the product of the length of any base and the length of a corresponding altitude. ($A = bh$)

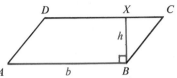

Given: $\square ABCD$ with $AB = b$, $\overline{BX} \perp \overleftrightarrow{CD}$, and $BX = h$.

To Prove: Area $\square ABCD = b \cdot h$.

Outline of Proof:

Case 1: Construct $\overline{AY} \perp \overleftrightarrow{DC}$ and show that the area of $\square ABCD$ is equal to the area of rect. $ABXY$.

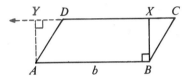

Proof

STATEMENT	REASON
1. Construct $\overline{AY} \perp \overleftrightarrow{DC}$.	1. At a point on a line . . .
2. $\overline{AY} \parallel \overline{BX}$.	2. Lines $\perp$ to same line . . .
3. $ABXY$ is a rect.	3. Definition of rect.
4. Rt. $\triangle AYD \cong$ Rt. $\triangle BXC$.	4. *HA* corollary.
5. Area $\triangle AYD =$ Area $\triangle BXC$.	5. If 2 $\triangle$ are $\cong$, they have equal areas.
6. Area trap. $ABXD =$ Area trap. $ABXD$.	6. Reflexive prop. of equality.
7. Area trap. $ABXD +$ Area $\triangle AYD =$ Area trap. $ABXD +$ Area $\triangle BXC$.	7. Add. prop. of equality.
8. Area trap. $ABXD +$ Area $\triangle AYD =$ Area rect. $ABXY$. Area trap. $ABXD +$ Area $\triangle BXC =$ Area $\square ABCD$.	8. Area-addition postulate.
9. Area rect. $ABXY =$ Area $\square ABCD$.	9. Subst. principle.
10. But, Area rect. $ABXY = bh$.	10. Rectangle area postulate.
11. Area $\square ABCD = bh$.	11. Subst. principle.

The proof shown for Theorem 15–1 is for the particular case where X lies between C and D. Pictures follow of parallelograms in which X lies in all other possible positions with respect to C and D. A complete proof of Theorem 15–1 involves a consideration of these four additional cases.

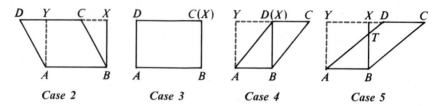

| Case 2 | Case 3 | Case 4 | Case 5 |

Case 2:

A method of proof similar to that used for Case 1 is possible.

Case 3:

$ABCD$ must be a rectangle. Therefore, P_{21} applies.

Case 4:

Area $\triangle AYD =$ Area $\triangle BXC$ since the $\triangle$ are $\cong$. Therefore, Area $\square ABCD =$ Area rect. $ABDY$.

Case 5:

Area $\triangle AYD =$ Area $\triangle BXC$ since the $\triangle$ are $\cong$.
Area $\square ABCD =$ Area $\triangle ABT +$ Area $\triangle BXC -$ Area $\triangle TDX$.
Area rect. $ABXY =$ Area $\triangle ABT +$ Area $\triangle AYD -$ Area $\triangle TDX$.
Therefore, Area $\square ABCD =$ Area rect. $ABXY$.

COROLLARY. Parallelograms having congruent bases and congruent altitudes have equal areas.

ORAL EXERCISES

1. What is the area of a square with a side $1\frac{1}{2}$ in. long? with a side k feet long?

2. Can you determine the length of a base and the length of a corresponding altitude of a rectangle if given only its area?

3. If two parallelograms have equal areas must they be congruent?

4. How is the area of a parallelogram affected if the lengths of its base and altitude are both doubled?

5. The lengths of sides of two squares have the ratio $1:3$. What is the ratio of the areas of the two squares?

6. If given the length of the base of a parallelogram and the area, can you determine the length of the altitude? the perimeter?

7. Can you find the area of a parallelogram if given only the lengths of its sides?

8. If two parallelograms are not congruent, can their perimeters be equal?

WRITTEN
EXERCISES

A

1. Find the area of a parallelogram if a base and corresponding altitude have the indicated lengths.

   a. base 8 in., alt. 4 in.   **c.** base $1\frac{1}{2}$ ft., alt. 6 in.

   b. base $3\frac{1}{2}$ ft., alt. $\frac{3}{4}$ ft.   **d.** base x yd., alt. y ft.

2. Find the area of a

   a. Square with a side $\frac{2}{3}$ in. long

   b. Square with perimeter 8 in.

   c. Rectangle with length 3 in. and perimeter 10 in.

   d. Square with perimeter $12\sqrt{3}$ in.

3. Given a rectangle with length 10 in. and width 5 in. and a parallelogram with base 12 in. and corresponding altitude 6 in. What is the ratio of the area of the rectangle to the area of the parallelogram?

4. What is the width of a rectangle with length 10 in. that has the same area as a rectangle with length 12 in. and width 9 in.?

5. Find the dimensions of a rectangle with a length five times its width and an area of 80 sq. in.

6. The area of a rectangle is 384 sq. ft. The lengths of the sides are in the ratio 2:3. Find the dimensions.

Find the area of parallelogram ABCD given $m\angle A = 30$ and

B

   7. $AB = 10$ in. $AD = 6$ in.

   8. $AB = 6$ ft. $AX = 3\sqrt{3}$ ft.

   9. $AD = 4\sqrt{3}$ in. $AB = 8$ in.

 10. $AX = 3$ ft. $AB = 4\sqrt{2}$ ft.

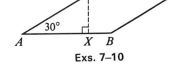

Exs. 7–10

If the area of a rectangle is to remain constant, what change must take place in the length of the base when the length of the altitude is

11. Multiplied by 3?   **13.** Increased by 25%?

12. Divided by 2?   **14.** Decreased by 25%?

15. A walk 3 ft. wide surrounds a rectangular grass plot 30 ft. long and 18 ft. wide. Find the area of the walk.

16. Find the area of a parallelogram with sides 12 in. and 8 in. long if one of its angles has measure 120.

17. The sides of a parallelogram are 6 in. and 8 in. long. Find the length of a longer altitude if a shorter altitude is 4 in. long.

18. A parallelogram with sides 6 in. and 10 in. long has an area of $30\sqrt{2}$ sq. in. Find the measure of each angle of the parallelogram.

C **19.** Find the area of a square inscribed in a circle of radius k.

20. By what per cent is the area of a rectangle increased if the length of each side is increased by 10 per cent?

21. Find the length of the sides of a rectangle of area 35 sq. in. and perimeter 24 in.

22. In a coordinate plane the vertices of a parallelogram are $A(-3, -2)$, $B(6, -2)$, $C(10, 3)$, and $D(1, 3)$. Find the area of $\square ABCD$.

15–3 Areas of Triangles and Trapezoids

THEOREM 15–2 The area of a triangle is one-half the product of the length of a base and the length of the altitude to that base. ($A = \frac{1}{2}bh$)

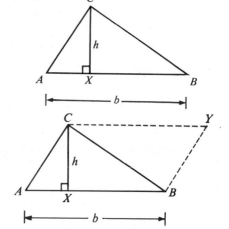

Given: $\triangle ABC$ with $AB = b$,
     $\overline{CX} \perp \overline{AB}$, and $CX = h$.

To Prove: Area $\triangle ABC = \frac{1}{2}bh$.

Outline of Proof:

Complete $\square ABYC$ by constructing $\overleftrightarrow{CY} \parallel \overline{AB}$ and $\overleftrightarrow{BY} \parallel \overline{AC}$. Show that area $\triangle ABC = \frac{1}{2}$ area $\square ABYC$.

Proof: The proof is left for you.

COROLLARY 1 Triangles with congruent bases and congruent altitudes have equal areas.

COROLLARY 2 The area of an equilateral triangle with side of length s is one-fourth the product of the square of s and $\sqrt{3}$. $\left(A = \dfrac{s^2}{4} \sqrt{3} \right)$

COROLLARY 3 The area of a rhombus is one-half the product of the lengths of its diagonals.

$$\left(A = \frac{d_1 \cdot d_2}{2}\right)$$

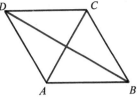

(*Hint:* At what angle do $\overline{AC}$ and $\overline{DB}$ intersect? What is true of the four △ formed?)

Whereas any side of a triangle or parallelogram can be taken as the base, only the parallel sides of a trapezoid are called bases. Recall that an **altitude of a trapezoid** is a perpendicular segment from any point in one base to a point in the line containing the other base.

THEOREM 15–3   The area of a trapezoid is one-half the product of the length of an altitude and the sum of the lengths of the bases. $A = \frac{1}{2}h(b_1 + b_2)$

Given: Trapezoid $ABCD$ with $AB = b_1$, $DC = b_2$, and $DX = h$.

To Prove: Area $ABCD = \frac{1}{2}h(b_1 + b_2)$.

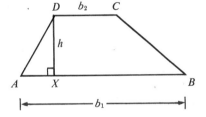

Outline of Proof:

Draw $\overline{DB}$ dividing $ABCD$ into △ABD and △DCB. Express the area of $ABCD$ as the sum of the areas of these △.

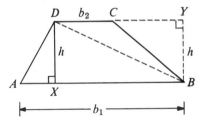

Proof: The proof is left for you.

ORAL EXERCISES

1. If given the area of a triangle and the length of each side, can you find the lengths of its three altitudes?

2. If two triangles have the same area, must they have congruent bases and congruent altitudes?

3. What is the locus in a plane of the vertex of a triangle with a given area when the base has a specified length and position?

4. In a triangle, side j is longer than side k. Is the altitude to j longer than the altitude to k?

5. Does the median of a trapezoid divide it into two trapezoids of equal area?

6. Does a segment joining the midpoints of the bases of a trapezoid divide it into two trapezoids of equal area?

7. Can you find the area of a trapezoid if given only the perimeter?

8. If given the length of the altitude of an equilateral triangle can you find the area of the triangle?

WRITTEN EXERCISES

Exercises 1–4 refer to triangles in which *b* is the length of the base, *h* is the length of the corresponding altitude, and *A* is the area. Supply the missing part in each exercise.

	b	**h**	**A**
1.	4 in.	6 in.	?
2.	?	5 in.	10 sq. in.
3.	5 ft.	?	12 sq. ft.
4.	$2\sqrt{3}$ in.	$3\sqrt{3}$ in.	?

Exercises 5–10 refer to trapezoids in which b_1 and b_2 are lengths of bases, *h* is the length of the altitude, and *A* is the area. Find the missing part in each exercise.

	b_1	b_2	**h**	**A**
5.	10 in.	6 in.	4 in.	?
6.	$\frac{1}{2}$ ft.	$\frac{1}{3}$ ft.	1 ft.	?
7.	5 cm.	3 cm.	?	24 sq. cm.
8.	6 cm.	?	2 cm.	18 sq. cm.
9.	?	5 yd.	3 yd.	12 sq. yd.
10.	$5\sqrt{2}$ in.	$3\sqrt{2}$ in.	?	$4\sqrt{6}$ sq. in.

Exercises 11–16 refer to a right triangle in which *a* and *b* are the lengths of the legs and *c* is the length of the hypotenuse. Find the area of the triangle.

11. $a = 6$ in., $b = 4$ in.

12. $a = 5$ ft., $c = 13$ ft.

13. $a = 5\sqrt{2}$ cm., $b = 4\sqrt{2}$ cm.

14. $b = 2$ in., $c = 6$ in.

15. $a = 2\sqrt{3}$ ft., $c = 4$ ft.

16. $a = \sqrt{\frac{2}{3}}$ cm., $b = \sqrt{\frac{2}{3}}$ cm.

EXAMPLE. Find the length of the side of an equilateral triangle of area $18\sqrt{3}$ sq. cm.

Solution: Let s be the length. Then $\dfrac{s^2}{4}\sqrt{3} = 18\sqrt{3}$.

$$\frac{s^2}{4} = 18$$

$$s^2 = 72 \quad s = 6\sqrt{2} \text{ cm.,} \quad \textbf{Answer.}$$

Exercises 17–22 refer to an equilateral triangle in which s is the length of a side, p is the perimeter, and A is the area. Find the missing parts in each exercise.

	s	p	A		s	p	A
17.	6 in.	?	?	**20.**	?	12 ft.	?
18.	5 ft.	?	?	**21.**	?	?	$9\sqrt{3}$ sq. ft.
19.	$2\sqrt{3}$ cm.	?	?	**22.**	?	?	$12\sqrt{3}$ sq. cm.

23. Find the area of a rhombus with diagonals 9 ft. and 12 ft. long.

24. Find the area of a rhombus with sides 13 in. long and one diagonal 10 in. long.

25. The area of a rhombus is 64 sq. in. Find the lengths of the diagonals if their lengths have the ratio 2:1.

26. The shorter diagonal of a rhombus has the same length as a side. Find the area of the rhombus if the longer diagonal is 12 in. long.

27. An isosceles trapezoid has base angles of measure 45 and bases 6 in. and 12 in. long. Find the area of the trapezoid.

28. Find the area of a trapezoid if the altitude is 6 in. long and the median 8 in. long.

29. $ABCD$ is a trapezoid with $\overline{AB} \parallel \overline{DC}$. Find the area of $ABCD$ given $AB = 25$, $BC = 20$, $CD = 4$, $DA = 13$.

30. Two sides of a triangle are 6 in. and 10 in. long respectively. Find the ratio of the areas of the two triangles into which the bisector of the angle determined by these sides divides the triangle.

31. In an equilateral triangle with side 6 in. long a segment is drawn parallel to one side so as to form a trapezoid with 4 in. legs. Find the areas of the trapezoid and the triangle into which the given triangle is divided.

32. An isosceles trapezoid with bases of lengths 12 and 16 is inscribed in a circle of radius 10. The center of the circle lies in the interior of the trapezoid. Find the area of the trapezoid.

33. Find the area of the quadrilateral whose vertices in a coordinate plane are $(2, -2)$, $(6, 4)$, $(-5, 2)$, and $(-1, 5)$.

34. Find the area of the isosceles trapezoid pictured if all of its sides are tangent to circle O.

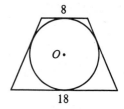

15–4   Comparing Areas of Similar Triangles

In our study of similar triangles we proved that the lengths of corresponding altitudes of two similar triangles have the same ratio as the lengths of any pair of corresponding sides. This property is useful in establishing a theorem about the ratio of the areas of two similar triangles.

THEOREM 15–4   The ratio of the areas of two similar triangles is the square of the ratio of the lengths of any two corresponding sides.

Given:

$\triangle ABC \sim \triangle RST$

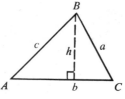

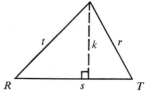

To Prove:

$$\frac{\text{Area } \triangle ABC}{\text{Area } \triangle RST} = \left(\frac{b}{s}\right)^2 = \left(\frac{a}{r}\right)^2 = \left(\frac{c}{t}\right)^2.$$

Outline of Proof:

Draw the altitudes from B and S. Designate their lengths by h and k.

$$\frac{\text{Area } \triangle ABC}{\text{Area } \triangle RST} = \frac{\frac{1}{2}b \cdot h}{\frac{1}{2}s \cdot k} = \frac{b \cdot h}{s \cdot k} = \frac{b}{s} \cdot \frac{h}{k}$$

But $\dfrac{h}{k} = \dfrac{b}{s}$.   (In $\sim \triangle$, the ratio of the lengths of corresponding

altitudes ...)

$$\frac{\text{Area } \triangle ABC}{\text{Area } \triangle RST} = \frac{b}{s} \cdot \frac{b}{s} = \left(\frac{b}{s}\right)^2$$

Since $\dfrac{b}{s} = \dfrac{a}{r} = \dfrac{c}{t}$, $\left(\dfrac{b}{s}\right)^2 = \left(\dfrac{a}{r}\right)^2 = \left(\dfrac{c}{t}\right)^2$

$$\frac{\text{Area } \triangle ABC}{\text{Area } \triangle RST} = \left(\frac{b}{s}\right)^2 = \left(\frac{a}{r}\right)^2 = \left(\frac{c}{t}\right)^2$$

1. Two equilateral triangles have sides 3 in. and 5 in. long respectively. What is the ratio of their areas? their perimeters? the lengths of their altitudes?

2. If the length of each side of a triangle is doubled, what change takes place in the area? the perimeter?

3. The areas of two similar triangles have the ratio 4:9. What is the ratio of the lengths of their sides? of their perimeters?

4. If the areas of two triangles have the ratio 1:4, must the triangles be similar with side lengths in the ratio 1:2?

5. A pair of corresponding sides of two similar triangles are $\sqrt{3}$ in. and 2 in. long. What is the ratio of the areas of the triangles?

6. Two similar triangles have areas in the ratio 3:4. What is the ratio of the lengths of a pair of corresponding sides?

WRITTEN

EXERCISES

In $\triangle ABC$, $\overline{XY} \parallel \overline{AB}$. Find the ratio of the area of $\triangle CXY$ to the area of $\triangle CAB$ when

1. $CX = 2$, $CA = 4$

2. $XY = 2$, $AB = 3$

3. $CY = \sqrt{2}$, $CB = 2$

4. $CX = 3$, $XA = 2$

5. $CX = 3$, $AX = 3$

6. $XY = 2\sqrt{3}$, $AB = 6$

7. $CX:XA = 2:3$

8. $BY:YC = 3:1$

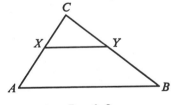

Exs. 1–8

9. Find the ratio of the areas of two similar triangles in which a pair of corresponding sides have lengths of $1\frac{1}{2}$ in. and $2\frac{1}{2}$ in. respectively.

10. The areas of two similar triangles are 36 sq. in. and 64 sq. in. respectively. Find the ratio of the lengths of a pair of corresponding sides.

11. Two similar triangles have areas of 144 sq. in. and 81 sq. in. respectively. If one side of the larger triangle is 18 in. long, find the length of the corresponding side of the smaller triangle.

12. Find the ratio of the perimeters of two similar triangles that have areas of 50 sq. cm. and 25 sq. cm. respectively.

13. The sides of a given triangle have lengths of 3 in., 5 in., and 7 in. Find the lengths of the sides of a similar triangle that has an area eight times that of the given triangle.

14. A pair of corresponding sides of two similar triangles have lengths of 5 in. and 8 in. respectively. The area of the larger triangle is 20 sq. in. Find the area of the smaller triangle.

In $\triangle RST$, $\overline{XY} \parallel \overline{RS}$. Find the ratio of the area of $\triangle TXY$ to the area of trapezoid *RSYX* when

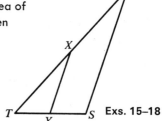

15. $TX = 1$, $TR = 2$

16. $TX = 2$, $XR = 3$

17. $XY = 2$, $RS = 3$

18. $XY = \sqrt{3}$, $RS = 2$

Exs. 15–18

19. The area of a triangle is 64 sq. in. Lines parallel to the base divide one side into four segments of equal length. Find the areas of the four nonoverlapping regions into which the triangle is divided.

20. Given a triangle with an altitude 10 in. long. How far above the base should a parallel line be drawn to divide the triangle into two parts whose areas have the ratio 2:3? (2 answers)

21. Given $\triangle ABC$ with base $\overline{AB}$ and corresponding altitude of length h. Describe a method of dividing $\triangle ABC$ into three parts of equal area by means of lines parallel to $\overline{AB}$.

22. The area of the larger of two similar triangles is 25 per cent more than the area of the smaller. By what per cent (correct to tenths) does the perimeter of the larger triangle exceed that of the smaller triangle?

■ Areas of Regular Polygons

15–5   Special Properties of a Regular Polygon

As previously defined, a **regular polygon** is a convex polygon that is both equiangular and equilateral. The theorems that follow deal with two special circles related to a regular polygon.

THEOREM 15–5   A circle can be circumscribed about any regular polygon.

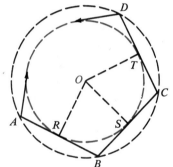

Given: A regular *n*-gon with vertices *A*, *B*, *C*, *D*, ...

To Prove: A circle can be circumscribed about the given regular *n*-gon.

Outline of Proof:

A circle with center *O* can be passed through noncollinear points *A*, *B*, and *C* $\angle ABC \cong \angle BCD$ and $\angle 1 \cong \angle 2$. Therefore, $\angle 3 \cong \angle 4$. $\triangle AOB \cong \triangle DOC$ (SAS), and $\overline{OD} \cong \overline{OA}$ (corres. parts). Thus $OA = OD$ and *D* lies on $\odot O$. By the same method remaining vertices taken successively can be shown to lie on $\odot O$.

THEOREM 15–6   A circle can be inscribed in any regular polygon.

Given: A regular *n*-gon with vertices *A*, *B*, *C*, *D*, ...

To Prove: A circle can be inscribed in the given regular *n*-gon.

Outline of Proof:

By Theorem 15–5, a circle can be circumscribed about the given *n*-gon. From *O*, the center of this circumscribed $\odot$, draw $\overline{OR} \perp \overline{AB}$, $\overline{OS} \perp \overline{BC}$, $\overline{OT} \perp \overline{CD}$, ... The sides of the given *n*-gon are congruent chords of the circumscribed circle. Therefore, $OR = OS = OT = \ldots$, since congruent chords of a circle are equidistant from its center. Hence, a circle with center *O* and radius *OR* will be tangent to each side of the *n*-gon at its midpoint and will be inscribed in the *n*-gon.

DEFINITIONS

1. The **center of a regular polygon** is the common center of its inscribed and circumscribed circles.
2. The **radius of a regular polygon** is the distance from the center of the polygon to a vertex.

3. The **apothem of a regular polygon** is the distance from the center of the polygon to a side.

4. **A central angle of a regular polygon** is an angle whose vertex is the center of the polygon and whose sides contain consecutive vertices of the polygon.

Apothem: OX
Radius: OA, OF
Central angle: ∠*AOF*

Apothem: OX
Radius: OR, OT
Central angle: ∠*ROT*

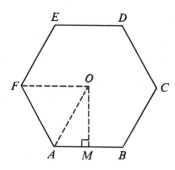

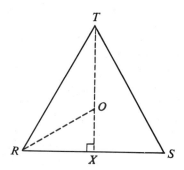

COROLLARY   A central angle of a regular *n*-gon has measure $\dfrac{360}{n}$.

ORAL EXERCISES

1. Is the apothem of a regular polygon greater than the radius of the polygon?

2. What is the measure of a central angle of a regular pentagon?

3. Can the number of sides of a regular polygon be found when the measure of a central angle is known?

4. If a circle can be circumscribed about a polygon, must the polygon be regular?

5. Does a central angle of a regular polygon have the same measure as an exterior angle of the polygon?

6. Name a quadrilateral that is equilateral but not necessarily regular.

7. If a circle can be circumscribed about a trapezoid, must the trapezoid be isosceles?

8. If a circle can be inscribed in a trapezoid, must the trapezoid be isosceles?

WRITTEN EXERCISES

In Exercises 1–6, find the apothem, radius, and measure of the central angle of the specified regular polygon.

A
1. Square, side 6 in. long.

2. Equilateral triangle, side 6 cm. long.

3. Regular hexagon, side 9 ft. long.

4. Square, side x cm. long.

5. Equilateral triangle, side k in. long.

6. Regular hexagon, side t ft. long.

7. Find the length of the side of a regular hexagon of radius 4 in.

8. Find the length of the side of an equilateral triangle of apothem $\sqrt{3}$ cm.

B
9. Find the radius of a circle circumscribed about an equilateral triangle with a 12 in. side.

10. What regular polygon has a radius equal to twice its apothem?

C
11. Prove: If a circle is divided into five congruent arcs, the chords of these arcs form a regular pentagon.

12. Prove: In a circle, the length of a side of an inscribed regular hexagon is equal to twice the apothem of an inscribed equilateral triangle.

15–6 Areas of Regular Polygons

Since the radii drawn to the vertices of a regular polygon of n sides divide it into n congruent triangles, it is not difficult to develop a formula for the area of the region bounded by a regular polygon. We shall refer to the area of such a region as the area of the regular polygon.

THEOREM 15–7 The area of a regular polygon is one-half the product of the apothem and the perimeter. ($A = \frac{1}{2}ap$)

Given: Regular n-gon with vertices R, T, U, V, ..., apothem a, side length s, perimeter p, and area A.

To Prove: $A = \frac{1}{2}ap$

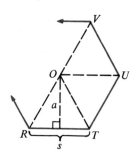

Outline of Proof:

If all radii are drawn, the n-gon is divided into n congruent $\triangle$.

The area of any one $\triangle$ is $\frac{1}{2}as$.

The area of the n-gon is $n(\frac{1}{2}as)$ or $\frac{1}{2}a(ns)$.

But, since $ns = p$, the area of the n-gon is $\frac{1}{2}ap$.

WRITTEN EXERCISES

Find the area of an equilateral triangle with a

A

1. 6 in. side. **3.** 3 ft. apothem. **5.** 3 in. radius.

2. 6 in. radius. **4.** $2\sqrt{3}$ cm. apothem. **6.** t in. perimeter.

Find the area of a regular hexagon with a

7. 4 in. side. **9.** 48 in. perimeter. **11.** k cm. side.

8. 6 in. radius. **10.** $2\sqrt{3}$ in. apothem. **12.** t in. apothem.

B

13. Find the area of a regular pentagon of perimeter 4 and apothem k.

14. Find the area of a regular octagon of t inch side and k inch apothem.

15. A regular decagon of perimeter 40 has an area of $40k$. Find its apothem.

16. Find the length of a side of a regular hexagon with area equal to that of an equilateral triangle with perimeter 36 in.

C

17. Prove: If an equilateral triangle and a regular hexagon have equal perimeters, their areas are in the ratio 2:3.

18. Prove: If an equilateral triangle and a regular hexagon have equal areas, their perimeters have the ratio of $\sqrt{6}$ to 2.

15–7   Comparing Areas of Similar Polygons

Consider two regular polygons that have the same number of sides, n. Each angle of each polygon has measure $\dfrac{(n-2) \cdot 180}{n}$. Since each polygon is equilateral, the ratio of the length of any side of one to any side of the other is the same number. You can therefore conclude that *two regular polygons that have the same number of sides are similar.* However, it does not follow that any two polygons that are similar must be regular.

Pictured below are two similar nonregular pentagons. From corresponding vertices A and L diagonals are drawn dividing the pentagons into the same number of correspondingly placed triangles.

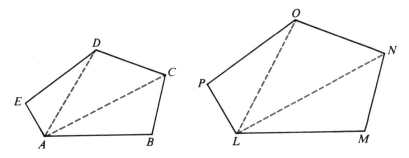

Select a pair of correspondingly placed triangles such as $\triangle ABC$ and $\triangle LMN$ and measure their corresponding angles with a protractor. Do the same for correspondingly placed triangles $\triangle ACD$ and $\triangle LNO$. Your measurements should suggest that correspondingly placed triangles are similar. We shall assume that this property holds for any two similar n-gons.

P22   If two polygons are similar, they can be separated into the same number of triangles similar each to each and in corresponding positions.

This postulate, together with the theorem about the ratio of the areas of similar triangles, will enable you to prove a corresponding theorem about the areas of similar polygons.

THEOREM 15–8 The ratio of the areas of two similar polygons is equal to the square of the ratio of the lengths of any pair of corresponding sides.

Given: n-gon *ABCDE* ... ~ n-gon *A′B′C′D′E′* ... with corresponding sides of lengths s and $s′$, t and $t′$, u and $u′$, ...

To Prove: $\dfrac{\text{Area } ABCDE ...}{\text{Area } A′B′C′D′E′ ...} = \left(\dfrac{s}{s′}\right)^2$

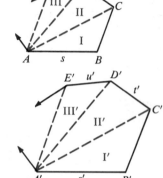

Outline of Proof:

By P_{22} diagonals can be drawn from corresponding vertices A and $A′$; dividing the n-gons into $n - 2$ correspondingly placed ~△.

$\dfrac{\text{Area } \triangle\text{I}}{\text{Area } \triangle\text{I}′} = \left(\dfrac{s}{s′}\right)^2 \qquad \dfrac{\text{Area } \triangle\text{II}}{\text{Area } \triangle\text{II}′} = \left(\dfrac{t}{t′}\right)^2 \qquad \dfrac{\text{Area } \triangle\text{III}}{\text{Area } \triangle\text{III}′} = \left(\dfrac{u}{u′}\right)^2$

Since $\dfrac{s}{s′} = \dfrac{t}{t′} = \dfrac{u}{u′}$, it follows that $\left(\dfrac{s}{s′}\right)^2 = \left(\dfrac{t}{t′}\right)^2 = \left(\dfrac{u}{u′}\right)^2$

Therefore, $\dfrac{\text{Area } \triangle\text{I}}{\text{Area } \triangle\text{I}′} = \dfrac{\text{Area } \triangle\text{II}}{\text{Area } \triangle\text{II}′} = \dfrac{\text{Area } \triangle\text{III}}{\text{Area } \triangle\text{III}′} = \cdots = \left(\dfrac{s}{s′}\right)^2$

Hence, $\dfrac{\text{Area } \triangle\text{I} + \text{Area } \triangle\text{II} + \text{Area } \triangle\text{III} + \ldots}{\text{Area } \triangle\text{I}′ + \text{Area } \triangle\text{II}′ + \text{Area } \triangle\text{III}′ + \ldots} = \left(\dfrac{s}{s′}\right)^2$

or $\dfrac{\text{Area } ABCDE ...}{\text{Area } A′B′C′D′E′ ...} = \left(\dfrac{s}{s′}\right)^2$

ORAL EXERCISES

1. Two similar pentagons have a pair of corresponding sides with lengths in the ratio 1:2. What is the ratio of the areas? of the perimeters?

2. The areas of two similar polygons have the ratio 4:9. What is the ratio of the lengths of two corresponding sides? of the perimeters?

3. Two similar hexagons have areas of 36 sq. in. and 64 sq. in. respectively. What is the ratio of the lengths of a pair of corresponding sides?

4. The perimeters of two similar polygons have the ratio $\sqrt{3}:4$. What is the ratio of the areas of the two polygons?

WRITTEN EXERCISES

A

1. Two regular pentagons have areas of 50 and 100 sq. in. Find the ratio of the lengths of a pair of corresponding sides.

2. The area of one n-gon is $\frac{25}{4}$ times that of a similar n-gon. Find the ratio of the perimeters of the two n-gons.

3. One side of a triangle is 15 in. long and the area is 90 sq. in. Find the area of a similar triangle in which the corresponding side is 9 in. long.

4. Points X, Y, and Z are the midpoints of the sides of triangle ABC. What is the ratio of the area of $\triangle XYZ$ to the area of $\triangle ABC$?

5. The shortest side of a polygon of area 196 sq. cm. is 4 cm. long. Find the area of a similar polygon whose shortest side is 8 cm. long.

6. The sides of a quadrilateral are 3 in., 4 in., 5 in., and 6 in. long. Find the lengths of the sides of a similar quadrilateral whose area is 9 times as great.

B

7. Two similar polygons have corresponding sides with lengths in the ratio 2:3. The sum of the areas of the polygons is 143 sq. in. Find the area of each.

8. The shortest sides of two similar polygons have lengths of 5 ft. and 12 ft. Find the length of the shortest side of a similar polygon whose area equals the sum of the areas of the two given polygons.

9. Given a circle with a radius of 6 in. Find the ratio of the areas of its inscribed and circumscribed equilateral triangles.

10. Two regular hexagons have apothems in the ratio 2:3. The difference of the areas of the hexagons is 245 sq. in. Find the area of each hexagon.

C

11. One regular hexagon is inscribed in, and another is circumscribed about, a circle of radius k. What is the ratio of the areas of the hexagons?

12. One of two similar polygons has an area 25 per cent more than that of the other. What is the ratio of the perimeters?

13. Pictured is a square inscribed in a semicircle of radius r. How does its area compare with that of a square inscribed in a circle of radius r?

14. A regular hexagon is inscribed in a circle, and a second regular hexagon is circumscribed about the same circle. If the sum of the areas of the two hexagons is $56\sqrt{3}$, find the radius of the circle.

■ Circles Sectors and Segments

15–8 The Circle as a Limiting Case of an Inscribed Regular Polygon.

In your previous mathematics courses you acquired a general under-standing of what is meant by the terms *circumference of a circle* and *area of a circle*. In proceeding to define these terms, we shall draw on that general understanding.

Pictured below are three regular polygons inscribed in congruent circles. Note that, as the number of sides of the inscribed polygon is increased, the following changes appear to take place:

1. The apothems increase, approaching the radius of the circle as a limit.

2. The perimeters increase, approaching the circumference of the circle as a limit.

3. The areas increase, approaching the area of the circle as a limit.

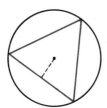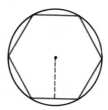

It is not possible to present a precise mathematical definition of *limit* that would be meaningful to you at this stage of your mathe-matical development. Without such a definition, it is impossible to establish deductively that the perimeters or the areas of regular inscribed polygons do approach limits, even though drawings suggest that they do. We shall assume that there are limits and define the circumference and the area of a circle, respectively, to be these limits.

The **circumference of a circle** (*c*) is the limit of the perimeters of the inscribed regular polygons. It is a positive number.

The **area of a circle** (*A*) is the limit of the areas of the inscribed regular polygons. It is a positive number.

On the basis of the foregoing definition of the circumference of a circle, it is possible to prove an important relationship that exists between the circumference and diameter of any circle.

THEOREM 15–9 The ratio of the circumference to the diameter is the same for all circles.

Given: ⊙O with radius r, diameter d, and circumference c.

⊙O' with radius r', diameter d', and circumference c'.

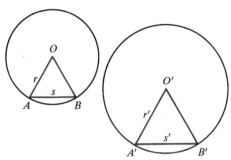

To Prove: $\dfrac{c}{d} = \dfrac{c'}{d'}$

Outline of Proof:

Using the same number of sides, inscribe regular n-gons with sides of length s and s' in each ⊙.

Shown is a side of each n-gon with radii drawn to the endpoints.

$\angle O \cong \angle O'$, for both have measure $\dfrac{360}{n}$; $\angle A \cong \angle A'$, for both have

measure $\dfrac{1}{2}\left(180 - \dfrac{360}{n}\right)$.

Thus, $\triangle AOB \sim \triangle A'O'B'$, and $\dfrac{s}{r} = \dfrac{s'}{r'}$. Therefore, $\dfrac{ns}{r} = \dfrac{ns'}{r'}$.

But ns and ns' are the perimeters p_n and p_n' of the respective polygons.

Hence, $\dfrac{p_n}{r} = \dfrac{p_n'}{r'}$.

Now as n increases without limit, $p_n \to c$ and $p_n' \to c'$. ($\to$ is read

'approaches as a limit'.) Therefore, $\dfrac{p_n}{r} \to \dfrac{c}{r}$ and $\dfrac{p_n'}{r'} \to \dfrac{c'}{r'}$. Since we have

shown that $\dfrac{p_n}{r}$ and $\dfrac{p_n'}{r'}$ are equal, it is reasonable to assume that their limits

are equal. Therefore, $\dfrac{c}{r} = \dfrac{c'}{r'}$ $\qquad \dfrac{c}{2r} = \dfrac{c'}{2r'}$ $\qquad \dfrac{c}{d} = \dfrac{c'}{d'}$

COROLLARY The circumferences of two circles have the same ratio as their radii or their diameters.

The number $\dfrac{c}{d}$, which is the same for all circles, is denoted by the

Greek letter π (pi). In other words, π is *defined* to be the ratio of c to d. It is an irrational number and so cannot be expressed as the ratio of two integers. The relationship between the circumference and diameter of any circle is such that when d is an integer, c is not an integer, and vice versa.

The most commonly used approximations for π are:

3.14 $\qquad\qquad \frac{22}{7} \qquad\qquad$ 3.1416

Two particularly useful formulas equivalent to $\dfrac{c}{d} = \pi$ are:

$c = \pi d \qquad\qquad\qquad c = 2\pi r$

Since π is an irrational number, only an approximation of the circumference is obtained when an approximate value is used for π. To express the *exact* circumference you do not replace π by an approximation. Thus, the *exact* circumference of a circle of radius 5 in. is 10π in. Some interesting facts about π are:

1. The Old Testament (I Kings 7:23) contains a passage which suggests that the Babylonians used the value 3 for the circumference-diameter ratio.

2. Archimedes (287–212 B.C.) showed that the value of the circumference-diameter ratio lies between $3\frac{1}{7}$ and $3\frac{10}{71}$.

3. The symbol π for the circumference-diameter ratio was not introduced until the 18th century.

4. The value of π correct to ten decimal places is 3.1415926536. If this approximation were used in computing the circumference of the earth, the result would be correct to inches.

5. Electronic computing machines have computed π correct to one hundred thousand places.

6. Given a unit of length, it is impossible to construct a segment of length π using straightedge and compass.

7. The number π plays an important role in both pure and applied mathematics in situations where no circle measurements are involved. A biologist investigating laws of bacterial growth and an insurance actuary computing probabilities both use π in their work.

ORAL EXERCISES

1. A square and a regular hexagon are inscribed in the same circle. Which has the greater perimeter? the greater apothem? the longer side?

2. Could the circumference of a circle be described as the limit of the perimeters of the circumscribed regular polygons?

3. If the perimeter of a billion-sided regular polygon were divided by the length of a diagonal which passed through the center, would the result be an approximation of π?

4. Which is the closer approximation of π: 3.14 or 3.15?

| WRITTEN
| EXERCISES

In Exercises 1–6 find the exact circumference of a circle with a radius of

A

1. 5 in.

2. 7 ft.

3. $3\frac{1}{2}$ cm.

4. $2\frac{1}{4}$ in.

5. $3k$ in.

6. $\dfrac{a}{2}$ cm.

In Exercises 7–12 find the approximate circumference of a circle having the given radius. For the approximation for π, round off 3.1416 to one more digit than there are digits in the given radius.

7. 4 in.

8. 6 ft.

9. 5.1 cm.

10. 4.6 in.

11. 3.21 ft.

12. 6.53 cm.

In Exercises 13–18 find the radius of a circle whose circumference is

13. 12π in.

14. 15π ft.

15. $6\sqrt{2}\,\pi$ in.

16. $5\sqrt{3}\,\pi$ cm.

17. $8k\pi$ ft.

18. π yds.

In Exercises 19–24 use approximations for π as directed in Exercises 7–12 and find the approximate radius of a circle whose circumference is

19. 10 in.

20. 18 cm.

21. 8.2 in.

22. 12.4 ft.

23. 5.34 ft.

24. 22.53 in.

In Exercises 25–32 use an approximation for π only when instructed to do so.

B

25. How far does a rolling wheel with an 8 in. radius travel in 6 revolutions?

26. Find the radius of a rolling wheel which makes 6 revolutions in traveling a distance of 66 ft. (Use $\pi \doteq \frac{22}{7}$.)

27. Given a square of perimeter $4k$. Find the ratio of the circumference of the inscribed and circumscribed circles.

28. Find the radius of a circle whose circumference is equal to the sum of the circumferences of two circles of radii 4 in. and 6 in.

29. The ratio of the circumferences of two circles is 5 to 8. If the smaller circle has a radius of 15 in., find the radius of the larger circle.

30. Given a circle of radius 4.2 in. By what amount is its circumference increased when its radius is increased by 1 in.? (Use $\pi \doteq 3.14$.)

C **31.** In a coordinate plane a circle with center $(2, 1)$ passes through the point $(5, -3)$. Find the circumference of the circle.

32. Find the circumference of a circle inscribed in an isosceles trapezoid with bases 8 and 18 inches long.

15–9 Area of a Circle

By definition, the area of a circle is the limit of the areas of the inscribed regular polygons. An investigation of this limit leads to a formula for the area of a circle.

THEOREM 15–10   The area of a circle is the product of π and the square of the radius of the circle ($A = \pi r^2$).

Given: Circle O with radius r, circumference c, and area A.

To Prove: $A = \pi r^2$.

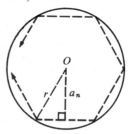

Outline of Proof:

Inscribe a regular n-gon with apothem a_n, perimeter p_n, and area A_n. Now, applying the formula for the area of a regular polygon, $A_n = \frac{1}{2}a_n p_n$. As n increases without limit:

$$a_n \rightarrow r$$
$$p_n \rightarrow c.$$

Therefore, $A_n \rightarrow \frac{1}{2}rc$.

But, by definition $A_n \rightarrow A$. Therefore, $A = \frac{1}{2}rc$.
Since $c = 2\pi r$, $A = \frac{1}{2}r(2\pi r) = \pi r^2$.

COROLLARY   The areas of two circles have the same ratio as the squares of their radii or the squares of their diameters.

| ORAL
| EXERCISES

1. If you know the circumference of a circle, can you determine the area?
2. What is the effect on the area of a circle if the radius is doubled?
3. Is the area of a circle always a number of square units?
4. What is the formula for the area of a circle in terms of its diameter?
5. Is the ratio of the area of a circle to the square of its radius a rational number?
6. If a regular hexagon has the same area as a circle, can it be inscribed in the circle?
7. What is the area of a circle in which the longest possible chord is 6 in. long?
8. The radii of two circles have the ratio $a:b$. What is the ratio of the areas of the two circles?

| WRITTEN
| EXERCISES

In Exercises 1–6 find the exact area of a circle having the given radius or diameter.

A

1. $r = 3$ in.
2. $d = 8$ in.
3. $r = 1\frac{1}{2}$ cm.
4. $d = 9$ ft.
5. $r = 2\sqrt{3}$ in.
6. $d = 3k\sqrt{2}$ cm.

In Exercises 7–12 find the exact area of a circle having a circumference of

7. 8π 8. 3π 9. $2\frac{1}{2}\pi$ 10. π 11. $4\sqrt{3}\,\pi$ 12. $6k\pi$

13. The circumference of a circle is 44 in. Find the area of the circle. (Use $\pi \doteq \frac{22}{7}$.)
14. Find the exact circumference of a circle with area 36π sq. in.
15. The circumferences of two circles are in the ratio $2:3$. What is the ratio of the areas of the two circles?
16. Find the exact area of the region bounded by two concentric circles with radii 10 in. and 6 in.

B

17. Given a square with side 7 in. long. By how much does its area exceed the area of the inscribed circle? (Use $\pi \doteq \frac{22}{7}$.)

18. Find the area of a circle circumscribed about an equilateral triangle whose side is 18 in. long.

19. The radii of two circles are in the ratio 3:1. Find the area of the smaller circle, if the area of the larger is 27π sq. in.

20. Find the radius of a circle whose area is equal to the sum of the areas of two circles with radii 2 and 3 respectively.

21. A 6 by 8 rectangle is inscribed in a circle. Find the area of that region bounded by the circle that contains no points in the interior of the rectangle. (Use $\pi \doteq 3.14$.)

22. An equilateral triangle of perimeter 18 inches is inscribed in a circle. Find the area of the region bounded by the circle but containing no points in the interior of the triangle.

23. A circle of radius 6 has half of its area removed by cutting away a border of uniform width. Find the width of the border.

24. Given a regular hexagon of area $48k^2\sqrt{3}$. Find the ratio of the areas of the inscribed and circumscribed circles.

C 25. The diagonals of a rhombus have lengths of 18 and 24. Find the area of a circle inscribed in this rhombus.

26. Prove: The area of the region bounded by two concentric circles is equal to the area of a circle whose radius is equal to half the length of any chord of the outer circle that is tangent to the inner circle.

15–10   Arcs, Sectors, and Segments

The meaning of the length of an arc can be described in terms of a limit. Think of arc $\overset{\frown}{AB}$ as divided by points $P_1, P_2, \ldots, P_{n-1}$ into n arcs of equal degree measure. Chords $\overline{AP_1}, \overline{P_1P_2}, \ldots, \overline{P_{n-1}B}$ can then be drawn. The *length of the arc* $\overset{\frown}{AB}$ is the limit of the sum of the lengths of these n chords as n increases indefinitely.

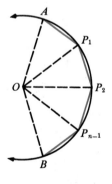

In dealing with lengths of arcs, it is convenient to consider an entire circle as an arc of degree measure 360. Then the ratio of the degree measure of an arc to 360 tells what fractional part of the circumference that particular arc is. This suggests the following formula for finding the length of an arc: (Recall that $m\overset{\frown}{AB}$ designates the degree measure of arc AB.)

$$\text{Length of } \overset{\frown}{AB} = \frac{m\overset{\frown}{AB}}{360}\,(2\pi r)$$

EXAMPLE. Find the length of an 80° arc in a circle of radius 6 in.

Solution: Length of arc = $\frac{80}{360}(2\pi \cdot 6) = \frac{8\pi}{3}$ in.

A **sector of a circle** is a region bounded by two radii and an arc of the circle. In the given circle:

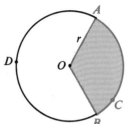

$O\text{-}\overparen{ACB}$ is a sector.
$O\text{-}\overparen{ADB}$ is a sector.
r is the radius of each sector.
$\overparen{ACB}$ is the arc of sector $O\text{-}\overparen{ACB}$.
$\overparen{ADB}$ is the arc of sector $O\text{-}\overparen{ADB}$.

$\dfrac{m\overparen{ACB}}{360}$ is the ratio of the area of the sector $O\text{-}\overparen{ACB}$ to the area of $\odot O$.

Thus, the area of sector $O\text{-}\overparen{ACB} = \dfrac{m\overparen{ACB}}{360} \cdot$ (Area $\odot O$). Therefore;

$$\text{Area of sector } O\text{-}\overparen{ACB} = \frac{m\overparen{ACB}}{360} \cdot \pi r^2.$$

EXAMPLE. Find the area and perimeter of a sector with a 60° arc in a circle with radius 12 in.

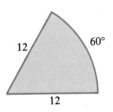

Solution: Area = $\frac{60}{360} \cdot \pi(12)^2 = 24\pi$ sq. in.
Perimeter = $\frac{60}{360} \cdot 2\pi(12) + (12 + 12)$
$= (4\pi + 24)$ in. **Answer.**

A **segment of a circle** is a region bounded by a chord and an arc of the circle. In the figure shown there are two segments: segment ABC and segment ABD.

The area of segment ACB is obtained by subtracting the area of $\triangle AOB$ from the area of sector $O\text{-}\overparen{ACB}$.

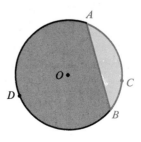

Area segment *ACB*

= Area sector *O-ACB* − Area triangle *AOB*.

    The area of segment *ABD* can be obtained either by subtracting the area of segment *ACB* from the area of the circle or by adding the area of △*AOB* to the area of sector *O-ADB*.

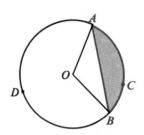

EXAMPLE. Given a circle with a 6 cm. radius. Find the area of a segment that has a 120° arc.

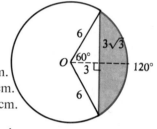

Solution: Area of sector = $\frac{1}{3}(36\pi) = 12\pi$ sq. cm.
          Area of △ = $\frac{1}{2}(6\sqrt{3})(3) = 9\sqrt{3}$ sq. cm.
          Area of segment = $(12\pi - 9\sqrt{3})$ sq. cm.

ORAL EXERCISES

1. What fractional part of the area of a circle is the area of a sector with arc of degree measure 1? 10? 40? 100?

2. Is the area of a sector doubled if the length of its arc is doubled while the radius remains fixed?

3. Given two circles each with a sector having an *x*° arc. If the circles have radii *a* and *b*, what is the ratio of the areas of the sectors?

4. If the area of a sector is one sixth that of a circle, what is the degree measure of its arc?

5. In a circle of radius 2*k* a sector has an arc of length *πk*. What is the degree measure of the arc of the sector?

6. In a given circle is it possible for a sector and its segment to have the same area?

WRITTEN EXERCISES

Express all answers in simplest exact form.

A

1. Find the length of an arc of degree measure 40 in a circle with an 8 in. radius.

2. Find the radius of a circle in which a 30° arc is 2*π* in. long.

3. Find the degree measure of an arc 4π cm. long in a circle of radius 10 cm.

4. Find the area of a sector with a 70° arc and an 8 in. radius.

5. Find the area of a sector with a 30° arc and a $3\sqrt{2}$ ft. radius.

6. In a circle of radius 10 cm., a sector has an area of 40π sq. cm. Find the degree measure of the arc of the sector.

B
7. An equilateral triangle is inscribed in a circle with a 6 in. radius. Find the area of a segment cut off by one side of the triangle.

8. What is the area of the smaller segment whose chord is 8 in. long in a circle with an 8 in. radius?

9. A segment of a circle has a 120° arc and a chord $8\sqrt{3}$ in. long. Find the area of the segment.

10. Express in terms of a the area of the smaller segment cut off by a side of an inscribed square in a circle with a radius of a units.

11. Find the perimeter of a segment of a circle having radius 8 in. and a 120° arc.

12. Two circles, each with a 4 in. radius, intersect so that their common chord is 4 in. long. Find the area of the region bounded by the two minor arcs.

13. Three circles, each with an 8 in. radius, are all tangent to each other. Find the area of the region between the circles.

14. From a given point, two tangent segments to a circle with a 6 in. radius intercept a 120° arc. Find the perimeter of the region bounded by the two tangents and the minor arc.

15. A circular grass plot 12 feet in diameter is cut by a straight gravel path three feet wide. One edge of the path passes through the center of the plot. Find the area of that part of the plot that is grass.

16. The radii of two concentric circles differ by $\sqrt{2}$. Find the radius of each circle, if the area of the ring formed is $2\pi + 6\sqrt{2}\,\pi$.

Find the area of the shaded portion in each figure.

C 17.

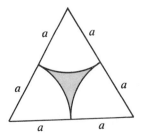

18.

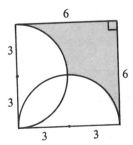

19.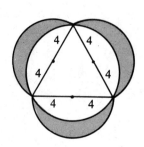

20.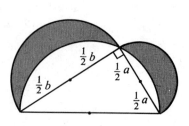

21. The arc of a sector has degree measure 60. The radius of the sector is 12 in. Find the area of the circle that can be inscribed in the sector.

22. Prove: The area of a circle having the hypotenuse of a right triangle as diameter is equal to the sum of the areas of the circles having the legs as diameters.

23. The sides of a triangle are 5, 5, and 6 in. long. Find the ratio of the areas of the inscribed and circumscribed circles.

24. Draw the graph of the circle with equation $x^2 + y^2 - 4x + 6y - 3 = 0$. Find the area of the two segments into which the y-axis divides the circle.

CHAPTER SUMMARY

Inventory of Structure and Methods

1. A polygonal region is the union of a finite number of non-overlapping coplanar triangular regions. Corresponding to every polygonal region there is a unique positive number called its area. Regions bounded by congruent triangles have equal areas. If a polygonal region is divided into n non-overlapping triangular regions its area is the sum of the areas of the n triangular regions.

2. Some formulas for areas of regions bounded by triangles, special quadrilaterals, or regular polygons are:

Triangle: $A = \frac{1}{2}bh$	Equilateral Triangle: $A = \dfrac{s^2}{4}\sqrt{3}$
Rectangle: $A = lw$	Rhombus: $A = \dfrac{d_1 d_2}{2}$
Parallelogram: $A = bh$	Square: $A = s^2$
Trapezoid: $A = \dfrac{h}{2}(b_1 + b_2)$	Regular Polygon: $A = \frac{1}{2}ap$

3. The ratio of the areas of two similar triangles is equal to the square of the ratio of the lengths of any two corresponding sides, medians, or altitudes.

4. A circle can be circumscribed about and inscribed in any regular polygon. As the number of sides of an inscribed regular polygon increases indefinitely, its perimeter approaches the circumference of the circle as a limit, and its area approaches the area of the circle as a limit.

5. The ratio of the circumference to the diameter of any circle is the irrational number π.

6. Some useful formulas for circles are:

$c = \pi d$

$c = 2\pi r$

$A = \pi r^2$

Length of $\overparen{AB}$: $\quad l = \dfrac{m\overparen{AB}}{360} \cdot 2\pi r$

Area of sector $O\text{-}\overparen{AB}$: $\quad A = \dfrac{m\overparen{AB}}{360} \cdot \pi r^2$

Vocabulary and Spelling

triangular regions (*p. 543*)
  non-overlapping (*p. 543*)
polygonal regions (*p. 544*)
  area of (*p. 544*)
square unit (*p. 547*)
base of parallelogram (*p. 548*)
altitude of parallelogram (*p. 548*)
regular polygon (*p. 558*)
  center of (*p. 559*)
  radius of (*p. 559*)
  apothem of (*p. 560*)
  central angle of (*p. 560*)

limit (*p. 566*)
circumference of a circle (*p. 566*)
area of a circle (*p. 566*)
π (pi) (*p. 567*)
length of an arc (*p. 572*)
sector of a circle (*p. 573*)
segment of a circle (*p. 573*)

CHAPTER TEST

15–1   Classify each statement as true or false

1. The area of any polygonal region is a positive number.
2. If two triangular regions have equal areas, the triangles bounding those regions must be congruent.
3. The area of a polygonal region cannot be an irrational number.
4. A rectangular region can be divided into two triangular regions that have equal areas.

15–2   Compute the area of each of the following quadrilaterals.

5. A rectangle with length 3 in. and width 6 in.
6. A square with a side $4\sqrt{2}$ in. long.
7. A parallelogram with adjacent sides 8 cm. and 6 cm. long and an included angle of measure 30.
8. A square with a perimeter of 6 ft.

15–3   In the given trapezoid *ABCD*

9. $DX = $ ___?___ .
10. Area $\triangle ABD = $ ___?___ .
11. Area trapezoid $ABCD = $ ___?___ .
12. $BC = $ ___?___ .

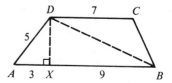

15–4   In $\triangle ABC$, $\overline{XY} \parallel \overline{AB}$. Find the ratio of the area of $\triangle CXY$ to $\triangle CAB$ when

13. $XY = 3$, $AB = 4$.
14. $CX = 2$, $CA = 3$.
15. $CY = 4$, $YB = 2$.

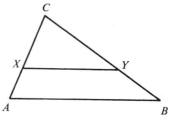

15–5   A regular hexagon is inscribed in a circle of radius 2k. What is the measure of its

16. Side?
17. Central angle?

18. Apothem?

19. Perimeter?

15–6 Find the area of each of the following *regular* polygons.

20. A pentagon with sides of length k and apothem t.

21. A hexagon with a perimeter of 24 inches.

15–7 Given two similar polygons with a pair of corresponding sides of lengths x and y $(x < y)$.

22. What is the ratio of the areas when $x = 8$ and $y = 12$?

23. What is the ratio of x to y when the areas have the ratio 12 to 16?

15–8 Given a circle of radius k and circumference c.

24. What is the ratio of c to $2k$?

25. Find c when $k = 6$.

26. Find k when $c = 20\pi$.

27. Find c when $k = \dfrac{4}{\pi}$.

15–9 Find the radius and circumference of a circle whose area is

28. 16π **30.** $4\pi a^2$

29. 12π **31.** π

15–10 The radius of $\odot O$ is k. $m\angle AOB = 60$.

32. $AB = \underline{\quad?\quad}$.

33. Length of $\overset{\frown}{ACB} = \underline{\quad?\quad}$.

34. Area of sector $O\text{-}\overset{\frown}{ACB} = \underline{\quad?\quad}$.

35. Area of segment $ACB = \underline{\quad?\quad}$.

36. Area of sector $O\text{-}\overset{\frown}{ADB} = \underline{\quad?\quad}$.

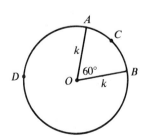

CHAPTER REVIEW

15–1 **What Area Means:** *Pages 543–547*
Basic Definitions and Postulates

1. The union of a triangle and its interior is called a __?__ .
2. If two triangles are congruent, then the triangular regions they bound have __?__ areas.
3. A region bounded by a circle __?__ (*is*, *is not*) a polygonal region.
4. The area of a polygonal region is a unique __?__ .

15–2 **Areas of Rectangles and Parallelograms** *Pages 547–552*

5. A square of perimeter $8k$ inches has an area of __?__ sq. inches.
6. A rectangle has a perimeter of $12a$ and a width of $2a$. The area of the rectangle is __?__ .
7. If the length of a rectangle is tripled and the width doubled, the area becomes __?__ times as great.
8. A square with a diagonal of length $3\sqrt{2}$ cm. has an area of __?__ sq. cm.

15–3 **Areas of Triangles and Trapezoids** *Pages 552–556*

9. The area of a right triangle is half the product of the lengths of the __?__ .
10. If two triangles have altitudes of equal length, then the ratio of the areas is equal to the ratio of the lengths of the __?__ .
11. A trapezoid with bases of lengths $6t$ and $4t$ units and altitude of length $3t$ units has an area of __?__ .
12. A rhombus with diagonals 8 in. and 6 in. long has an area of __?__ sq. in.

15–4 **Comparing Areas of Similar Triangles** *Pages 556–558*

13. If the areas of two similar triangles have the ratio 4:9, any pair of corresponding sides have lengths in the ratio __?__ : __?__ .
14. A side of one of two similar triangles is 3 times as long as the corresponding side of the other triangle. If the area of the smaller triangle is 5 sq. cm., the area of the larger triangle is __?__ sq. cm.
15. Two equilateral triangles have perimeters in the ratio $\sqrt{2}$:3. The ratio of their areas is __?__ : __?__ .

15–5   **Special Properties of a Regular Polygon**   *Pages 558–561*

16. The distance from the center of a regular polygon to a side is called the __?__ of the polygon.

17. A regular polygon with a central angle of measure 45 has __?__ sides.

18. A regular hexagon of radius k units has apothem __?__.

15–6   **Areas of Regular Polygons**   *Pages 561–562*

19. A regular pentagon with a side k units long and apothem t units has a perimeter of __?__ and an area of __?__.

20. A regular hexagon with perimeter 24 in. has area __?__ sq. in.

15–7   **Comparing Areas of Similar Polygons**   *Pages 563–565*

21. Two similar pentagons with perimeters in the ratio $2\sqrt{3}:5$ have areas in the ratio __?__:__?__.

22. In a circle of radius k, the ratio of the area of an inscribed square to that of a circumscribed square is __?__:__?__.

15–8   **The Circle as a Limiting Case**   *Pages 566–570*
      of an Inscribed Regular Polygon

23. The ratio of the __?__ of a circle to the __?__ is the number π.

24. As the number of sides of a regular inscribed polygon increases, its apothem __?__ (*increases, decreases*).

15–9   **Area of a Circle**   *Pages 570–572*

25. A circle of circumference 10π has an area of __?__.

26. Two circles have areas of 18π and 32π. The ratio of their radii is __?__:__?__.

15–10   **Arcs, Sectors, and Segments**   *Pages 572–576*

27. In a circle of radius 9 in., a 40° arc is __?__ in. long.

28. In a circle with an 8 cm. radius, a sector with an area of 16π sq. cm. has an arc of degree measure __?__.

● EXTRA FOR EXPERTS

The Area of a Triangle in Terms of the Lengths of its Sides

Hero of Alexandria, a first century A.D. mathematician, devised a means of finding the area of a triangle when the lengths of its sides were known. The proof of what is now called *Hero's Formula,*

$$A = \sqrt{s(s-a)(s-b)(s-c)},$$

calls for skillful rearranging of terms and the factoring of the difference of two squares. See if you can follow this derivation of Hero's Formula.

Problem: Express the area of $\triangle ABC$ in terms of a, b, and c, the lengths of its sides.

$$h^2 = a^2 - x^2 \qquad (\text{rt. } \triangle BDC)$$
$$h^2 = b^2 - (c+x)^2 \quad (\text{rt. } \triangle ADC)$$
$$a^2 - x^2 = b^2 - (c+x)^2$$
$$a^2 - x^2 = b^2 - c^2 - 2cx - x^2$$
$$2cx = b^2 - c^2 - a^2$$
$$x = \frac{b^2 - c^2 - a^2}{2c}$$

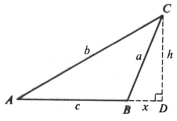

Since $h^2 = a^2 - x^2$, $h^2 = (a-x)(a+x)$.
Substituting for x in $h^2 = (a-x)(a+x)$, you get

$$h^2 = \left[a - \frac{(b^2 - c^2 - a^2)}{2c}\right] \cdot \left[a + \frac{(b^2 - c^2 - a^2)}{2c}\right]$$

$$h^2 = \left[\frac{a^2 + 2ac + c^2 - b^2}{2c}\right] \cdot \left[\frac{b^2 - (a^2 - 2ac + c^2)}{2c}\right]$$

$$h^2 = \left[\frac{(a+c)^2 - b^2}{2c}\right] \cdot \left[\frac{b^2 - (a-c)^2}{2c}\right]$$

Factoring the difference of two squares,

$$h^2 = \left[\frac{(a+c+b)(a+c-b)}{2c}\right]\left[\frac{(b+a-c)(b-a+c)}{2c}\right]$$

Now let $a + b + c = 2s$. Then, $a + c - b = 2s - 2b$ or $2(s-b)$
$$b + a - c = 2s - 2c \text{ or } 2(s-c)$$
$$b - a + c = 2s - 2a \text{ or } 2(s-a)$$

Then, by substitution,

$$h^2 = \left[\frac{2s \cdot 2(s-b)}{2c}\right] \cdot \left[\frac{2(s-c) \cdot 2(s-a)}{2c}\right]$$

$$h^2 = \frac{4s(s-a)(s-b)(s-c)}{c^2}$$

or

$$h^2c^2 = 4s(s-a)(s-b)(s-c)$$

$$hc = 2\sqrt{s(s-a)(s-b)(s-c)}$$

The area of $\triangle ABC = \frac{1}{2}hc$.

Therefore, $\quad$ Area $\triangle ABC = \frac{1}{2} \cdot 2\sqrt{s(s-a)(s-b)(s-c)}$

Area $\triangle ABC = \sqrt{s(s-a)(s-b)(s-c)}$ $\quad$ **(Hero's Formula)**

EXAMPLE. Find the area of a triangle with sides 8 in., 10 in., and 12 in. long.

Solution: Let $a = 8$, $b = 10$, $c = 12$

Then $s = \dfrac{8 + 10 + 12}{2} = 15$

Area $= \sqrt{(15)(7)(5)(3)} = 15\sqrt{7}$ sq. in.

EXERCISES

Find the area of a triangle with sides a, b, and c units long when

1. $a = 6$, $b = 8$, $c = 10$.

2. $a = 9$, $b = 11$, $c = 13$.

3. $a = 4$, $b = 5$, $c = 6$.

4. $a = 7$, $b = 8$, $c = 9$.

5. Given a triangle with sides 4, 6, and 8 in. long. Find the length of the altitude upon the shortest side.

6. Given a triangle with sides 10, 12, and 14 in. long. Find the length of the altitude upon the 12 in. side.

7. Find the radius of the circle inscribed in a triangle with sides 3, 4, and 5 in. long.

8. Find the radius of the circle inscribed in a triangle with sides 7, 9, and 11 cm. long.

9. Find the area of a parallelogram with two adjacent sides 8 in. and 10 in. long and one diagonal 12 in. long.

10. Find the area of quadrilateral $RSTV$ if $m\angle R = 90$, $RS = 12$, $ST = 8$, $TV = 7$, and $VR = 5$.

16

Areas and
Volumes of Solids

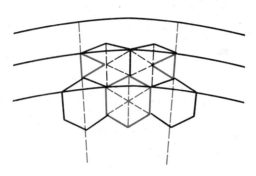

*Interlocking hexagons in
the dome of the
Missouri Botannical
Garden in St. Louis
closely approximate a
spherical surface.*

This chapter deals with methods of computing the areas and volumes of certain geometric solids. You will find that a rigorous deductive approach to the study of volumes is not taken. Some terms are described rather than defined, and no attempt is made to list postulates and prove theorems. Although a rigorous deductive approach is possible, it would involve a more detailed and exacting study than time permits.

■ Prisms and Pyramids

16–1 Vocabulary for Prisms and Pyramids

Pictured at the left below are parallel planes M and M' with polygonal region $ABCDE$ lying in M and line l intersecting both planes, but not intersecting the given polygonal region. For each point X of polygonal region $ABCDE$ let $\overline{XX'}$ be the segment parallel to l with endpoint X' in M'. The union of all such segments $\overline{XX'}$, pictured at the right below, is called a **prism.**

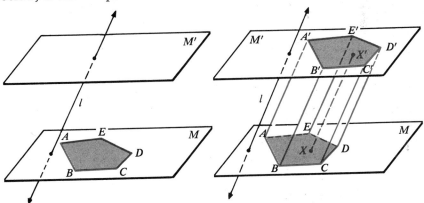

The polygonal regions $ABCDE$ and $A'B'C'D'E'$ are **bases** of the prism. Vertex A of the lower base and vertex A' of the upper base are *corresponding vertices of the bases.* Similarly, side $\overline{AB}$ and side $\overline{A'B'}$ are *corresponding sides of the bases* and $\angle ABC$ and $\angle A'B'C'$ are *corresponding angles.* The bases of a prism are parallel, equal in area, and are bounded by polygons whose corresponding sides and angles are congruent.

585

Segments $\overline{AA'}$, $\overline{BB'}$, $\overline{CC'}$, $\overline{DD'}$, and $\overline{EE'}$ are *lateral edges* of the prism. A **lateral edge** of a prism is a segment that joins two corresponding vertices of the bases. The lateral edges of a prism are parallel and congruent.

A **lateral face** of a prism is the union of the segments joining points on a side of one base with corresponding points of the corresponding side of the other base. The region bounded by $ABB'A'$ is a lateral face of the prism shown on p. 585. Can you identify the other four lateral faces? Each lateral face of a prism is a parallelogram.

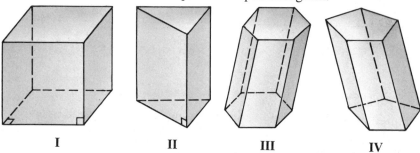

I	**II**	**III**	**IV**

Prisms I and II are *right prisms*. In a **right prism** the lateral edges are perpendicular to the planes of the bases. A prism is classified according to the type of polygonal region that is its base. Hence, Prism I is a *right rectangular* prism. (Any pair of opposite faces of a right rectangular prism can be viewed as bases and the remaining four faces as lateral faces.) Prism II is a *right triangular* prism.

Prisms III and IV are *oblique prisms*. In an **oblique prism** the lateral edges are *not* perpendicular to the planes of the bases. Prism III is an *oblique hexagonal* prism. Prism IV is an *oblique pentagonal* prism.

An **altitude of a prism** is a segment perpendicular to the planes of the bases with one endpoint in each plane. The length of an altitude is the **height** (h) of the prism.

A **pyramid** is the union of all segments that join points lying in a polygonal region to a point not in the plane of that region. Pictured is the pyramid V-$ABCD$ with region $ABCD$ as **base** and with point V as **vertex**. The segments that join V to the

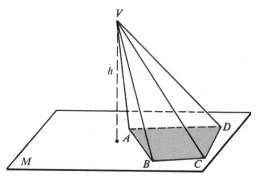

vertices of the base are **lateral edges.** Each region bounded by two lateral edges and a side of the base is a **lateral face.** The **altitude of a pyramid** is a segment from the vertex perpendicular to the plane of the base. Its length is the **height** (*h*) of the pyramid.

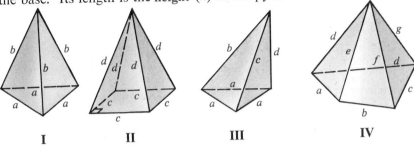

| I | II | III | IV |

Pyramids I and II are *regular pyramids.* A **regular pyramid** has a base that is bounded by a regular polygon and lateral edges of equal length. The altitude of a regular pyramid meets the base at the center of the regular polygon that bounds the base. The lateral faces are bounded by congruent isosceles triangles.

Pyramids III and IV are *nonregular pyramids.* In pyramid III the lateral edges are not congruent. In pyramid IV the base is not a regular polygon.

The **slant height** (*l*) **of a regular pyramid** is the length of the altitude of any one of its lateral faces. *Slant height is defined only for regular pyramids.*

ORAL EXERCISES

1. Can the two bases of a prism differ in number of sides?
2. Can a prism have lateral faces that are triangular regions? pentagonal regions? hexagonal regions?
3. How many lateral faces does a prism have if its bases are octagonal regions?
4. Are all lateral faces of a right prism rectangular regions?
5. Can the bases of an oblique prism be bounded by regular polygons?
6. Can the base of a pyramid be a triangular region?
7. Can the base of a regular pyramid be bounded by a trapezoid?
8. How many lateral faces does a pyramid have if its base is bounded by a pentagon? a hexagon? an *n*-gon?

9. If two pyramids have bases of equal area must the polygons bounding those bases have the same number of sides?

10. In a regular pyramid is the length of the altitude greater than that of a lateral edge?

WRITTEN EXERCISES

In exercises 1–6 classify the given statement as true or false. For each statement you classify as false make a sketch to support your answer.

1. Each lateral face of a prism is bounded by a rectangle.

2. Every prism has at least three lateral faces.

3. The lateral faces of a pyramid are bounded by isosceles triangles.

4. The height of an oblique prism is greater than the length of a lateral edge of the prism.

5. A pyramid must have at least four lateral edges.

6. Each lateral face of a cube has the same area as a base.

Sketch each of the following geometric solids.

7. A right triangular prism.

8. An oblique pentagonal prism.

9. A pyramid with triangular base.

10. A right pyramid with square base.

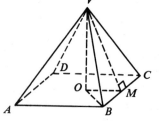

Pictured at the right is a regular square pyramid with altitude $\overline{OV}$. If all lateral faces are equilateral triangles and $AB = 6$, find the length of:

11. The altitude.

13. $\overline{VM}$

12. A lateral edge.

14. $\overline{OB}$

A regular hexagonal pyramid has an altitude of length 6 and a base of perimeter 24. Sketch a figure and find:

15. The length of a lateral edge.

16. The slant height.

17. The area of the base.

18. The area of a lateral face.

16–2   Area and Volume of a Prism

The **lateral area** (L.A.) of a prism is the sum of the areas of its lateral faces. The **total area** (T.A.) of a prism is the sum of the lateral area and the areas of its two bases.

Formulas for the lateral area and the total area of a *right* prism in terms of the length (h) of its altitude, the perimeter (p) of its base, and the area (B) of its base are not difficult to develop.

Assume the right prism shown has an n-sided polygon as base. The lateral area is the sum of the areas of n rectangles each having one pair of opposite sides of length h.

$$\text{L.A.} = s_1h + s_2h + \cdots + s_nh$$
$$= (s_1 + s_2 + \cdots + s_n)h$$

But $s_1 + s_2 + \cdots + s_n = p$ (the perimeter of the base)

$$\textbf{L.A.} = \textbf{\textit{ph}} \quad \text{and} \quad \textbf{T.A.} = \textbf{\textit{ph}} + \textbf{2B}$$

EXAMPLE. Find the lateral area and the total area of a right triangular prism if its height is 4 in. and its base is an equilateral triangle with sides 6 in. long.

Solution: $p = 3 \cdot 6$ $= 18$ in.
 L.A. $= 4(18)$ $= 72$ sq. in. **Answer.**

$$B = \frac{(6)^2}{4} \sqrt{3} \quad = 9\sqrt{3} \text{ sq. in.}$$

T.A. $= 72 + 2(9\sqrt{3}) = (72 + 18\sqrt{3})$ sq. in. **Answer.**

In our formal study of areas in Chapter 15 we started by postulating a formula for the area of a rectangle and then used that formula in developing formulas for the areas of other polygons. A similar approach is used in developing formulas for the volumes of various types of solids. We begin our informal study of volumes by accepting a formula for the volume of a right rectangular prism.

The volume of a right rectangular prism is the product of the area (B) of the base and the length (h) of an altitude to the base.

$$V = Bh$$

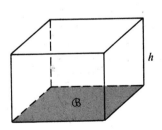

Since $B = l \cdot w$ in the case of a rectangular base, this formula is equivalent to $V = lwh$. Can you state a simple formula for the volume of a cube with edges of length e?

Pictured is a solid C made up of thin rectangular cards, all having the same dimensions. By exerting pressure horizontally you can change the shape of C without changing its volume. Resulting solids such as D and E have the same volume as C.

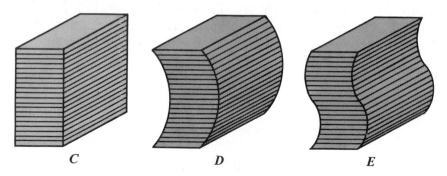

C   D   E

Suppose solids G and H are made up of equal numbers of thin cards of uniform thickness. Assume also that each card in H has the same face area as the correspondingly placed card in G. Intuition suggests that the two solids have equal volumes.

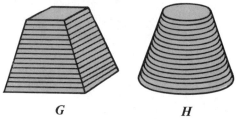

G   H

The preceding observations about volumes of solids made up of cards suggest a basic principle about volumes first formulated by the Italian mathematician Bonaventura Cavalieri (1599–1647).

Cavalieri's Principle: Given two solids R and S and a plane M that does not intersect either solid. Suppose that: (1) Every plane X_n parallel to M either intersects both R and S or does not intersect either solid. (2) When X_n intersects both R and S, the area of the cross section of R equals the area of the cross section of S. Then, solids R and S have equal volumes.

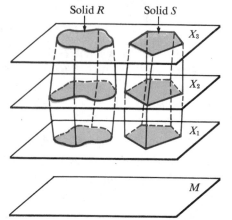

Solid R Solid S

X_3

X_2

X_1

M

By comparing the volume of an oblique prism with that of a right rectangular prism having the same base area (B) and altitude length (h), it is possible to obtain a formula for the area of any prism.

Given right rectangular prism P_1 and oblique prism P_2 both with altitude length h and base area B. Let plane X be any plane that intersects both P_1 and P_2 and is parallel to the plane M that contains their bases. The region intersected by

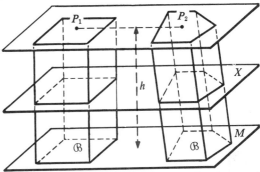

X on each prism has the same size, shape, and area as the base of that prism. (This is a property that can be proved but which we shall assume here.) From Cavalieri's Principle, it follows that prisms P_1 and P_2 have the same volume. Since $V = Bh$ for prism P_1, $V = Bh$ for prism P_2.

The volume of any prism is the product of the area (B) of the base and the length (h) of an altitude to that base.

$$V = Bh$$

EXAMPLE. Find the volume of a prism of height 8 in. if its base is bounded by a regular hexagon with 4 in. sides.

Solution: $B = 6(\frac{16}{4})\sqrt{3} = 24\sqrt{3}$ sq. in.
$h = 8$ in.
$V = 8 \times 24\sqrt{3} = 192\sqrt{3}$ cu. in., **Answer.**

ORAL EXERCISES

1. Is the total area of a prism necessarily greater than the lateral area?
2. If two prisms have the same volume, must they have the same total area?
3. How many blocks, each a cube with 1 in. edge, will fit into a container which is a cube with 2 in. edge?
4. If a cube has a total area of $6x^2$, what is the volume of the cube?
5. Two triangular prisms have equal heights and equal volumes. Must the triangles bounding their bases be congruent? equal in area?
6. What is the volume of a right rectangular box with dimensions l, w, and h?

WRITTEN EXERCISES

In Exercises 1–4 find the lateral area, total area, and volume of a right rectangular prism in which *l* and *w* are base dimensions and *h* is the length of the altitude.

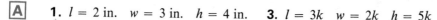

A

1. $l = 2$ in. $w = 3$ in. $h = 4$ in.   **3.** $l = 3k$ $w = 2k$ $h = 5k$

2. $l = 1$ ft. $w = 2$ ft. $h = 3$ ft.   **4.** $l = 2\sqrt{3}$ $w = \sqrt{3}$ $h = 4$

5. Find the lateral area, total area, and volume of a cube with an edge 3 in. long.

6. What is the volume in cubic yards of a classroom 24 ft. by 30 ft. by 12 ft.?

B

7. Find the volume of a cube that has a total area of 96 sq. in.

8. Find the volume of a cube that has a lateral area of 36 sq. in.

9. The base of a right prism is bounded by an equilateral triangle with sides 6 cm. long. The prism has a height of 10 cm. Find the volume and total area of the prism.

10. A right prism of height 12 in. has a base bounded by a rhombus whose diagonals are 6 in. and 8 in. long. Find the volume and lateral area of the prism.

11. Find the volume of a cube that has a diagonal $6\sqrt{3}$ ft. long.

12. The diagonal of one face of a cube is 4 in. long. Find the total area of the cube.

13. A right prism with a 4 in. height has a regular hexagonal base. If the prism has a lateral area of 144 sq. in., find the volume.

14. How many bricks 8 in. by 4 in. by 2 in. are necessary to build a wall 20 ft. by 6 ft. by 1 ft., if 12 per cent of the wall is mortar?

C

15. Two dimensions of a right rectangular prism are 6 and 8. If the length of the diagonal of the prism is 12, find the third dimension.

16. A right rectangular tank with a 12 in. by 8 in. base is filled with water to a depth of 5 in. If the water rises $\frac{2}{3}$ in. when a solid cube is completely submerged in the tank, find the length of an edge of the cube.

17. The altitude of a right hexagonal prism is twice as long as the edge of the base. If the prism has a volume of $192\sqrt{3}$ cu. in., find the lateral area.

18. A right rectangular prism of total area 236 sq. in. has an altitude 6 in. long. The width of the base is 2 in. less than the length. Find the volume of the prism.

16–3   Area and Volume of a Pyramid

The **lateral area** of a pyramid is the sum of the areas of the lateral faces. The **total area** of a pyramid is the sum of the lateral area and the area of the base.

If a pyramid is *nonregular*, its lateral area and total area cannot be computed unless enough measures are given to enable you to find the area of each face. However, if a pyramid is *regular*, both the lateral and total areas can be computed when enough measures are given to enable you to compute the area of one face and the base.

Since the lateral faces of a regular pyramid are equal in area ($\cong \triangle$), formulas for the lateral area and total area are not difficult to develop.

Assume the regular pyramid shown has slant height l, an n-sided base of perimeter p, and area B.

Area of one lateral face $= \frac{1}{2}al$.

Area of n lateral faces $= n(\frac{1}{2}al)$
$\qquad\qquad\qquad\qquad = \frac{1}{2}(na)l$.

But $na = p$.

$\therefore$ **$L.A. = \frac{1}{2}pl$** and **$T.A. = \frac{1}{2}pl + B$**

EXAMPLE. Find the lateral area and total area of a regular square pyramid with a base edge 8 in. long and lateral edge 10 in. long.

Solution: $l = \sqrt{(10)^2 - (4)^2} = 2\sqrt{21}$ in.

$p = 4(8) = 32$ in.

L.A. $= \frac{1}{2}(32)(2\sqrt{21}) = 32\sqrt{21}$ sq. in.   **Answer.**

T.A. $= (32\sqrt{21} + 64)$ sq. in.   **Answer.**

Pictured are two pyramids with the same base area B and the same height h. Let X represent any plane parallel to M and intersecting both pyramids. The intersection of X with each pyramid is a polygonal

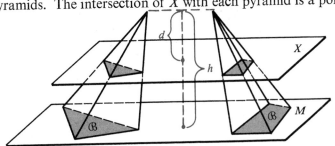

region called a **cross section.** In each pyramid the polygon bounding the cross section is similar to the polygon bounding the base of that pyramid. It can be proved that in each pyramid the ratio of the area of the cross section to the area of the base is d^2 to h^2. But, since both bases have the same area B, any pair of corresponding cross sections formed by X have equal areas. Thus, Cavalieri's Principle enables us to make the following assertion:

If two pyramids have the same base area B and the same height h then they have the same volume.

From the above statement it follows that if we can develop a formula for the volume of a triangular pyramid, we can generalize about the volumes of pyramids whose bases are non-triangular.

Consider the triangular pyramid V-ACD with base area B and height h. On the base of V-ACD construct a prism with base area B and height h. This prism can be considered to be the union of the three non-over-lapping pyramids shown below at the right.

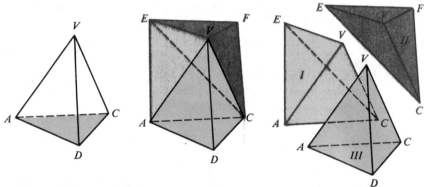

Pyramid I may be viewed as having vertex V and base bounded by $\triangle AEC$. Pyramid II may be viewed as having vertex V and base bounded by $\triangle FEC$.

Since $ACFE$ is a rectangle, $\triangle AEC \cong \triangle FEC$. Thus, pyramids I and II have bases of equal area lying in the same plane. Since V is the vertex of both pyramids, they have the same height. Therefore, **Vol. pyramid I = Vol. pyramid II.**

Pyramid II may be viewed as having vertex C and base bounded by $\triangle EVF$. Pyramid III may be viewed as having vertex V and base bounded by $\triangle ADC$.

Since $\triangle EVF$ and $\triangle ADC$ are bases of a prism, they are congruent and have equal areas. The height of both pyramid II and pyramid III is h, the height of the prism. Therefore, **Vol. pyramid II = Vol. pyramid III.**

Since the volume of the prism is Bh and the three non-overlapping pyramids forming it have equal volumes, each has a volume of $\frac{1}{3}Bh$. Therefore, the volume of the given pyramid V-ACD is $\frac{1}{3}Bh$.

Recall that earlier we concluded that a non-triangular pyramid of base area B and height h has the same volume as a triangular pyramid with the same base area B and same height h. Thus, any pyramid of base area B and height h has volume $\frac{1}{3}Bh$.

The volume of any pyramid is one third the product of the area (B) of the base and the length (h) of the altitude.

$$V = \tfrac{1}{3}Bh.$$

EXAMPLE. Find the volume of a regular hexagonal pyramid with a base edge 6 in. long and a lateral edge 10 in. long.

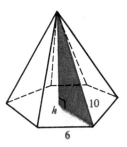

Solution: $h = \sqrt{(10)^2 - (6)^2} = 8$ in.

$B = 6(\frac{36}{4}\sqrt{3}) = 54\sqrt{3}$ sq. in.

$V = \frac{1}{3}(54\sqrt{3})8 = 144\sqrt{3}$ cu. in., **Answer.**

ORAL EXERCISES

1. Is each lateral face of a regular pyramid bounded by an isosceles triangle?

2. If a prism and pyramid have the same base area and the same height, how do their volumes compare?

3. The base of a regular pyramid is a square with a 4 in. side. How far from each vertex of the base is the point where the altitude meets the base?

4. The base of a regular pyramid is a regular hexagon with a 6 in. side. How far from each vertex of the base is the point where the altitude meets the base?

5. How many lateral faces does a pentagonal pyramid have?

6. If two pyramids have the same lateral area, must they have the same volume?

A   1. Find the volume of a pyramid with base area 24 sq. in. and height 8 in.

2. Find the lateral area of a regular pyramid with base perimeter 18 in. and slant height 10 in.

3. A pyramid has a base of area 16 sq. in. and a volume of 32 cu. in. Find the length of the altitude to that base.

4. Find the volume of a regular square pyramid that has an altitude 3 in. long and a base edge 2 in. long.

5. Find the lateral area of a regular hexagonal pyramid with a base edge 4 ft. long and slant height 6 ft.

6. Find the slant height of a regular triangular pyramid with a base edge 12 cm. long and a lateral edge 10 cm. long.

B   7. All six edges of a triangular pyramid are 4 in. long. Find the total area of the pyramid.

8. A regular hexagonal pyramid has a height of 8 in. and a base edge 6 in. long. Find the volume of the pyramid.

9. The base of a pyramid is a square with sides 10 ft. long. Each lateral edge is 13 ft. long. Find the total area of the pyramid.

10. Find the volume of a regular square pyramid that has a base edge 6 cm. long and a lateral edge 10 cm. long.

C   11. A lateral edge of a regular pyramid is 7 in. long. The base is a regular hexagon with sides 4 in. long. Find the lateral area and volume of the pyramid.

12. Find the lateral area, total area, and volume of a regular triangular pyramid with a lateral edge a in. long and a slant height of b in.

13. Find the volume of a regular triangular pyramid if all edges are 3 cm. long.

14. In a regular square pyramid, a lateral edge is 6 in. long. Each lateral edge determines a 60° angle with its projection in the base. Find the volume of the pyramid.

16–4   Area and Volume of a Right Circular Cylinder

A *circular cylinder* can be defined using the same approach as that taken in defining a prism. Let M and M' be two parallel planes with circular region R lying in M and line l intersecting M and M' but not region *R*. For each point *X* of region *R* let $\overline{XX'}$ be the segment parallel to *l* with endpoint *X'* in *M'*. The union of all such segments $\overline{XX'}$ is called a **circular cylinder**.

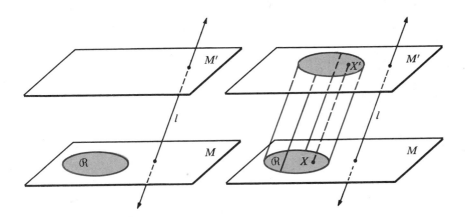

The **bases** of a circular cylinder are bounded by circles of equal radii.

The **axis of a circular cylinder** is the segment which joins the centers of the bases.

A **right circular cylinder** is a circular cylinder in which the segment joining the centers *O* and *O'* of its bases is perpendicular to the planes of both bases. As in a prism, an **altitude of a circular cylinder** is a perpendicular segment from a point in one base to a point in the plane of the other base.

Pictured is a right prism whose bases are bounded by regular polygons. The prism is inscribed in a right circular cylinder. Suppose you double the number of sides of the bases again and again for any prism with bases bounded by regular polygons. Just as the polygon bounding the base of the prism more nearly resembles the circle in which it is inscribed, so the prism more nearly resembles

the cylinder in which it is inscribed. We shall assume that the lateral area, total area, and volume of the prism have limits and these limits are, respectively, the lateral area, total area, and volume of the cylinder. Based upon this assumption we can derive formulas for a right circular cylinder based on those for a right prism.

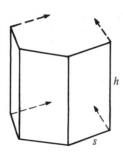
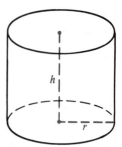

Prism   *Right Circular Cylinder*

$$\left. \begin{array}{c} \textbf{\textit{L.A.}} = \textbf{\textit{ph}} \\ \textbf{\textit{T.A.}} = \textbf{\textit{ph}} + \textbf{\textit{2B}} \\ \textbf{\textit{V}} = \textbf{\textit{Bh}} \end{array} \right\}$$
As *n* is doubled and redoubled indefinitely,
$$p \rightarrow 2\pi r$$
$$B \rightarrow \pi r^2$$
$$\left\{ \begin{array}{c} \textbf{\textit{L.A.}} = \textbf{\textit{2}}\boldsymbol{\pi}\textbf{\textit{rh}} \\ \textbf{\textit{T.A.}} = \textbf{\textit{2}}\boldsymbol{\pi}\textbf{\textit{rh}} + \textbf{\textit{2}}\boldsymbol{\pi}\textbf{\textit{r}}^2 \\ \textbf{\textit{V}} = \boldsymbol{\pi}\textbf{\textit{r}}^2\textbf{\textit{h}} \end{array} \right.$$

EXAMPLE. Find the lateral area, total area, and volume of a right circular cylinder with 4 in. radius and 6 in. height.

Solution: L.A. $= 2\pi(4)(6) = 48\pi$ sq. in.
T.A. $= 48\pi + 2\pi(4)^2 = 80\pi$ sq. in.
V $= \pi(16)(6) = 96\pi$ cu. in.

WRITTEN EXERCISES

Find the lateral area, total area, and volume of a right circular cylinder in which

1. $r = 3$ in. $h = 5$ in.   **3.** $r = 2k$ in. $h = 3k$ in.

2. $r = 2$ cm. $h = 3$ cm.   **4.** $r = \sqrt{3}$ ft. $h = 2$ ft.

5. Two cylinders have bases of equal radii. The ratio of the lengths of the altitudes is $1:2$. Find the ratio of **(a)** the volumes **(b)** the lateral areas.

6. Find the volume of a cylinder of height 6 in. and base circumference 16π in.

7. The radius of a cylinder is 5 in. and the lateral area is 70π sq. in. Find the length of the altitude.

8. The adjacent figure shows a cylinder inscribed in a cube. If the edge of the cube is 6 in. long, find the volume and total area of the cylinder.

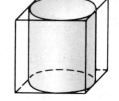

9. A cylinder has volume 320π cu. in. and height 5 in. Find the radius of the cylinder.

10. Find the total area of the cylinder generated (formed) by rotating an 8 in. by 10 in. rectangle about its shorter side as an axis.

11. The adjacent figure shows a cylinder circumscribed about a cube. If the edge of the cube is 3 in. long find the volume and total area of the cylinder.

12. In a certain cylinder the sum of the areas of the two bases is equal to the lateral area. How is the length of the altitude related to the radius?

13. Find the per cent increase in the volume of a cylinder when the length of the altitude is increased by 10 per cent and the radius is increased by 25 per cent.

14. A cylindrical tank 20 ft. long and 8 ft. in diameter is placed so that its axis is horizontal. When the tank is filled to a depth of 2 ft., how many cubic feet of liquid does it contain?

16–5   Area and Volume of a Right Circular Cone

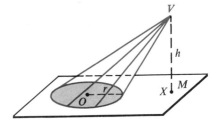

A **circular cone** is the union of all segments that join points lying in a circular region to a point not in the plane of that region. Pictured is a cone with circular region O as *base*, point V as *vertex*, and $\overline{VX}$ as *altitude*. ($\overline{VX} \perp$ plane M at point X.)

The **axis of a cone** is the segment $\overline{VO}$ that joins the vertex to the center of the base.

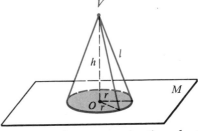

A **right circular cone** is a circular cone whose vertex is equidistant from all points lying on the circle that bounds the base. The altitude of a right circular cone intersects the base at the center of the bounding circle. The distance from any point on the bounding circle to the vertex is the *slant height l*.

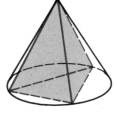

Suppose that the number of sides of the base of a regular pyramid inscribed in a cone is doubled and redoubled indefinitely. By assuming that the limits of the lateral areas, total areas, and volumes of the pyramids exist and are the corresponding measures of the cone, you can obtain formulas for the cone.

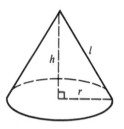

Right Pyramid   **Right Circular Cone**

$$L.A. = \tfrac{1}{2}pl \\ T.A. = \tfrac{1}{2}pl + B \\ V = \tfrac{1}{3}Bh$$

as n is doubled and
redoubled indefinitely,

$$p \rightarrow 2\pi r \\ B \rightarrow \pi r^2$$

$$L.A. = \pi rl \\ T.A. = \pi rl + \pi r^2 \\ V = \tfrac{1}{3}\pi r^2 h$$

EXAMPLE. Find the lateral area, total area, and volume of a right circular cone with a 4 in. radius and a 6 in. height.

Solution: L.A. $= (\pi)(4)(\sqrt{36 + 16}) = 8\pi\sqrt{13}$ sq. in.
   T.A. $= 8\pi\sqrt{13} + \pi(4)^2 = (8\pi\sqrt{13} + 16\pi)$ sq. in.
   $V = \dfrac{\pi(16)(6)}{3} = 32\pi$ cu. in.

WRITTEN EXERCISES

In Exercises 1–6 two measures of a right circular cone are given. Find the other measures.

	r	h	l	L.A.	T.A.	V
1.	3	4	?	?	?	?
2.	5	?	13	?	?	?
3.	2	?	?	12π	?	?
4.	5	?	?	?	?	100π
5.	?	?	$2a$	$2\pi a^2$	?	?
6.	?	$3a$	?	?	?	πa^3

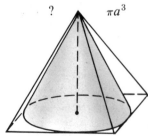

7. A cone of radius 3 in. has a total area of 24π sq. in. Find the volume.

8. The given figure shows a cone inscribed in a regular square pyramid. Find the volume of the cone if the pyramid has slant height 9 in. and a base edge 6 in. long.

9. A solid metal cylinder of radius 2 in. and height 6 in. is melted down and recast as a cone with radius 3 in. Find the height of the cone.

10. The lateral area of a cone is three-fifths of the total area. What is the ratio of the radius to the slant height?

11. Show that the volume of the solid generated by revolving a region bounded by an equilateral triangle of side s about one side is $\frac{1}{4}\pi s^3$.

12. Show that the volume of the solid generated by revolving a region bounded by a square of side s about one diagonal is $\frac{1}{6}\pi s^3\sqrt{2}$.

13. A conical tent is made by using a semicircular piece of canvas of radius 6 yds. Find the number of cubic ft. of air inside the tent.

14. A cone and a cylinder have equal radii and equal heights. What is the ratio of their lateral areas?

16–6 Volume and Surface Area of a Sphere

Formal proofs leading to formulas for the volume and surface area of a sphere will not be developed here. However, the discussions that follow should help you to recognize the reasonableness of the formulas that are stated.

Suppose you wished to find the volume of the unshaded solid pictured below. This solid consists of those points of the cylinder that are not in either of the cones. Do you see that you can find this volume by subtracting volumes?

Vol. Unshaded Solid = Vol. Cylinder − 2 (Vol. of Cone)

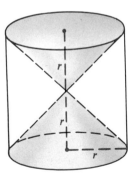

$$= (\pi r^2)(2r) - 2 \cdot (\tfrac{1}{3}\pi r^2)(r)$$
$$= 2\pi r^3 - \tfrac{2}{3}\pi r^3$$
$$= \tfrac{4}{3}\pi r^3$$

Now let us compare the volume of this special solid with that of a sphere of radius r. In the diagram on the next page, X is parallel to M. h is the distance of X from the vertex of the cones. As indicated below the diagram, the area of the intercepted ring-shaped region on the special solid equals the area of the circular region on the sphere.

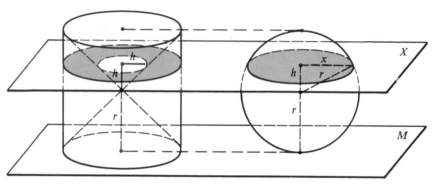

Areas of Cross Sections

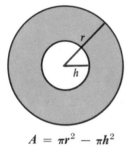

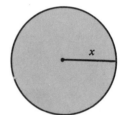

$$A = \pi r^2 - \pi h^2$$

$$A = \pi x^2$$
$$\text{But } x^2 = r^2 - h^2$$
$$\therefore A = \pi r^2 - \pi h^2$$

Cavalieri's Principle enables us to assert that the volume of the sphere is the same as that of the special solid. Recall that we found that volume to be $\frac{4}{3}\pi r^3$.

The volume of a sphere of radius r is $\frac{4}{3}\pi r^3$.

$$V = \frac{4}{3}\pi r^3$$

Think of the surface of the sphere as being divided into a large number of regions of the type shown. Suppose segments are drawn joining the vertices of each region to the center of the sphere. The sphere could then be described as the union of a large number n of such

non-overlapping "curved-base" pyramids each of altitude r. If B_1 is the area of the base of one such pyramid, $\frac{1}{3}B_1 r$ is a reasonable approximation of the volume of that pyramid. Assuming there are n

pyramids, the sum of their volumes is the volume of the sphere.

$$\tfrac{1}{3}B_1r + \tfrac{1}{3}B_2r + \cdots + \tfrac{1}{3}B_nr = \text{Volume of Sphere}$$
$$\tfrac{1}{3}r(B_1 + B_2 + \cdots + B_n) = \tfrac{4}{3}\pi r^3$$
$$\text{But } B_1 + B_2 + \cdots + B_n = \text{The surface area } (S) \text{ of the sphere}$$
$$\therefore \tfrac{1}{3}rS = \tfrac{4}{3}\pi r^3$$
$$S = 4\pi r^2$$

The Surface Area (S) of a sphere of radius r is $4\pi r^2$.

$$S = 4\pi r^2$$

WRITTEN EXERCISES

1. Find the surface area and volume of a sphere of radius

   a. 3 in. **b.** 4 cm. **c.** $2t$ in. **d.** $\sqrt{3}$ cm.

2. Find the surface area and volume of a sphere of diameter

   a. 4 in. **b.** 3 cm. **c.** t ft. **d.** $\sqrt{3}$ in.

3. A plane through the center of a sphere divides it into two parts called *hemispheres.* Find the volume of a hemisphere of radius 4 in.

4. Find the volume of the sphere generated by rotating a semicircular region of radius 4 in. about its diameter as an axis.

5. Find the volume of a sphere that has a surface area of 16π sq. in.

6. Find the surface area of a sphere that has a volume of 288π cu. in.

B

7. A sphere of radius 10 in. is cut by a plane perpendicular to a radius at a point 6 in. from the center. Find the area of the circular cross section.

8. The ratio of the surface areas of two spheres is 4:9. What is the ratio of their volumes?

9. The cross section shown is that of a spherical shell with center O, inner radius 5 in., and outer radius 6 in. Find the volume of the shell.

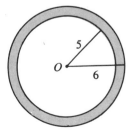

10. A cylinder is shown circumscribed about a sphere. Prove that the surface area of the sphere is equal to the lateral area of the cylinder. **Ex. 10**

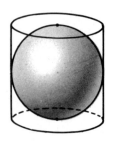

C 11. Two tangent spheres with radii of 6 in. and 10 in. rest on a table. How far apart are the points at which they touch the table?

12. Pictured is a cylinder inscribed in a sphere of radius 4 in. The height of the cylinder is twice the radius of the cylinder. Find the volume of the cylinder. **Ex. 12**

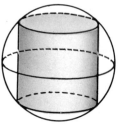

13. Two metal spheres of radii k and $2k$ are melted and recast as a single cylinder of altitude $3k$. Find the radius of the cylinder.

14. A cylinder of height 8 in. is inscribed in a sphere of radius 5 in. Find the volume of the cylinder.

15. Cross section ABC of the cone-shaped container shown is an equilateral triangle with sides 4 in. long. A sphere rests in the container so that the lid just touches the sphere. Find the radius of the sphere.

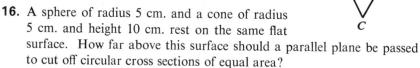

16. A sphere of radius 5 cm. and a cone of radius 5 cm. and height 10 cm. rest on the same flat surface. How far above this surface should a parallel plane be passed to cut off circular cross sections of equal area?

■ Areas and Volumes of Similar Solids

16–7 Areas of Similar Solids

Two right prisms, or two regular pyramids, are said to be **similar** if their bases are bounded by similar *n*-gons and the lengths of their altitudes have the same ratio as the lengths of any two corresponding edges of their bases.

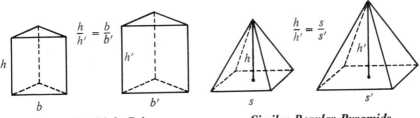

Similar Right Prisms　　　**Similar Regular Pyramids**

Two right circular cylinders, or right circular cones, are said to be similar if the lengths of their altitudes have the same ratio as their radii.

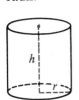 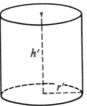 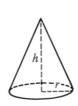

Similar Right Circular Cylinders　　**Similar Right Circular Cones**

For any two similar polygons we know that perimeters have the same ratio as the lengths of any pair of corresponding sides and that areas have the same ratio as the squares of the lengths of any pair of corresponding sides. This suggests the possibility that some special relationship exists between the lateral areas of two similar solids.

Given: Rt. Prism $X \sim$ Rt. Prism X' with base perimeters p and p' and heights h and h' respectively.

1. Let e and e' be the lengths of two corresponding base edges.
2. Since the bases are $\sim$ polygons, $\dfrac{p}{p'} = \dfrac{e}{e'}$.
3. Since the prisms are similar, $\dfrac{e}{e'} = \dfrac{h}{h'}$.
4. Therefore, $\dfrac{p}{p'} = \dfrac{e}{e'} = \dfrac{h}{h'}$.
5. $\dfrac{\text{L.A. of } X}{\text{L.A. of } X'} = \dfrac{ph}{p'h'} = \dfrac{p}{p'} \times \dfrac{h}{h'} = \dfrac{h^2}{(h')^2} = \dfrac{e^2}{(e')^2}$.

Thus, *the lateral areas of two similar right prisms have the same ratio as the squares of the lengths of any two corresponding base edges or the squares of the lengths of the altitudes.*

Now let us consider similar right circular cones, this time working with total areas, to see if the relationship developed for prisms will hold.

Given: Cone $Y \sim$ Cone Y' (both rt. circular).

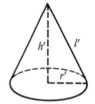

1. Since the cones are similar,

$$\frac{l}{l'} = \frac{r}{r'} = \frac{h}{h'}.$$

2. By a property of equal ratios,

$$\frac{l+r}{l'+r'} = \frac{l}{l'} = \frac{r}{r'} = \frac{h}{h'}.$$

3. $\dfrac{\text{T.A. of } Y}{\text{T.A. of } Y'} = \dfrac{\pi r l + \pi r^2}{\pi r' l' + \pi (r')^2} = \dfrac{\pi r(l+r)}{\pi r'(l'+r')} = \dfrac{r}{r'} \cdot \dfrac{(l+r)}{(l'+r')}$

$$= \frac{r^2}{(r')^2} = \frac{l^2}{(l')^2} = \frac{h^2}{(h')^2}.$$

Thus, *the total areas of two similar right circular cones have the same ratio as the squares of their radii, the squares of the lengths of their altitudes, or the squares of their slant heights.*

Arguments similar to those shown can be developed for other solids to support the conclusion:

The lateral areas and total areas of two similar solids have the same ratio as the squares of the lengths of any pair of corresponding segments.

ORAL EXERCISES

1. Are all right rectangular prisms similar?

2. Do the slant heights of similar right circular cones have the same ratio as the radii?

3. A plane is passed through a cone parallel to the base. Is the smaller cone which it cuts off similar to the original cone?

4. Each of two similar right triangular regions is rotated about the longer leg of the bounding triangle. Are the cones that are generated similar?

A

1. The altitudes of two similar cones are 3 in. and 5 in. long. The radius of the smaller cone is 6 in. Find the radius of the larger cone.

2. The areas of two spheres have the ratio 9 to 16. What is the ratio of the radii? the diameters?

3. Two cubes have edges that are respectively 4 cm. and 6 cm. long. What is the ratio of the total areas of the cubes? the lateral areas?

4. Two similar right prisms have total areas of $18k^2$ and $50k^2$. Find the ratio of the lengths of the sides of the bases.

5. Two similar cylinders have radii of 2 in. and 3 in. The total area of the smaller is 8π sq. in. Find the total area of the larger cylinder.

6. The lateral edges of two similar regular pyramids are 3 ft. and 4 ft. long. The total area of the larger pyramid exceeds the total area of the smaller by 14 sq. ft. Find the total area of each pyramid.

B

7. A given sphere has a radius of 3 ft. Find the radius of a sphere that has two-thirds the area of the given sphere.

8. The sum of the total areas of two similar cones is 195π. The radii have the ratio 2:3. Find the total area of each cone.

9. The lengths of the edges of two cubes differ by 14 in. Find the length of the edge of each cube if the total areas have the ratio 9:25.

10. Cubes are inscribed in and circumscribed about a sphere of radius 6 cm. Find the ratio of the total areas of these cubes.

C

11. The sum of the radius and slant height of a right circular cone is 8 in. A similar cone with a radius twice as great has a total area of 96π sq. in. Find the radius and height of the smaller cone.

12. The sum of the total areas of two similar right circular cones is $25\pi(1 + \sqrt{5})$ sq. cm. Find the total area of each cone if the heights have the ratio 3 to 4.

16–8 Volumes of Similar Solids

To investigate the possibility of a special volume-ratio relationship between two similar solids, we shall again consider two types of similar solids.

Given: Similar right circular cylinders X and X' with radii r and r' and heights h and h' respectively.

1. Since X and X' are similar,

$$\frac{h}{h'} = \frac{r}{r'}.$$

2. $\dfrac{\text{Volume } X}{\text{Volume } X'} = \dfrac{\pi r^2 h}{\pi (r')^2 h'} = \dfrac{r^2}{(r')^2} \times \dfrac{h}{h'} = \dfrac{r^3}{(r')^3} = \dfrac{h^3}{(h')^3}.$

Thus, *the volumes of two similar right circular cylinders have the same ratio as the cubes of their radii or the cubes of their heights.*

Given: Similar regular pyramids Y and Y' with base areas B and B', heights h and h', and base edge lengths e and e', respectively.

1. Since the bases are $\sim$ polygons, $\dfrac{B}{B'} = \dfrac{e^2}{(e')^2}.$

2. Since Y and Y' are similar, $\dfrac{h}{h'} = \dfrac{e}{e'}.$

3. $\dfrac{\text{Vol. } Y}{\text{Vol. } Y'} = \dfrac{\frac{1}{3}Bh}{\frac{1}{3}B'h'} = \dfrac{B}{B'} \times \dfrac{h}{h'} = \dfrac{e^2}{(e')^2} \times \dfrac{e}{e'} = \dfrac{e^3}{(e')^3} = \dfrac{h^3}{(h')^3}.$

Thus, *the volumes of two similar regular pyramids have the same ratio as the cubes of the lengths of their base edges or the cubes of their heights.*

Arguments similar to those shown can be developed for other types of solids to support the conclusion:

The volumes of two similar solids have the same ratio as the cubes of the lengths of any pair of corresponding segments.

ORAL EXERCISES

1. The lengths of the edges of two cubes have the ratio 2 to 3. What is the ratio of the volumes of the cubes? of the total areas of the cubes?

2. The areas of two spheres have the ratio 16 to 25. What is the ratio of the radii? of the volumes?

3. The volumes of two similar regular pyramids are $2a^3$ and $16b^3$. What is the ratio of the lengths of the lateral edges of these pyramids?

4. The total area of one of two similar right prisms is $2\frac{1}{4}$ times that of the other. How are the volumes related?

WRITTEN EXERCISES

A 1. Find the ratio of the volumes of two cubes whose total areas are in the ratio 25:49.

2. Two similar regular pyramids have volumes of 16 cu. in. and 54 cu. in. What is the ratio of their heights? of their total areas?

3. Two similar right circular cylinders have total areas of 18π sq. cm. and 50π sq. cm. What is the ratio of their volumes?

4. Two similar right circular cones have volumes of 108π cu. in. and 500π cu. in. Find the ratio of their total areas.

5. The radius of one sphere is equal to the diameter of another sphere. What is the ratio of the areas? of the volumes?

6. A right rectangular solid has dimensions 3 in., 4 in., and 5 in. Find the length of the diagonal of a similar right rectangular solid that has a volume eight times as great.

B 7. The slant heights of two similar right circular cones are 9 ft. and 15 ft. The volume of the larger cone is 625π cu. ft. Find the volume of the smaller cone.

8. Two similar right prisms have total areas of $18\sqrt{2}$ sq. in. and $50\sqrt{2}$ sq. in. If the volume of the smaller is 81 cu. in., what is the volume of the larger?

9. Given a cube with edge length t, what is the ratio of the volume of the inscribed and circumscribed spheres?

10. Two similar regular pyramids have total areas of $16t^2$ and $72t^2$. If the volume of the smaller is $8\sqrt{2}k^3$, find the volume of the larger.

C 11. The sum of the volumes of two spheres is 105π cu. in. Their areas have the ratio 4:9. Find the volume of each sphere.

12. By what per cent is the volume of a sphere decreased when the radius is decreased by 20 per cent?

13. How far above the base of a right circular cone of height h should a plane parallel to the base be passed to cut off a cone that has a volume equal to half the volume of the original cone?

14. A solid metal regular pyramid is cut by a plane parallel to the base. If the height of the smaller pyramid cut off is three-fifths that of the original pyramid, find the ratio of the weights of the two solids into which the pyramid is divided.

MISCELLANEOUS PRACTICAL PROBLEMS

Use the following approximations:

$$\pi \doteq 3.14 \qquad 1 \text{ cu. ft.} \doteq 7\tfrac{1}{2} \text{ gallons} \qquad 1 \text{ gal.} \doteq 231 \text{ cu. in.}$$

1. What is the capacity in gallons of a cylindrical oil tank that has a 15 ft. altitude and a 3 ft. radius?

2. How many feet of copper wire $\frac{1}{8}$ in. in diameter can be made from 1 cu. ft. of copper?

3. The vertical cross section of a concrete dam is a trapezoid with an altitude 40 ft. long and bases 90 ft. and 20 ft. long. The dam is 60 ft. long. Find the number of cubic yds. of concrete in the dam.

4. If oranges $2\frac{1}{2}$ in. in diameter sell for 54 cents a dozen while oranges 3 in. in diameter sell for 72 cents a dozen, which size is more economical for someone making orange juice?

5. A cylindrical tank 10 ft. long and 3 ft. in diameter is placed so that its axis is horizontal. It is filled with oil to a depth of $2\frac{1}{4}$ ft. How many gallons of oil are in the tank?

6. In manufacturing buck shot, lead cylinders of radius 1 in. and height 8 in. are melted and recast as spherical shot of diameter $\frac{1}{16}$ in. How many shot can be made from one cylinder, assuming no waste?

7. If a cylindrical gallon measure has a radius of 2 in., what is the height?

8. A conical container of slant height 9 in. is made to hold exactly 2 qts. of water. How far from the vertex should a mark be placed to indicate a measure of one quart?

9. If water is flowing through a pipe of diameter 10 in. at the rate of 350 ft. per minute, what is the rate of flow in gallons per hour?

10. The cross section of a steel rod is a regular hexagon $\frac{1}{2}$ in. on an edge. Find the weight of a 12 ft. rod made of steel weighing 480 lbs. per cubic foot.

CHAPTER SUMMARY

Inventory of Structure and Methods

1. Notation:

h, length of altitude	l, slant height	$T.A.$, total area
e, length of base edge	B, area of base	S, surface area of sphere
p, perimeter of base	$L.A.$, lateral area	V, volume

2. Area and Volume Formulas:

Right Prism	*Regular Pyramid*	*Rt. Circular Cylinder*
$L.A. = ph$	$L.A. = \frac{1}{2}pl$	$L.A. = 2\pi rh$
$T.A. = ph + 2B$	$T.A. = \frac{1}{2}pl + B$	$T.A. = 2\pi rh + 2\pi r^2$
$V = Bh$	$V = \frac{1}{3}Bh$	$V = \pi r^2 h$

Rt. Circular Cone

$L.A. = \pi rl$
$T.A. = \pi rl + \pi r^2$
$V = \frac{1}{3}\pi r^2 h$

Sphere

$S = 4\pi r^2$
$V = \frac{4}{3}\pi r^3$

3. The lateral areas and total areas of two solids have the same ratio as the squares of the lengths of any pair of corresponding segments.

4. The surface areas of two spheres have the same ratio as the squares of the radii. The volumes have the same ratio as the cubes of the radii.

5. The volumes of two similar solids have the same ratio as the cubes of the lengths of any pair of corresponding segments.

Vocabulary and Spelling

prism (*p. 585*)
  bases (*p. 585*)
  lateral edge (*p. 586*)
  lateral face (*p. 586*)
  altitude (*p. 586*)
  height (*p. 586*)
right prism (*p. 586*)
oblique prism (*p. 586*)
pyramid (*p. 586*)
  base (*p. 586*)
  vertex (*p. 586*)
  lateral edge (*p. 587*)
  lateral face (*p. 587*)
  altitude (*p. 587*)
  height (*p. 587*)
regular pyramid (*p. 587*)
  slant height (*p. 587*)
nonregular pyramid (*p. 587*)
lateral area of a prism (*p. 588*)
total area of a prism (*p. 588*)

Cavalieri's Principle (*p. 590*)
lateral area of a pyramid (*p. 593*)
total area of a pyramid (*p. 593*)
circular cylinder (*p. 596*)
  bases (*p. 597*)
  axis (*p. 597*)
  altitude (*p. 597*)
right circular cylinder (*p. 597*)
  lateral area (*p. 598*)
circular cone (*p. 599*)
  vertex (*p. 599*)
  base (*p. 599*)
  axis (*p. 599*)
  altitude (*p. 599*)
right circular cone (*p. 599*)
  slant height of (*p. 599*)
  lateral area (*p. 600*)
sphere (*p. 601*)
  surface area of sphere (*p. 603*)
similar solids (*p. 604*)

CHAPTER TEST

16–1   **1.** A hexagonal prism has __?__ lateral faces and __?__ bases.

2. The lateral edges of a prism are __?__ and are __?__ in length.

3. A pyramid must have at least __?__ lateral faces.

4. Each lateral face of a regular pyramid is a(n) __?__ triangle.

16–2   Given the right rectangular prism shown with $AB = 4k$, $BC = 2k$, and $BF = 3k$.

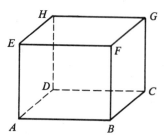

5. Area Base $ABCD$ = __?__

6. Lateral Area = __?__

7. Total Area = __?__

8. Volume = __?__

16–3   Given the regular square pyramid shown with $AB = 10$ in. and $PO = 12$ in.

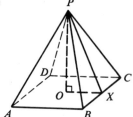

9. Slant Height = __?__

10. Lateral Area = __?__

11. Total Area = __?__

12. Volume = __?__

16–4   Given a right circular cylinder with radius r and height h.

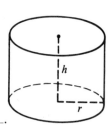

13. If $r = 6$ and $h = 4$, then $L.A.$ = __?__ .

14. If $L.A. = 30\pi$ and $r = 6$, then h = __?__ .

15. If $r = 5$ and $h = 4$, then V = __?__ .

16. If $T.A. = 55\pi$ and $L.A. = 30\pi$, then r = __?__ .

16–5   Given a right circular cone with radius 5 in. and height 11 in.

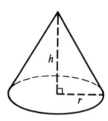

17. Slant Height = __?__

18. Lateral Area = __?__

19. Total Area = __?__

20. Volume = __?__

16–6   **21.** A sphere of radius 3 cm. has a surface area of __?__.

      22. A sphere of radius 8 in. has a volume of __?__.

      23. A sphere of surface area 16π has a radius of __?__.

16–7   **24.** Two cubes with total areas in the ratio 4:9 have sides with lengths in the ratio __?__.

      25. If the ratio of the radii of two spheres is 3:5, the ratio of the surface areas is __?__.

      26. Two similar cones have radii in the ratio 3:7. If the height of the smaller cone is 9 in., the height of the larger cone is __?__.

16–8   **27.** The volumes of two similar right circular cylinders of radii 3 in. and 5 in. have the ratio __?__.

      28. Given a sphere of radius k. A sphere with volume twice as great has a radius of __?__.

CHAPTER REVIEW

16–1   **Vocabulary for Prisms and Pyramids**   *Pages 585–588*

      1. Each lateral edge of a right prism is __?__ to the bases of the prism.

      2. Each lateral face of a prism is a region bounded by a __?__.

      3. The lateral edges of a pyramid intersect at the __?__ of the pyramid.

      4. The lateral area of a pyramid is __?__ ($<$, $=$, $>$) the area of the base.

16–2   **Area and Volume of a Prism**   *Pages 588–592*

      5. A right prism with base area $24k^2$ and height $3k$ has volume __?__.

      6. A cube with edges 5 in. long has a total area of __?__ sq. in.

      7. The lateral area of a right prism is the product of the __?__ of its base and the __?__ of a lateral edge.

      8. A prism with a total area of $30a^2$ and a lateral area of $18a^2$ has a base area of __?__.

16–3   **Area and Volume of a Pyramid**   *Pages 593–596*

      9. A regular pyramid with a base area of 12 sq. in. and a height of 6 in. has a volume of __?__ cubic in.

      10. If each lateral face of a regular square pyramid is an equilateral triangle of side k, the lateral area is __?__.

11. The slant height of a regular pyramid is __?__ ($<$, $=$, $>$) the height.

12. The altitude of a regular square pyramid with base edge 6 in. long intersects the base at a point that is __?__ in. from each vertex of the base.

16–4 Area and Volume of a Right   *Pages 596–599*
Circular Cylinder

Given a right circular cylinder of radius 2k and height 3k.

13. The area of a base is __?__.

14. The lateral area is __?__.

15. The total area is __?__.

16. The volume is __?__.

16–5 Area and Volume of a Right   *Pages 599–601*
Circular Cone

In each exercise the cone described is a right circular cone.

17. A cone of radius 4 in. and height 6 in. has a lateral area of __?__ sq. in.

18. A cone of radius 3 cm. and height 4 cm. has a volume of __?__ cubic cm.

19. A cone with a slant height of 10*k* and an altitude of length 8*k* has a radius of __?__.

20. A cone and cylinder with equal radii and equal heights have volumes in the ratio __?__.

16–6 Volume and Surface Area of a Sphere   *Pages 601–604*

21. A sphere with radius *k* has surface area __?__ and volume __?__.

22. A sphere with surface area 36π sq. in. has a radius of __?__ in.

23. A sphere inscribed in a cube with edges of length 6 in. has a volume of __?__ sq. in.

24. A hemisphere of diameter 4*k* has a volume of __?__.

16–7 Areas of Similar Solids   *Pages 604–607*

25. Two cubes with edges 3 in. and 5 in. long respectively have total areas that are in the ratio __?__.

26. The areas of two spheres are 18π and 50π. The ratio of their radii is __?__.

16–8 Volumes of Similar Solids   *Pages 607–610*

27. Two similar circular cones have radii of 2*k* and 3*k*. The ratio of the volumes of the two cones is __?__.

28. The areas of two spheres are 25π and 49π. The ratio of the volumes of the two spheres is __?__.

● EXTRA FOR EXPERTS

Frustums of Cones and Pyramids

That part of a pyramid or a cone that is included between the plane of the base and a plane that is parallel to the base and intersects the edges is called a **frustum.** Pictured are a frustum of a regular pyramid and a frustum of a right circular cone.

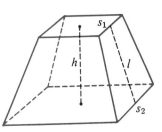
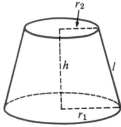

Lateral Area:

The *lateral area of a frustum of a regular pyramid* with n-gons as bases is the sum of the areas of n trapezoids, each of which has an area of $\frac{1}{2}l(s_1 + s_2)$. Therefore, where p_1 and p_2 are the perimeters of the upper and lower bases of the frustum, respectively,

$$\textbf{L.A.} = \tfrac{1}{2}l(s_1 + s_2) \cdot n = \tfrac{1}{2}l(ns_1 + ns_2) = \tfrac{1}{2}l(p_1 + p_2)$$

A formula for the *lateral area of a frustum of a right circular cone* can be obtained by substituting $2\pi r_1$ and $2\pi r_2$ for the perimeters of the bases in the formula for a frustum of a pyramid.

$$\textbf{L.A.} = \tfrac{1}{2}l(2\pi r_1 + 2\pi r_2) = \pi l(r_1 + r_2)$$

EXERCISES

Find the lateral area and the total area of each of the following frustums.

1. A frustum of a regular square pyramid that has bases with edges 6 in. and 4 in. long and has a slant height of 3 in.

2. A frustum of a right circular cone that has bases of radii 8 in. and 4 in. and has a slant height of 5 in.

3. A frustum of a regular triangular pyramid that has bases with edges 6 in. and 4 in. long and a slant height of 8 in.

4. A frustum of a right circular cone that has bases of radii 12 in. and 6 in. and has height $3\sqrt{3}$ in.

Volume:

You can develop a formula for the volume of a frustum of a regular pyramid by subtracting the volume of the pyramid cut off from the volume of the complete pyramid.

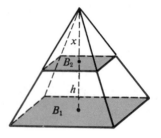

Volume Frustum: $V = \frac{1}{3}B_1(h + x) - \frac{1}{3}B_2x = \frac{1}{3}B_1h + \frac{1}{3}(B_1 - B_2)x$ (1)

Since the pyramids are similar, $\dfrac{(x)^2}{(x + h)^2} = \dfrac{B_2}{B_1}$ or $\dfrac{x}{x + h} = \dfrac{\sqrt{B_2}}{\sqrt{B_1}}$ (2)

Solving (2) for x, $x = \dfrac{h\sqrt{B_2}}{\sqrt{B_1} - \sqrt{B_2}}$ or $x = \dfrac{h\sqrt{B_1B_2} + hB_2}{B_1 - B_2}$ (3)

Substituting for x in (1), $V = \frac{1}{3}B_1h + \frac{1}{3}(B_1 - B_2)\left(\dfrac{h\sqrt{B_1B_2} + hB_2}{B_1 - B_2}\right)$

Simplifying, $V = \frac{1}{3}h(B_1 + B_2 + \sqrt{B_1B_2})$

To obtain the formula for the Volume of a frustum of a right circular cone, you merely replace B_1 and B_2 by πr_1^2 and πr_2^2.

$$V = \tfrac{1}{3}h(\pi r_1^2 + \pi r_2^2 + \sqrt{(\pi r_1)^2 \cdot (\pi r_2)^2})$$

$$V = \tfrac{1}{3}\pi h(r_1^2 + r_2^2 + r_1r_2)$$

EXERCISES

Find the volume of each of the following frustums.

1. A frustum of a regular square pyramid that has bases with edge length 8 in. and 3 in. long and a height of 4 in.

2. A frustum of a right circular cone that has bases of radii 5 in. and 2 in. and a height of 3 in.

3. The frustum formed when a regular square pyramid with height 8 in. and base edge 4 in. long is cut by a plane parallel to the base and 2 in. from the vertex.

4. The frustum formed by cutting a right circular cone of 6 in. radius and 8 in. altitude with a plane parallel to the base and lying 4 in. above the base.

▶ The Fourth Dimension

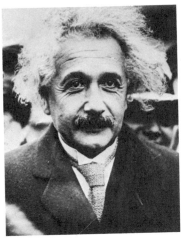

There once was a lady named Bright
Who could travel far faster than light,
She set out one day,
In a relative way,
And came back the previous night.

This well-known limerick, though delightfully absurd, has a sobering side. People find it just as hard to accept parts of Einstein's theory as to believe the fanciful tale above. In fact, Albert Einstein himself once said:

> The nonmathematician is seized by a mysterious shuddering when he hears of four-dimensional things, by a feeling not unlike that awakened by thoughts of the occult. And yet, there is no more commonplace statement than that the world in which we live is a four-dimensional space-time continuum.

It is not our intent here to explain what is meant by a four-dimensional space-time continuum. We hope only to acquaint you with a few details about the life of a humble man who can truly be called a genius. However, you should realize that any proposed fourth dimension cannot be like the familiar three: length, width, and height. You can think of it as time. For example, to describe the position of a satellite you need four numbers: latitude, longitude, altitude, and time.

For a person destined to startle the world with ideas such as those of four dimensions and curved space, Einstein led an unspectacular early life. Slow in speech as a young child, he remained shy as a student. He intensely disliked all forms of regimentation and military procedure, in particular the required memory work and rote drill which characterized the German schools he attended in his youth.

In spite of his brilliance in mathematics and physics, Einstein actually failed in his first attempt to enter the Swiss Federal Polytechnic School. After an additional year of preparation, he entered the school. During his years at the Polytechnic he developed the habit of approaching his studies with two basic questions in mind: How? Why?

While working at a modest job in the Swiss Patent Office, Einstein began writing his epoch-making papers. In 1905 the twenty-six year old announced his Special Theory of Relativity. Perhaps you have already encountered the equation $E = mc^2$ in your reading. This simple looking equation, just one outcome of the Theory of Relativity, opened the door to experiments which led to the development of atomic power.

Einstein left Europe during the turbulent years preceding World War II, and came to the United States where he received a lifetime appointment at the Institute for Advanced Study in Princeton, New Jersey. There he lived as a humble, kindly scholar until his death in 1955.

Einstein discusses his Theory of Relativity before the American Association for the Advancement of Science at Carnegie Institute of Technology in 1934.

CUMULATIVE REVIEW: CHAPTERS 8–16

TRUE-FALSE EXERCISES

1. An angle inscribed in a major arc of a circle is obtuse.
2. If two triangles have equal areas, they are congruent.
3. If an acute angle of one right triangle is complementary to an acute angle of a second right triangle, then the triangles are similar.
4. The transformation specified by the equations $x' = -x$ and $y' = y$ is a reflection of the plane in the y-axis.
5. Tangent segments to a circle from the same external point have equal lengths.
6. Given a segment of length a it is possible to construct a segment of length $\frac{2}{3}a$.
7. If the radius of a sphere is doubled, the volume is exactly doubled.
8. The geometric mean of x and y is $\sqrt{xy}$.
9. A circle with circumference 6π has area 9π.
10. The area of a rhombus is equal to the product of the lengths of its diagonals.
11. In space, the locus of points equidistant from two points is a plane.
12. If two circles intersect in two points, then the center of one circle lies in the exterior of the other circle.
13. Under a reflection in the y-axis, every vertical line maps into a vertical line.
14. If a polygon can be inscribed in a circle, then it must be a regular polygon.
15. The point $(3, -2)$ lies on the graph of $2x + 3y = 12$.
16. The length of the chord of an arc is double the length of the chord of half the arc.
17. A median of a triangle divides the triangle into two triangles of equal area.
18. If two chords of a circle have unequal lengths, the longer chord is further from the center.
19. Two isosceles right triangles are similar.
20. Under the transformation specified by $x' = 3x$ and $y' = 3y$, the origin is a fixed point.
21. The graph of $y = \dfrac{6}{x}$ is a line.

22. A cube with edge 3 in. long has a volume of 27 cu. in.
23. Two externally tangent circles have exactly 4 common tangents.
24. In a plane, the locus of points equidistant from 3 noncollinear points is a circle.
25. A line with slope $-\frac{2}{3}$ is perpendicular to a line with slope $\frac{3}{2}$.
26. The lateral area of a pyramid must be greater than the area of the base of the pyramid.
27. A triangle with vertices $(a, 0)$, $(-a, 0)$ and $(0, a)$ is equilateral.
28. The locus of the midpoints of all 6 in. chords in a circle of radius 5 in. is a circle of radius 4 in.
29. The slope of the line $ax + by = c$ is not defined when $a = 0$.
30. The ratio of the volume of a sphere to that of a circumscribed cube is $\pi:6$.

ALWAYS-SOMETIMES-NEVER EXERCISES

Classify each statement as *Always True* (A), *Sometimes True* (S), or *Never True* (N).

1. If two chords of a circle are equal in length, then they are parallel.
2. The projection of a segment into a plane is a point.
3. In a 30°–60°–90° triangle, the ratio of the lengths of the legs is 1:2.
4. A trapezoid inscribed in a circle is isosceles.
5. The medians of an equilateral triangle are also the altitudes.
6. A triangle with angle measures in the ratio 1:2:3 is a right triangle.
7. A line perpendicular to a radius is a tangent.
8. The center of a circle circumscribed about an obtuse triangle lies in the exterior of the triangle.
9. The area of a circle is equal to one-half the product of the circumference and the radius.
10. Two parallelograms that have equal areas have equal perimeters.
11. The length of a diagonal of a right rectangular prism is less than the length of the diagonal of any lateral face.
12. A median of a triangle divides the triangle into 2 nonsimilar triangles.
13. It is possible to construct a triangle with sides having lengths $2k$, $3k$, $5k$ $(k > 0)$.
14. If two right triangles have the same area, the triangles are congruent.
15. If, under a transformation, point $(-2, 1)$ is mapped into point $(2, 1)$ the transformation is a reflection of the plane in the y-axis.

SHORT COMPUTATION EXERCISES

1. The line passing through points (3, 4) and (5, −1) has a slope of __?__.
2. The geometric mean of 4 and 9 is __?__.
3. If $5x = 3y$, the ratio of x to y is __?__.
4. A square of perimeter $8k$ has an area of __?__.
5. For any circle, the ratio of the circumference to the diameter is __?__.
6. If the graph of $y = kx$ passes through point $(-2, 4)$, then k is __?__.
7. A circle with circumference 12π in. has area __?__ sq. in.
8. Under the transformation $M: (x, y) \rightarrow (3x, 4y)$, the image of the point $(2, 3)$ is point __?__.
9. A cube with a side 3 cm. long has a volume of __?__ cu. cm.
10. In a circle of radius 5 in. the midpoint of a 6 in. chord is __?__ in. from the center.
11. If the hypotenuse of an isosceles right triangle is 8 in. long, then each leg is __?__ in. long.
12. If point X is located on $\overline{AB}$ so that $AX = 4$ and $BX = 11$, the ratio $BX:AB$ is __?__.
13. Under the translation specified by $x' = x + 4$ and $y' = y - 2$, the image of the point $(7, 2)$ is __?__.

14. A cube with an edge 4 in. long has a diagonal that is __?__ in. long.
15. The perimeters of two similar pentagons of areas $2k^2$ and $18k^2$ have the ratio __?__.
16. The coordinates of the midpoint of a segment joining points $(-4, 3)$ and $(6, 7)$ are __?__.
17. A trapezoid with bases 5 cm. and 8 cm. long and an area of 26 sq. cm. has an altitude __?__ cm. long.
18. In a circle of radius 8 in. a central angle of measure 45 intercepts an arc of length __?__ in.
19. A right circular cone of radius 6 and height 8 has a lateral area of __?__.
20. In a circle of radius 6, a 40° sector has an area of __?__.
21. A circle with center at the origin and radius 3 has the equation __?__.
22. Under the transformation specified by $x' = x + 2$ and $y' = y - 1$, the preimage of point $(4, 5)$ is __?__.
23. A circle inscribed in an equilateral triangle of perimeter 18 has area __?__.
24. An equation of the line passing through pts. $(0, 4)$ and $(2, 2)$ is __?__.

25. A line that is perpendicular to the line $2x - 3y = 9$ has slope __?__.

26. The midpoint of $\overline{AB}$ has coordinates $(\frac{1}{2}, \frac{3}{2})$. If the coordinates of A are (4, 8), then the coordinates of B are __?__.

27. In a circle of radius 2 in., a sector with area $\dfrac{4\pi}{5}$ sq. in. has a central angle of measure __?__.

28. A plane parallel to the base of a right circular cone and bisecting the altitude divides the cone into two solids whose volumes have the ratio __?__.

29. A right circular cylinder of volume 320π cu. in. and height 5 in. has a radius of __?__ in.

MULTIPLE CHOICE EXERCISES

A

1. If the length of the shorter leg of a 30°–60°–90° triangle is 3, then the length of the longer leg is

  a. 6   **b.** $3\sqrt{2}$ **c.** 3   **d.** $3\sqrt{3}$

2. The median to the hypotenuse of a right triangle divides the triangle into two triangles that are

  a. congruent   **c.** isosceles

  b. similar   **d.** acute

3. A segment joining the midpoints of two sides of a triangle divides it into a triangle and trapezoid whose areas have the ratio

  a. 1:1   **b.** 1:2   **c.** 1:3   **d.** 1:4

4. In a plane, the locus of points at a given distance from a given point is

  a. a line   **b.** a circle   **c.** two lines   **d.** a sphere

5. A line passing through the points $(-1, 2)$ and $(3, 5)$ has a slope of

  a. $-\frac{3}{4}$ **b.** $\frac{3}{4}$ **c.** $\frac{3}{2}$ **d.** $-\frac{4}{3}$

6. The locus of the centers of all circles tangent to both sides of a given angle is a

  a. line   **c.** segment

  b. ray, except for its endpoint   **d.** point

7. If $\triangle ABC$ is inscribed in a circle of diameter 8 and $\angle A$ is acute, the length of side $\overline{BC}$ is such that

  a. $BC < 4$ **c.** $BC < 8$

  b. $BC = 4$ **d.** $BC = 10$

8. The lateral faces of all oblique prisms are

  a. squares   **b.** rectangles   **c.** parallelograms   **d.** trapezoids

9. If the area of a square is 18, the length of each diagonal is

  a. $3\sqrt{2}$ **b.** $6\sqrt{2}$ **c.** 4   **d.** 6

10. If the measure of each angle of a regular polygon is greater than 120, then the number of sides the polygon has is

  a. 6   **b.** at least 7   **c.** at most 6   **d.** 7

11. A trapezoid with bases having lengths 6 and 12 and legs having lengths 5 and 5 has an area of

  a. 14   **b.** 45   **c.** 36   **d.** $14\sqrt{2}$

12. Under the translation specified by $x' = x + 4$ and $y' = y - 2$, the preimage of $(6, -8)$ is

  a. $(2, 6)$ **b.** $(-2, -6)$ **c.** $(10, -10)$ **d.** $(2, -6)$

13. If the ratio of the volumes of two similar pyramids is $8:27$, the ratio of their total areas is

  a. $2:3$ **b.** $8:27$ **c.** $4:9$ **d.** $16:81$

B 14. The locus of points at a distance k from a given plane M and at a distance d from a fixed point in M, where $k > d$, is

  a. 2 circles   **b.** 1 circle   **c.** 2 lines   **d.** Ø

15. If two points P and Q have images P' and Q' under the stretching $x' = 3x$ and $y' = y$, then

  a. $PQ < P'Q'$ **b.** $PQ \le P'Q'$ **c.** $PQ > P'Q'$ **d.** $PQ \ge P'Q'$

16. A reflection in the x-axis is specified by the pair of equations

  a. $x' = -x$ **b.** $x' = -x$ **c.** $x' = x$ **d.** none of these
   $y' = y$ $y' = -y$ $y' = -y$

17. A line through the point $(3, -2)$ with slope $-\frac{2}{3}$ will pass through point

  a. $(-2, 3)$ **b.** $(6, 0)$ **c.** $(-3, 6)$ **d.** $(0, 0)$

18. Given a triangle with sides having lengths 3, 4, and 5. A similar triangle with perimeter 24 has area

  a. 12   **b.** 24   **c.** 48   **d.** 36

19. If $x^2 - x - 12 < 0$, then

  a. $-3 < x < 4$ **c.** $x > 4$ or $x < -3$
  b. $-4 < x < 3$ **d.** $x < 4$

20. The ratio of the surface area of a sphere to the lateral area of a circumscribed right circular cylinder is

  a. $1:2$ **b.** $1:1$ **c.** $\pi:1$ **d.** $\sqrt{2}:3$

CIRCLES: ANGLE AND SEGMENT EXERCISES

A   **1.**

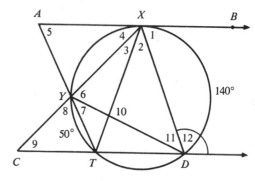

Given: $\overleftrightarrow{AB}$ tangent at X.
$\overleftrightarrow{AB} \parallel \overleftrightarrow{CD}$;
$m\widehat{XD} = 140$;
$m\widehat{YT} = 50$.

$m\angle 1 = $ __?__	$m\angle 4 = $ __?__	$m\angle 7 = $ __?__	$m\angle 10 = $ __?__
$m\angle 2 = $ __?__	$m\angle 5 = $ __?__	$m\angle 8 = $ __?__	$m\angle 11 = $ __?__
$m\angle 3 = $ __?__	$m\angle 6 = $ __?__	$m\angle 9 = $ __?__	$m\angle 12 = $ __?__

Given: tangent $\overline{AB}$ Given: $MT > TN$ Given: secants $\overline{AP}$ and $\overline{CP}$

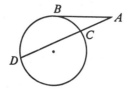   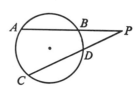

B   **2.** $AC = 3$
$CD = 5$
$AB = $ __?__

3. $AB = 4\sqrt{3}$
$AC = 4$
$DC = $ __?__

4. $AB = 3\sqrt{3}$
$DC = 6$
$AC = $ __?__

5. $RT = 3$
$TS = 8$
$MN = 10$
$MT = $ __?__
$TN = $ __?__

6. $RS = 9$
$RT:TS = 1:2$
$MN = 11$
$MT = $ __?__
$NT = $ __?__

7. $AB = 5$
$BP = 4$
$CP = 12$
$DP = $ __?__
$CD = $ __?__

8. $AB = 3$
$AP = 8$
$CD = 6$
$DP = $ __?__

COORDINATE PLANE EXERCISES

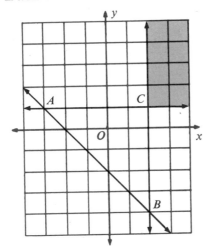

In the coordinate system pictured state:

A

1. The coordinates of A.
2. The distance from A to B.
3. The slope of $\overleftrightarrow{AB}$.
4. An equation of $\overleftrightarrow{AB}$.
5. An equation of $\overleftrightarrow{AC}$.
6. The slope of any line $\perp \overleftrightarrow{AB}$.
7. The coordinates of the midpoint of $\overline{AB}$.
8. The measure of $\angle BAC$.

B

9. The area of $\triangle ABC$.
10. The perimeter of $\triangle ABC$.
11. The coordinates of the image of C under the transformation: $x' = 2x, y' = 3y$.
12. The coordinates of the image of A under the transformation $x' = x + 2$, $y' = y - 1$.

C

13. An equation of the circle with center at O and passing through C.
14. An equation of the line through C and parallel to $\overleftrightarrow{AB}$.
15. An equation of the line through C and perpendicular to $\overleftrightarrow{AB}$.
16. A pair of open sentences that describe points of the shaded region.
17. An equation of the circle that has $\overline{AC}$ as diameter.
18. An equation of the circle passing through A, B, and C.

MATCHING EXERCISES

Write the numbers from 1 to 20 on your paper. Alongside each number write the letter that identifies the algebraic expression by which you can compute the measure named. The terms "cylinder" and "cone" refer to right circular solids.

A

1. Area of a circle
2. Volume of a cube
3. Distance between points
4. Lateral area of a cone
5. Volume of a pyramid
6. Total area of a cylinder
7. Length of a diagonal of a rectangular solid
8. Slope of a line
9. Area of an equilateral triangle
10. Circumference of a circle
11. Volume of a sphere
12. Lateral area of a cube
13. Area of a rhombus
14. Area of a sphere
15. Volume of a cylinder
16. Length of diagonal of a cube
17. Lateral area of a cylinder
18. Area of a trapezoid
19. Total area of a cone
20. Sum of the measures of the interior angles of a polygon

a. $\frac{1}{3}Bh$

b. e^3

c. $\sqrt{l^2 + w^2 + h^2}$

d. $\frac{1}{2}h(b_1 + b_2)$

e. $\frac{s^2}{4}\sqrt{3}$

f. $\frac{4}{3}\pi r^3$

g. $4\pi r^2$

h. $\frac{1}{2}d_1 d_2$

i. $\frac{y_2 - y_1}{x_2 - x_1}$

j. $4e^2$

k. $e\sqrt{3}$

l. πr^2

m. $\pi r^2 h$

n. $2\pi rh$

o. $\sqrt{(x_2 - x_1)^2 + (y_2 - y_1)^2}$

p. $2\pi r$

q. $180(n - 2)$

r. πrl

s. $\pi rl + \pi r^2$

t. $2\pi rh + 2\pi r^2$

CONSTRUCTION EXERCISES

On your paper draw two segments having lengths a and b where $a > b$. Then construct

A

1. An equilateral triangle with sides a units long.
2. An isosceles right triangle with legs $(a + b)$ units long.
3. A rhombus in which the diagonals have lengths a and b.
4. A segment of length $\sqrt{2ab}$.

B

5. A segment of length $\sqrt{a^2 + b^2}$.
6. A circle with area $\pi(a^2 + b^2)$.
7. A square with radius $a\sqrt{2}$.
8. Any isosceles trapezoid with bases having lengths a and b.

MORE DIFFICULT EXERCISES

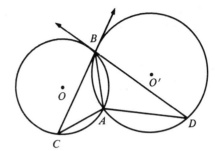

C **1.** Prove: The opposite angles of an inscribed quadrilateral are supplementary.

2. Given: $\overline{BC}$ tangent to $\odot O'$ at B.
$\overline{BD}$ tangent to $\odot O$ at B.

Prove: $\triangle CBA \sim \triangle BDA$.

3. Using a coordinate system prove that an isosceles triangle has two congruent medians.

4. From the vertex B of an inscribed isosceles $\triangle ABC$ ($\overline{AB} \cong \overline{CB}$) a chord $\overline{BE}$ is drawn intersecting the base in D. Prove that $(AB)^2 = BD \cdot BE$.

5. In $\triangle ABC$ the length of the median drawn from the vertex A is equal to one-half BC. Prove that the area of $\triangle ABC$ is equal to one-half the product of AB and AC.

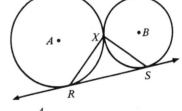

6. Given: $\odot A$ and $\odot B$ tangent at X;
$\overleftrightarrow{RS}$ tangent to $\odot A$ and $\odot B$.

Prove: $\overline{RX} \perp \overline{SX}$.

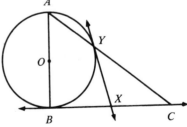

7. Given: $\overleftrightarrow{BC}$ is tangent to $\odot O$ at B;
$\overleftrightarrow{XY}$ is tangent to $\odot O$ at Y.

Prove: $BX = XC$.

8. Using a coordinate system, prove that the line segment joining the midpoints of the non-parallel sides of a trapezoid has a length equal to one-half the sum of the lengths of the two bases.

9. Prove: The sum of the lengths of the perpendiculars drawn from any point within an equilateral triangle to the sides is equal to the length of an altitude.

10. In quadrilateral $ABCD$ segments $\overline{AE}$ and $\overline{CF}$ are drawn to the midpoints of $\overline{BC}$ and $\overline{AD}$ respectively. Prove that the area of quadrilateral $AECF$ is equal to the sum of the areas of $\triangle BEA$ and $\triangle CFD$.

Values of Trigonometric Ratios

Angle Measure	Sine	Cosine	Tangent	Angle Measure	Sine	Cosine	Tangent
1°	.0175	.9998	.0175	46°	.7193	.6947	1.0355
2°	.0349	.9994	.0349	47°	.7314	.6820	1.0724
3°	.0523	.9986	.0524	48°	.7431	.6691	1.1106
4°	.0698	.9976	.0699	49°	.7547	.6561	1.1504
5°	.0872	.9962	.0875	50°	.7660	.6428	1.1918
6°	.1045	.9945	.1051	51°	.7771	.6293	1.2349
7°	.1219	.9925	.1228	52°	.7880	.6157	1.2799
8°	.1392	.9903	.1405	53°	.7986	.6018	1.3270
9°	.1564	.9877	.1584	54°	.8090	.5878	1.3764
10°	.1736	.9848	.1763	55°	.8192	.5736	1.4281
11°	.1908	.9816	.1944	56°	.8290	.5592	1.4826
12°	.2079	.9781	.2126	57°	.8387	.5446	1.5399
13°	.2250	.9744	.2309	58°	.8480	.5299	1.6003
14°	.2419	.9703	.2493	59°	.8572	.5150	1.6643
15°	.2588	.9659	.2679	60°	.8660	.5000	1.7321
16°	.2756	.9613	.2867	61°	.8746	.4848	1.8040
17°	.2924	.9563	.3057	62°	.8829	.4695	1.8807
18°	.3090	.9511	.3249	63°	.8910	.4540	1.9626
19°	.3256	.9455	.3443	64°	.8988	.4384	2.0503
20°	.3420	.9397	.3640	65°	.9063	.4226	2.1445
21°	.3584	.9336	.3839	66°	.9135	.4067	2.2460
22°	.3746	.9272	.4040	67°	.9205	.3907	2.3559
23°	.3907	.9205	.4245	68°	.9272	.3746	2.4751
24°	.4067	.9135	.4452	69°	.9336	.3584	2.6051
25°	.4226	.9063	.4663	70°	.9397	.3420	2.7475
26°	.4384	.8988	.4877	71°	.9455	.3256	2.9042
27°	.4540	.8910	.5095	72°	.9511	.3090	3.0777
28°	.4695	.8829	.5317	73°	.9563	.2924	3.2709
29°	.4848	.8746	.5543	74°	.9613	.2756	3.4874
30°	.5000	.8660	.5774	75°	.9659	.2588	3.7321
31°	.5150	.8572	.6009	76°	.9703	.2419	4.0108
32°	.5299	.8480	.6249	77°	.9744	.2250	4.3315
33°	.5446	.8387	.6494	78°	.9781	.2079	4.7046
34°	.5592	.8290	.6745	79°	.9816	.1908	5.1446
35°	.5736	.8192	.7002	80°	.9848	.1736	5.6713
36°	.5878	.8090	.7265	81°	.9877	.1564	6.3138
37°	.6018	.7986	.7536	82°	.9903	.1392	7.1154
38°	.6157	.7880	.7813	83°	.9925	.1219	8.1443
39°	.6293	.7771	.8098	84°	.9945	.1045	9.5144
40°	.6428	.7660	.8391	85°	.9962	.0872	11.4301
41°	.6561	.7547	.8693	86°	.9976	.0698	14.3007
42°	.6691	.7431	.9004	87°	.9986	.0523	19.0811
43°	.6820	.7314	.9325	88°	.9994	.0349	28.6363
44°	.6947	.7193	.9657	89°	.9998	.0175	57.2900
45°	.7071	.7071	1.0000				

POSTULATES

P₁ A line contains at least two points; a plane contains at least three points not all on one line; and space contains at least four points not all in one plane.

P₂ Through any two different points there is exactly one line.

P₃ Through any three points that are not on one line, there is exactly one plane.

P₄ If two points lie in a plane, then the line containing them lies in that plane.

P₅ If two different planes intersect, then their intersection is a line.

P₆ Between any two points there is a unique distance.

P₇ The set of points on a line can be put in one-to-one correspondence with the real numbers in such a way that:
(1) Any particular point is paired with zero;
(2) The distance between any two points is equal to the absolute value of the difference between the numbers corresponding to those points. (Ruler postulate)

P₈ To every angle there corresponds a unique real number greater than 0 and less than 180. (Angle measurement postulate)

P₉ In the union of a half-plane and its edge, the set of rays with a common endpoint in the edge of the half-plane can be put in one-to-one correspondence with the real numbers from 0 to 180 inclusive in such a way that:
(1) One of the two opposite rays lying in the edge is paired with 0 and the other is paired with 180.
(2) The measure of any angle whose sides are rays of the given set is equal to the absolute value of the difference between the numbers corresponding to its sides. (Protractor postulate)

P₁₀ If two parallel lines are cut by a transversal, corresponding angles are congruent.

P₁₁ If two lines are cut by a transversal so that corresponding angles are congruent, the lines are parallel.

P₁₂ If three sides of one triangle are congruent to three sides of another triangle, the triangles are congruent. (SSS postulate)

P₁₃ If two sides and the included angle of one triangle are congruent to two sides and the included angle of another triangle the triangles are congruent. (SAS postulate)

P₁₄ If the hypotenuse and a leg of one right triangle are congruent to the hypotenuse and a leg of another right triangle, the triangles are congruent. (HL postulate)

P_{15} If two angles and the included side of one triangle are congruent to two angles and the included side of another triangle, the triangles are congruent. (ASA postulate)

P_{16} If two angles of one triangle are congruent to two angles of another triangle, the triangles are similar. (AA postulate)

P_{17} If the intersection of arcs $\overarc{DE}$ and $\overarc{EF}$ of a circle is the single point E, then $m\overarc{DE} + m\overarc{EF} = m\overarc{DEF}$. (Arc addition postulate)

P_{18} Corresponding to each polygonal region there is a unique positive number called the **area** of that region.

P_{19} If two triangles are congruent, then the regions they bound have the same area.

P_{20} If a polygonal region is the union of n non-overlapping polygonal regions, then its area is the sum of the areas of those n regions.

P_{21} The area of a rectangle is the product of the length of a base and the length of an altitude to that base. ($A = bh$)

P_{22} If two polygons are similar, they can be separated into the same number of triangles similar each to each and in corresponding positions.

THEOREMS

Deduction and Geometry

3–1 If two lines intersect, they intersect in exactly one point.

3–2 If a point lies outside a line, exactly one plane contains the line and the point.

3–3 If two lines intersect, exactly one plane contains both lines.

3–4 On a ray there is exactly one point at a given distance from the endpoint of the ray.

3–5 A segment has exactly one midpoint.

Angle Relationships; Perpendicular Lines

4–1 If $\overrightarrow{OE}$ lies between $\overrightarrow{OD}$ and $\overrightarrow{OF}$ in a half-plane, then $m\angle DOE + m\angle EOF = m\angle DOF$. (Angle addition theorem)

4–2 If the exterior sides of two adjacent angles are opposite rays, the angles are supplementary.

4–3 In a half-plane, through the endpoint of a ray lying in the edge of the half-plane, there is exactly one other ray such that the angle formed by the two rays has a given measure between 0 and 180.

4–4 An angle has exactly one bisector.

4–5 All right angles are congruent.

4–6 If two lines are perpendicular, they meet to form right angles.

4-7 If two lines meet to form a right angle, the lines are perpendicular.

4-8 If two adjacent acute angles have their exterior sides in perpendicular lines, the angles are complementary.

4-9 In a plane, through a given point of a line, there is exactly one line perpendicular to the line.

4-10 If two angles are supplementary to the same angle or to congruent angles, they are congruent to each other.

4-11 If two angles are complementary to the same angle or to congruent angles, they are congruent to each other.

4-12 If two lines intersect, the vertical angles formed are congruent.

4-13 Congruence of segments is reflexive, symmetric and transitive.

4-14 Congruence of angles is reflexive, symmetric, and transitive.

Parallel Lines and Planes

5-1 If two parallel planes are cut by a third plane, the lines of intersection are parallel.

5-2 If a transversal is perpendicular to one of two parallel lines, it is perpendicular to the other one also.

5-3 If two parallel lines are cut by a transversal, alternate interior angles are congruent.

5-4 Through a point outside a line not more than one parallel can be drawn to the line.

5-5 Through a point outside a line a parallel can be drawn to the line.

5-6 Through a point outside a line, exactly one line can be drawn perpendicular to the line.

5-7 In a plane, if two lines are perpendicular to a third line, they are parallel to each other.

5-8 If two lines are cut by a transversal so that alternate interior angles are congruent, the lines are parallel.

5-9 The sum of the measures of the angles of a traingle is 180.

5-10 The measure of an exterior angle of a triangle is equal to the sum of the measures of the two remote interior angles.

5-11 The sum of the measures of the angles of a convex quadrilateral is 360.

Congruent Triangles

6-1 Congruence of triangles is reflexive, symmetric and transitive.

6-2 If the legs of one right triangle are congruent to the legs of another right triangle, the triangles are congruent. (LL theorem)

6-3 If two angles and a not-included side of one triangle are congruent to the corresponding parts of another triangle, the triangles are congruent. (AAS theorem)

6–4 If two sides of a triangle are congruent, then the angles opposite those sides are congruent. (Base angles of an isosceles triangle are congruent.)

6–5 If two angles of a triangle are congruent, then the sides opposite those angles are congruent.

Applying Congruent Triangles

7–1 A diagonal of a parallelogram separates the parallelogram into two congruent triangles.

7–2 The diagonals of a parallelogram bisect each other.

7–3 If two sides of a quadrilateral are congruent and parallel, the quadrilateral is a parallelogram.

7–4 If both pairs of opposite sides of a quadrilateral are congruent, the quadrilateral is a parallelogram.

7–5 If the diagonals of a quadrilateral bisect each other, the quadrilateral is a parallelogram.

7–6 The segment joining the midpoints of two sides of a triangle is parallel to the third side and its length is half the length of the third side.

7–7 If three parallel lines cut off congruent segments on one transversal, they cut off congruent segments on every transversal.

7–8 The diagonals of a rectangle are congruent.

7–9 The diagonals of a rhombus are perpendicular.

7–10 Each diagonal of a rhombus bisects two angles of the rhombus.

7–11 The median of a trapezoid is parallel to the bases; it has a length equal to half the sum of the lengths of the bases.

7–12 Base angles of an isosceles trapezoid are congruent.

7–13 The diagonals of an isosceles trapezoid are congruent.

7–14 If two sides of a triangle are not congruent, then the angles opposite those sides are not congruent and the angle opposite the longer side is the larger.

7–15 If two sides of a triangle are not congruent, then the sides opposite those angles are not congruent and the side opposite the larger angle is the longer side.

7–16 The sum of the lengths of any two sides of a triangle is greater than the length of the third side.

7–17 If two sides of one triangle are congruent to two sides of another triangle, but the included angle of the first triangle is larger than the included angle of the second, then the third side of the first triangle is longer than the third side of the second.

7–18 If two sides of one triangle are congruent to two sides of another triangle, but the third side of the first triangle is longer than the third side of the second, then the included angle of the first triangle is larger than the included angle of the second.

Similar Polygons

8-1 Similarity of convex polygons is reflexive, symmetric, and transitive.

8-2 If two polygons are similar, the ratio of their perimeters equals the ratio of the lengths of any pair of corresponding sides.

8-3 If a line is parallel to one side of a triangle and intersects the other two sides, it divides them proportionally.

8-4 If a ray bisects an angle of a triangle, it divides the opposite side into segments whose lengths are proportional to the lengths of the other two sides.

8-5 If two triangles are similar, the lengths of corresponding altitudes have the same ratio as the lengths of any pair of corresponding sides.

Similar Right Triangles

9-1 If the altitude is drawn to the hypotenuse of a right triangle, the two triangles formed are similar to the given triangle and to each other.

9-2 Pythagorean Theorem — In any right triangle the square of the length of the hypotenuse is equal to the sum of the squares of the lengths of the legs.

9-3 If the sum of the squares of the lengths of two sides of a triangle is equal to the square of the length of the third side, the triangle is a right triangle. (Converse of the Pythagorean Theorem)

9-4 If the acute angles of a right triangle have measures 30 and 60, the hypotenuse is twice as long as the shorter leg and the longer leg is $\sqrt{3}$ times as long as the shorter leg. (30°–60°–90° theorem)

9-5 If each acute angle of a right triangle has measure 45, the hypotenuse is $\sqrt{2}$ times as long as a leg.   (45°–45°–90° theorem)

Circles

10-1 A line in the plane of a circle and containing an interior point of the circle intersects the circle in two points.

10-2 A tangent to a circle is perpendicular to the radius drawn to the point of tangency.

10-3 A line in the plane of a circle and perpendicular to a radius at its outer endpoint is tangent to the circle.

10-4 If in the same circle or congruent circles, two central angles are congruent, their arcs are congruent.

10-5 If in the same circle or congruent circles, two minor arcs are congruent, their central angles are congruent.

10-6 In the same circle or in congruent circles, congruent chords have congruent arcs.

10-7 In the same circle or in congruent circles, congruent arcs have congruent chords.

10-8 A diameter that is perpendicular to a chord bisects the chord and its two arcs.

10–9 In the same circle or in congruent circles, chords that are equally distant from the center are congruent.

10–10 In the same circle or in congruent circles, congruent chords are equally distant from the center.

10–11 The measure of an inscribed angle is equal to half the measure of its intercepted arc.

10–12 The measure of an angle formed by a secant ray and a tangent ray drawn from a point on a circle is equal to half the measure of the intercepted arc.

10–13 The measure of an angle formed by two secants intersecting inside a circle is equal to half the sum of the measures of the arcs intercepted by the angle and by its vertical angle.

10–14 The measure of an angle formed by two secant rays with a common endpoint outside a circle equals one-half the difference of the measures of the intercepted arcs.

10–15 The measure of an angle formed by a tangent ray and a secant ray or by two tangent rays with a common endpoint outside a circle is equal to half the difference of the measures of the intercepted arcs.

10–16 If two chords intersect within a circle, the product of the lengths of the segments of one chord equals the product of the lengths of the segments of the other.

10–17 If two secant segments are drawn to a circle from an outside point, the product of the length of one secant segment and the length of its external secant segment is equal to the product of the length of the other secant segment and the length of the external secant segment.

10–18 If a tangent segment and a secant segment are drawn to a circle from an outside point, the length of the tangent segment is the geometric mean between the length of the secant segment and the length of the external secant segment.

Coordinate Geometry — Methods

12–1 The distance d between two points (x_1, y_1) and (x_2, y_2) is:

$$d = \sqrt{(x_2 - x_1)^2 + (y_2 - y_1)^2}.$$

12–2 The circle with center (a, b) and radius r has the equation $(x - a)^2 + (y - b)^2 = r^2$.

12–3 All points whose coordinates satisfy the equation $(x - a)^2 + (y - b)^2 = r^2$, $r > 0$, lie on the circle with center (a, b) and radius r.

12–4 The midpoint of the segment joining the points (x_1, y_1) and (x_2, y_2) is the point $\left(\dfrac{x_1 + x_2}{2}, \dfrac{y_1 + y_2}{2}\right)$.

12–5 Two nonvertical lines are parallel if and only if they have equal slopes.

12–6 Two nonvertical lines are perpendicular if and only if the slope of one line is the negative reciprocal of the slope of the other line.

$$m_1 = -\frac{1}{m_2}, \text{ or } m_1 \cdot m_2 = -1$$

12–7 The graph of any equation that can be written in the form $ax + by = c$, a and b not both 0, is a line.

12–8 The equation of the line passing through the point (x_1, y_1) and having slope m is $y - y_1 = m(x - x_1)$.

Areas of Polygons and Circles

15–1 The area of a parallelogram is the product of the length of any base and the length of a corresponding altitude. $(A = bh)$

15–2 The area of a triangle is one-half the product of the length of a base and the length of the altitude to that base. $(A = 1/2\ bh)$

15–3 The area of a trapezoid is one-half the product of the length of an altitude and the sum of the lengths of the bases. $A = 1/2h(b_1 + b_2)$.

15–4 The ratio of the areas of two similar triangles is the square of the ratio of the lengths of any two corresponding sides.

15–5 A circle can be circumscribed about any regular polygon.

15–6 A circle can be inscribed in any regular polygon.

15–7 The area of a regular polygon is one-half the product of the apothem and the perimeter. $(A = \frac{1}{2}ap)$

15–8 The ratio of the areas of two similar polygons is equal to the square of the ratio of the lengths of a pair of corresponding sides.

15–9 The ratio of the circumference to the diameter is the same for all circles.

15–10 The area of a circle is the product of π and the square of the radius of the circle. $(A = \pi r^2)$

GLOSSARY

Absolute value: The **absolute value** of any real number a is the greater of the number a and its opposite $-a$. (p. 13)

Acute angle: An angle of measure less than 90. (p. 38)

Adjacent angles: Two angles in the same plane that have a common vertex and a common side but have no interior points in common. (p. 38)

Alternate exterior angles: When two lines are cut by a transversal, two angles such as $\angle 1$ and $\angle 8$ that are on opposite sides of the transversal, are both exterior, and have different vertices. (p. 152)

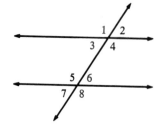

Alternate interior angles: When two lines are cut by a transversal, two angles such as $\angle 3$ and $\angle 6$ that are both interior, are on opposite sides of the transversal, and have different vertices. (p. 152)

Altitude of a circular cylinder: A perpendicular segment from a point in one base of the cylinder to the plane of the other base. (p. 597)

Altitude of a parallelogram: A perpendicular segment from a point in one side, considered the *base* of the parallelogram, to the line containing the opposite side. (p. 548)

Altitude of a prism: A segment perpendicular to the planes of the bases with one endpoint in each plane. (p. 586)

Altitude of a pyramid: A perpendicular segment from the vertex of the pyramid to the plane of the base. (p. 587)

Altitude of a trapezoid: A segment perpendicular to one base of the trapezoid from any point in the other base. (p. 553)

Altitude of a triangle: The perpendicular segment from any vertex of the triangle to the line that contains the opposite side. (p. 215)

Analysis: A brief description of the plan to be used in a proof. (p. 137)

Angle: The union of two noncollinear rays that have the same endpoint. The two rays are called the **sides** of the angle and their common endpoint the **vertex** of the angle. (p. 29)

Angle of depression: When a person at B looks down at A, angle B is the **angle of depression.** (p. 346)

Angle of elevation: When a person at A looks up at B, angle A is the **angle of elevation.** (p. 346)

Apothem of a regular polygon: The distance from the center of the regular polygon to a side. (p. 560)

Area of a circle: The limit of the areas of the inscribed regular polygons. (p. 566)

Auxiliary line: A line introduced to make a proof of a theorem possible. (p. 161)

Axioms, or postulates: Fundamental statements accepted as true without proof. (p. 91)

Axis of a circular cylinder: The segment which joins the centers of the bases of the cylinder. (p. 597)

Axis of a cone: The segment that joins the vertex to the center of the base. (p. 599)

Base of a parallelogram: Any side of a parallelogram may be considered the base. (p. 548)

Base of an isosceles triangle: In an isosceles triangle, the side that is not one of the two congruent sides. (p. 214)

Bases of a trapezoid: The two parallel sides of the trapezoid. (p. 244)

Betweenness of rays: $\overrightarrow{OB}$ is said to lie between $\overrightarrow{OA}$ and $\overrightarrow{OC}$ when:

1. All three rays have a common endpoint.
2. All three rays lie in the union of a halfplane and its edge.
3. The real numbers x, y, and z which correspond to $\overrightarrow{OA}$, $\overrightarrow{OB}$, and $\overrightarrow{OC}$ respectively are such that either $z > y > x$ or $x > y > z$. (p. 118)

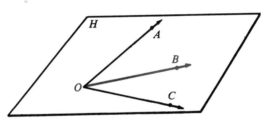

Betweenness of points: Point B is said to lie between points A and C if and only if all three points are distinct points on a line and $AB + BC = AC$. (p. 25)

Biconditional or equivalence: The statement $p \leftrightarrow q$ is biconditional when the conditional $p \rightarrow q$ and its converse $q \rightarrow p$ are both true. (p. 80)

Bisector of an angle: Ray $\overrightarrow{BD}$ is the bisector of $\angle ABC$ if D lies in the interior of $\angle ABC$ and $\angle ABD \cong \angle DBC$. (p. 39)

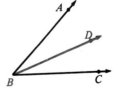

Bisector of a segment: A line, ray, segment, or any other set of points whose intersection with a given segment $\overline{AB}$ is the midpoint of $\overline{AB}$. (p. 26)

Center of an arc: The center of the circle that contains the arc. (p. 370)

Center of a circle: See *Circle.* (p. 57)

Center of a regular polygon: The common center of the inscribed and circumscribed circles of the regular polygon. (p. 559)

Central angle of a circle: An angle having its vertex at the center of the circle. (p. 365)

Central angle of a regular polygon: An angle whose vertex is the center of the polygon and whose sides contain consecutive vertices of the polygon. (p. 560)

Chord: A segment having its endpoints on a circle. (p. 57)

Circle: The set of all points in a plane that are at a given distance from a given point in the plane. That given point is the **center.** (p. 57)

Circular cone: The union of all segments that join points lying in a circular region to a point not in the plane of that region. (p. 599)

Circular cylinder: Let M and M' be two parallel planes with circular region R lying in M and line l intersecting M and M' but not region R. For each point X of region R let $\overline{XX'}$ be the segment parallel to l with endpoint X' in M'. The union of all such segments $\overline{XX'}$ is called a **circular cylinder.** (p. 596)

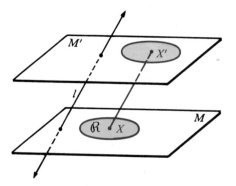

Circumference of a circle: The limit of the perimeters of the inscribed regular polygons. (p. 566)

Circumscribed circle: A circle is circumscribed about a polygon when each vertex of the polygon is a point of the circle. (p. 372)

Circumscribed polygon: A polygon each of whose sides is tangent to a circle. The circle is **inscribed** in the polygon. (p. 361)

Collinear points: A set of points all of which lie on the same line. (p. 24)

Common tangent: A common tangent of two coplanar circles is a line that is tangent to each circle. If a tangent line is such that it intersects the segment joining the centers, the tangent is a **common internal tangent.** Otherwise the tangent is a **common external tangent.** (p. 361)

Common tangent of two spheres: A line that is tangent to both spheres. (p. 60)

Common tangent plane of two spheres: A plane that is tangent to both spheres. (p. 60)

Complement of a set: A set of elements in the universal set but not in the given set. (p. 9)

Complementary angles: Two angles the sum of whose measures is 90. Each angle is called a **complement** of the other. (p. 39)

Concentric circles: Two or more circles that lie in the same plane and have the same center. (p. 57)

Conclusion of a conditional: See *Conditional.*

Conditional: Where p and q represent statements, the compound statement "*If p, then q*" is called a **conditional** or **implication** and expressed in symbols by $p \rightarrow q$. Statement p is the **hypothesis** and statement q the **conclusion** of the conditional $p \rightarrow q$. (p. 72)

Congruence between triangles: If a correspondence between the vertices of two triangles is such that each side and each angle of one triangle is congruent to the corresponding part of the other triangle, then the correspondence is called a **congruence** between the triangles. (p. 192)

Congruent angles: Angles which have the same measure. (p. 39)

Congruent arcs: Arcs which have equal measures in the same circle or in congruent circles. (p. 366)

Congruent circles: Circles that have congruent radii. (p. 365)

Congruent segments: Two segments are said to be **congruent** if they have the same length. The symbol $\cong$ stands for "is congruent to." (p. 26)

Conjunction of two statements: Where p and q represent any statements, the compound statement "*p and q*," written $p \wedge q$, is called the **conjunction** of p and q. (p. 67)

Consecutive sides of a polygon: Two sides of the polygon that intersect. (p. 178)

Consecutive vertices of a polygon: The endpoints of one side of a polygon. (p. 178)

Construction: An imaginary drawing in which required points or lines are determined by use of just two idealized instruments, a compass and a straightedge. In practice, a *constructed figure* is made on paper when a compass and straightedge are used according to certain rules. No other instrument is used. (p. 407)

Contraction of plane: For each positive number k the transformation specified by the equations $x' = kx$ and $y' = ky$ is called a **contraction** of the plane when $0 < k < 1$. (p. 518)

Contrapositive of a conditional: Where *If p, then q* is any conditional, the new conditional *If not-q, then not-p* is called the **contrapositive** of the original conditional. Thus, the contrapositive of $p \rightarrow q$ is $\sim q \rightarrow \sim p$. (p. 80)

Converse of a conditional: If you interchange the statements p and q in the conditional *If p, then q*, you get a new conditional *If q, then p* called the **converse** of the original conditional. (p. 79)

Convex polygon: A polygon is a **convex polygon** if there is no line that contains more than two points of the polygon unless it contains a side of the polygon. (p. 177)

Coordinate axes of a plane: A pair of perpendicular number lines in the plane. (p. 443)

Coordinate system for a line: A coordinate system is established on a line when: (a) to every point of the line there corresponds exactly one real number, (b) to every real number there corresponds exactly one point of the line, and (c) the distance between any two points is the absolute value of the difference of the corresponding numbers. (p. 13)

Coordinate system for a plane: A one-to-one correspondence between the set of points in the plane and the set of ordered pairs of numbers. (p. 444)

Coplanar points: A set of points all of which lie in the same plane. (p. 25)

Corollary: A statement that is readily proved by applying a theorem. (p. 172)

Corresponding angles, corresponding sides: For the correspondence $ABC \leftrightarrow XNT$ between $\triangle ABC$ and $\triangle XNT$, the **corresponding angles** are $\angle A$ and $\angle X$, $\angle B$ and $\angle N$, and $\angle C$ and $\angle T$. **Corresponding sides** are $\overline{AB}$ and $\overline{XN}$, $\overline{BC}$ and $\overline{NT}$ and $\overline{AC}$ and $\overline{XT}$. (p. 192)

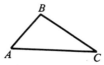

Corresponding angles formed by two lines and transversal: Two angles such as $\angle 1$ and $\angle 5$, one exterior and one interior, but on the same side of the transversal, are called **corresponding angles.** (p. 152)

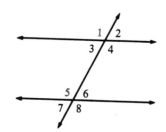

Cosine of an acute angle of a right triangle: For right triangle ABC,

$$\cos A = \frac{b}{c}$$

$$\cos j° = \frac{\text{length of adjacent side}}{\text{length of hypotenuse}} \cdot \text{ (p. 342)}$$

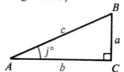

Cross section of a pyramid: A polygonal region that is the intersection of the pyramid and a plane parallel to the base of the pyramid. (p. 594)

Deductive reasoning: The process of accepting some statements and reasoning from them to a conclusion. (p. 63)

Diagonal of a polygon: A segment joining two nonconsecutive vertices of the polygon. (p. 178)

Diagonal of a rectangular solid: A segment whose endpoints are vertices not in the same face of the solid. (p. 331)

Diameter: A chord of a circle that contains the center. (p. 57)

Dihedral angle: The union of a line and two noncoplanar half-planes having the line as edge. Each half-plane is called a **face** of the dihedral angle. (p. 40)

Disjoint sets: Two sets that do not intersect. (p. 6)

Disjunction of two statements: Where p and q represent any statements, the compound statement "p *or* q," written $p \lor q$, is called the **disjunction** of p and q. (p. 68)

Distance between two parallel lines: The length of the perpendicular segment drawn from any point in one line to the other line. (p. 233)

Distance between two points: Corresponding to any two points A and B there is a unique positive number called the **distance** between them. (This number is denoted by AB or BA.) The distance between two points on the number line is the absolute value of the difference of their coordinates. (p. 13)

Distance between a point and a line (or a plane): The length of the perpendicular segment from the point to the line (or plane). (p. 232)

Distance from a point to a figure: The length of the shortest segment that can be drawn from the given point to any point of the figure. (p. 232)

Drawing: A representation made on paper using any suitable drawing instruments such as a protractor, T-square, marked ruler, compass, and straightedge. (p. 407)

Edge of a polyhedron: Any segment formed by the intersection of two faces of the polyhedron. (p. 331)

Empty set: A set that contains no members is called the **empty set** or the **null set** and is designated by the symbol $\emptyset$. (p. 2)

Equal sets: Two sets are said to be **equal sets** if and only if they contain the same members. (p. 2)

Equiangular polygon: A polygon having congruent angles. (p. 178)

Equilateral polygon: A polygon having congruent sides. (p. 178)

Equivalent statements: When the conditional $p \rightarrow q$ and its converse $q \rightarrow p$ are both true, p and q are said to be **equivalent statements.** (p. 80)

Expansion of plane: For each positive number k the transformation specified by the equations

$$x' = kx$$
$$y' = ky$$

is called an **expansion of the plane** when $k > 1$. (p. 518)

Extended proportion: Two or more equal ratios expressed in the form:

$$\frac{a}{b} = \frac{c}{d} = \frac{e}{f} = \frac{g}{h}. \text{ (p. 278)}$$

Exterior of an angle: The set of all points that are in the plane of the angle and are neither in the angle nor in the interior of the angle. (p. 30)

Exterior angle of a triangle: For $\triangle RST$, $\angle TSX$ is an exterior angle when $\overrightarrow{SX}$ and $\overrightarrow{SR}$ are opposite rays. (p. 171)

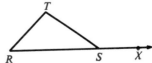

Exterior sides of two adjacent angles: The rays not common to both adjacent angles. (p. 38)

External secant segment: See *Secant segment.*

Face of a dihedral angle: See *Dihedral angle*.

Face: The rectangular solid shown has six rectangular faces. The opposite faces are parallel; adjacent faces are perpendicular. Take face *ABCD* to be the base. Then the faces that intersect base *ABCD* are called **lateral faces.** (p. 586)

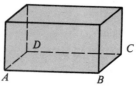

Finite set: If the elements of a set can be counted with the counting process coming to an end, the set is said to be a **finite set** (**fy**-nite). Otherwise, it is an **infinite set** (**in**-fi-nit). (p. 2)

Fixed point: A point that maps into itself. (p. 514)

Frustum: That part of a pyramid or a cone that is included between the plane of the base and a plane that is parallel to the base and intersects the edges. (p. 615)

Geometric mean: For any positive numbers *a*, *b*, and *x*, if $\dfrac{a}{x} = \dfrac{x}{b}$, then *x* is called the **geometric mean,** between *a* and *b*. Note that $x = \sqrt{ab}$. (p. 314)

Graph: A set of points whose coordinates meet certain algebraic conditions. (p. 450)

Half-plane: The diagram pictures a line *l* in plane *M*. Line *l* separates *M* into three subsets of points. One subset is *l*. Each of the other subsets is an infinite set of points called a **half-plane** of *M*. Each of the half-planes had edge *l*. Neither half-plane contains *l*. Coplanar half-planes that have the same edge are called *opposite half-planes*. (p. 30)

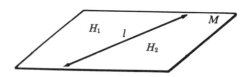

Hypotenuse: The side that lies opposite the right angle in a right triangle. (p. 199)

Hypothesis of a conditional: See *Conditional*.

Image: If a mapping carries point *P* into point *P′*, *P′* is called the **image** of *P* and *P* is called the **preimage** of *P′*. (p. 514)

Included angle: The included angle for two sides of a triangle is the angle whose rays contain those sides. (p. 193)

Included side: The included side for two angles of a triangle is the side whose end-points are the vertices of the two angles. (p. 193)

Induction: The process of finding a general principle based upon the evidence of specific cases. The statement of the general principle is also called an **induction.** (p. 52)

Inscribed angle: An angle is said to be **inscribed** in an arc and to be an **inscribed angle** if its sides contain the endpoints of the arc and its vertex is a point of the arc other than an endpoint. (p. 376)

Inscribed circle: See *Circumscribed polygon.*

Inscribed polygon: A polygon is said to be **inscribed in a circle** when each vertex of the polygon is a point of the circle. (p. 373)

Intercepted arc: An angle is said to **intercept** an arc if
1. The endpoints of the arc lie on the sides of the angle with at least one endpoint on each side.
2. All points of the arc, other than the endpoints, lie in the interior of the angle. (p. 376)

Interior angles formed by two lines and transversal: With respect to lines *m* and *n* cut by transversal *t*, angles 3, 4, 5, and 6 are called **interior angles.** (p. 152)

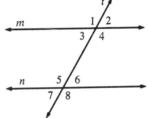

Interior of an angle: The **interior** of ∠*ABC* is the intersection of the half-plane that contains *C* and has edge $\overrightarrow{AB}$ and the half-plane that contains *A* and has edge $\overrightarrow{BC}$. (p. 30)

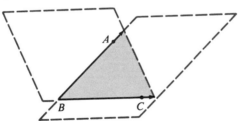

Interior of a circle: The interior of a circle with center *P* and radius *r* is the set of all coplanar points whose distance from *P* is less than *r*. (p. 57)

Intersect: Two sets *A* and *B* are said to **intersect** if there is at least one element that belongs to both sets. (p. 6)

Intersection: The **intersection** of two sets *A* and *B* is the set whose elements belong to *both A and B.* The intersection of sets *A* and *B* is expressed in symbols by *A* ∩ *B* (read "the intersection of *A* and *B*"). (p. 6)

Intuition: That kind of mental activity which gives you information or beliefs which are based on hunches or insight. (p. 53)

Inverse of a conditional: Where *If p, then q* is any conditional, the new conditional *If not-p, then not-q* is called the **inverse** of the original conditional. Thus, the **inverse** of $p \rightarrow q$ is $\sim p \rightarrow \sim q$. (p. 80)

Irrational number: A nonrepeating, nonterminating decimal numeral names an *irrational number*. (p. 15)

Isosceles trapezoid: A trapezoid with congruent legs. (p. 244)

Isosceles triangle: A triangle with at least two congruent sides. The congruent sides are called *legs,* and the third side is called the *base*. The angles that include the base are called *base angles;* the third angle is called the *vertex angle*, and its vertex is often referred to as *the* vertex of the triangle. (p. 214)

Lateral area of a prism: The sum of the areas of the lateral faces of the prism. (p. 588)

Lateral area of a pyramid: The sum of the areas of the lateral faces of the pyramid. (p. 593)

Lateral edge of a prism: A segment that joins two corresponding vertices of the bases of the prism. (p. 587)

Lateral face of a prism: The union of the segments joining points on a side of the base of the prism with corresponding points of the corresponding side of the other base. (p. 586)

Legs of an isosceles triangle: For an isosceles triangle, the two congruent sides. (p. 214)

Legs of a right triangle: In any right triangle the two sides that intersect at the vertex of the right angle. (p. 199)

Legs of a trapezoid: The two nonparallel sides of a trapezoid. (p. 244)

Length of segment: The length of a segment is the distance between its endpoints. The length of $\overline{AB}$ is therefore designated by writing AB or BA. The length of a segment is a positive number. (p. 25)

Line segment: For any two distinct points A and B, line segment AB is the set of points consisting of A, B and all points between A and B. A line segment is usually referred to simply as a segment. The symbol for segment AB is $\overline{AB}$. (p. 25)

Locus: The set of all points that satisfy a given condition and containing no points that do not satisfy the condition. (p. 426)

Major arc of a circle: The union of two points of the circle, not the ends of a diameter, and all points of the circle which lie in the exterior of the central angle whose sides contain the two points. (p. 365)

Measure of an angle: A number that is the absolute value of the difference between the numbers corresponding to the sides of the angle. (p. 32)

Measure of a major arc: The measure of a major arc $\overset{\frown}{AXB}$ is 360 minus the measure of minor arc $\overset{\frown}{AB}$. (p. 365)

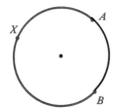

Measure of a minor arc: The measure of the central angle that intercepts the arc. (p. 365)

Median of a trapezoid: The segment joining the midpoints of the legs of the trapezoid. (p. 244)

Median of a triangle: The segment from any vertex of the triangle to the midpoint of the opposite side. (p. 215)

Midpoint of a segment: The point that is on the segment and divides it into two congruent segments. (p. 26)

Minor arc of a circle: The union of two points of the circle, not the ends of a diameter, and all points of the circle that lie in the interior of the central angle whose sides contain the two points. (p. 365)

Negation of a statement: Where p represents any statement, the statement *It is false that p*, usually shortened to *not-p*, written $\sim p$, is called the **negation** of p or the **negative** of p. (p. 68)

Number line: A line on which a coordinate system has been established. (p. 13)

Oblique prism: A prism whose lateral edges are *not* perpendicular to the planes of the bases. (p. 586)

Obtuse angle: An angle of measure greater than 90 but less than 180. (p. 38)

One-to-one correspondence: A one-to-one correspondence between two sets A and B is a matching that pairs each element of A with exactly one element of B, and pairs each element of B with exactly one element of A. (p. 12)

Opposite rays: $\overrightarrow{AB}$ and $\overrightarrow{AC}$ are called opposite rays if A, B, and C lie on a line and A is between B and C. (p. 26)

Ordered pair of numbers: A pair of numbers is an **ordered pair** when the order in which they are named has significance. (p. 443)

Parallel lines: Lines that lie in the same plane and have no point in common. (p. 147)

Parallel line and plane: A line and a plane that have no point in common. (p. 147)

Parallel planes: Planes that have no point in common. (p. 148)

Parallelogram: A quadrilateral in which both pairs of opposite sides are parallel. (p. 231)

Perimeter of a polygon: The sum of the lengths of the sides of the polygon. (p. 288)

Perpendicular bisector of a segment: A line, ray, or segment which is perpendicular to a segment at its midpoint. (p. 56)

Perpendicular lines: Two lines that meet to form congruent adjacent angles. (p. 56)

Perpendicular planes: Two planes such that one of them contains a line **perpendicular** to the other. (p. 149)

Polygon: When $P_1, P_2, \ldots, P_n$ are n distinct points in a plane, the union of the segments $\overline{P_1P_2}, \overline{P_2P_3}, \ldots, \overline{P_{n-1}P_n}, \overline{P_nP_1}$ is said to be a **polygon** if (a) no two of the segments intersect except at their endpoints, (b) no two segments with a common endpoint are collinear. (p. 177)

Polygonal region: The union of a finite number of non-overlapping coplanar triangular regions. (p. 544)

Polyhedron: An enclosed region of space that is bounded by many planes. (p. 330)

Postulate: See *Axiom*.

Preimage: See *Image*.

Prism: Given two parallel planes M and M' with polygonal region $ABCDE$ lying in M and line l intersecting both planes, but not intersecting the given polygonal region. For each point X of polygonal region $ABCDE$ let $\overline{XX'}$ be the segment parallel to l with endpoint X' in M'. The union of all such segments $\overline{XX'}$, is called a **prism.** (p. 585)

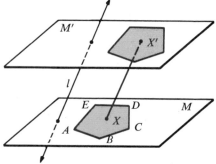

Product of transformations: Let g be any transformation that maps each point P into the unique point P'. Let f be a transformation that maps point P' into the unique point P''. Under the successive transformations, g followed by f, each point P is paired with a unique point P''. The mapping that maps P into P'' is said to be the **product of transformations** f and g. It is denoted by fg. (p. 530)

Projection of a point on a line: The point of intersection of the line and the perpendicular from the point to the line. When a point lies on a line it is considered to be its own projection on that line. (p. 314)

Projection of a point into a plane: The point of intersection of the plane and the perpendicular segment from the point to the plane. When a point lies in a plane, the projection of that point into the plane is the point itself. (p. 334)

Proportion: For nonzero numbers a, b, c, d, an equation written in the form $\frac{a}{b} = \frac{c}{d}$, or $a:b = c:d$, is called a **proportion.** (p. 278)

Protractor: An instrument consisting of a semicircular scale marked off in units from 0 to 180 used to find the approximate measure of an angle in degrees. (p. 32)

Pyramid: The union of all segments that join points lying in a polygonal region to a point not in the plane of that region. (p. 586)

Quadrant: Any of the four regions into which a plane is separated by a pair of coordinate axes. (p. 443)

Quadrilateral: A polygon having exactly four sides. (p. 231)

Radical: An indicated root of a number. $\sqrt{3}$, $\sqrt[3]{2}$, $\sqrt[4]{5}$ are radicals. The **radical sign,** ($\sqrt{}$) indicates the positive square root. The **radicand** is the number appearing under the radical sign. (p. 316)

Radius: A segment joining the center of a circle to a point on the circle. (p. 57)

Radius of a regular polygon: The distance from the center of the polygon to a vertex. (p. 559)

Ratio: If a and b are numbers and $b \neq 0$, the ratio of a to b is the number $\dfrac{a}{b}$.

(p. 277)

Rational number: A repeating or terminating decimal numeral names a *rational number*. (p. 15)

Ray: Ray AB is the union of segment $\overline{AB}$ and the set of all points X such that B lies between X and A. A is called the **endpoint** of the ray AB. The symbol $\overrightarrow{AB}$ is used to designate "ray AB." (p. 26)

Real number: Either a rational number or an irrational number. The set of real numbers $\Re$ is the union of two disjoint sets — the set of rational numbers and the set of irrational numbers. (p. 15)

Rectangle: A parallelogram with four right angles. (p. 240)

Reflection: A transformation under which one line or plane bisects each line segment determined by a point and its image. (p. 526)

Reflection of the plane in the x-axis: The transformation specified by the equations $x' = x$ and $y' = -y$. (p. 527)

Reflection of the plane in the y-axis: The transformation specified by the equations $x' = -x$ and $y' = y$. (p. 527)

Regular polygon: A convex polygon that is both equiangular and equilateral. (p. 558)

Regular pyramid: A pyramid having a base that is bounded by a regular polygon and lateral edges of equal length. (p. 587)

Remote interior angle of a triangle: With respect to an exterior angle of a triangle, either of the two nonadjacent interior angles of the triangle. (p. 171)

Rhombus: A parallelogram with four congruent sides. (p. 240)

Right angle: An angle of measure 90. (p. 38)

Right circular cone: A circular cone whose vertex is equidistant from all points lying on the circle that bounds the base. (p. 599)

Right circular cylinder: A circular cylinder in which the segment joining the centers of its bases is perpendicular to the planes of both bases. (p. 597)

Rigid transformation of the plane: A transformation such that distances between points and measures of angles do not change under the transformation. (p. 522)

Secant line: A line that contains a chord of a circle. (p. 57)

Secant ray: A ray that lies on a secant line and contains both points of intersection with the circle. (p. 379)

Secant segment: If $\overleftrightarrow{RT}$ is a secant intersecting circle O at S and T, and R is in the exterior of circle O, then $\overline{RT}$ is a **secant segment** and $\overline{RS}$ an **external secant segment** to the circle from R. (p. 389)

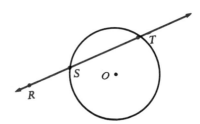

Sector of a circle: A region bounded by two radii and an arc of the circle. (p. 573)

Segment of a circle: A region bounded by a chord and an arc of the circle. In the figure shown there are two segments: segment ABC and segment ABD. (p. 573)

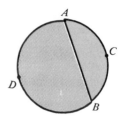

Semicircle: The union of the endpoints of a diameter and all points of the circle lying on one side of the diameter. (p. 365)

Shrinking of the plane: For each positive number k, $0 < k < 1$, the equations $x' = kx$ and $y' = y$ determine a transformation called a *shrinking of the plane.* (p. 517) Also when $0 < k < 1$ and $x' = x$ and $y' = ky$. (p. 518)

Similarity between polygons: If a correspondence between the vertices of two convex polygons is such that the *measures of corresponding angles are equal* and the *lengths of corresponding sides are in proportion*, then the correspondence is called a similarity between the polygons. (p. 285)

Sine of an acute angle of a right triangle: For right triangle ABC,

$$\sin A = \frac{a}{c}$$

$$\sin j° = \frac{\text{length of opposite side}}{\text{length of hypotenuse}} \cdot \quad \text{(p. 342)}$$

Skew lines: Two lines that do not lie in any one plane. (p. 147)

Skew quadrilateral: A four-sided figure having sides that are not all contained in any one plane. (p. 231)

Slant height of a regular pyramid: The length of the altitude of any one of its lateral faces. *Slant height is defined only for regular pyramids.* (p. 587)

Slant height of a right circular cone: The distance from any point on the bounding circle to the vertex of the cone. (p. 599)

Slope of a line: The slope of a line is $\dfrac{y_2 - y_1}{x_2 - x_1}$, where pts. (x_1, y_1) and (x_2, y_2) are any two points of the line, and $x_2 \neq x_1$. Whenever $x_2 = x_1$ the line is vertical and has no slope. (p. 461)

Sphere: The set of all points at a given distance from a given point. (p. 59)

Square: A rectangle with two consecutive sides congruent. (p. 241)

Stretching of the plane: For each positive number $k > 1$, the equations $x' = kx$ and $y' = y$ determine a transformation called a **stretching of the plane.** (p. 517) Also if $k > 1$ and $x' = x$ and $y = ky$. (p. 518)

Subset: When two sets A and B are such that every element of A is an element of B, A is said to be a **subset** of B. (p. 5)

Supplementary angles: Two angles the sum of whose measures is 180. Each angle is called a **supplement** of the other. (p. 39)

Symmetry with respect to a line: A figure has **symmetry with respect to a line** l if for every point Q of the figure there is a corresponding point Q' in the figure such that l is the perpendicular bisector of $\overline{QQ'}$. (p. 447)

Symmetry with respect to a plane: A figure has **symmetry with respect to a plane** Z if for every point Q of the figure there is another point Q' in the figure such that Z is the perpendicular bisector of $\overline{QQ'}$. (p. 447)

Symmetry with respect to a point: A figure has **symmetry with respect to a point** P if for every point Q in the figure there is a corresponding point Q' in the figure such that P is the midpoint of $\overline{QQ'}$. (p. 447)

Tangent of an acute angle of a right triangle: For right triangle ABC,

$$\tan A = \frac{a}{b}$$

$$\tan j° = \frac{\text{length of opposite side}}{\text{length of adjacent side}}.$$

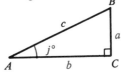

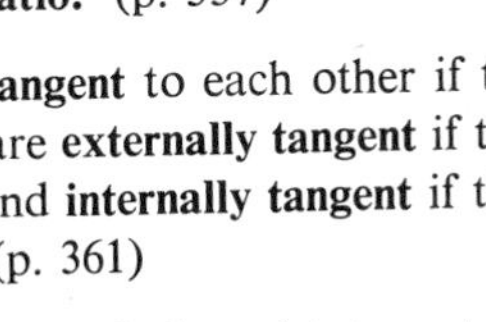

The number $\tan A$ is often referred to as the **tangent ratio.** (p. 337)

Tangent circles: Two coplanar circles are said to be **tangent** to each other if they are tangent to the same line at the same point. They are **externally tangent** if their centers lie on opposite sides of the common tangent and **internally tangent** if their centers lie on the same side of the common tangent. (p. 361)

Tangent line to a circle: A line that lies in the plane of the circle and intersects the circle in exactly one point. The point of intersection is called the **point of tangency** or **point of contact.** A ray or segment that contains the point of tangency and is a subset of a tangent line is also referred to as a tangent. (p. 359)

Tangent ray: A ray that lies on a tangent line and contains the point of tangency. (p. 379)

Tangent segment: If $\overleftrightarrow{AB}$ is tangent to circle O at point B, then segment $\overline{AB}$ is a **tangent segment** from A to circle O. (p. 389)

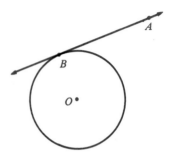

Theorem: A statement that can be proved. (p. 93)

Total area of a prism: The sum of the lateral area and the areas of the two bases of the prism. (p. 588)

Total area of a pyramid: The sum of the lateral area and the area of the base of the pyramid. (p. 593)

Transformation of the number line (plane): A mapping that carries each point of the number line (plane) into a unique point of the number line (plane). (p. 514)

Translation of the plane: A transformation specified, for any real numbers h and k, by the equations $x' = x + h$ and $y' = y + k$. (p. 522)

Transversal: A line that intersects two or more other lines in different points. See p. 151 for restrictions placed on "transversal" in this course.

Trapezoid: A quadrilateral with exactly two sides parallel. (p. 244)

Triangle: The union of the three segments determined by three noncollinear points. (p. 170)

Triangular region: The union of a triangle and its interior. (p. 543)

Union of two sets: The **union** of two sets A and B is the set of all elements that belong to *at least* one of the two sets. The union of A and B is written $A \cup B$ (read "the union of A and B"). (p. 6)

Universal set (universe): When each set in a particular discussion is thought of as a subset of some particular set U, the set U is called the **universal set** or **universe.** (p. 9)

Vector: An ordered pair of real numbers. (p. 503)

Vertex of an angle: The common endpoint of the two rays of the angle. (p. 29)

Vertex of a polyhedron: Any point which is the intersection of two edges of the polyhedron. (p. 331)

Vertex angle of an isosceles triangle: For an isosceles triangle, the angle having rays that contain the two congruent sides. (p. 214)

Vertical angles: Angles with sides forming two pairs of opposite rays. (p. 38)

X-coordinate (y-coordinate) of a point: The **x-coordinate** of a point is the number that corresponds to the projection of the point on the x-axis. The **y-coordinate** of a point is the number that corresponds to the projection on the y-axis. (p. 444)

INDEX